Computer Communications

VOLUME II
SYSTEMS AND APPLICATIONS

Computer Communications

VOLUME II
SYSTEMS AND APPLICATIONS

EDITOR

Wushow Chou

North Carolina State University

CONTRIBUTORS

Wushow Chou
Wesley W. Chu
Mario Gerla
Kathryn W. Hanson
Donald L. Nielson
R. Andrew Pickens
Louis Pouzin
David C. Wood

Prentice-Hall, Inc.,
Englewood Cliffs, New Jersey 07632

001.64404
C7395
V.2

Library of Congress Cataloging in Publication Data
(Revised for volume 2)
Main entry under title:

Computer communications.

Includes bibliographies and index.
Contents: v. 1. Principles—v. 2. Systems and
applications.
1. Computer networks.   2. Data transmission systems.
I. Chou, Wushow.
TK5105.5.C637   1983   001.64′404   82-3833
ISBN 0-13-165043-2 (v. 1)
ISBN 0-13-165050-5 (v. 2)

Manufacturing buyer: Gordon Osbourne

© 1985 by Prentice-Hall, Inc., Englewood Cliffs, New Jersey 07632

All rights reserved. No part of this book may be
reproduced, in any form or by any means,
without permission in writing from the publisher.

Printed in the United States of America

10   9   8   7   6   5   4   3   2   1

ISBN   0-13-165050-5   01

Prentice-Hall International, Inc., *London*
Prentice-Hall of Australia Pty. Limited, *Sydney*
Editora Prentice-Hall do Brasil, Ltda., *Rio de Janeiro*
Prentice-Hall Canada Inc., *Toronto*
Prentice-Hall of India Private Limited, *New Delhi*
Prentice-Hall of Japan, Inc., *Tokyo*
Prentice-Hall of Southeast Asia Pte. Ltd., *Singapore*
Whitehall Books Limited, *Wellington, New Zealand*

Contents

Preface

The economy and convenience of extending the use of computing resources have promoted the development and expansion of communication-based computer systems. In 1970 there were fewer than 250,000 data terminals in the United States. Today there are more than 3 million, plus 200,000 facsimile machines. The expected growth rate in their numbers is over 20% per year. Present estimates are that there are 1 billion electronic messages per year generated or received by such devices. Within three years the number should almost double.

Another perspective on growth is that 70% of first-class mail is generated by computers. Almost all Fortune 500 companies are expected to have electronic mail systems in the next few years. Statistics indicate that we are inevitably heading toward an information society. This trend will be a continuing stimulation for new applications and new users. As a result, the rate of innovations in system design concepts, hardware features, and transmission services is accelerating; and as new applications become economically and operationally practical, demands increase and the cycle continues. The data terminals, or multimode terminals combining data, voice, and video capabilities, will outnumber the telephone sets used only for transmitting voice. Clearly, computer communication networks are needed.

One part of computer communication network design involves networking strategies. Volume I begins with a classification of networking alternatives (Chapter 1). Closely related are the control procedures used in the networks for managing traffic. Chapter 2 addresses control procedures at the link level. Chapter 3 deals with control procedures at higher levels; IBM's System Network Architecture and ARPANET are used as examples. Multiaccess schemes that allow a large number of terminals and computers to contend for a high-capacity channel are the topic in Chapter 4.

Another part of computer communication network design involves selection of digital transmission facilities. When common carriers provide all transmission facilities, people involved in planning computer communications systems do not need to understand the characteristics of the transmission facilities. The increasing need for wideband transmission facilities that are not provided by common carriers requires an understanding of the characteristics. Therefore, material on radio links, satellite channels, coaxial cables, and fiber optics are provided in Chapters 5, 6, and 7.

Control procedures are implemented in devices, and the devices are connected by transmission facilities to form networks. The communication devices and their functions are discussed in Chapter 8.

With the proliferation of equipment and use of computer communications, one issue that cannot be ignored is the security and integrity of the data flowing through various networks. Chapter 9 presents encryption possibilities, including data encryption standards and public key systems.

Two very important and interesting parts of computer communications network design deal with the problems of analysis and optimization of large teleprocessing networks. In Chapter 10 is a presentation of stochastic analytic methods for determining network performance, with emphasis placed on those that are practical, yet robust. A unified approach to the optimization of communication networks is given in Chapter 11, contained in Volume II. The unified approach combines exact and heuristic methods.

One of the most exciting aspects of computer communication technology is the emerging use of broadband facilities in networks. There will be wide use of satellite networks ranging from point-to-point to pervasive networks, cable networks that provide capacity for hundreds of megabits per second, and packet and cellular radio networks that can be used in situations where wired networks are less convenient. A possible scenario for new networks is that satellite channels be used as part of the backbone network, radio networks be included in the regional networks for local access or in place of telephone companies' local loops, and cable networks be used for limited-distance local networks. Examples of satellite networks, cable networks, and radio networks are given in Chapters 5, 6, and 7. Packet radio networks are discussed in Chapter 12.

The multiaccess schemes used on wideband facilities will make possible increased office automation and will be essential in the office of the future. The wide adaptation of limited-distance local networks, the topic of Chapter 13, will come first. The wide acceptance of the services available through local networks will prompt and accelerate the demand for communications and services that are not available locally. Users on one local network will be able to communicate with users on a geographically remote local network or access information and network services from a remote location.

For a user to access various possible network services not available locally or to communicate with another user at a remote site, there must be networks in between. Some of these networks will be in the form of public data networks. The discussion and comparison of several public data networks, as well as several private data networks, are given in Chapter 14. The issue of interconnecting the networks is considered in Chapter 15.

Another phenomenon is that of integration, that is, the integration of packet and circuit switching into the same architecture. Because of the growing conversion to computer-controlled digital switches, more telephone plants are converting from analog to digital. As a consequence, data, digitized voice, and other digital signals can be mixed in the same network, called an integrated services digital network. The integration of packet and circuit switching is addressed in Chapter 16. The combination of voice, data, still image, and video in the same network is addressed in Chapter 17.

While economy and convenience have resulted in the acceleration of demand in computer communication usage, they themselves are a direct consequence of advances in microelectronics, digitization techniques, and wideband digital transmission facilities. The availablity of low-cost, high-performance microelectronic components allows the development of new applications of data communications usage and new data communication technologies which would otherwise be economically infeasible. The advancement of digitization techniques facilities sharing of common transmission facilities for data, voice, and video traffic. Digitization techniques and the availablity of wideband digital transmission facilities together open a new horizon for applications. Applications that require inexpensive, low-error-rate, high-bandwidth facilities, such as high-speed digitial video transmission, are becoming practical. Chapter 18 presents these driving technologies that advance computer communications.

Many new network services will be developed to satisfy various application needs. A very important one is the access of distributed data bases. The issues of locating, managing, and coordinating distributed data bases are presented in Chapter 19.

Illustrated in Fig. A.1 are the interrelationships of topics covered in the book. However, each chapter is written to stand alone. Because of this, some overlap of material between certain chapters exists. Any apparent inconsistencies in terminology are attributable to the fact that definitions have not yet been agreed upon by all persons in the field of computer communications; conceptual differences may also exist between different individuals. No attempts have been made to unify definitions among the various authors. Indeed, the editor believes it is advantageous to be exposed to different definitions.

Wushow Chou
North Carolina State University

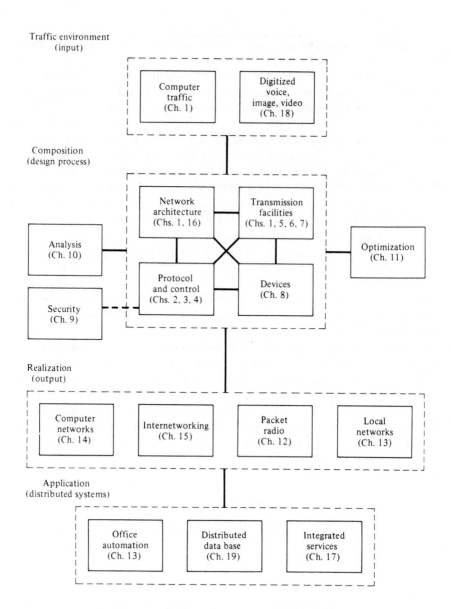

Traffic environment
(input)

Composition
(design process)

Realization
(output)

Application
(distributed systems)

Computer
traffic
(Ch. 1)

Digitized
voice,
image, video
(Ch. 18)

Network
architecture
(Chs. 1, 16)

Transmission
facilities
(Chs. 1, 5, 6, 7)

Analysis
(Ch. 10)

Optimization
(Ch. 11)

Protocol
and control
(Chs. 2, 3, 4)

Devices
(Ch. 8)

Security
(Ch. 9)

Computer
networks
(Ch. 14)

Internetworking
(Ch. 15)

Packet
radio
(Ch. 12)

Local
networks
(Ch. 13)

Office
automation
(Ch. 13)

Distributed
data base
(Ch. 19)

Integrated
services
(Ch. 17)

Figure A.1. Profile of computer communications.

Computer Communications

VOLUME II
SYSTEMS AND APPLICATIONS

11

Optimization of
Data/Computer Networks

W. CHOU

North Carolina State University
Raleigh, North Carolina

11.1 INTRODUCTION

Geographically distributed data terminal equipment (DTE), such as terminals, data processing facilities, or computer resources, communicate with each other through data/computer communications networks. Figure 11.1 illustrates one such network. The data/computer communication network architectures used in the distributed environment are those illustrated in Figs. 11.2 to 11.4.

Figure 11.2 depicts the tree-shaped, hierarchical architecture, in which the local access network, defined as the circuits interconnecting the terminals and/or terminal control units, are connected to the concentrating devices, most likely multiplexers, statistical multiplexers, or concentrators. (See Chap. 8 and [CHOU 76] for a description of these devices.) The concentrating devices are in turn connected to the host computer. (The concentrating functions may be performed as part of a remote processor's responsibility.) The circuits shown interconnecting the concentrating devices and the host computers are called the *backbone network*. Both the local access and the backbone networks may be point-to-point or tree-shaped connections. Occasionally, ring-shaped connections of terminals may also occur. Often, the local access networks terminate directly at the host computer instead of through the concentrating devices.

The mesh-shaped switching architecture is illustrated in Fig. 11.3. In this architecture the local access network is comprised of both the terminal devices and the host computers connected in either a point-to-point or multipoint configuration. The local access networks are connected to the switches. The backbone network for this architecture is defined as the interconnecting circuits between the switches. The backbone network of this nature is usually mesh shaped (but not necessarily), and may employ circuit, message, packet, or integrated switching.

Figure 11.4 presents the architecture associated with a ring-shaped, ring-

1

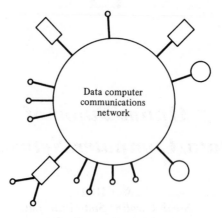

Figure 11.1. Communications network for a distributed data processing system. Rectangle, host computer; large circle, remote processor; small circle, terminal or terminal control unit.

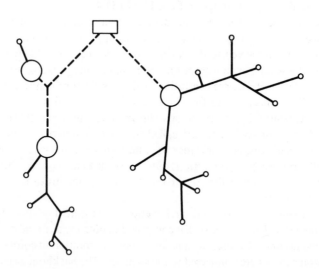

Figure 11.2. Tree-shaped, hierarchically controlled data communication network architecture. Rectangle, host computer; large circle, remote processor or concentrator; small circle, terminal or terminal control unit. Dashed line, backbone; solid line, local access.

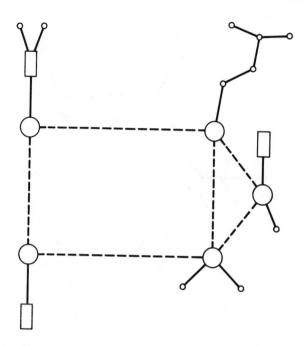

Figure 11.3. Mesh-shaped architecture. Rectangle, host computer; large circle, (packet) switch; small circle, terminal or terminal control unit. Dashed line, backbone; solid line, local access.

switching design. The local access network in this case is the same as that defined earlier for the mesh-shaped network architecture. Similarly, the backbone network is defined by the circuits interconnecting the switches, in this case specified as ring switches.

For completeness, it should be noted at this point that terminals controlled by a terminal control unit (TCU) usually form, on a second-order local level, a star or ring network, as shown in Fig. 11.5.

It is evident from the figures that the concentrating devices, the (packet) switches, and the ring switches interface with the local access and backbone networks. In this chapter these devices and switches will be generically referred to as *network access facilities* (NAFs). (For more detailed descriptions of the data network architectures, see Chap. 1 and [CHOU 75].)

The network optimization problem of a distributed system therefore consists of the determination of the number and locations for NAFs; the configuration of the local access networks, including point-to-point, tree-shaped multipoint, and ring-shaped multipoint; and the configuration of the backbone network, including point-to-point, tree-shaped multipoint, ring-shaped multipoint, and mesh-shaped switching architectures. Of course, methods for solving each of these network problems are not new; good heuristic algorithms have been widely used in many data/computer

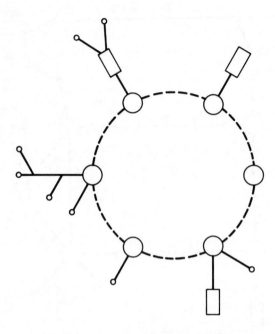

Figure 11.4. Ring architecture. Rectangle, host computer; large circle, ring switch; small circle, terminal or terminal control unit. Dashed line, backbone; solid line, local access.

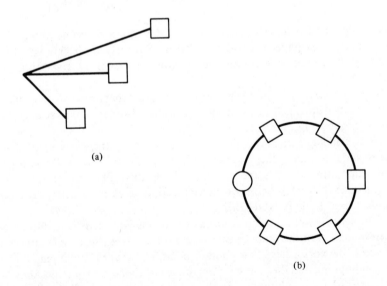

Figure 11.5. TCU–terminal configurations: (a) star configuration; (b) ring configuration. Circle, terminal control unit; square, unintelligent terminal.

communication networks. However, new emphasis on the distributed data processing systems has lessened the applicability of these algorithms. The following sections of this chapter discuss the algorithms and implementation approaches that are felt to be suitable to the new distributed processing network environment.

For local access networks with geographically dispersed terminal devices, "effective" algorithms for optimization have existed for over a decade [ESAU 66, CHOU 73]. The term *effective* implies that an algorithm leads to a good solution, one near the theoretic optimum. When the number of terminals is in the hundreds or even thousands, the efficiency of the algorithms in terms of computer memory requirements and execution time becomes important. The effectiveness of the algorithms is irrelevant if they are too expensive to implement. Section 11.3 describes the most effective algorithm now known for the optimization of tree-shaped multipoint networks and shows how it can be implemented efficiently.

The concept of ring switching has been proved workable for quite a few years [FAR 73], and there are ring-shaped local access networks in operation (e.g., the IBM 3600 and the IBM 8100 systems). However, with few exceptions, devices on the same ring are generally located in the same proximity. Therefore, topological optimization has never been a concern. Nevertheless, it is expected that in some applications the ring network may be more desirable than the tree network, even for geographically dispersed devices. Section 11.4 describes algorithms, based on modifications of graph-theoretic results [LIN 65, CLAR 64], for designing ring-shaped networks.

The problem of optimizing the packet-switching network dominates the backbone network optimization problem. The bulk of the research in the optimization of packet-switching networks has been supported by the Advanced Research Projects Agency from 1969 through 1976. Naturally, the algorithm that has been widely used in networks is the one sponsored by the ARPA; and, just as naturally, these algorithms have been biased by the ARPANET environment during that period [GERL 74, BOOR 77]. Section 11.5 describes the biases and specifies a modified algorithm without such biases [SAPI 78, CHOU 82].

When conventional approaches are used to design a distributed network as shown in Figs. 11.2, 11.3, or 11.4, the number and locations of the NAFs, the configuration of the local access network, and the configuration of the backbone network are each treated as separate optimization problems. The optimal network cannot be realized by simply overlaying three optimized subnetworks. To avoid such a suboptimum design, it is necessary to integrate consideration of the subnetworks in the final and overall optimization process. Section 11.6, in conjunction with the determination of the number and locations of NAFs, introduces an integrated approach that combines the three optimization problems into one.

11.2 BASIC CONCEPTS OF HEURISTIC PROCEDURES

Almost all the heuristics used in designing communication networks are iterative techniques. Even those that may not appear to be iterative can often be restructured to be equivalent to iterative techniques. Iterative techniques used in network design involve applications of the following perturbation methods: deleting a link, adding a link, adding a link while simultaneously deleting another link, exchanging the position of another link, adding an NAF to the network, deleting an NAF, or other small changes of the network in order to determine structures with better cost and performance. Figure 11.6 graphically illustrates the procedure. It begins with a "reasonable starting" network, either selected by a human being or generated by a simple computer program. That network's cost and performance, usually in terms of throughput, response time, and reliability, are determined by a simulation or analysis. Then perturbation methods are applied, according to a heuristic algorithm or judiciously selected link(s) or NAF(s). The cost and performance of the modified network are determined by analysis or simulation and compared with those of the starting network. If a certain percentage of improvement cannot be achieved, a different set of link(s) or NAF(s) of the starting network are perturbed. The procedure is then repeated until a perturbed network that can achieve a certain amount of improvement is found. This perturbed network becomes the new starting network. This iterative process is continued until all constraints are satisfied and cost can no longer be lowered.

Some seeingly different architectures may use the same heuristics with different performance and analysis approaches. For example, the packet-switching architecture and the circuit-switching architecture may use the same heuristics except that

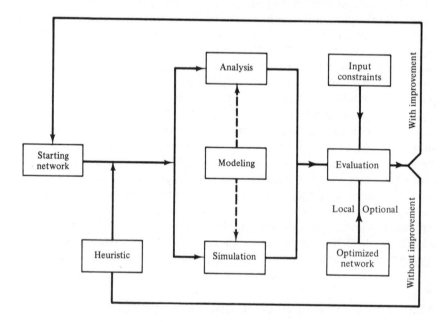

Figure 11.6. Heuristic procedure.

formulas of the Pollazcek–Khinchine type are used to determine the response time-throughput relationship for the packet-switching architecture, while formulas of the Erlang–C/B type may be used to determine the grade of service for the circuit-switching architecture (see Chap. 10).

Various performance criteria and analysis techniques have been discussed in Chap. 10. This chapter concentrates on the heuristic techniques.

11.3   TREE-SHAPED MULTIPOINT CONFIGURATION

The basic problem of tree-shaped multipoint line design can be stated as: Given a geographic distribution of terminals, locations of roots (network access facilities, host computers), line speeds, line cost functions (telephone companies' tariffs), and constraints, design a least-cost network connecting the terminals to the roots. The constraints may be one or more of the following: terminal response times, reliability criteria, maximum amount of traffic allowed per line, maximum number of terminals permitted per line, and maximum amount of traffic permitted per line as a function of the terminals on the line.

Many, mainly heuristic, techniques have been developed for the optimization of tree-shaped networks in data communication systems [ESAU 66, KRUS 56, PRIM 57, SHAR 70, KARN 75, CHOU 73]. The techniques, although differing, are all constrained minimum spanning tree algorithms. They design minimum-cost, tree-shaped networks satisfying the constraints. Each of these algorithms starts with the terminals in separate components and subsequently joins pairs of components. They differ only in the order in which they consider joining components. If no constraints are imposed, they all yield a least-cost, tree-structured network. Since the grouping of a given set of terminals into one component (i.e., placing them on the same multidrop line) restricts subsequent merging with other components because of the constraints, these algorithms, in general, yield different solutions. For example, Prim's algorithm [PRIM 57] chooses a terminal whose distance to any terminal already in the tree is minimal as a basis for joining components to the tree. Kruskal's algorithm [KRUS 56] evaluates a least-cost line connecting a pair of components and joins the components by that line. (See [CHOU 73] or [KERS 74] for a description and comparison of various algorithms of this class.)

Based on the principle outlined above, Chou and Kershenbaum [CHOU 73, KERS 74] have developed a unified algorithm which allows the network designer to take advantage of features offered by other algorithms or to experiment with new algorithms by simply varying parameters. In addition, while other techniques allow only one root for all the tree networks during the execution of the algorithm and, in the case of multiple roots or NAFs, require a preprocessing step of clustering terminals for each of the roots or NAFs, the Chou–Kershenbaum algorithm allows multiple NAF sites to be considered during the execution of their algorithm. A modified version of the algorithm is given below.

Chou-Kershenbaum's Unified Algorithm for Tree Network Optimization

Algorithm	*Comments*

STEP 0—INITIALIZATION

$A \triangleq \{1, 2,...,N_t\}$	(Set of all terminals, N_t = number of terminals)
$B \triangleq \{N_t + 1,...,N_t + N_{NAF}\}$	(Set of all NAFs, N_{NAF} = number of NAFs)
$C_i \triangleq \{i\} \; \forall_i \; \varepsilon \; A \cup B$	(C_i is the component, or the set of nodes, that contains i; initially, each component C_i contains one node.)
Define W_i	[Weighting function associated with C_i (e.g., minimum connecting cost from C_i to any concentrator)]
$t_{ij} = W_i - d_{ij}$; $i \; \varepsilon \; A, j \; \varepsilon \; A \cup B$	(Cost trade-off function of connecting C_i and C_j, d_{ij} = cost of connecting i and j)
$N_L = 0$	(Number of connected links = 0)

STEP 1—DEFINE MAXIMUM COST TRADE-OFF FUNCTION

$t_{i*j*} \triangleq$ Max t_{ij}	
$i \; \varepsilon \; C_i \cap A$	(i must be a terminal)
$j \; \varepsilon \; C_i$	(j may be either)
$C_i \not\subseteq C_j - \beta$	(i and j not in the same set)

STEP 2—ADD LINKS

If $C_{i*} \cup C_{j*}$ does not violate constraints (e.g., number of terminals, amount of traffic, response time):

Add $(_{i*}, _{j*})$	(Add a link)
Let $C_{i*} \leftarrow C_{i*} \cup C_{j*}$	(Merge two components)
$\qquad N_L \leftarrow N_L + 1$	(Increment N_L)
Update W_i and t_{ij}	(W_i may vary with configurations)
Otherwise, let $t_{i*j*} = -\infty$	[$(i*, j*)$ are not allowed]

STEP 3—CHECK NUMBER OF CONNECTED LINKS

If $N_L < N_t$, go to step 1	(End the algorithm if the number of links is equal to the number of terminals)
Otherwise, stop	

The algorithm does not restrict the definition of the terminal weight, W_i. However, Chou and Kershenbaum [CHOU 73] suggest the following definition:

$$W_i = a[b \times d_{i,0} + (1 - b) \times d_{i,2}]$$

where $d_{i,0}$ = cost of connecting terminal i to the closest NAF
$\quad d_{i,2}$ = cost of connecting i to the second nearest neighbor
$\quad a, b$ are parameters of the algorithm such that $a > 0, 0 \leq b \leq 1$

The parameters a and b, when varied, allow the Chou–Kershenbaum algorithm to essentially perform operations similar to those of other algorithms. For example, by setting $a = 0$, Kruskal's algorithm is simulated; or by setting $a = b = 1$, Esau–William's algorithm results.

Before the publication of [CHOU 73], Chandy and Russell [CHAN 72] proved that most previously published heuristic algorithms, particularly the Esau–William algorithm [ESAU 66], achieve near-theoretic-optimum results. Cain [CAIN 74] then showed that the Chou–Kershenbaum algorithm always outperforms the Esau–William algorithm, in some cases by as much as 14 percent.

The Chou–Kershenbaum algorithm and others referenced in this section can all be classified as first-order greedy algorithms. At every step, two components are merged if the merge does not violate the performance constraint and if the merge results in the best cost trade-off. In a second-order greedy algorithm, the satisfaction of these two conditions would not necessarily result in the merging of the two components. Instead, an alternative least-cost design is sought under the condition that the two components are not merged. The cost of the design with the two merged and the cost of the least-cost design with the two not merged are compared and the one with lower cost is chosen. The second-order greedy algorithms can usually outperform the first-order greedy algorithms by a couple of percent, but at the expense of increased computational complexity. For detailed discussion on the second-order greedy algorithms, refer to [KERS 80] and [KARN 75].

In a large network with many terminals, large memory requirements and long execution times are primarily the result of determination and updating of t_{ij} values. Technically, determination of minimum t_{ij} implies the computation and storage of (t_{ij}) for all i and j. With 1000 terminals, this means that almost 1,000,000 lines have to be considered in calculating cost at each stage of the algorithm. The memory and computation time requirements, given large N, can be expressed as $K_m N^{a_m}$ and $K_t N^{a_t}$, where K_m, a_m, K_t, and a_t are constants and N is the number of terminals. With a straightforward implementation, a_m is 2 and a_t is 2 or 3 [WHIT 70]. Even if N is in the low hundreds, the computation time is so large that the algorithm is impractical to use.

To improve the efficiency of computation time, we must lower the value of a_m and a_t. It can be observed that by proper preprocessing, the value of K_t is increased with companion consequence of lowering the value of a_t. With the following two schemes, it can be shown that we are able to reduce a_m and a_t close to 1. For large practical networks, a_m and a_t can actually be reduced to a value less than 1. (The net result is that memory storage size and computation time are increased by the schemes for small N due to the increase in K_l, K_m but are reduced for large N.)

Scheme A.   Only Terminals within a Neighborhood
Being Considered for Connections

Without significant degradation in the resulting solution, the cost calculations can be reduced by considering only a few t_{ij}. This scheme is based on the premise that, in the optimum network design, it is very unlikely that a terminal will be connected directly to a very distant terminal.

Significant execution time savings can be obtained in determining the nearest neighbors instead of evaluating all interterminal costs, if the area containing the terminals is partitioned into grids. Then, for each terminal, the nearest neighbors are found by considering only the terminals contained either within the same grid or in the next adjacent grid area.

The computation time for evaluation and updating of t_{ij} can be reduced by maintaining the neighbors as a list-data structure with associated nearest-neighbor trade-off parameters. This structured list is referred to as a *heap*. Updating a heap structured array can be shown to be much more efficient than resorting an identically sized array. This is in part due to the fact that the least element is always located at the top of the heap. Maintaining the neighbors in a linked list has the advantage that after merging link (i) with its immediate neighbor link (j), and simply adjusting appropriate pointers, immediate neighbors of link (j) can be assigned as link (i)'s immediate neighbor. Note, once link (j) has been merged with link (i), it is no longer necessary to consider the link (i, j).

This scheme has been programmed in FORTRAN on an IBM 370/158. Figure 11.7 illustrates the nearly linear relationship between computation time and the number of different terminal locations when scheme A is used. Also shown is a predicted curve if costs are calculated for all terminals. Let K_t' represent K_t in an implementation with scheme A and K_t'' represent K_h in an implementation without scheme A. We *conservatively* assume that $K_t' = 50\ K_t''$, and *optimistically* assume that $a_t = 2$ for the curve without scheme A. (K_t' is found to be 0.075.)

With scheme A, the computation time can be expressed as $C_0 + C_l \log N + K_l'N$. For large N, the term $C_0 + C_l \log N$ is insignificant.

Scheme B.   Preprocessing Terminals in the Same Locality

Frequently, several terminals are located within a geographic area that is served by the same telephone central office or exchange. When these terminals are interconnected, often no mileage charges are levied. Thus they can form components and be interconnected based only on traffic or other constraints. By only increasing the number of terminals in each locality without increasing the number of localities, the value of N in $K_t N^{a_t}$ is hardly increased and the computation time is increased only slightly. For systems with more than a couple of hundred terminals, it is likely that many locations have multiple terminals. The multiplicity of terminals per location

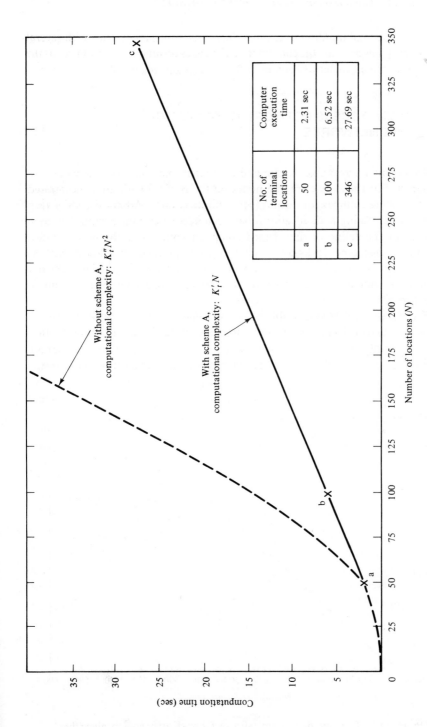

Figure 11.7. Computation complexity of Chou–Kershenbaum algorithm with scheme A.

	No. of terminal locations	Computer execution time
a	50	2.31 sec
b	100	6.52 sec
c	346	27.69 sec

Without scheme A, computational complexity: $K_t'' N^2$

With scheme A, computational complexity: $K_t' N$

Computation time (sec)

Number of locations (N)

increases as the total number of terminals increases. Thus, for systems with several hundred terminals or more, the computation time goes up much less than linear as the number of terminals increases. Figure 11.8 illustrates this relationship.

11.4 LOCAL ACCESS NETWORK OPTIMIZATION: RING NETWORKS

Only a very small percentage of data and computer communication networks are ring-shaped. For those that are, the nodes on the ring network are concentrated within a building complex, or the number of nodes is small. Ad hoc design of such networks (after noting node locations) has been adequate; no algorithm has been published for the design of ring-shaped computer communication networks. To consider ring-shaped networks covering larger geographical areas, good algorithms are needed. Good algorithms do exist; however, they were not inspired by data and computer communication networks, but are directly applicable to the layout of ring-shaped data communication networks.

The topological layout problem for the ring-shaped data networks can be classified into two problems. One problem is to connect terminals or communication devices into a ring (loop)-shaped network with minimum total transmission-line cost, given the locations of the devices. This problem is equivalent to the traveling salesman

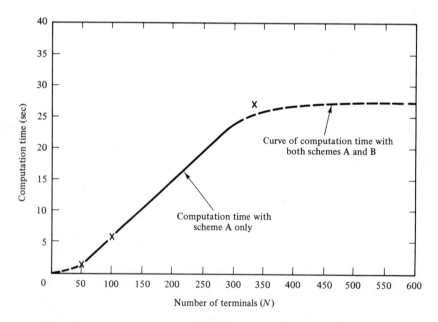

Figure 11.8. Computation complexity of Chou–Kershenbaum algorithm with schemes A and B.

problem of determining a minimum-cost tour for a salesman visiting every city exactly once. It can be effectively solved by the following steps. Start from an arbitrary initial ring interconnecting the nodes; add or drop links between one or more pairs of nodes while keeping the network in the ring shape; if the exchange does not result in a net cost saving, restore the original network; otherwise, use the new network and repeat the interchange process until no appreciable improvement can be made [LIN 65].

A second problem involves the layout of multiple ring-shaped networks. In this case, the number of terminal devices that can share a loop is often constrained by the terminal-generated traffic and by the link capacities. This second problem is the constrained loop problem, and can be considered an extension of the traveling salesman problem. Instead of having one salesman visiting all the cities, there are now several salesmen visiting different cities. Each salesman must start from the central office. The number of salesmen and the number of cities to be visited by a salesman depend on the sales load at the cities. The problem can be solved effectively by partitioning the terminals into separate rings and then optimizing each of these rings as a separate traveling salesman problem.

A very good algorithm for partitioning the terminals is the following one based on an algorithm developed by Clark and Wright [CLAR 64]. Initially, consider every terminal as forming a separate ring connected to the central node (communication device or host computer) by two links. Merge the two rings that result in the largest cost saving without violating constraints. Each time two rings are merged, two of the four links connecting them to the central node are removed and one link connecting the two individual rings is added. This process continues until no more rings can be merged without violating the constraints. This Clark–Wright algorithm gives good results for the terminal layout design problem even without the link exchange reoptimization of the individual rings. It is also interesting to note that the basic principle of their algorithm is quite similar to the one for tree network design. The Clark–Wright algorithm is presented below in a form similar to tree network design algorithms.

Modified Clark-Wright Algorithm for Ring Networks

STEP 0—INITIALIZATION

Algorithm	**Comments**
$A = \{1, 2, 3, ..., N_t\}$	(A is the set of nodes that are directly connected to the NAF; initially it is the set of all nodes; N_t = number of terminals)
$C_i = \{i\}$ for all $\forall\ i\ \varepsilon\ A$	(C_i is the component, or set of nodes, that contains i; initially, each component C_i contains one node)
$t_{ij} = \text{Max}\ \{d_i + d_j - d_{i,j}\}$ $\forall\ i, j\ \varepsilon\ A$ $C_i \neq C_j$	(Determine the cost trade-off functions of merging C_i, C_j; d_k = the cost con-

necting k to NAF)

STEP 1—DETERMINE THE MAXIMUM COST TRADE-OFF FUNCTION

$t_{i*,j*} \triangleq \text{Max } t_{i,j}, \quad i, j \, \varepsilon \, A$ (i, j must be terminals that are directly connected to the NAF)

STEP 2—MERGING TWO LOOPS BY ADDING A NEW LINK

If $C_{i*} \cup C_{j*}$ does not violate constraints (e.g., no more than a certain number of terminals per ring):

Add $(_{i*,j*})$ (Add a link)

$C_{i*} \leftarrow C_{i*} \cup C_{j*}$ (Merge two components)

$A \leftarrow A - \{i*\} - \{j*\}$ (Update the set of nodes that are directly connected to the NAF)

Update $t_{i,j}$ (Update trade-off function)

Otherwise, $t_{i*,j*} = -\infty$ [*Link (i*, j*)* is not allowed]

STEP 3—CHECK FOR ANY POSSIBLE FURTHER MERGE

If $t_{i,j} = -\infty \quad \forall \, i, \quad i \, \varepsilon \, A$,   (No components can be further
     go to step 4   merged)

Otherwise,
     go to step 1   (Go back to step 1 for considering further merge)

STEP 4—COMPLETE RINGS

Add a link from NAF to the free end
points of $C_i, \, \forall \, i \, \varepsilon \, A$; if $|C_i| = 1$,   (Form a ring-shaped network for each
add two links   component)

Stop

11.5 BACKBONE NETWORK OPTIMIZATION: PACKET-SWITCHING NETWORKS

A backbone network can be point-to-point, tree-shaped, ring-switched, or packet-switched. For the first three types, the techniques and algorithms given in Secs. 11.3 and 11.4 apply. This section discusses the optimization of packet-switching networks.

The topological design of distributed packet-switching networks was first discussed by Frank et al. [FRAN 70]. They described the application of branch exchange techniques in conjunction with branch deletion and addition techniques to the optimization of ARPANET. A summary of experience with branch exchange techniques for ARPANET optimization is given in [FRAN 72] and [BOOR 77].

Similar techniques are discussed in [LAVI 75]. Basically, these techniques seek repetitive cost or throughput improvement by adding, deleting, or simultaneously adding and deleting links (branches, lines) to a starting network until there are no modifications that result in an appreciable improvement. An evolution from the branch addition, deletion and exchange is the cut-saturation algorithm [GERL 74], which improves both the effectiveness of the design and efficiency of the computer program execution time. A cut is any set of lines whose removal will disconnect the network. A cut is saturated if the traffic load of every link in the cut is at capacity. There are, typically, a large number of cuts in a network. When the traffic load grows, one of the cuts approaches saturation. Then the only way the capacity of the network can be increased is by increasing the capacity of at least one link in the cut or by adding links across the cut. These ways form the basis for the cut-saturation algorithm. The algorithm attempts to satisfy throughput and response-time requirements while keeping overall cost low. It has been successfully applied to the various stages of the ARPANET, among others, and has been shown to be nearly optimum for problems under consideration [GERL 77].

Another class of heuristic algorithms for designing packet-switching networks are called concave branch elimination algorithms [YAGE 71, FRAT 73, GERL 77]. However, their limited applicability make them less useful than the cut-saturation approach [MARU 78].

However, the cut-saturation algorithm as given in [GERL 74] and [NAC 74] is somewhat biased by the ARPANET environment and is limited in its applicability to more general packet-switching networks. Specifically:

1. It always assumes a good starting design and uses the optimization algorithm to improve upon it (in a general environment, a "good" starting design is not always available).
2. It pays little attention to the applicability of multiple capacities and parallel links (with the proliferation of line tariffs, such considerations are likely).
3. The criterion to determine the locations to add links across a cut is derived purely from the experience of ARPANET network structure (therefore, it is not likely to be well suited to other environments).

A generalized cut-saturation algorithm for packet-switching network optimization has been developed with those deficiencies eliminated. The algorithm is quite complicated. Presented below is a simplified version. For a detailed discussion, see [SAPI 78] and [CHOU 82].

STEP 1—GENERATING A STARTING NETWORK

The starting network is generated by continuously adding one link at a time between nodes that are yet not connected. The choice of the node pair is based on the considerations of link costs, traffic requirements, and the total capacities of the links that have been connected to each of the nodes.

a. Let TRM (k) = kth largest element in $\{TR(i, j)\}$, where $TR(i, j)$ is the traffic requirement from packet switch i to j.

b. Reorder the first N_l elements in TRM according to ascending link costs, where N_l is determined by a prespecified parameter A such that N_l maximizes $TRM(1)/TRM(N_1) \leq A$. Let the vector be TRCOST.

c. Let the end points of the line represented by TRCOST (1) be i and j. If the sum of the line capacity connected to k divided by $\Sigma\ TR(k,l)$, $k = i$ or j, does not exceed a preset limit, B, line (i, j) is added. Otherwise, eliminate this link from the list and a new link is picked from TRM and reorder TRCOST.

d. Process c is repeated until all the nodes are connected.

Parameters A and B affect computer running time. For small networks, they may be set to infinity. For large networks, they should be set small. But if too small, a feasible network cannot be realized.

STEP 2—DEFINE GENERALIZED LINK CAPACITIES

A link can assume a generalized link capacity C_m. C_m, in general, consists of parallel lines of different speeds or capacities. Among them there are m_i parallel lines with speed S_i, for $i = 1, 2, ..., N_S$. The value of m_i can be zero.

Let $(S_i \mid i = 1, ..., N_S)$ be the set of available link speeds (capacities). The set of generalized capacities $(C_m \mid C_m < C_{m+1}, m = 0, 1, 2, ...)$ are defined as:

$$C_0 = 0$$
$$C_m = \sum_{i=1}^{N_S} m_i S_i, \qquad m_i = 1, 2, 3, ...$$

STEP 3—ROUTING

The routing operation determines the path(s) for every pair of nodes, upon which traffic should be sent. It checks whether a network can support the required throughput or can support more traffic than the original network. It is performed after each network modification and is used to generate a new optimal link flow. The routing operation is a necessary step regardless of which topological optimization technique is used.

One routing strategy is to send traffic along the shortest paths. Traffic that is overflowing from the shortest paths is sent via the second and third shortest paths and so on [CHOU 72].

STEP 4—SATURATED CUTSET DETERMINATION

The cutset that has been newly saturated must be determined after each operation. Link flows are calculated. The minimal cutset that has the highest utilization is the saturated cutset [CHOU 72].

STEP 5—ADD-ONLY ALGORITHM

If the network structure under consideration cannot accommodate the required throughput, an add-only algorithm determines the "best" link to be added across the two components separated by the saturated cutsets.

Let C_{nk} be the generalized capacity on link k. The "adding" of a link is used in a generic sense to mean the upgrading of the value of capacity for link k from C_{nk} to C_{nk+1} or higher. If link k did not exist before, this operation becomes the addition of a new link. Otherwise, this operation may upgrade the capacity of individual lines in link k or add parallel lines to link k.

Let $D_k(C_m)$ be the line cost of link k if link k assumes a capacity value of C_m. Link k must be either an existing or a potential new link across the saturated cut. Either of the following two criteria may be used:

Criterion 1. Upgrade the link whose upgrading results in minimum additional costs; that is, upgrade link k if

$$D_k(C_{nk+1}) - D_k(C_{nk}) = \min_i \; [D_i(C_{ni+1}) - D_i(C_{ni})]$$

Criterion 2. Upgrade the link whose upgrading appears to result in minimum additional costs per bit; that is, upgrade k if

$$\frac{(D_k(C_{nk+1}) - D_k(C_{nk})}{C_{nk+1} - C_{nk}}$$

$$= \min \; \frac{D_i(C_{ni+1} - D_i(C_{ni})}{C_{ni+1} - C_{ni}}$$

For computer running-time efficiency, only a subset of possible k's should be considered. In particular, choose only those links whose end points have high unsatisfied traffic requirements for nodes across the saturated cut.

STEP 6—DELETE-ONLY ALGORITHM

This algorithm may be applied if the throughput supported by the network structure under consideration is higher than the requirement. The Delete-Only operation begins with a highly connected topology and "deletes" one "link" at each iteration, continuously reducing cost and throughput. The deleting of link k is used in a general sense to mean the degrading of link k's generalized capacity from C_{nk} to C_{nk-1} or lower. If C_{nk-1} is zero, this operation eliminates link k. Otherwise, this operation reduces the capacities of individual lines in link k or reduces the number of parallel lines in link k.

Either of the following two criteria may be used for "degrading."

Criterion 1. Degrade the link that has the most residue capacity; that is, degrade link k if

$$C_{n_{k-1}} - f_k = \max_i (C_{n_{i-1}} - f_i) > 0$$

where f_i is traffic flow on link k.

Criterion 2.   Degrade the link whose degrading will result in the maximum costs per bit savings; that is, degrade link k if

$$\frac{D_k(C_{n_k}) - D_k(C_{n_k-1})}{f_k - C_{n_k-1}}$$

$$= \max_i \frac{D_i(C_{n_i}) - D_i(C_{n_i-1})}{f_i - C_{n_i-1}}$$

for $f_i < C_{n_i-1}$.

STEP 7—EXCHANGE

This operation combines Add-Only and Delete-Only operations and is used to improve the throughput or the cost. One link is deleted according to the Delete-Only algorithm and one or more links is added according to the Add-Only algorithm. Exchange operation is performed when the Add-Only algorithm cannot further improve appreciably the throughput and the Delete-Only algorithm cannot further improve appreciably the cost.

Figure 11.9 demonstrates the efficiency and effectiveness of the generalized cut-saturation algorithm. Figure 11.9b is a network design that was designed with several executions of the ARPANET-based optimization algorithm and with a substantial amount of human interface, including specification of the starting network design. Figure 11.9a shows the design obtained by a single execution of the generalized cut-saturation algorithm. The throughput and response-time requirements were the same as for Fig. 11.9b and no starting network was specified. It was designed within 28 sec. of processing time on an IBM 370/168 machine (at a computing cost of $2.20). Yet this design realizes savings of over $200,000 (11%) annually. Figure 11.9c summarizes the comparison.

11.6   INTEGRATED OPTIMIZATION AND NAF PLACEMENT

11.6.1   Integrated Optimization Process

The communications cost for a data/computer network in general consists of the costs of NAFs, the local access network, and the backbone network. Minimizing the costs for one of the three elements is likely to increase the overall cost. It is important that to optimize the overall communication network costs, the three design problems should be treated as an integrated one. (All conventional approaches, however, have treated them as separate optimization or design problems resulting in potentially an overall suboptimized network.)

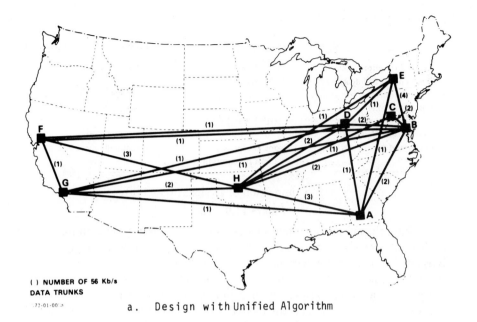

( ) NUMBER OF 56 Kb/s
DATA TRUNKS

a. Design with Unified Algorithm

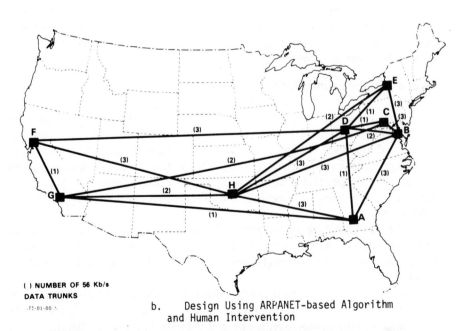

( ) NUMBER OF 56 Kb/s
DATA TRUNKS

b. Design Using ARPANET-based Algorithm
and Human Intervention

Figure 11.9. Comparison of network design with and without the generalized cut-saturation algorithm: (a) design with generalized cut-saturation algorithm; (b) design using ARPANET-based algorithm and human intervention; (c) comparison of designs (a) and (b).

	Generalized Cut-Saturation Algorithm	ARPANET-Based Algorithm
Network throughput	1529.2 kbps	1635.43 kbps
Average end-to-end delay	0.1233 sec	0.1233 sec
Communication cost per year	$1,675,411	$1,881,474
Computation time	28 sec (IBM 370/168)	Substantially more
Computer time charge	$2.20	Substantially more
Human interface	None except input preparation	Substantially more

(c) Comparison of Designs (a) and (b)

Figure 11.9. *(cont.)*

Since the number and locations optimization impact directly on the costs of both local access and backbone networks, it is only logical to implement the integrated optimization process in conjunction with the optimal placement process of the NAFs. Figure 11.10 is a simplified version illustrating the interrelation of the integrated process and the three optimization processes. Basically, whenever a set of locations are considered as potential NAF sites, the integrated process interfaces the local access optimization and the backbone network optimization process to determine the costs of the two subnetworks under this set of NAFs. The network costs either may be determined by a complete optimization procedure or estimated by a heuristic. Section 11.6.2 describes the algorithm combining the integrated process and the NAF optimization process.

11.6.2 Optimization of NAF Placement

The problem of determining the number and location of NAFs is very similar to the classic warehouse (or plant) location problem. The warehouse location problem is to determine the number, location, and capacity of source sites that minimize the cost of satisfying shipping requirements [COOP 62]. A "warehouse" corresponds to an "NAF," and shipping requirements correspond to traffic requirements. Many techniques and algorithms for warehouse location problems have been applied to the NAF problem.

A general NAF location algorithm has (heuristic) procedures for as many as four problems: determining potential sites, iteratively placing NAFs at the potential sites, estimating the cost of local access networks, and estimating the cost of the backbone networks.

If the number of sites on which NAFs may be placed is small, every one can be designated as a potential site. If not, only a subset of all the possible sites should be designated as potential sites to reduce the computational complexity. Iterative procedures are then used to determine the number of NAFs and the eventual NAF sites among the potential NAF sites. The optimal number and locations of NAFs depend on the costs of the network. These network costs are sometimes estimated instead of being determined exactly.

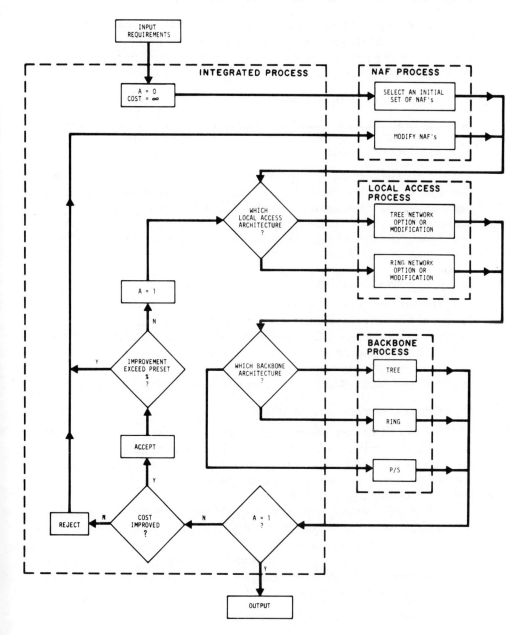

Figure 11.10.   Integrated optimization process.

Many algorithms, with different degrees of applicability to real problems, have been developed and published [BAHL 72; WOO 73; GREE 73; DIRI 76; HSIE 76A, B; MCGR 77; CHOU 78A, B; TANG 78]. Classification and comparison of many of these algorithms can be found in [MCGR 77] and [CHOU 78A]. Presented in this section is the Integrated Network Access Facility (INAF) Location Algorithm given in [CHOU 78A, B]. (For a formal presentation of the algorithm, refer to [CHOU 78A].) The INAF algorithm possesses several important features that are not available with other algorithms.

A.   Integrated optimization process

It incorporates the integrated optimization process discussed in Sec. 11.6.1.

B.   Exact network costs

At every step in the iterative process, when one chosen set of NAF locations is compared with another alternative, the costs of NAFs, terminal or local access networks, and backbone networks are all included. One consequence of using the integrated process is the availability of the exact costs of the two networks. (Otherwise, some of the network costs may have to be estimated and the accuracy of the result would be affected.)

C.   Universal applicability

It is often desirable to evaluate alternatives of different network architectures. Instead of one NAF location algorithm for each type of architecture, INAF is implemented in a generalized form which enables it to handle different types of NAF problems based on input parameters. This is not difficult to achieve. It is basically a problem of providing the interface between different types of local access and backbone networks, and being able to determine costs of these networks.

D.   Consolidated heuristic techniques

The experience learned from packet-switching network optimization [GERL 74, BOOR 77] is that appplication of a single heuristic technique may not always result in a good design. Therefore, the INAF algorithm to be described incorporates several techniques which are applied interchangeably to a problem as required. These are: add, drop, exchange, and merge.

The first two techniques have been used in both the NAF problem and the warehouse allocation problem (see [COOP 62]). The idea of the exchange technique, where one NAF is dropped and another is added simultaneously, is borrowed from the packet-switching network optimization problem. The merge technique basically combines terminal clusters associated with two NAFs into one, deletes the two NAFs, and chooses a new NAF from the new cluster.

E.   Variable NAF capacities

It is not unusual that different types of NAFs with different characteristics, capacities, and costs are used in the same system; or that multiple NAFs are located at the same site. In INAF, the cost of an NAF is defined as a function of throughput and number of lines it handles, which is usually a step function. This is a general way to accommodate different types of NAFs. Therefore, when INAF selects an NAF site, the type of NAF to be located at that site is also determined. In addition, when INAF is adding an NAF, it also permits the new NAF to be located at a site where at least one other NAF has been placed.

Integrated NAF Location Algorithm

STEP 1—SELECT A SUBSET OF PERMISSIBLE SITES
AS POTENTIAL NAF SITES

a.   *Check the size of locations permissible as NAF sites.* Certain locations may be designated as mandatory NAF sites and certain others as permissible. If the sum of the two sets is reasonably small, they are all designated as potential NAF (PNAF) sites and steps 1b, c, and d are skipped. (A mandatory site is a location where an NAF must be placed independent of cost considerations. Mandatory sites are specified as input constraints. A permissible site is a location where an NAF may be placed if it is cost effective to do so. Permissible sites are also given as input constraints. Potential NAF sites are a subset of the permissible sites that are determined by the INAF as candidates for NAF sites.)

b.   *Cluster terminals.* If the input-specified permissible NAF set is large, the magnitude of the design problem may be reduced by initially clustering the terminals. Intuitively, a good location for a NAF is the center of a cluster of terminals. Thus, by considering only the centers of a set of clusters, the magnitude of the initial problem may be significantly reduced. The number of initial clusters and the cluster size can be provided by input specifications or can be calculated by the algorithm. The clustering can be performed by using Kruskal's algorithm [KRUS 56].

c.   *Determine center of mass of the clusters.* The centers of mass (COMs) for the clusters are determined. Only those clusters that have permissible NAF sites but not mandatory NAF sites need be considered. For each such cluster, define the COM by:

$$V \text{ coordinate of COM} = \frac{\displaystyle\sum_{1}^{N_c} t_i V_i}{\displaystyle\sum t_i}$$

$$H \text{ coordinate of COM} = \frac{\displaystyle\sum_{1}^{N_c} t_i H_i}{\displaystyle\sum t_i}$$

where t_i = traffic from node i
   $V_i, H_i = (V, H)$ coordinates of node i
   N_c = number of nodes in cluster

d.   *Refine the center of mass.* The COM as defined above is a mathematically defined location and hence may not correspond to a physical node location. Determine a permissible NAF site closest to each COM amd assign it as a PNAF.

STEP 2—DESIGN LOCAL ACCESS NETWORK

This step designs the local access network. Initially, assume that all PNAF locations are NAF locations. Using algorithms in earlier sections, the local access network can be designed.

STEP 3—DESIGN BACKBONE NETWORK

Having designed the local access network, the traffic emanating from each PNAF can be assessed. Three distinct types of backbone network designs are considered: (a) point-to-point, (b) multipoint, and (c) packet-switched. For (a), connect each NAF to the closest CPU. For (b), connect the NAFs to the CPUs via multipoint trees using similar algorithms defined earlier. For (c), use packet-switching techniques defined earlier for the backbone network.

STEP 4—SELECT THE NAF SITES

a.   *Drop algorithm.* In this step, for each PNAF that is nonmandatory and has been selected as an NAF site in the current design step, the potential cost savings to be obtained by dropping it is evaluated. This consists of (a) savings in backbone network, and (b) savings in local access network. A PNAF whose removal yields maximum positive savings is permanently dropped from the network. If the cost saving is negative, this step is concluded. The savings (a) and (b) can be either evaluated exactly or estimated using heuristics.

- *Heuristic cost adjustment for backbone.* If the PNAF considered for dropping is singly connected to another node, the backbone cost saving simply equals the line cost plus the physical cost of the NAF. If the PNAF is connected to more than one node, consider all the nodes directly connected to this PNAF. Consider, in turn, each of these nodes for direct connection to the rest of the nodes. Whichever of these yields the least cost is considered the alternative. The cost saving equals the line cost of the new configuration minus the line cost of the previous configuration plus the NAF cost.

- *Heuristic cost adjustment for local access.* Consider all the lines that were connected to this PNAF. For each of these lines determine the closest NAF (other than the NAF under consideration) and check if this NAF can accommodate one additional input port. If not, dropping the NAF is infeasible. If it can, consider this the alternative local access configuration. As before, the cost saving equals the new line cost minus the previous line cost.

After each K is an input parameter) iterations, reoptimize the local access and backbone networks. (If $K = 1$, the heuristic cost adjustment is not necessary. The larger the value of K, the less computer execution time that is needed, but at the expense of a possible sacrifice in accuracy.)

b.   *Add algorithm.* This step considers the cost saving to be obtained by adding an NAF site. For this purpose, PNAFs that are not selected for the current design and that are farthest from the current set of PNAFs are considered for potential addition. The cost saving can be estimated heuristically with similar steps as those in the drop algorithm. The PNAF whose addition results in the greatest positive saving is added to the network. If the saving is negative, conclude this step. If the number of iterations equals K, reoptimize the local access and backbone networks.

c.   *Split algorithm.* This step considers the cost saving that can result if a PNAF having a large number of terminals is replaced by two PNAFs. Consider KS (input parameter) PNAFs that have the most number of terminals. For each of these, heuristically adjust the cost saving by replacing it with two NAFs. If the maximum cost saving is positive, make the split permanent; if not, conclude this step. After K iterations, reoptimize the local access and backbone networks.

d.   *Exchange algorithm.* This step examines the cost saving obtainable by exchanging NAF locations. It considers unselected PNAF locations that are farthest from the current set of selected PNAFs; each of these locations is examined for the effect of making it an NAF and simultaneously dropping the selected PNAF that is closest to it. As before, make permanent an exchange that yields the most positive heuristic cost-saving adjustment. After each K iteration, reoptimize the local access and backbone networks.

e.   *Merging algorithm.* This step examines the cost saving obtainable by merging two neighboring terminal clusters into one, ignoring the two selected PNAFs associated with the two clusters and selecting a new PNAF for the combined cluster.

In any one design run, all substeps need not be executed. For a given design problem one of these steps may be more useful than the others in achieving low-cost networks. The designer can experiment with the order and number of these heuristics to be applied.

STEP 5—REFINEMENT AND REOPTIMIZATION

If any network adjustments have been made since the last redesign of the network, reoptimize both the local access and backbone networks.

11.6.3   Performance Analysis

11.6.3.1   *Cost Comparison of Integrated and Nonintegrated Approaches*

Figure 11.11a compares the costs between the designs obtained from the integrated and nonintegrated approaches. Cost information for the nonintegrated approach was derived from data presented by McGregor and Shen [MCGR 77]. Only local access, backbone line cost, and concentrator costs were considered in doing the comparative evaluation. Locations of terminals used in the data presented in Fig. 11.11 were obtained from a uniformly random distribution of sites taken over a rectangle 2000 by 3000 miles in size.

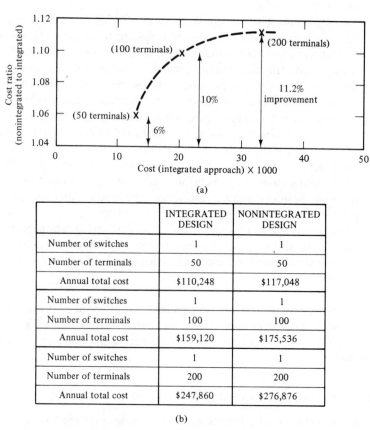

(a)

	INTEGRATED DESIGN	NONINTEGRATED DESIGN
Number of switches	1	1
Number of terminals	50	50
Annual total cost	$110,248	$117,048
Number of switches	1	1
Number of terminals	100	100
Annual total cost	$159,120	$175,536
Number of switches	1	1
Number of terminals	200	200
Annual total cost	$247,860	$276,876

(b)

	COST BASIS
Concentrator (NAF)	$200/month
Line charges/mile	$0.50/mile
Termination charge	$40/termination

(c)

Figure 11.11. Cost comparison information: (a) cost comparison curve; (b) cost comparison table; (c) charges considered in determining communication cost.

The specific cost comparisons of the two approaches for three network designs are given in the table in Fig. 11.11b. Figure 11.11c gives the cost information on lines and devices. Figure 11.12 is the plot of one of the network designs (200-terminal design). In the comparisons above it should be noted that the reason for using McGregor–Shen's data is that the McGregor–Shen COM algorithm has been demonstrated to be the best heuristic algorithm among the nonintegrated approaches.

11.6.3.2 *Comparison of Heuristic Techniques*

In iteratively determining a best set of NAF sites, one or more of the following heuristic techniques can be used within the INAF algorithm: "drop," "add," "exchange," and "merge." In examining the effectiveness of each of these techniques, and whether there is any need to combine more than one of these techniques experiments were carried out on a 50-terminal network, a 100-terminal network, and a 150-terminal network [CHOU 78A]. For each of the networks, the NAF algorithm was evaluated applying only the drop heuristic, only the add heuristic, the drop–add–exchange–merge sequence, and the add–drop–exchange–merge sequence. In every one of the three networks, it was indicated from the results that application of the "drop" algorithm could not be improved by using any of the other heuristic approaches. On applying the "add" heuristic process, a network design that was approximately two to four percent more expensive than that obtained by applying

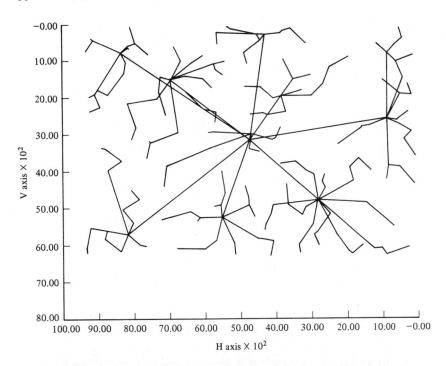

Figure 11.12. Integrated algorithm network design (200 terminals).

only "drop" resulted. This design (obtained using "add" only) was improved upon by one to two percent through the application of the "exchange" technique. The improvement was achieved within one iteration. Further application of the "exchange," or the application of "merge" techniques, resulted in no additional improvements in network costs. The cost comparison of the "drop" only, "add-- exchange," and "add"-only techniques is shown in Fig. 11.13.

Because of the limited number of samples, no definite conclusion can be drawn from these experiments. However, they do provide an insight into the tendency of how these heuristics perform. The "drop" technique seems to be the best. It outper- forms the "add" technique and does not require application of the other techniques to provide an optimal solution.

The fact that the "merge" technique was not able to improve the results

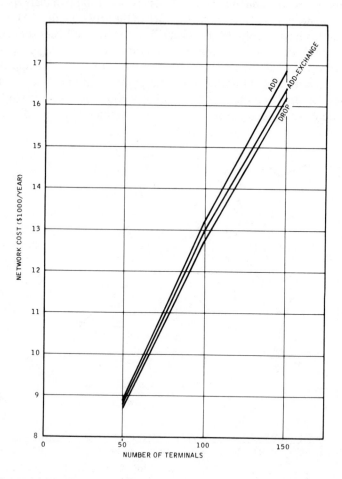

Figure 11.13. Cost comparison of drop only, add only, and add-exchange heuristics.

obtained from applying either the "drop" or the "add" and that use of the "exchange" technique improved the results provided by the "add" technique by only one to two percent implies that both "drop" and even "add" are quite robust, particularly the "drop" technique. Although one cannot prove or claim that the "drop" technique results in the absolute optimal solution, the "drop" heuristics do appear to provide, in most cases, the most nearly-optimal solution possible with the methods available. Because of the robustness of the "drop" and even "add" techniques, "exchange" and "merge" are not much needed. However, no matter how well a heuristic process may seem to perform, in most cases poor results for certain pathological cases are possible. Hence refinements in a design applying different techniques should normally be attempted. Thus "exchange" and "merge" heuristics may be viewed as insurance against the pathological cases, in that the heuristics may catch and improve specific problem designs.

11.7 NETWORK MODELS FOR SATELLITE COMMUNICATIONS

A satellite communication channel of a certain bandwidth or capacity can be configured either as a cable in the sky that connects two earth stations (point-to-point access) or as a facility that is shared by several earth stations (multiple access). In the point-to-point mode, the satellite channel is used like a terrestrial channel and can be modeled in the same manner (i.e., a line connecting two end points).

In the multiple-access mode, the allocation of the channel can be either static or dynamic. With the static allocation, the channel is further divided into subchannels and each user is dedicated a subchannel. All subchannels need not be assigned the same capacity. This can be achieved by time-division multiplexing, frequency-division multiplexing, or other appropriate multiple-access schemes. Once a sub-channel is assigned to a user or an earth station, other users or stations cannot send information through this subchannel, even if it is idle. However, any user or earth station may receive information from other subchannels because of the broadcast nature of the satellite downlink. This fixed-allocation broadcast approach is termed channel-division multiple access. In essence, every earth station is given a fixed allocation of the uplink channel, while the downlink channel is broadcast. With the dynamic allocation, the users seek access to the same channel independently. A set of built-in rules schedule the traffic so as to optimize channel utilization and minimize conflicts.

The multiple-access satellite channel can be represented with the model shown in Fig. 11.14, consisting of $2N_E + 1$ simplex links (where N_E is the number of earth stations) and two hypothetical store-and-forward switches. The uplinks are all connected to one switch and the downlinks are all originated from the other switch. A simplex link connects the first switch to the second one. The link capacity values for both the channel division model and the dynamic access model are shown in Fig. 11.14.

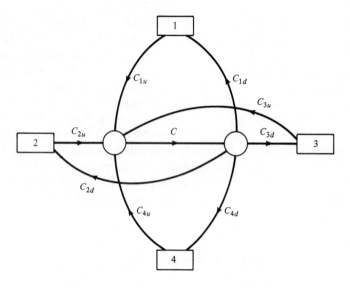

For channel-division multiple access:

$C_{iu} = C_i$ = capacity for uplink subchannel assigned to earth station i, $\forall\,i$
$C_{id} = \infty\;\forall\,i$; $C = \infty$

For random or dynamic multiple access:

$C_{iu} = C_{id} = \infty\;\forall\,i$
C = total channel capacity

Figure 11.14. Network model for multiple access satellite communication channel. Rectangle, earth station; circle, hypothetical S/F switch.

11.8 LINE COST MODEL

The model given in Fig. 11.15 can probably represent almost any line cost tariff. It consists of one main channel segment, two extension channel segments, and two local loop segments. The telephone central offices that are linked by the main channels serve the areas where the communication services are normally provided. Service under a particular tariff is sometimes restricted to certain geographic locations. For example, AT&T's DDS is available only to a certain specific set of high-traffic-usage locations. However, the service can be extended to areas served by central offices near the DDS central offices. These two types of central offices are linked generically by extension channels. In most cases, there are no extension channels, or equivalently, the distance of the extension channel is zero. The local loop is the portion that connects the user equipment to the central office.

The tariff so modeled can be further characterized by the maximum number of channels or speed the link can handle, the locations when the service is available, and the locations where the extension service is available.

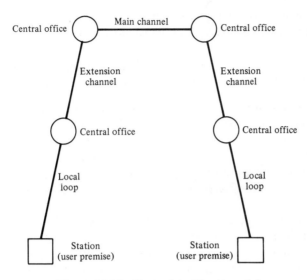

Figure 11.15. General tariff cost model.

The end-to-end cost is determined by (1) the main channel mileage charge as a step function of the mileage, parameterized by the number of channels, (2) extension channel mileage charge as another function of distance, (3) the local loop mileage charge (usually distance independent), (4) channel termination charges for the main channel and extension channel (distance independent), and (5) the station termination charges as a function of the number of station terminations at the same premise or in the same central office service area. (When there is no extension channel, the costs associated with it are all zero.)

11.9 SOFTWARE TOOLS

Because of the complexity of the algorithms, software tools are necessary for all but the most trivial networks. Such tools, with various levels of sophistication, are widely available. One of them is ACK/TOPS [CHOU 78, CHOU 81A], which incorporates algorithms and models similar to those in Chap. 10 and those in this chapter. Another one is MIND [KOZI 81], which incorporates mainly the Chou–Kershenbaum algorithm, and the simulation of multipoint polled networks [CHOU 81A]. Discussion of several others can be found in [KONS 80]. When software tools are developed, attention should be paid to two issues: (1) transformation of the abstraction of the models and algorithms into the design of specific types of networks, and (2) the ease of using the tools. Examples of using software tools are given in the Appendix.

11.9.1   Analysis and Design Problems
That Can Be Handled by Software Tools

Specific analysis and design problems that can be solved by software tools are numerous. Listed below are several typical ones. There are many other possibilities.

1. *Terminal response-time analysis.* Given the operating environment of a polled line (configuration, traffic characteristics, protocols), determine the average response time, the time that is greater than 90% of the response times, 95%, or other figure.
2. *Traffic sensitivity analysis.* Given the operating environment of a polled line, determine the average response time as a function of the variations of the traffic loads specified by the input.
3. *Traffic loading table determination.* Determine the maximum amount of traffic a line can handle as a function of the number of terminals.
4. *Centralized teleprocessing network design.* Determine the least-cost network design satisfying traffic and response-time requirements for the situation where all the terminal access lines are terminating at a single host computer.
5. *Distributed teleprocessing network design.* Determine the least-cost network design satisfying traffic and response-time requirements for the situation where terminal access lines are terminating at geographically distributed multiple-host sites. (Note that the difference between this problem and the preceding problem is that we have geographically distributed multiple-host sites instead of just one host computer site.)
6. *Teleprocessing network design with unspecified NAF locations.* Determine the least-cost network design satisfying traffic and response-time requirements that include the terminal access network; the determination of the number, the locations and the size of the NAFs; and the backbone network.
7. *Teleprocessing network design with specified NAF locations.* Make the same determination as for problem 6 except that some of the NAF locations are constrained by the input.
8. *Designing terminal access network for accessing public data networks.* Determine the least-cost terminal access network that terminates at public data network's access points or switches. (Note that this is a special application of problems 4, 5, 6, and 7, by simply treating the public data network's access points or switches as host computer sites.)
9. *Determining number and size of satellite Earth stations.* Given the terminal locations, determine the number and size of satellite earth stations in order to achieve the minimum total cost for the earth segments and the satellite segments. (This is a special application of problem 6 or 7 by treating the satellite as a pseudo-host computer site and treating the satellite channel as a pseudo-line tariff whose cost is independent of distance.)
10. *Packet-switching network performance analysis.* Given the control procedure, traffic characteristics, and network configuration and sizing, evaluate the throughput and end-to-end delay relationship.

11. *Packet-switching network design with given switch locations.* Given the control procedure, traffic characteristics, traffic and performance requirements, switch locations, and cost information, determine the least-cost network configuration.

12. *Packet-switching network design without prespecified switch locations.* Similar to problem 11 except that the switch locations are not specified and are determined based on terminal locations.

13. *Reliability analysis.* Based on the link and failure rates, determine the network reliability (such as percentage of time the network is not connected, etc.).

14. *Designing CCSA (common control switching arrangement) networks.* Determine the number and locations of the switches and the number of trunks between the switches for CCSA networks. (This is a special application of packet-switching networks by substituting the entries and delays with blocking probability and substituting the trunk capacity with number of trunks.)

11.9.2   Features Aimed for Ease of Use

The usefulness of a software tool depends more on human engineering considerations than on the sophistication of algorithms and models. Examples of this are the design of interactive input that can be easily learned and used, the input–output formats, the input data preparation and manipulation of output, and the inclusion of various defaults. Listed below are examples of features that are nice to have.

Data Link Control Procedures

- User-selectable, built-in data link control procedures. Typical control procedures, such as BSC (Binary Synchronous Control), SDLC (Synchronous Data Link Control), and start/stop procedures, should be built into the program system to allow users to select either of them at the time of specifying inputs.
- User-definable data link control procedures. If a user has a data link control procedure that deviates from built-in ones, he or she should be able to specify the data link control procedure during the input process.

Line Tariffs

- User-selectable, built-in line tariffs. Commonly used line tariffs (line cost structure) should be contained in the program system. Users may specify any of them.
- User-definable line tariff. If user needs a line tariff that is not one of the built-in ones, he or she should be allowed to specify it.

Constraints

- Response time considerations. The user should be able to specify response time, line utilization, and/or number of terminals per line as constraints.

- Reliability considerations. It is desirable to have the ability to design networks with different reliability considerations (which, of course, will result in different costs).

Trunk Sizing

Depending on the traffic loading from terminal lines, the program system should be capable of automatically sizing the trunks with different line speeds.

Network Access Facilities Sizing

Based on traffic conditions, each NAF needs to be configured individually and its cost calculated individually. For example, in using multiplexers the specific model and number of ports of a multiplexer would depend on the number of terminal lines it is connected to.

Traffic Sensitivity Analysis

To estimate the traffic requirement for any network is not an exact science. The capability to evaluate the variation in performance as a function of the variations of estimated traffic load is desirable.

One-Step Design Process and Total Design Capability

From constraints specified by the input, the software should be capable of determining the total design in a single execution, including the traffic loading as a function of the number of terminals; the number, sizing, and location of NAFs; the backbone network; the capacity and tariff for each of the backbone trunks; and the terminal access network.

Easy to Use

The users should have no need to remember the symbols and key words to input parameters.

Efficiency and Effectiveness

- Accuracy. The degree of accuracy depends on the sophistication of algorithm schemes used.
- Efficiency in human time. If the one-step design process is used, every time a design is being made the human time and the real time can both be much less.
- Efficiency in computer execution time. With proper choice of algorithms and heuristics, the execution time for using the program can be made to increase as little as approximately linearly with the number of terminals.

ACKNOWLEDGMENT

The work in this chapter is supported by NSF Grant ENG-77-24110.

Appendix

Applications and Examples

If traffic parameters, performance constraints, control procedures and system parameters, line tariffs (cost functions), hardware costs, and terminal/host locations are all specifically defined or known, then the algorithms discussed in this chapter lead to the procedures of a single network design. Often, however, there are unknowns or uncertainties in some of these elements. When this is so, multiple network designs are necessary. The choice of the final design will then be based on considerations beyond those of network analysis and design issues.

In this section two examples are given. The first one involves the uncertainty of choosing between deterministic and adaptive routings for packet switching networks spanning several time zones. The second example deals with the uncertainty of estimated traffic volumes.

EXAMPLE 11.A.1: COST IMPACT OF ROUTING PROCEDURES ON NETWORKS SPANNING SEVERAL TIME ZONES

There have been differences in opinion regarding whether an adaptive routing or a deterministic routing procedure is better in general for use in packet switching networks [CHOU 79], [CHOU 81B]. There are, of course, specific cases where one is better than the other. It appears potentially possible that a network spanning several time zones may benefit from adaptive routing procedures [CHOU 82]. There are times of the day when one part of the network is under peak load while other parts of the network generate very little traffic. It is conceivable that under the adaptive routing procedure the part of the network generating the peak traffic load can route part of the traffic through other parts of the network. It is, therefore, reasonable to assume that the network costs of the network using adaptive routing can be less than that of the network using deterministic routing. The example in this subsection designs two networks under, respectively, the adaptive and deterministic routing procedures and compares their costs.

1. Assumptions

Locations:

Switch Site	Time Zone
1 New York	Eastern
2 Philadelphia	Eastern
3 Detroit	Eastern
4 Baltimore	Eastern
5 Washington	Eastern
6 Chicago	Central
7 Houston	Central
8 Dallas	Central

9	Milwaukee	Central
10	Memphis	Central
11	Los Angeles	Pacific
12	San Francisco	Pacific
13	Seattle	Pacific
14	San Diego	Pacific
15	Portland	Pacific

Packet size:

Average 1,000 bits/packet

Traffic volume (average):

- For any pair of switches in the same time zone
  1.2 Kbps during working hours
  33% higher during peak hours
  Almost zero during non-working hours
- For switches between different zones
  Average of the two values of the traffic between switches in the individual zones

Performance constraints:

Average 0.5 seconds end-to-end

Control procedures and overhead:

Emulated to be similar to those in ARPANET, except for the deterministic routing procedure which follows the minimum hop paths.

Line tariffs:

MPL and DDS (for 19.2 Kbps, two DDS lines are used)

2. Results

Figures 11.A.1 and 11.A.2 are network topologies representing the designs for deterministic and adaptive routings, respectively. Tables 11.A.1 and 11.A.2 list link locations and associated costs. (Because of the fact that under the adaptive routing strategy a link can be used by peak-hour traffic of different time zones at different times, the link speeds in this situation can be lower than those under the deterministic strategy. Consequently, the total line cost for networks using the adaptive routing strategy is lower.) The cost difference between these two designs is $10,734, and the network design under adaptive routing procedures is 11% lower than that under the deterministic routing procedures. The cost difference listed here is that of the network. It is conceivable that there would be higher costs on software and packet switches and higher complexity in control associated with the adaptive routing procedures. The

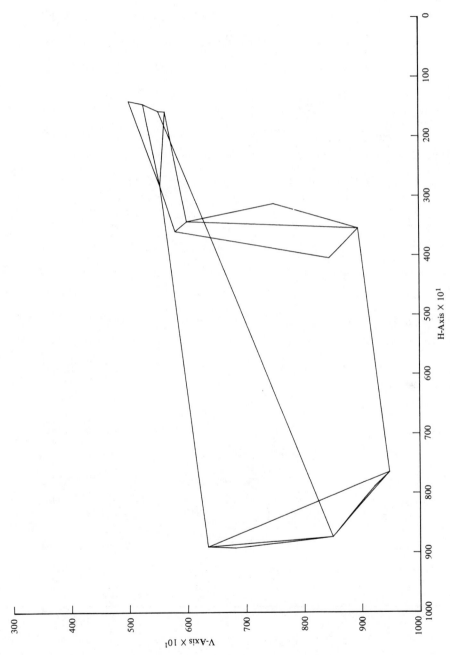

Figure 11.A.1. Network topology for Example 11.A.1, with a deterministic routing strategy.

H-Axis X 10^1

V-Axis X 10^1

37

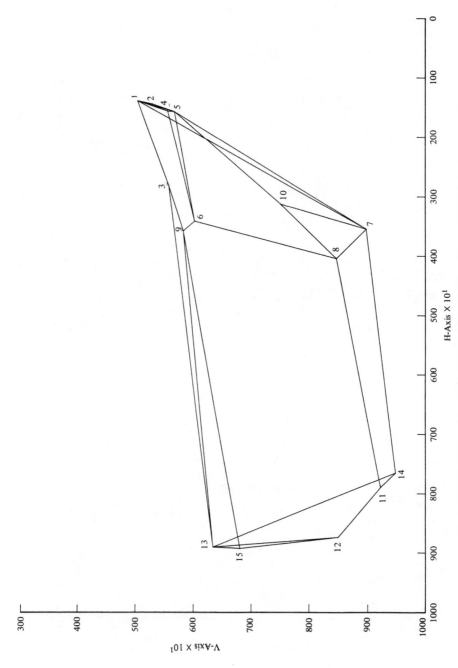

Figure 11.A.2. Network topology for Example 11.A.1, with an adaptive routing strategy.

H-Axis X 10¹

V-Axis X 10¹

38

Table 11.A.1. *Link Locations and Costs for Example 11.A.1, With a Deterministic Routing Strategy.*

Location	Speed	Cost $/Month	Tariff
New York - Philadelphia	19200	2,159.52	DDS2
New York - Detroit	19200	2,934.12	DDS2
Philadelphia - Baltimore	19200	2,185.44	DDS2
Philadelphia - Detroit	19200	2,862.68	DDS2
Detroit - Washington	56000	4,557.10	DDS
Detroit - Seattle	56000	10,114.81	DDS
Baltimore - Washington	19200	2,010.48	DDS2
Baltimore - San Francisco	19200	5,590.68	DDS2
Washington - Chicago	56000	5,497.10	DDS
Houston - Chicago	56000	7,095.10	DDS
Houston - Dallas	56000	3,753.40	DDS
Houston - Memphis	19200	2,936.00	DDS2
Houston - San Diego	56000	8,288.00	DDS
Chicago - Milwaukee	19200	2,159.52	DDS2
Chicago - Memphis	19200	2,932.24	DDS2
Dallas - Milwaukee	19200	3,627.84	DDS2
San Diego - Seattle	56000	7,600.70	DDS
San Diego - Los Angeles	19200	2,242.28	DDS2
San Diego - San Francisco	19200	2,900.28	DDS2
Seattle - Portland	56000	3,391.50	DDS
Seattle - San Francisco	19200	3,317.64	DDS2
Los Angeles - San Francisco	19200	2,689.72	DDS2
Portland - San Francisco	19200	3,043.16	DDS2

decision between the two must be made based on all the factors considered and not on the network costs alone.

EXAMPLE 11.A.2: DESIGN OF HOST-ORIENTED, CENTRALLY CONTROLLED TELEPROCESSING NETWORKS UNDER UNCERTAIN TRAFFIC ESTIMATES

It is quite common that at the time of designing a network, the traffic to be generated by the terminals is unknown, or the estimation of the traffic to be generated is far from accurate, or the traffic volume is expected to grow rapidly. Under these conditions the design of a single least-cost network does not always make sense. Sensitivity analyses should be made. A set of network topologies are designed based on a range of traffic volumes. The traffic level upon which to design the network can then be decided.

Table 11.A.2. *Link Locations and Costs for Example 11.A.1, With an Adaptive Routing Strategy.*

Location	Speed	Cost $/Month	Tariff
New York - Philadelphia	56000	3,024.80	DDS
New York - Detroit	56000	4,961.30	DDS
New York - Baltimore	56000	3,504.30	DDS
New York - Washington	19200	2,417.12	DDS2
New York - Houston	9600	2,196.78	DDS
Philadelphia - Washington	19200	2,262.96	DDS2
Detroit - Milwaukee	19200	2,507.36	DDS2
Detroit - Seattle	19200	4,995.60	DDS2
Baltimore - Chicago	9600	1,583.62	DDS
Baltimore - Washington	56000	2,652.20	DDS
Washington - Houston	9600	2,080.78	DDS
Washington - Chicago	19200	3,148.44	DDS2
Washington - Memphis	19200	3,462.40	DDS2
Houston - Dallas	19200	2,450.96	DDS2
Houston - Memphis	19200	2,936.00	DDS2
Houston - San Diego	19200	4,264.80	DDS2
Chicago - Milwaukee	19200	2,159.52	DDS2
Chicago - Dallas	19200	3,531.96	DDS2
Dallas - Memphis	19200	2,819.44	DDS2
Dallas - Los Angeles	19200	4,189.40	DDS2
Milwaukee - Seattle	9600	2,353.96	DDS
Milwaukee - Portland	19200	4,738.08	DDS2
San Diego - Seattle	19200	3,989.88	DDS2
San Diego - Los Angeles	19200	2,242.28	DDS2
Seattle - Portland	9600	1,153.10	DDS
Seattle - San Francisco	19200	3,317.64	DDS2
Los Angeles - San Francisco	19200	2,689.72	DDS2
Portland - San Francisco	9600	1,521.58	DDS

1. Assumptions

Host computer location: New York City
Terminal locations: 200 of the largest cities in the continental U.S.
Number of terminals: 823 terminals dispersed among the 200 locations

Traffic characteristics:

Message size: On the average, 15 characters per message from terminal to host computer and 150 characters per message from host to terminals.
Base traffic volume: 24 messages per hour per terminal
Line control procedures: BSC

Performance constraints (terminal response time):

15 seconds for at least 95% of the messages

Terminal line speed:

2400 bits per second

Line tariff:

MPL for terminal lines

MPL and DDS for trunk lines between multiplexors and host computer (for 19.2 Kbps, two DDS lines are used)

Hardware costs:

$45 per month per host port

$100 per month per pair for multiplexors that can handle up to 4 low-speed ports each (T-4)

$150 per month per pair for multiplexors that can handle up to 16 low-speed ports each (T-16)

$35 per month per pair of multiplexor ports

2. Results

Figure 11.A.3 shows the network costs as a function of traffic volume. At the

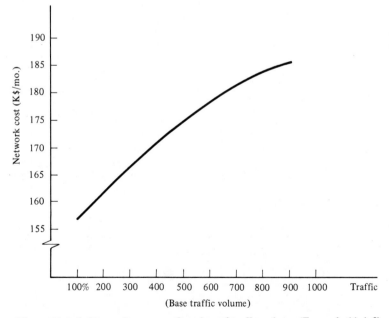

Figure 11.A.3. Network cost as a function of traffic volume (Example 11.A.2).

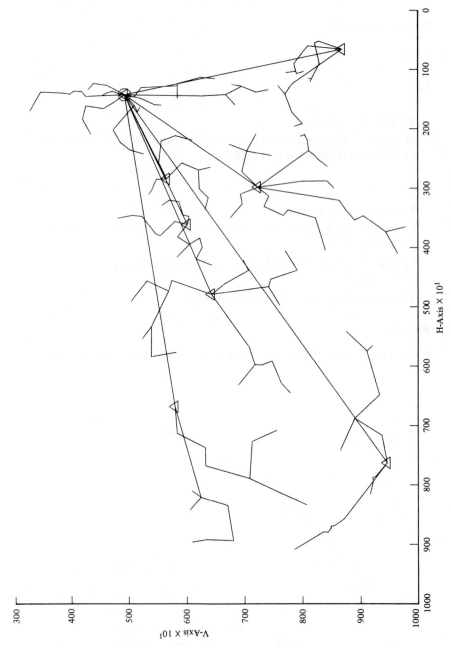

H-Axis × 10¹

V-Axis × 10¹

Figure 11.A.4. Network topology for Example 11.A.2, with base traffic volume.

42

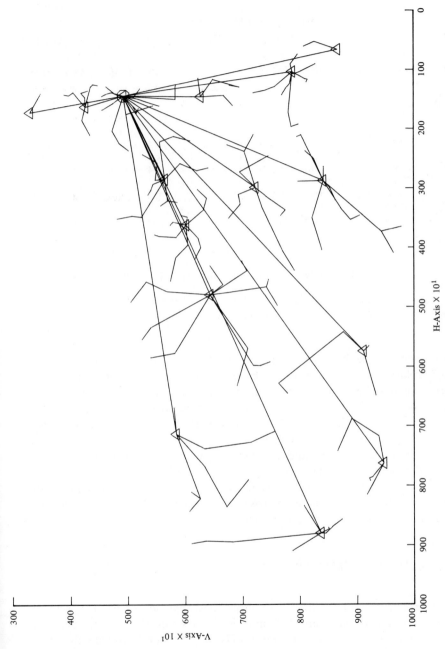

H-Axis × 10¹

V-Axis × 10¹

Figure 11.A.5. Network topology for Example 11.A.2, with nine times base traffic volume.

43

Table 11.A.3.   *Trunk Locations and Costs for Example 11.A.2, With Base Traffic Volume*

Network Configuration Summary

Host	Trunks				Trunk Access Devices			Access Line	
ID	Speed	Trff	Mles	Cost $/Mo.	Location	Type	Cost $/Mo.	No. Ckts	No. Term
1					New York N NY	Host	405.00	9	213
1	9600	MPL	500	1260.92	Toledo O OH	T-4	240.00	4	66
1	7200	MPL	2424	2556.84	San Diego C CA	T-4	205.00	3	81
1	9600	MPL	769	1513.78	De Kalb I IL	T-4	240.00	4	81
1	9600	MPL	1161	1824.30	Sioux City I IA	T-4	240.00	4	102
1	19200	DDS2	877	3678.60	Jackson T TN	T-16	360.00	6	134
1	9600	MPL	1208	1851.56	Key West F FL	T-4	240.00	4	84
1	7200	MPL	1679	2218.65	Glasgow M MT	T-4	205.00	3	62

Total backbone network line cost is 14904.64 dollars/mo.
Total cost of network access facilities is 2135.00 dollars/mo.

base traffic volume the cost per month is $156,941.12. In this particular case when traffic volume is three times as much, the network cost is $166,525.06 per month, an increase of about only six percent. When traffic is nine times as much, the network cost is $185,423.25 per month, only about an eighteen percent increase in costs. The decision one must make then is whether the network should be overdesigned to take care of the possible underestimation of the traffic volume and to take care of the future growth in traffic with the additional costs stated above. Figure 11.A.4 shows the network topology for the network design based on the base volume and Table 11.A.3 lists the trunk locations and associated costs. Figure 11.A.5 is the topology for network design with nine times the base volume traffic, and Table 11.A.4 lists the locations of the trunks and associated costs.

CONCLUDING REMARKS

The use of heuristic algorithms is the only practical approach for designing network topologies of data and computer communication systems. However, the heuristics might not always give cost-effective results. The way to ensure the cost effectiveness of the designs is to use the "human" aided design approach, i.e., the use of human intelligence and manual interfacing to help the heuristic algorithm and the associated software tools produce cost-effective network topological designs. The goodness of an

Table 11.A.4. *Trunk Locations and Costs for Example 11.A.2, With Nine Times the Base Traffic Volume*

Network Configuration Summary

Host	Trunks				Trunk Access Devices			Access Line	
ID	Speed	Trff	Mles	Cost $/Mo.	Location	Type	Cost $/Mo.	No. Ckts	No. Term
1					New York N NY	Host	450.00	10	119
1	19200	DDS2	500	2969.84	Toledo O OH	T-16	395.00	7	78
1	9600	MPL	2565	2638.62	Santa Rosa C CA	T-4	240.00	4	48
1	7200	MPL	2424	2556.84	San Diego C CA	T-4	205.00	3	36
1	19200	DDS2	769	3475.56	De Kalb I IL	T-16	395.00	7	72
1	19200	DDS2	1161	4096.60	Sioux City I IA	T-16	430.00	8	85
1	19200	DDS2	877	3678.60	Jackson T TN	T-16	360.00	6	64
1	9600	MPL	220	997.72	W. River JN V VT	T-4	240.00	4	47
1	7200	MPL	427	1192.30	Raleigh N NC	T-4	205.00	3	29
1	4800	MPL	1895	1936.02	Las Cruces N NM	T-4	170.00	2	25
1	19200	DDS2	1195	4136.04	.Baton Rouge L LA	T-16	430.00	8	79
1	4800	MPL	1208	1537.56	Key West F FL	T-4	170.00	2	16
1	19200	DDS2	943	3802.68	Orlando F FL	T-16	395.00	7	77
1	4800	MPL	526	1065.27	Fort Kent M ME	T-4	170.00	2	6
1	9600	MPL	1820	2300.43	Havre M MT	T-4	240.00	4	42

Total backbone network line cost is 36384.06 dollars/mo.
Total cost of network access facilities is 4495.00 dollars/mo.

algorithm or software tool cannot be measured in absolute terms. They should be judged by comparing with others in terms of human effort and the cost effectiveness of the final design.

Because of the involvement of human judgement, the network topological design is a process combining both science and art. This is true particularly for the design of packet switched networks. The effectiveness of currently available optimization algorithms is very sensitive to the starting networks, and no algorithms are available that can generate good starting networks. In Example 11.A.1 the initial design from the software tools was not a good one because it did not have a good starting network topology, which had been generated internally by the software tools. Here the "human" aided design process comes into play. This initial design was used as a basis to construct a good starting network topology as an externally defined starting network to the software. Network optimization algorithms are then applied to the starting network topology. The topologies shown in the example, as depicted in Figures 11.A.1 and 11.A.2, are the end results of the above process. Because of the involvement of human intelligence in constructing a good starting network and since the final result is sensitive to the starting network, the end result is, of course, sensitive to the skill of the designer [1].

The algorithms for tree-type teleprocessing networks do not need separately generated starting networks. These algorithms in general work much better than those of packet switched networks. The results shown in Example 11.A.2 did not involve human interface for the final designs. While it cannot be proven the designs shown are optimum, it is not obvious that human eyeballing can reduce the cost of the design.

The algorithms presented in this chapter are probably the best available for designing network topologies for data and computer communication systems. But there is definitely room for improvement, in particular for those associated with packet switched networks.

REFERENCES

BAHL 72 Bahl, L. R., and D. T. Tang, "Optimization of Concentrator Locations in Teleprocessing Networks," *Proc. Symp. Comput.-Communi. Networks Teletraffic*, Polytechnic Institute of Brooklyn, Brooklyn, N.Y., April 1972.

BOOR 77 Boorstyn, R. R., and H. Frank, "Large Scale Network Topological Optimization," *IEEE Trans. Commun.*, January 1977.

CAIN 74 Cain, J. B., "Centralized Network Design with Multidrop Lines," Memo Report No. 47, Harris Corporation, May 1974.

CHAN 72 Chandy, K. M., and R. A. Russell, "The Design of Multipoint Linkages in a Teleprocessing Tree Network," *IEEE Trans. Comput.*, Vol. C-21, October 1972, pp. 1062–1066.

CHOU 72 Chou, W., and H. Frank, "Routing Strategies in Computer Networks," *Proc. Symp. Comput.-Commun. Networks Teletraffic*, Polytechnic Institute of Brooklyn, Brooklyn, N.Y., 1972.

CHOU 73 Chou, W., and A. Kershenbaum, "A Unified Algorithm for Designing Multidrop Teleprocessing Networks," *Proc. 3rd Data Commun. Symp.*, November 1973; also *IEEE Trans. Commun.*, November 1974.

CHOU 75 Chou, W., "Computer Communications Networks—Parts Make Up the Whole," *Proc. 1975 NCC.*

[1] The designs shown in the example were performed by George Varghese.

CHOU 76   Chou, W., and M. Gerla, "Satellite Technology Impact on Large Data Network Designs," *Proc. Symp. Trends Appl.: Comput. Networks*, October 1976.

CHOU 78A   Chou, W., F. Ferrante, M. Balagangadhar, and L. Gerke, "An Algorithm for Optimally Locating Network Access Facilities," *Proc. 1978 ICC*, June 1978.

CHOU 78B   Chou, W., F. Ferrante, and M. Balagangadhar, "Integrated Optimization of Distributed Processing Networks," *Proc. 1978 NCC*, June 1978.

CHOU 79   Chou, W., J. D. Powell, and A. W. Bragg, Jr., "Comparative Evaluation of Deterministic and Adaptive Routing," *Proc. Flow Control in Computer Networks,* Paris, February 1979, North-Holland.

CHOU 81A   Chou, W., "ACK/TOPS—An Integrated Network Design Tool," *Proc. 1981 ICC*, June 1981.

CHOU 81B   Chou, W., A. W. Bragg, Jr., and A. A. Nilsson, "The Need for Adaptive Routing in the Chaotic and Unbalanced Traffic Environment," *IEEE Trans. Commun.,* April 1981.

CHOU 82   Chou, W., and D. L. Sapir, "A Generalized Cut-Saturation Algorithm for Distributed Computer Communications Network Optimization," *Proc. 1982 ICC*, June 1982.

CLAR 64   Clarke, G., and J. W. Wright, "Scheduling of Vehicles from a Central Depot to a Number of Delivery Points," *ORSA*, December 1964.

COOP 62   Cooper, L., "Location–Allocation Problems," *Oper. Res.*, 1962, pp. 331–343.

DIRI 76   Dirilter, H., and R. W. Donaldson, "Topological Design of Teleprocessing Networks Using Linear Regression Clustering," *IEEE Trans. Commun.,* October 1976.

ESAU 66   Esau, L. R., and K. C. Williams, "On Teleprocessing System Design, Part II," *IBM Syst. J.*, Vol. 5, No. 3, 1966, pp. 142–147.

FARB 73   Farber, D. J., et al., "The Distributed Computing System," *Digest of Papers, COMPOCON '73.*

FRAN 70   Frank, H., I. T. Frisch, and W. Chou, "Topological Considerations in the Design of the ARPA Computer Network," *Proc. Spring Joint Comput. Conf.*, 1970, pp. 581–587.

FRAN 72   Frank, H., and W. Chou, "Topological Optimization of Computer Networks," *Proc. IEEE*, Vol. 60, November 1972, pp. 1385–1397.

FRAT 73   Fratta, L., M. Gerla, and L. Kleinrock, "The Flow Deviation Method: An Approach to Store-and-Forward Communications Network Design," *Networks*, Vol. 3, No. 2, 1973.

GERL 74   Gerla, M., H. Frank, W. Chou, and J. Eckl, "A Cut Saturation Algorithm for Topological Design of Packet-Switched Communications Networks," *Proc. 1974 NTC.*

GERL 77   Gerla, M., and L. Kleinrock, "On the Topological Design of Distributed Computer Networks," *IEEE Trans. Commun.*, January 1977.

GREE 73   Greenberg, D. A., "A New Approach for the Optimal Placement of Concentrators in a Remote Terminal Communications Network," *Proc. Natl. Telecommun. Conf.*, Atlanta, November 26–28, 1973, pp. 37D-1 to 37D-7.

HSIE 76A   Hsieh, W., M. Gerla, P. McGregor, and J. Eckl, "Locating Backbase Switches in a Large Packet Network," *Proc. 1976 ICCC.*

HSIE 76B   Hsieh, W., "Backbone Switch Location Problem for Mixed Large Packet Switch Networks," *Proc. 1976 NTC.*

KARN 75   Karnaugh, M., "A New Class of Algorithms for Multipoint Network Optimization," *Proc. 1975 ICC.*

KERS 74   Kershenbaum, A., and W. Chou, "A Unified Algorithm for Designing Multidrop Teleprocessing Networks," *IEEE Trans. Commun.*, November 1974; also *Proc. 3rd Data Commun. Symp.*, November 1973.

KERS 80   Kershenbaum, A., R. Boorstyn, and R. Oppenheim, "Second-Order Greedy Algorithms for Centralized Teleprocessing Network Design," *IEEE Trans. Commun.*, October 1980.

KONS 80   Konsynski, B. R., and W. E. Bracker, "Software Packages for Solving Network Puzzles," Data Commun., July 1980, pp. 69–77.

KOZI 81   Kozicki, Z., "MIND—An Interactive Networks Design Tool," *Proc. 1981 ICC*, June 1981.

KRUS 56   Kruskal, J. B., "On The Shortest Spanning Subtree of a Graph and the Traveling Salesman Problem," *Proc. Am. Math. Soc.*, Vol. 7, 1956.

LAVI 75   Lavi, A., and L. E. Manning, "Topological Optimization of Packet-Switched Communications Networks," CCNG Report E-35, University of Waterloo, October 1975.

LIN 65   Lin, S., "Computer Solutions of the Traveling Salesman Problem," *Bell Syst. Tech. J.*, Vol. 44, 1965, pp. 2245–2269.

MARU 78   Maruyama, K., IBM Corp., Private communication, 1978.

MCGR 77   McGregor, M., and D. Shen, "Locating Concentration Points in Data Communication Networking," *Proc. 4th Data Commun. Symp.*, November 1975; and *IEEE Trans. Commun.*, January 1977.

NAC 74   Network Analysis Corporation, *The Practical Impact of Recent Computer Advances on the Analysis and Design of Large Scale Networks*, 1974. (Network Analysis Corporation is now Contel Information System, Great Neck, N.Y.)

PRIM 57   Prim, R. C., "Shortest Connection Networks and Some Generalizations," *Bell Syst. Tech. J.*, Vol. 36, 1957, pp. 1389–1401.

SAPI 78   Sapir, D. L., "A Generalized Cut-Saturation Algorithm for Distributed Computer Communications Network Optimization," M.S. thesis, Computer Studies Program, North Carolina State University, Raleigh, N.C., 1978.

SHAR 70   Sharma, R. L., and M. T. El-Bardai, "Suboptimal Communication Network Synthesis," *Proc. 1970 ICC*, pp. 19.11–19.16.

TANG 78   Tang, D. T., L. S. Woo, and L. R. Bahl, "Optimization of Teleprocessing Networks with Concentrators and Multiconnected Terminals," *IEEE Trans. Comput.*, Vol. C-27, No. 7, 1978, pp. 594–604.

WHIT 70   Whitney, V. K. M., "Comparison of Network Topology Optimization Algorithms," *Proc. 1970 ICC*, pp. 332–337.

WOO 73 Woo, L. S., and D. T. Tang, "Optimization of Teleprocessing Networks with Concentrators," *Proc. 1973 Natl. Telecommun. Conf.*

YAGE 71 Yaged, B., Jr., "Minimum Cost Routing for Static Network Models," *Networks*, Vol. 1., 1971, pp. 139–172.

12

Packet Radio:
An Area-Coverage Digital
Radio Network

DON NIELSON
SRI International
Menlo Park, CA 94025

12.1   PACKET-SWITCHING TECHNOLOGY
AND THE RADIO CHANNEL

12.1.1   Need for Area-Coverage Digital Radio

The transmission media for computer networks need not consist only of wire, cable, or fiber optics. For many applications a radio alternative can serve equally well, and in some applications radio is essential. In this chapter we examine some of these applications and some design approaches to *digital radio networks* (DRNs). Before starting we need to define what we mean by a DRN. As used here a DRN is an aggregation of radios operating in mutual support to transport digital information from a network source to a network destination. It is perhaps the most general of digital radio network concepts and although it could embrace point-to-point micro-wave or digital forms of land-mobile radio, it is exclusively neither. A DRN may involve fixed or mobile nodes or directive or nondirective antennas. Intelligent nodes, capable of storing and selectively forwarding data, almost uniformly rely on micro-processors, a key component in future DRNs. The particular type of DRN discussed here shares in common with land-mobile radio the capability to provide area coverage. But since mobility is not an *essential* element, we shall occasionally refer to it as *area-coverage digital radio.*

There has been very little use of area-coverage digital radio (including land-mobile digital radio) to date, but the potential applications are clearly there. For example, this new medium can provide communications between the various ele-ments of a computer network. This and other potential uses with some corresponding radio features are given in Tab. 12.1.

Table 12.1.   *Uses of Area-Coverage Digital Radio.*

Category	Uses	Features
General	Communications among data terminals and host computers	Mobile nodes Network transparency Real-time response (low-delay) Internet capability
Government and military	Military tactical radio (autonomous operation or as local area distribution for a trunking system)	Rapid deployment Data integrity and security Access control Effective network control
	Telemetry nets (seismic, weather, meteorological, utility services)	Automated network management High operational reliability
	Public safety (police record traffic)	Interoperability with other networks Efficient spectrum utilization Wide range of terminal devices
Business and personal	Mobile delivery and freight	Low nodal cost Adequate area coverage
	Time-sharing computer systems in developing countries	Interconnection to landline network Multiple access
	Local distribution for special carrier or private trunks	
	Paging	
	Personal data terminals	

As indicated in Tab. 12.1, the transmission of information in digital form can at times offer greater spectrum efficiency than can typical analog forms. These situations are usually those in which data can be substituted for voice of equivalent information content. When speaking we convey in direct information the equivalent of only about 100 bps, yet normal radio-telephone transmissions are given a channel bandwidth of 15 to 25 kHz. Even allowing for bandwidth expansion similar to that used in the normal FM land mobile channel and frequency guardbands equal to one full channel, over thirty 100-Hz digital channels could still be fit into one 25-kHz voice channel. As an example of the use of such a channel, consider the use of digital transmission to a small printer in a freight pickup van. Not only could the route details be communicated when the driver was not in the truck, but doing so would require far less bandwidth.

Straightforward digital conversion of analog voice, on the other hand, leads to significant bandwidth expansion unless speech compression techniques are also used. Many such techniques are elaborate and presently require expensive and complex hardware to regain the equivalent analog voice bandwidth. Should these techniques eventually become inexpensive, the digital channel could provide voice service as ubiquitously as analog systems have.

Although several of these applications are useful and now in some stage of fulfillment, perhaps the most important question is whether radio can provide a practical alternative to the local loop offered by the telephone companies. Through the FCC's permitting of competition at the end-device level in 1968 [FCC 68] and at the trunking level in 1971 [FCC 71], significant alternative communication services have been provided. But in the critical and expensive local switching and distribution portion of the system, there is still no alternative. The use of local satellite terminals located on the roof and directly connected to a wideband network or a PBX has been proposed under some filings [FCC 76], but for the foreseeable future the satellite earth terminals will be too expensive for all but the largest users, thus generally requiring sharing among different users. To reach out from the earth station to its various customers the Xerox Telecommunications Network (XTEN) proposed to use a network of directional microwave links that fed cells of subscribers [FCC 80]. These subscribers accessed more omnidirectional antennas at the center of these individual cells. Although this service was to provide an alternative means of local distribution, the venture was terminated by Xerox in May 1981. The FCC has termed this type of distribution the Digital Termination Service and other companies are pursuing it.

One possible candidate for such a local distribution network is illustrated schematically in Fig. 12.1. Radio networks, located atop the buildings of a city with connectivity to nearby satellite terminals, can perhaps provide a valid alternative to the increasingly expensive wire network beneath the city. The approach most resembling the DRN in Fig. 12.1 is the experimental Packet Radio system now under development by the Defense Advanced Research Projects Agency (DARPA) for tactical military application [BURC 75; FRAL 75A,B; FRAN 75; GRON 80; KAHN 75; KAHN 77; KAHN 78; KLEI 75B; LAWS 78; ROBE 72]. It provides reliable terminal–host and host–host data channels in a fixed or mobile, military or commercial [SHOC 79] environment. The term *packet radio*, while somewhat generic, refers most often to the DARPA's particular embodiment (when it does we shall capitalize it). The name derives from the use of packet-switching concepts [ROBE 78] in a radio network.

Motorola has also introduced a multiple-access, nonswitched digital radio system that permits up to 32 hand-held digital radio terminals to access an IBM 360/370 computer via a radio controller/interface. Process control and inventory taking are some of its potential uses. Packet radio has also been examined for potential use in satellite communications [PARK 80, ROBE 80B], but commercialization has been slow.

12.1.2   Attributes of Radio

Before examining some specific area-coverage DRNs, let us describe some of the attributes of radio for data communcation. Consider the simple wired star network shown in Fig. 12.2. Since all outlying nodes in this example have direct access to the central node, some type of multiplexing or multiple access is required to accommodate the inbound legs. If we now assume for a moment that each wire line is replaced

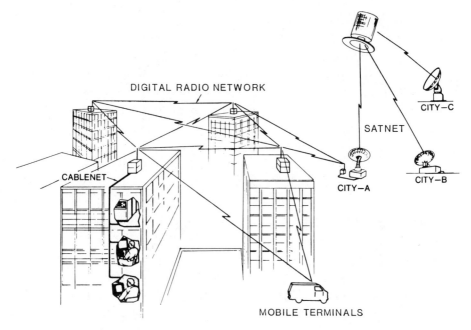

Figure 12.1. Typical use of a digital radio network.

by two directive antennas and frequency assignments are available to match the transmission capability of the wire, the transition to radio will be transparent to the user.

If directional antennas are now replaced with nondirectional ones, the broadcast attributes of radio can offer some new network features and perhaps economies. The last three networks in Fig. 12.2 show network topologies in which the power of the radios are either uniformly or individually adjusted to produce a desired result. This power control, particularly if exercised dynamically, creates topologies not easily duplicated with wire. Certainly, if one or more of the nodes were mobile, then radio provides a logical and perhaps unique capability.

But radio has its constraints. Depending on the carrier frequencies used and the competition for spectral resource, bandwidths characteristic of wire or cable may not be available. The use of radio for nonmobile networks nearly always requires a trade-off between the cost of obtaining and using the radio spectrum (including protection against possible interference) and the cost of wire or cable (possibly including right-of-way). Generalizations about this trade-off are normally not possible. It is safe to say, however, that the greatest impediment to the use of data radio comes from the allocation of adequate spectrum. New concepts for the movement of digital data via radio may have to be accompanied by new concepts of spectrum utilization.

One important approach to extending the available frequency spectrum is to reuse it in space. Rather than building more powerful transmitters with higher antennas to give greater and greater area coverage, it is often more sensible to use

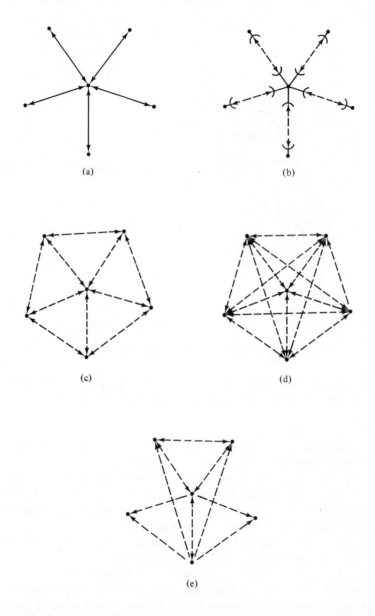

(a)

(b)

(c)

(d)

(e)

Figure 12.2. Example of a broadcast radio network: (a) bidirectional wired star; (b) direct radio replacement using directional antennas (may require up to 10 frequency assignments or other means of sharing the channel); (c) limited-range radio using omnidirectional antennas (sharing of channel implicit); (d) full-range radio using omnidirectional antennas (sharing of channel implicit); (e) power-dependent topology using omnidirectional antennas (sharing of channel implicit). Dashed line, radio link; solid line, wire link.

smaller transmitters, each responsible for a small cell of space. Thus a single radio-frequency channel could be reused a number of times within a large metropolitan area. This is essentially the approach proposed by AT&T (and Illinois Bell) for the introduction of a cellular system into the Chicago area Advanced Mobile Phone System [BELL 79, COX 71B; COX 72B, FREN 70, PORT 71, SCHI 70, SCHU 60]. Since terrain is nearly always irregular, cell size is often determined by topography and statistical propagation parameters. This system is intended for land-mobile radio telephone and as such is circuit oriented; that is, an individual channel is dedicated until surrendered by the using parties. A mobile unit is assigned a specific cell based on the signal level of its transmitter at various voting receivers. As the mobile unit crosses cell boundaries, frequency channel assignments are likely to change. This requires an elaborate and extensive system of frequency management, particularly if the channels allocated to any group of cells are dynamically reassigned.

Although the cellular approach has been intended for radio-telephone use, it could conceivably satisfy the needs of a DRN. This would be true only if the channel is protected against the use of signals inimical to data transmission. These may occur at times of transmitter or receiver hand-over or perhaps even incidentally. But since the approach is circuit oriented, the algorithms for channel assignments will probably not be the most efficient for the class of digital traffic characterized by high peak-to-average data rates typically found in computer communications.

Methods of dividing up the frequency spectrum other than frequency channelization are also possible. Time division and code division are two examples, and these are discussed later. Just how the signal space is divided up is a complex trade-off, but there remains the inalterable need to reuse the spectrum in any dimension where isolation (orthogonality) is possible, including space. Packet radio uses a single-frequency spread-spectrum concept that can employ pseudo-random codes to isolate individual users transmitting in the same geographical area. Much of its ability to share the resource, however, comes simply from the unscheduled, asynchronous participation by users with the type of bursty transmissions mentioned above.

Depending on the local environment, a radio link may also have some limitation in coherent bandwidth (i.e., the bandwidth for signaling) due to multipath. This limitation ultimately governs the practical capacity of a given radio link. Terminals immersed in rough terrain or urban areas are much more limited in this respect than are elevated terminals with uncluttered foregrounds. More detail on this constraint is given at the end of the section.

12.1.3 Brief History of the ALOHA System and Packet Radio

12.1.3.1 ALOHA System

The first packet DRN was probably that developed under DARPA sponsorship at the University of Hawaii [ABRA 70, BIND 75]. It offered a higher-capacity network than the existing telephone system for the connection of data terminals to the university computer and at a potentially lower cost. This system used two 100-kHz-bandwidth UHF radio channels (in the government band) in a configuration shown in Fig. 12.3. In the inbound direction the system is multiple access, with all users vying for the centralized node (computing resource or internetwork gateway). In the outbound direction the system is pure broadcast, with relays as necessary.

The inbound multiple-access problem led to a number of channel-access protocols, some of which still carry the ALOHA name. The basic ALOHA protocol permits transmission at any time, regardless of channel occupancy at that time. Channel activity is determined by a co-located receiver that is either in the process of receiving a packet or in some less specific monitoring of the channel. Should a collision occur between the transmissions of two nodes at the input to a third, that receiving node will likely fail to give a positive acknowledgment to either source. This failure may cause transmitting nodes or perhaps ultimately end devices to try recovering from that failure using retransmissions. To avoid synchronized retransmissions, a random delay can be added to the retransmission interval at each node. This access protocol was essentially that used in the ALOHANET.

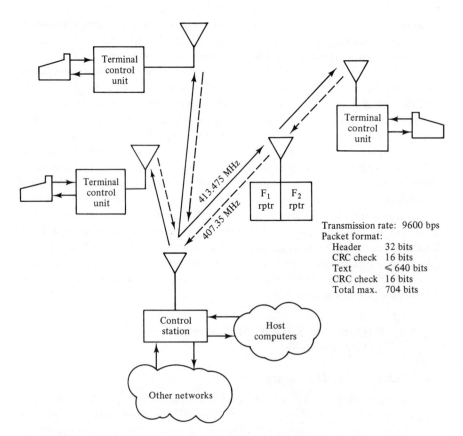

Figure 12.3. Schematic of the ALOHA system. Dashed line, multiple-access channel; solid line, broadcast channel.

A very simple model of such a protocol serves to illustrate a common multiple-access problem, an unstable or infinitely increasing delay as the number of users becomes large.[1] To illustrate this effect, we assume an infinite and independent population of users who are transmitting packets randomly in an attempt to access a common point. All users continue to transmit a given packet until they succeed. If the aggregate process is Poisson, an average offering rate S can be defined which is the number of *new* packets offered per packet interval. Under assumptions of statistical equilibrium, S is also the channel throughput.

Because of retransmissions, however, there is another, total packet transmission rate, G, that under the conditions noted above is assumed to be Poisson distributed. As indicated by Abramson [ABRA 70],

$$S = Gp$$

where $p = Pr$ [no transmission in a two-packet interval]. Thus

$$S = Ge^{-2G}$$

Consider now multiple collisions for the same packet offered. The average number of such offerings is

$$n = \frac{1}{p} = e^{2G}$$

Then the net rate of new packets into the net is

$$S = \frac{\ln(n)}{2n}$$

This is plotted as "pure" ALOHA in Fig. 12.4 and shows the significant network delays mentioned above. Other, more intelligent access mechanisms mentioned in the figure will be discussed later in conjunction with network protocols, but it is clear that in each case operation must be maintained below the knee of the curve. There reasonable throughput can be achieved at tolerable delay. Notice that in pure ALOHA the channel throughput is limited to $1/2e$ or about 18%. If the user is required to begin transmission only at the beginning of defined time slots that are of one packet duration, the maximum throughput is doubled to about 37% but still far from the channel capacity.

The ALOHANET pioneered the concept of packet radio and achieved its original objectives. But there were several recognized limitations inherent in this approach and it eventually gave way to a second-generation network.

These limitations were:

1. Repeaters were simple access extensions of the central node and could not switch packets. Thus even with repeaters it remained, from a logical viewpoint, a one-hop or star network.

[1]This characteristic is also true of more complex access protocols in multiple hop nets whenever flow and congestion control are not exercised.

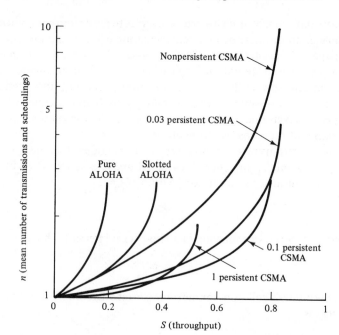

Figure 12.4. Performance curves for various multiple-access techniques. (After [Klei 75C].)

2. The separate radio channels, while providing some isolation of inbound and outbound traffic, made acknowledgment protocols difficult for packets on the multiple-access channel and somewhat dubious for packets on the single-hop, noncontention, broadcast channel.

3. The dual channel could not allow flexible adjustment to channel capacity, as the traffic flow favored either inbound or outbound traffic.

4. Two channels meant more complex receivers than a single-channel system, wherein all receivers were single frequency and identical.

12.1.3.2 Packet Radio Program

The *DARPA Packet Radio Network* (PRNET) is a packet-switched, broadcast DRN operating on a single wideband L-band (about 1800 MHz) channel to provide area coverage and real-time response to a number of fixed and mobile users. It is both multiple-hop (store-and-forward) and multiply accessible over its area of coverage. Because of the single radio-frequency channel, all transmissions are effectively half-duplex. However, since all users are assumed to have intermittent traffic, each access is treated independently regardless of previous traffic.

The Packet Radio program was created in 1973 by DARPA to remove some of the limitations of the ALOHANET concept noted above, to provide a more natural way to extend such a network geographically, and to increase network capacity. The new network was philosophically different and was to have some specific innovations:

1. An intelligent store-and-forward switch common to every node. These switches would relay traffic, provide switching, measure traffic flow, implement hop-transport protocol, and at the behest of a control node, help organize the network and control traffic.

2. A common radio-frequency channel that simplified the interaction between nodes for purposes of packet relaying and acknowledgment.

3. A spread-spectrum modulation that potentially offered a favorable multiple-access technique [DIXO 76] (explained as code-division multiple access in Sec. 12.2.1).

4. Controlling node(s), capable of continually assessing network conditions and managing the network to offer the best service to users.

5. An ability to self-organize and in particular to cope automatically with maintaining connectivity to mobile units.

Ultimately, the movement of packets in the PRNET is governed by one or more controlling nodes called *stations* [BURC 75]. The control nodes are responsible for using other nodes present to create a workable topology through granting each node a network role and a unique network label. The labels are authorizations to participate in the network and are addresses used within the packet header to define a unique route within the network. A later version of the PRNET is station-free (distributed control).

The packet used in the PRNET has four major parts, and a simplified outline is shown in Fig. 12.5. These parts are described in detail in Sec. 12.3. An example of a PRNET is shown in Fig. 12.6. The solid lines indicate paths of hierarchical control

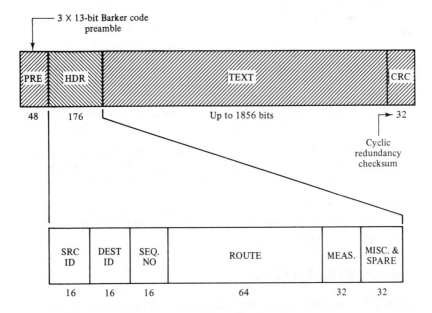

Figure 12.5. PRNET header (simplified).

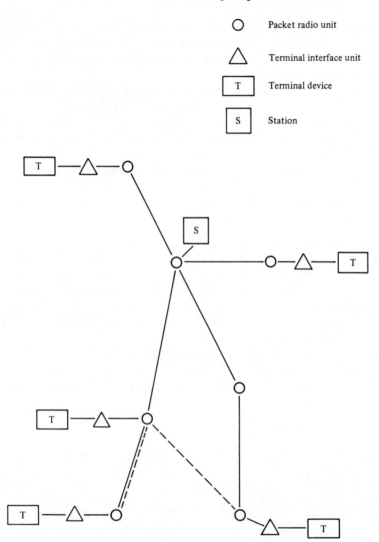

Figure 12.6. Schematic of a PRNET. Circle, packet radio unit; square, station minicomputer; triangle, terminal interface unit; rectangle, terminal device. Dashed line, point-to-point route; solid line, hierarchical routes.

over all nodes by the station(s) and are not necessarily the required routes for traffic. We will characterize this network in more detail following a brief introduction to the radio channel such digital networks must use.

12.1.4   Digital Radio Channel

A wealth of information exists on the land-mobile radio channel, at least as it serves traditional frequency-modulated, narrowband voice needs [CLAR 68, GANS 72,

JAKE 67, MOTO 73, OKAM 65, OSSA 64, REUD 72, YOUN 52]. Much of this information comes from the work of the purveyors of land-mobile radio services. Narrowband channels, typically 15- or 25-kHz assignments, are characterized by an inability to resolve in the time domain the individual rays that by various paths reach the receiver. This phenomenon is referred to as *multipath*. Since at any point in space the narrowband signal is the vector sum of these various ray paths, the result is an interference field where at some points the signal is very strong and at others very weak. Movement of a receiver in this field causes the fading common to land-mobile radio channels. Higher frequencies (shorter wavelengths) and greater terminal velocity result in higher fading rates [COX 71A, COX 72A]. In some instances spatial diversity is needed to reduce the impact of these fades. This momentary loss of signal is much more inimical to digital transmissions than to analog voice. This fact is due to the highly redundant characteristics of voice and to the typical uses of digital data that require higher-fidelity transmission. For example, voice may tolerate equivalent error rates as high as 1 in 100, whereas digital data with that error rate are often useless.

Modern approaches to area-coverage digital radio should, however, look beyond the conventional narrowband assignments to explore the possible benefits of wider bandwidths.[2] Wider bandwidths unfortunately mean higher carrier frequencies and their correspondingly higher fading rates for a given terminal velocity. The number and depth of such fades are a complicated function of the signal bandwidth, the detection technique, the terminal vector velocity, and the time profile of multipath (i.e., the response of the channel to a single impulse).

Signals received over traditional narrowband channels are usually described as having a Rayleigh amplitude distribution over small distances (10 to 20m) and log-normal distributions over larger distances that might include the shadows of large obstacles such as hills or buildings [OKAM 65, REUD 72]. This characterization helps specify the fades encountered and the consequent need for diversity. Applying digital data to the narrowband channel requires additional channel measures, particularly about multipath. The amount of detail needed about multipath is defined to a large extent by the ability of the communication signal to resolve individual ray paths. The greater the RF bandwidth (and hence multipath resolution), the more important become features such as the number of ray paths received during a single signaling element or baud, and the relative spacing and strength of the various ray-path components [TURI 72]. DARPA's Packet Radio system uses spread-spectrum modulation (RF bandwith $\gg$ information bandwidth) to offer, among other features, a multiple-access capability. To the extent that wide bandwidths resolve multipath components, they avoid the interference fading mentioned earlier and provide a form of path diversity. That is, being resolved, the paths are now impulses isolated from one another in time delay. Vector cancellations (or reinforcements) are less likely to occur and each nonfading ray path becomes an independent route from transmitter to receiver—in effect, path diversity. We will discuss how to

---

[2]Wide bandwidths are here taken to mean signaling element durations of the order of the multipath delay spread. Ultra-wide bandwidths, where the bit rate far exceeds the inverse of the multipath duration, are also feasible but are not discussed here.

take advantage of this result after a little more introduction to multipath at micro-wave frequencies.

To aid in system design, some wideband propagation data were taken in DARPA's Packet Radio program [NIEL 75, NIEL 77]. Examples of typical multi-path waveforms for an urban area are given in Fig. 12.7. The signal used had a 9-MHz postdetection bandwidth, not unlike the standard packet radio unit but centered at 1340 MHz. Using this bandwidth, one is able to illustrate (resolve) many of the discrete ray paths that contribute to the overall signal received. As just mentioned, in a narrowband implementation where the inter-ray path delays are short compared to the baud length, these separate paths add together or cancel to cause large swings in received signal level as a function of space. On the other hand, appropriate processing of the wideband signal shown in Fig. 12.7 can result in all of the integrated signal energy being applied to the decision circuitry.

A somewhat more synoptic view of the multipath profile in a dense urban environment is shown in Fig. 12.8. These data show for a typical received signal the

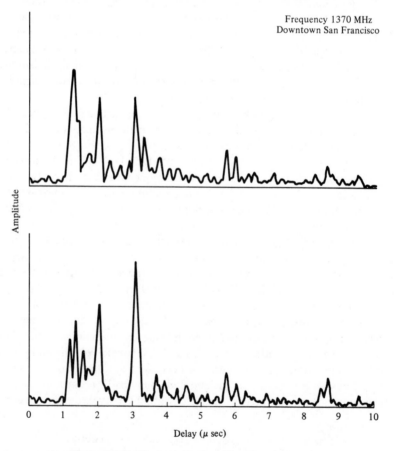

Figure 12.7. Some typical multipath waveforms.

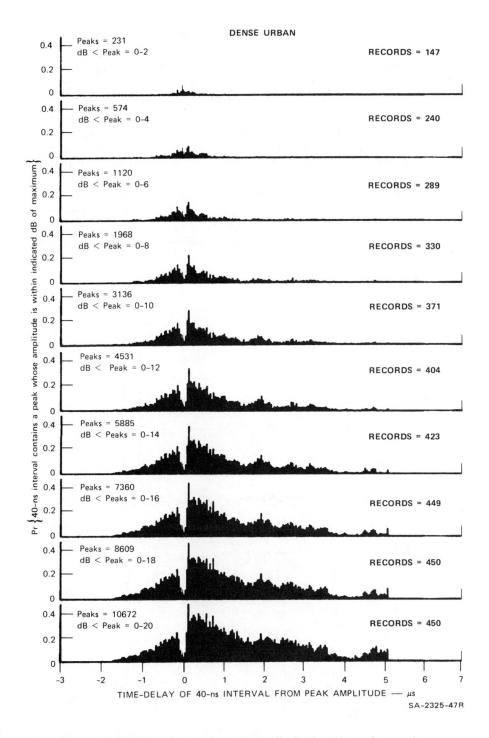

Figure 12.8. Peak-referenced multipath distributions in a dense urban environment.

distribution of individual ray-path peaks with respect to the maximum peak and depict a multipath delay of less than about 5 usec. This delay corresponds to a nominal maximum bit rate of about 100 to 200 kbps.

But even signal bandwidths of the order of 10 MHz do not always resolve multipath components. To the extent that they do not an apparent "single ray path" may fade abruptly. This characteristic is shown in Fig. 12.9, where two consecutive pulses were received over a distance separation of 20 cm. Any system that employs a narrow detection window (such as window A) is susceptible to synchronization loss over the course of a packet if the velocity of the receiver is sufficient.

To correct this problem it is necessary to obtain greater diversity by integrating the signal over a larger portion of the baud interval. To avoid the vector cancellation (fading), common in predetection filtering, the detection technique indicated in Fig.

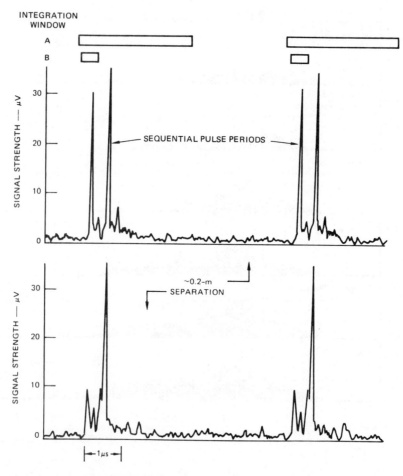

Figure 12.9. Rapid fading of unresolved multipath components and the need for adequate integration–diversity.

12.10 can be used. This scheme uses the resolution inherent in the wide bandwidth to reduce the likelihood of a fade of the entire signal by accumulating the energy (power over time) in the various multipath components. For example, extending the postdetection integration to window B in Fig. 12.9 would encompass more than one multipath component. However, the price for this improved reception is a reduced ability to discriminate against (decorrelate) other signals using the same spread spectrum code, with slightly different time delay, and trying intentionally or unintentionally to access the same receiver. Thus the amount of integration directly affects the number of simultaneous users that can be accommodated in a single code-division multiple-access channel.

Several more recent studies have examined the performance of packet radio networks with fading included [DASI 79, GRIE 79, ROBE 80A].

The noise environment must also be reconsidered in the transition from analog voice to digital data. Wideband noise impulses, common to an urban environment, are often only an annoyance to voice communications, but cause serious errors in digital data. Moreover, because the noise sources are often very close to the receiver, the impulses may be strong enough to make infeasible their neutralization by simply increasing transmitter power.

Most urban impulse noise stems from ignition noise [SPAU 72]. This noise is characterized by very wide bandwidths (an essentially flat spectrum up to several gigahertz) and hence can be said to be bandwidth limited by virtually all receivers. If so, then two characteristics of the noise signal are important to describe it: the energy in an impulse and the rate at which the impulses arrive. Data relevant to those points are given in Fig. 12.11, also obtained during the DARPA Packet Radio program.

A principal method of dealing with the high peak power of impulse noise is to

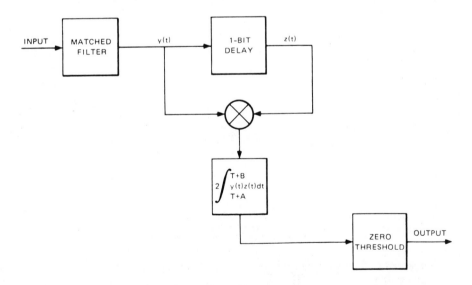

Figure 12.10. Postdetection signal integration technique.

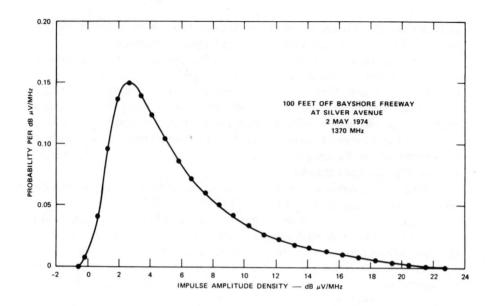

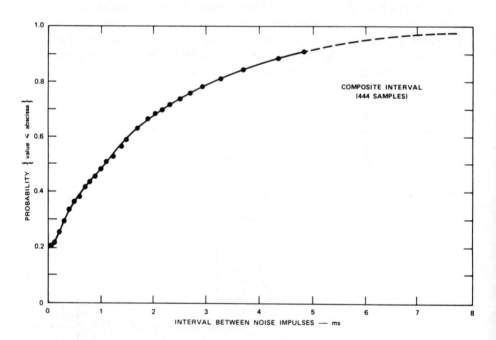

Figure 12.11. Model of impulsive noise from automobile ignition systems in city traffic.

use filters to decorrelate or destroy the coherence of the noise spike. The spread-spectrum waveform used in Packet Radio and its associated matched filter accomplish this very effectively. Should sufficient noise energy still reach the decision circuitry and cause an error, a remaining solution is the use of error-correcting codes. In this case a certain fraction of the packet is devoted to information redundancy. Codes are available [PETE 72] to detect such errors and correct the altered bit(s) without the need for retransmission or for increasing transmitter power to unreasonable levels. A necessary condition, however, is that the impulses occur relatively infrequently.

12.2   PACKET RADIO CHARACTERIZATION

12.2.1   Broadcast/Multiple-Access Channel

One desirable feature of radio is the ease of broadcasting; that is, enabling multiple destinations to receive simultaneously a single transmission. (A common wire bus and a satellite system are also broadcast media.) Broadcasting normally implies transmission over a single hop. In the radio transmission of digital data, however, a broadcast network can be defined as one in which all transmissions are heard by all nodes having radio connectivity with the transmitter. This is not necessarily all nodes in the network. In a ground radio channel this usually implies the use of omnidirectional antennas and a deliberate network topology in which each transmitting node has at least two receiving nodes (e.g., broadcast for redundancy). Conversely, if two or more elements in such a network wish to access a single node, then a multiple-access technique is also needed. Thus broadcast DRNs are often multiple-access networks. If a common frequency is used throughout, the contention occurs in the receivers themselves rather than in some attached device.

In addition to providing the capability to reach a number of destination points in parallel rather than through serial access, broadcasting offers the reliability of redundant coverage without extensive reprogramming of the network. In a network with relay points a broadcast mode enables more than one node to participate, when necessary, in the forwarding of a packet. It is not always necessary to reroute formally a packet that encounters a blockage. Simple alternative routing methods can be implemented that take advantage of the broadcast feature.

Although it is perhaps obvious, a final advantage of a broadcast network is the inherent ease and flexibility of route assignment. In such a network, radio connectivity between candidate relay points is perhaps the only essential condition for forming a route. Omnidirectional antennas and a common frequency greatly simplify the criteria to be satisfied.

But given a certain assigned bandwidth for a packet radio system, one must decide how best to use the resource. If the total bandwidth available is small compared to the average total required data rate, resource sharing may be highly contentious. If the reverse is true, various interesting design options may be explored to assign individual channels that are roughly equivalent in bandwidth to individual user data rates. The three principal options are:

1. To use one or more signals, each of whose bandwidths greatly exceeds the average data rate of any individual user and which have some orthogonality in code space
2. To divide the bandwidth into many narrowband channels, each of which is comparable to the average data rate
3. To divide time into small increments (channels), during each of which a single user transmitter shall be assigned the entire available bandwidth

These approaches are called code-, frequency-, and time-division multiple-access methods, respectively (CDMA, FDMA, and TDMA). These three methods usually involve assigning a channel for some continuous period and each technique has its advantages and disadvantages, as outlined in Tab. 12.2. Under the most idealized conditions all three options occupy equal signal space and have equal capacities. Our present technologies, however, make certain approaches more feasible than others. Which multiple-access approach is best is heavily dependent on the particular application. For example, the inherent interference protection in CDMA may be traded for the higher practical capacities of FDMA or TDMA. Other possible trade-offs are also apparent from Tab. 12.2.

Once the channelization has been defined, there remains the possibility of sharing the individual channels. In any of the foregoing multiple-access techniques, each channel can be accessed under a fixed plan or schedule, or it can be contended for by the potential users. Fixed assignments can lead to poor channel utilization if individual traffic duty cycles are low. In this case contention access among such users leads to more efficient utilization, and a variety of digital radio systems, including Packet Radio, use this approach. Contention is simply another approach to resource sharing, in this case at the channel level. Here another plethora of multiple-access techniques exist, some of which involve direct contention through the transmission of the packet, and others that involve indirect contention as through a reservation system. Two were selected for Packet Radio: ALOHA and carrier sense. These have been extensively examined analytically but with models that are necessarily simplified to one- or at most two-hop accesses of a single node [BOOR 80; GITM 75; KLEI 74; KLEI 75A,C; KLEI 77; KLEI 80; TOBA 80A,B].

12.2.2 Channel Multiple-Access Methods for Intermittent Traffic

12.2.2.1 Aloha

The ALOHA protocol described earlier is the least disciplined of all access protocols. Even though simple, the protocol is of limited value since any node capable of both transmitting and receiving would not logically interrupt a packet being received just to transmit at an arbitrary time. Waiting until the air is clear, on the other

Table 12.2.   *A Brief Comparison of Multiple-Access Methods.*

Condition	Access Scheme		
	CDMA	*FDMA*	*TDMA*
Requirement for maximum spectral efficiency	Orthogonal code-words for all time shifts (cannot be found)	Zero adjacent chan-nel interference (need nonrealiz-able brick wall filter)	Zero timing error (impossible for mobile users)
Practical require-ment for good spectral efficiency	Quasi-orthogonal codewords (resulting in added noise)	Frequency guard band	Time guard band
User transmission characteristics	Continuous	Continuous	Intermittent (Buffers required)
User data rate	Most efficient for users with one data rate, or mul-tiple of it	Users with different data rate require-ment assigned different **BW**	Users with different data rate require-ment assigned different time slot lengths
System requirement	Codeword assign-ment, no network synch	Frequency slot assignment, no network synch	Time slot assignment, need network tim-ing
Flexibility of adding new unscheduled users	Yes, with graceful degradation	No	No
Transmitter power requirement	Average power	Average power	Peak power
Antijamming capa-bility	Inherent antijam-ming capability	Vulnerable to selective jamming	Vulnerable to selective jamming

hand, adds discipline, decreases access randomization, and puts the access in the realm of carrier-sense methods to be discussed below.

A second variation of ALOHA is slotted ALOHA [TOBA 78B]. Instead of transmitting at arbitrary times, transmission can occur only during well-defined time intervals. This modest discipline decreases the chance for overlap and consequently increases the maximum throughput, both by a factor of 2. The characteristic curve for slotted ALOHA was shown in Fig. 12.4. To derive this increased performance, slotted ALOHA requires a synchronization of network nodes that is accurate to a small portion of a packet length.

12.2.2.2   Carrier Sense

As the name implies, this access method involves listening before transmitting. To listen first is to avoid possible packet collisions and therefore subsequent retrans-missions. This procedure is defined, however, only for nodes within radio connectivity of one another. For example, if node B finds that it can hear both nodes A and C but A and C cannot hear one another, A and C may well collide at B, even if they both use a carrier-sense technique. This is known as the *hidden terminal problem* and as far as A and C are concerned the access is pure ALOHA. One partial remedy for this is to devote a small portion of the bandwidth of each transmitter (i.e., a control channel) that radiates a busy tone whenever a node, such as B, is receiving [TOBA 75]. Since both A and C would hear the tone, they would not transmit during that time.

Using the same idealized scenario of independent transmitters as in Sec. 12.3, carrier-sense access results in greater net channel utilization. Just how much improvement is obtained in a given network depends on the extent to which hidden terminals are a problem and also on what action is taken after the channel is sensed. Table 12.3 shows some of the carrier-sense options and the corresponding through-put/delay curves are plotted in Fig. 12.4 [KLEI 74, KLEI 75A,C, TOBA 75, TOBA 77A]. Thus several specific types of carrier-sense algorithms are appropriate for the broadcast networks depicted so far. Other multiple-access techniques for packet radio can be found in GITM 74, KLEI 77, TOBA 76A.

But carrier-sense methods are susceptible to other external, non-network transmissions that can prohibit (jam) normal network activity. In the case of DARPA Packet Radio the spread-spectrum demodulator decorrelates some types of interfering signals, so the carrier sensing (detection) is made on the so-called coherent carrier (i.e., the one following the matched filter for the spread-spectrum waveform).

12.2.3   Routing and Alternate Routing[3]

Although we have spoken favorably of a broadcast technique for network radio, when using it certain restrictions on packet movement are necessary to keep the network from becoming too inefficient: that is, too many transmissions per delivered packet. These restrictions are:

1.   A specific route is preselected for each packet so that only a limited number of nodes must act on it. These nodes are followed sequentially using selective call or route indicators.

Table 12.3. *Definition of Various Random-Access Modes.*

Mode	Definition
ALOHA	Initiate transmission at arbitrary times
Slotted ALOHA	Initiate transmission at the beginning of prescribed time windows
Carrier sense	
Persistent	Transmits packet as soon as channel is clear
Nonpersistent	If channel is busy; transmission is scheduled for random delay; transmits when channel is clear
p-Persistent	If channel is clear, transmits with probability p; With probability $1 - p$ it delays transmission by a random amount; if channel is busy, it waits until clear, then operates as above

[3]Even though routing may be considered a part of network protocol, we discuss PRNET routing here in the setting of a broadcast network.

2.   Any given packet will be retransmitted only a limited number of times before being discarded.

3.   Any given repeater will be permitted to receive and forward a given packet only once in a time duration equal to the maximum packet lifetime in the network.

The second condition means that the user cannot assume that the network will deliver the packet with probability 1; that is, the network is lossy. The third condition is necessary because retransmissions lead to duplicate packets, which ultimately must be filtered out.

The broadcast mechanism very naturally leads to the possibility of spatially redundant paths. As implied above, a single, primary route can be invoked and, barring failure, will carry the packet to its destination. Should any node along that route fail, however, it would be desirable to provide an automatic means to circumvent the blockage. Since the failing node is not known a priori, the alternate-routing technique must have flexibility. One rather natural alternate-routing technique to use in a broadcast network is as follows: First each node must become aware of its neighbors; that is, who within one hop distance can it communicate with easily? With this information, and upon encountering blockage at a certain node, the packet route can be broadened temporarily as shown in Fig. 12.12. The last node that received the

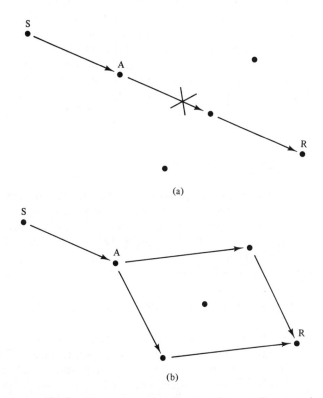

(a)

(b)

Figure 12.12. Alternate routing in a broadcast radio network.

packet correctly, in this case node A, sets a bit in the header that permits *any* of its neighbors to accept the packet. They, in turn, transmit the packet if they find in their list of neighbors any node in the route (contained in the packet header) closer to the destination than themselves. Several strategies of this type are possible with variations, for example, in how many retransmissions are invoked for both the directed and alternate-routed path.

An alternative approach has the route (or partial route) of each packet contained in all nodes, indexed by destination. Then those nodes having the same destination in their forwarding tables qualify as alternate-routing candidates and are eligible to relay the packet to the prescribed adjacent node.

Two prominent types of routing in a packet-switched radio net are hierarchical and point-to-point (PTP) [GITM 76A]. *Hierarchical routing* means all packet routes pass through a central, usually controlling, node. This routing is shown by the solid lines in Fig. 12.6 and leads directly to (1) the notion of inbound and outbound directions with consequent asymmetries in the ability to alternate route, and (2) spatially dependent traffic patterns with the greatest concentration at the central node. There are few advantages to hierarchical routing and, unless the link capacities are increased appropriately as the central node is reached, many parts of the network suffer poor utilization. This important constriction is antithetical to the flexible and improved network resource utilization embodied in packet switching.

PTP routines place no such restrictions on route selection. It is more typically minimum-hop routing, such as that shown by the dashed line in Fig. 12.6. As the name implies, minimum-hop routing means that the assigned route minimizes the number of relays between end points. In a spatially distributed network, PTP routing tends to use the available network capacity more completely since all routes do not have to go through the same point. Alternate-routing possibilities are also symmetrical with respect to packet direction. The present DARPA PRNET employs PTP routing.

12.2.4   The Switching Node Itself

The appearance of packet switching has been made possible by the advent of affordable processors. These processors are used as economic, intelligent, store-and-forward switches that can now proliferate the interior of a network to provide greatly increased network flexibility and reliability (see Fig. 12.13). This proliferation is often desirable in radio networks where the terrain is irregular or if individual links are marginal. The PRNET switching nodes are a marriage of an L-band (1800-MHz) transceiver and a microprocessor that is intended to temporarily store only those packets destined for it or packets that it must relay. The unit is intended to operate unattended in a difficult environment.

But with the proliferation of nodes comes a need for commonality. As indicated in Fig. 12.6 all nodes within the PRNET have a common element called a packet radio unit (PRU). This unit is shown schematically and pictorially in Fig. 12.14. As mentioned, it consists of an L-band transceiver and a microprocessor. The role of the

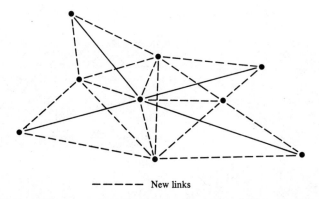

— — — — — New links

Figure 12.13. Effect of switch proliferation. Dashed line, new links.

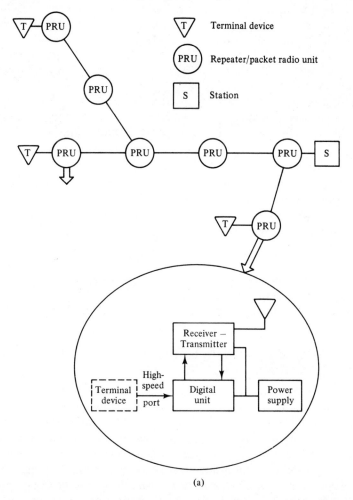

(a)

Figure 12.14. Packet Radio unit: (a) block diagram; (b) photograph.

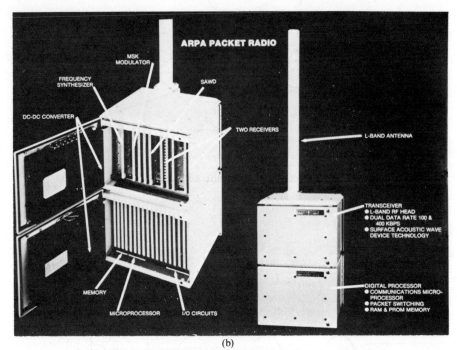

(b)

Figure 12.14 *(continued).*

PRU is determined by what is connected to its processor. If nothing is connected to it, the PRU is a repeater; if a terminal interface unit (TIU) and an end device are connected, the combination can become a user terminal or perhaps a network host; and if a specially programmed minicomputer is connected, it is a network controlling node or station. The commonality of the PRU has several advantages: the interchangeability of nodes, the minimization of maintenance procedures and parts inventory, and lower unit cost stemming from large procurements.

Major characteristics of the experimental PRU are listed in Tab. 12.4. More details on this and more advanced units are given in [KAHN 78].

12.3 PROTOCOL DESIGN: RELIABILITY IN A MARGINALLY RELIABLE MEDIUM

With the general network arrangement and routing concepts described in the preceding section (and in Fig. 12.6), we now proceed to a more detailed examination of the movement of packets within the PRNET. The first topic will be a general look at the subnet itself and its role in packet delivery. Beyond that, two aspects will be considered: protocol layering including some specifics of internetting, and error control. We will see in Sec. 12.4 the network management methods that provide the mechanical framework for such data flow but since the establishment of that framework relies in part on protocols, we discuss those first.

Table 12.4.   *Experimental Packet Radio Characteristics.*

Radio	
Frequency band	1710–1850 MHz
Tuning	Digitally controlled synthesizer
Occupied bandwidth	20 MHz
Maximum output power	10 watts
Power control	20 dB in 5-dB steps
Size	1.3 cu ft
Spread-spectrum technique	Direct sequence PN code
Signal processing	
Data rates (dual)	100 (400) kbps
Data modulation	DCPSK
Chip rate	12.8 Mchips/sec
Spread factor (chips/bit)	128(32)
Chip modulation	MSK (minimum-shift keyed)
Processing gain	21 dB (15 dB)

12.3.1   Reliability of the Subnet

In the preceding section a set of conditions on packet handling was given, one stipulation being that a node in the subnet would try only a limited number of times to relay a packet before discarding it. This condition is really an architectural issue in subnet design: the extent to which the subnet accepts the responsibility for packet delivery. Providing the end user of a packet network with a given set of characteristics involves among other things the persistence of the subnet in delivering to a specified address (subnet port) each packet it accepts for transmission. We examine here some of the rationale for where the responsibility for reliability is to be placed: in the subnet or in the end devices. Should each hop of the subnet be made ultrareliable so that several hops in tandem yield an adequate likelihood of packet delivery, or is it preferable to place in the end devices the ability to retry the subnet enough times to achieve a comparable reliability with a less reliable subnet? Although the following model is greatly simplified, it is instructive in addressing this question.

Let us assume for a moment that the transmissions on each leg of a N-hop path are independent network transmissions and that the probability of success, p, is the same for each transmission. Up to K retransmissions are permitted on each hop before discarding a packet and up to I retransmissions are permitted on an end-to-end (ETE) basis. As a measure of network performance, we then examine the average number of transmissions per hop required to achieve a given ETE reliability, P. The independence assumption presupposes a large number of nodes trying to access a given node and the fact that $p < 1$ is due only to packet collisions.

Using the assumptions above, the equations for the average number of transmissions along a given route can be found as follows [LEUN 79]:

For no ETE retransmissions but up to K transmissions on each hop, the total number of transmissions are:

$$\text{For one hop:} \quad T_K = \frac{P_K}{p}$$

$$\text{For } N \text{ hops: } T_{KN} = \frac{T_K F_{KN}}{F_K}$$

With up to I ETE transmissions:

$$\text{For } N \text{ hops: } \quad T_{KNI} = \frac{T_{KNI} \, P_{KNI}}{P_{KN}}$$

where $p = \text{Pr [success for each hop transmission]}$

$\qquad P_K = 1 - (1 - p)^K = \text{Pr [exactly one success for each hop in at most } K \text{ trials]}$

$\qquad F_K = (1 - p)^K = \text{Pr [failure on each hop in } K \text{ trials]}$

$\qquad P_{KN} = P_K^N = \text{Pr [success on each ETE transmission over an } N\text{-hop path]}$

$\qquad F_{KN} = 1 - P_K^N = \text{Pr [failure on each ETE transmission over an } N\text{-hop path]}$

$\qquad P_{KNI} = 1 - F_{KN}^I = \text{Pr [exactly one success in at most } I \text{ ETE transmissions over an } N\text{-hop path]}$

Dividing T_{KN} or T_{KN} by N yields the average number of transmissions per hop.

From these expressions and the corresponding plots in Fig. 12.15, we can draw some important conclusions about the subnet:

1. If a given hop probability, p, is so low that the subnet cannot satisfy the ETE probability, P, then repeated transmissions at the hop level (K) or the ETE level (I) are necessary.
2. Considering only subnet retransmissions ($K \geq 1$), there is a trade-off between p and K to achieve a given ETE reliability $P (=P_{KN})$. Figure 12.15a shows the trade-off between K and p for various N. Obviously, higher values of p mean a lower number of subnet transmissions.
3. Considering both subnet and ETE retransmissions ($K, I \geq 1$), there is a trade-off between K and I for a given p and P. This can be seen in Fig. 12.15b. Suppose that $p = 0.6$ and $N = 5$. To achieve a $P (= P_{KNI})$ of 0.95, you can, for example, select $K = 5$ and $I = 1$ or $K = 2$ and $I = 5$. Using the former, the average transmissions per hop is 1.6, whereas in the latter case it is 2.15, a difference of nearly 3 transmissions per ETE transit, or over a one-third increase in traffic. (Furthermore, that higher traffic level would result in a lower value of p and hence an even greater number of transmissions to achieve the same P. This feedback is, of course, not represented in this model.)
4. Under the assumptions stated, ETE retransmission is not the more efficient method for improving the overall likelihood of packet delivery. It is better to try all possible means to persist or circumvent the problem locally in the subnet than to back up and start again. One might conclude that, from a transmission

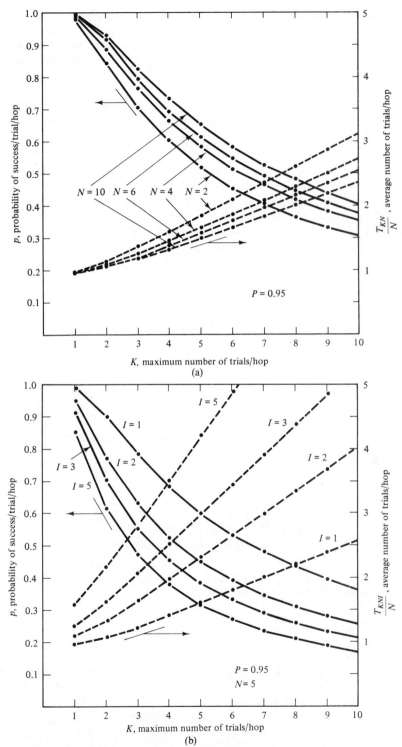

Figure 12.15. Effect of (a) hop and (b) ETE retransmissions on multihop success and average number of transmissions.

efficiency standpoint, it is not sensible to retransmit ETE unless a new and presumably better route is available! Some of these conclusions were voiced by Gitman [GITM 76B] when he was looking more specifically at delay.

With this reasoning, then, why use ETE protocols that rely on ETE retransmission? First, in a network with mobile operation a node could conceivably accept responsibility for forwarding a packet and then abruptly lose its connectivity entirely. This in itself requires ETE backup. Second, a requirement for high subnet reliability plus an inflexible queue discipline in the switch (such as persistent retransmission) may cause greater average delay in the network. Third, with ETE retransmission exists the ability to gain a new route in the face of difficulty on a primary route. Since it is the nature of a well-designed packet-switched system to seek routes of high probability of delivery on a packet-by-packet basis, holding a packet for persistent retransmission at a blockage may not provide adequate route alternatives. A fourth reason for leaving some responsibility for delivery outside the subnet itself is that different types of traffic may require different reliability. Making the subnet meet the users' highest level of reliability may be inefficient and unnecesary. ETE protocols also serve other functions, as we shall see later.

It is also possible to relate p to a hypothetical user population if we make some further assumptions, such as to the nature of their access method. In particular, if we make the same assumptions as for the ALOHA multiple-access method described in Sec. 12.1.3.1, where

$$p = \frac{1}{n} = e^{-2G}$$

then the net rate of new packets per packet interval for a node whose probability of access if p is given by

$$S = \frac{p}{2}(\ln \frac{1}{p})$$

The value may be found by entering the ordinate of Fig. 12.4 with p (= $1/n$) and reading S using the pure ALOHA curve. If M users are to share the channel (where M is not small), then S/M packets per interval may be transmitted by each user. This assumes persistent users; in other words, K is large, say greater than 10. If K is smaller, allowance must be made for failure from nonpersistent K values. In all cases though, the maximum value of S remains $1/2e$.

12.3.2   Protocol Layering and Internet Protocols

The basic function of the communication protocols used in the PRNET is to ensure reliable and robust operation. The protocols themselves are layered by function. This layering permits the modification of selected portions of the protocol or the associated equipment without necessarily altering the rest of it. With proper design, complementary functions at the ends of a link or circuit may have a virtual relationship with one another that is based only on services provided by the next lowest layer.

All other lower layers are transparent. Through functional decomposition the layered approach also offers some simplification to a complex process, as well as the ability to specify functions more accurately. This logical layering of protocols has become an important data communications concept [MCQU 78].

The communications protocols of the PRNET are implemented in the PRU subnet, the station, and the end subnet devices (TIUs). They include a channel access protocol (CAP), used for network access and hop transport; a station-to-PRU protocol (SPP), used for the reliable delivery of network control packets; and a transmission control protocol (TCP) [CERF 74], used for the end-to-end movement of data packets on both an intranet and internet basis. (Traffic between TIUs in the same PRNET is considered intranet traffic.) The structure of these protocols is shown in Fig. 12.16.

12.3.3. Channel Access Protocol (CAP)

CAP is implemented in the digital section of each PRU and provides the basic packet transport mechanism within the PRNET. CAP performs the function of radio channel access, packet routing, hop-by-hop (HBH) acknowledgment and retransmission, and system monitoring.

It makes use of the packet header (shown in Fig. 12.5), which contains addressing, sequencing, routing, status, and control information to help implement the protocols as the packet moves through the subnet. PRNET packets are variable in size, up to 2112 bits; 48 bits of preamble to acquire synchronization, 176 bits of header to define packet handling, up to 1856 bits of text, and a 32-bit cyclic redundancy checksum (CRC) that constitutes the only error detection in the subnet.

12.3.3.1   Radio Channel Access

A single radio channel is used for PRNET communication in all directions. Bit rates of 100 or 400 kbps can be used, the slower rate being most appropriate for severe noise and propagation conditions such as those encountered by moving terminals. These conditions might consist of both high multipath and low signal level. PRUs can access this common channel by either of two asynchronous multiple-access techniques: a variant of nonslotted ALOHA, or nonpersistent carrier sense. The choice of access mode is programmable, and can be remotely selected by a control message from the station. In the ALOHA mode, packets are transmitted as soon as they reach the top of the transmit queue without consideration of channel activity, save an in-progress reception in the PRU in question. Having transmitted, the PRU awaits acknowledgment of correct receipt by the next node; if the acknowledgment does not arrive within a specified time interval, the packet is presumed lost or mutilated and is retransmitted after that timeout interval, which is randomized to reduce the probability of subsequent collisions. Although ALOHA access is simple to implement, it results in low throughput. The carrier-sense mode improves channel utilization by reducing the chances of packet collisions. If the channel is busy, the PRU waits a random time and senses the state of the channel again. The improve-

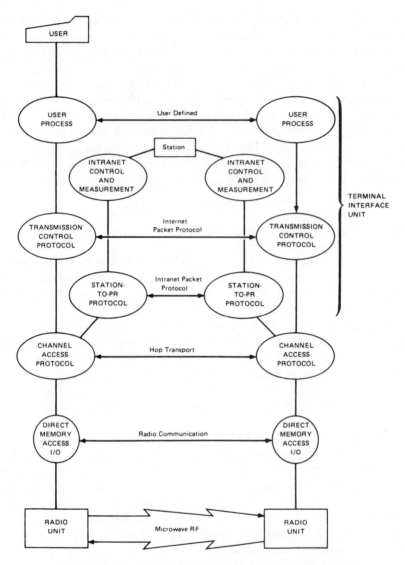

Figure 12.16. Layering of Packet Radio network protocols.

ment obtained with carrier sense is a function of radio connectivity between active PRUs; the greatest improvement occurs when all contending transmitters can hear each other, whereupon the efficiency approaches 80 to 90%.

12.3.3.2   Routing

As described earlier, the PRNET packet routing data are contained in the packet header. Hierarchical routing is used for control messages to and from the station, whereas data packets are routed via a direct point-to-point route assigned by the station.

The alternate-routing mechanisms described earlier are built into the HBH protocol to provide local protection against node congestion or outright node failure. Mechanisms are also provided for notifying the station whenever a PRU is having a problem forwarding traffic.

12.3.3.3   System Monitoring and Control

In the first implementation each PRU in the network periodically announced its existence by transmitting special "hello" packets which were routed to the station. This function provided the station with information on node status and the radio connectivity among the labeled (known) PRUs in the network. It also provided a mechanism for detecting when new nodes wished to join the network. To avoid flooding the station node with these special packets, the present system first collects connectivity and congestion statistics for the local neighborhood around each PRU. The PRU processes this information for its own inbound link quality and periodically forwards only that result to the station. These techniques are described in more detail in Sec. 12.4.3.

12.3.3.4   Hop-by-Hop Acknowledgment and
Retransmission

A packet may be lost as it travels the subnet. To improve the probability of success in traversing many hops and to restrain the number of unnecessary transmissions, a positive acknowledgment/retransmission scheme is used at each hop. The PRU saves a copy of each packet that it transmits and awaits an acknowledgment from the next PRU along the route. This acknowledgment is implicit if the PRU hears the packet being forwarded at the next hop; the acknowledgment is explicit at the last hop, where only the packet's header need be transmitted back as an acknowledgment. If the PRU has not heard the acknowledgment within some time interval, it retransmits the packet. Retransmission occurs a set number of times until the PRU gives up and discards the packet, freeing its buffer. The use of an HBH acknowledgment results, of course, in a reduced capacity for normal traffic [TOBA 78A]. However, not using it may cause a greater channel congestion under the appropriate conditions (see Sec. 12.3.1.)

Another consideration of the acknowledgment scheme described above is whether any new packet should come to the top of the transmit queue until an acknowledgment is received for the packet most recently transmitted. If the choice is to await the acknowledgment, a buffer must be held open to receive it. Seven buffers are presently used in each Packet Radio unit.

The HBH retransmission mechanism obviously may introduce duplicate packets into the system. Some, but not all, of these duplicates created through retransmission are detected and discarded by the PRUs (on the basis of a table of unique packet identifiers stored within the PRUs). Since the HBH protocols are not infinitely persistent, some packets may not get through. Finally, packets may arrive at their destination out of order. To keep the subnet protocols simple, a final filtering for missing, duplicate, or out-of-order packets is done in the end devices.

12.3.4 End-to-End Protocols

Although each node in the network performs a moderately persistent attempt to transport packets hop by hop, end-to-end (ETE) protocols are also used, to guarantee delivery and to control the rate of flow from source to destination. The guarantee of delivery is made possible by persistent attempts by a sender to retransmit a packet until it receives an ETE acknowledgment indicating the packet's arrival at the destination.

Station-to-PRU Protocol (SPP) is an intranet ETE protocol used in the PRNET for control traffic, and *Transmission Control Protocol* (TCP) [CERF 74] is a more powerful internet ETE protocol used in the PRNET for movement of data traffic. A brief description of each follows.

12.3.4.1 Station-to-PRU Protocol (SPP)

The station node continuously gathers network status information and uses this to control dynamically the topology of the network and the routes assigned. SPP is an ETE protocol optimized specifically for the PRNET and used by the station in its capacity as the network controlling node. It provides a reliable connection with one outstanding packet at a time and is used to exchange control information and a limited amount of PRNET data between the PRUs and the station. SPP uses the same source address, destination address, and sequence number fields as CAP, to minimize header-space requirements.

As with the CAP HBH protocol, SPP achieves reliable ETE communication through error detection and retransmission; a packet being sent is saved by the source SPP until a corresponding acknowledgment is received. If no acknowledgment arrives within a specified time interval, the packet is retransmitted; if one does arrive, the packet is discarded. After a set number of unsuccessful retransmission attempts, the SPP discards the undeliverable packet and communicates its failure to the originating process.

Generally, the station opens and closes SPP connections. To open a connection, two SPPs exchange "open" control messages for establishing mutually acceptable initial sequence numbers (ISNs) for the connection, one in each direction; successive packets sent must bear sequence numbers that increase monotonically from the ISN for that direction. When a packet is received by the destination SPP, the packet sequence number is used to determine whether the packet is the next in sequence; if so, its correct arrival is acknowledged by returning a special control message acknowledgment bearing the packet's sequence number. Out-of-sequence packets from the past (sequence number lower than the expected sequence number) are acknowledged and discarded; those from the future may be discarded or saved and acknowledged when the preceding packets in the sequence have arrived.

12.3.4.2   Internetwork Protocols: Datagrams and TCP

Internetwork data communications carries the implication that the communicating parties are separated not only by distance but also potentially by the design of their resident networks. Each network may have different data structures, switching methods, capacities, and so on. As data networks proliferate, internet protocols are being designed to enable different packet-switched networks to be linked in ways that are, hopefully, network independent. Two protocols important to this process are the *Internet Datagram Protocol* (IDP) and the *Transmission Control Protocol* (TCP) [CERF 74].

To avoid some of the inconsistencies among different networks the IDP provides variable-length *data envelopes*. These packets use the transport mechanisms of the individual networks in combination with special processors at the interfaces between networks (termed *gateways*). To accomplish this transport, internet source and destination addresses are appended to each IDP packet. (An IDP header, defined by a DARPA internet working group, is shown in Fig. 12.17a.) Fragmentation may occur at gateways when going from a network with large packet size to one with smaller packets.

The higher-level internet protocol, TCP, is a process-to-process arrangement that calls on IDP for its internet transport process. The present TCP header is shown in Fig. 12.17b and carries information needed for the following functions of TCP:

- Basic data transfer—byte oriented in record or stream mode; pipelining (multiple packets outstanding)
- Reliability—based on sequencing and positive acknowledgments
- Flow control—based on receiver-controlled windowing
- Connections—status information relevant to a single data stream
- Multiplexing—multiple connections per host

TCP is used within the PRNET for high-performance intranet communication as well as for internetwork communication among the PRNET, the ARPANET [ROBE 73], the DARPA Satellite Network [JACO 78], and other interconnected networks, including other PRNETS [CERF 78]. As far as the PRNET is concerned, the gateway process connecting these nets may reside in any terminal node that has the appropriate processor and physical internet connections. A more detailed discussion of TCP is beyond the scope of this chapter.

12.3.5   Error Control

Error control in the PRNET is vested mainly in the requirement for a packet to be received correctly before it is accepted (and possibly relayed) by a PRU. This check is in the form of a polynomial-based cyclic redundancy check (CRC), mentioned above and noted in Fig. 12.5. The CRC is computed as the final PRU task prior to transmission and is appended to the end of the packet. If the receiver fails to replicate the identical CRC bit pattern, the packet is flushed and the transmitter must retransmit. The 32-bit CRC results in a probability of an undetected packet error of 1 in 2^{32} (or a binary rate of better than 1 in 10^{12}) and permits the PRNET to be an extremely reliable computer data link. This methodology, combined with the protocols in the end devices (TIUs), means that even the PRU's radio can be momentarily disabled and, upon restoration, the data flow will continue, error free! To those familiar with the vargaries of the land-mobile radio channel, this capability is impressive.

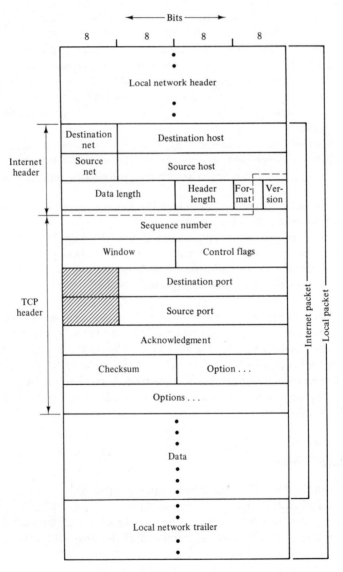

Figure 12.17. Format of headers for (a) internet datagram and (b) TCP.

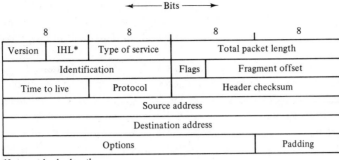

*Internet leader length.

(a)

Source port	Destination port		
Sequence number			
Acknowledgment number			
TCP header length	Reserved	Control	Window
Checksum		Urgent call pointer	
Options			Padding
Data			

(b)

Figure 12.17. *(continued)*

12.4   NETWORK MANAGEMENT

One of the most important contributions of the DARPA Packet Radio program to the science of DRNs has been a sophisticated system of network management. In this section we examine that subject plus some of the operational aspects of packet radio networks: how they are established, what measurements are needed to intelligently manage and control them, and how they can provide special features, such as mobile operation.

12.4.1   Centralized versus Decentralized Control

The PRNET has centralized control and decentralized (point-to-point) routing. Centralized control, vested in the station, has both advantages and disadvantages. Although centralization certainly affords a greater sophistication of network control algorithms and may cover a greater variety of contingencies, concentration of control is also a *network-wide* vulnerability. On the other hand, decentralization may represent some loss of control that may itself be critical to the integrity of the network. Other comparative factors, such as the amount of control traffic and the rapidity of network response to change, are too dependent on individual implementations to favor one approach over the other. To avoid the vulnerability of centralized control, the present PRNET also has decentralized control (multiple stations).

Of course, as networks move from decentralized control to distributed control, the intelligence that formerly resided at the control nodes must be relegated to the individual switching nodes. The ARPANET is a classical example of such distributed control [ROBE 73]. To examine a simple concept of distributed control, consider the example shown in Fig. 12.18. Here the nodes continually provide one another with special packets that are used to estimate the average delay on each link. (Although an average may exist for each direction, the value for only one direction is shown here.) Separate packets originate at terminal nodes and flow through the network, picking up link performance parameters (the link delay value) as they go. The packet, in turn, deposits at each node the value of delay accumulated since leaving its source. By considering the value associated with each route from a single source, a node can develop a table showing the best (lowest delay) route to any terminal. This approach ignores other valid criteria for route selection, such as whether a node at any given moment has memory space to receive a packet; but it illustrates the concept.

12.4.2 Criteria for Topology

Arriving at a proper topology for a radio network requires significantly greater study and care than for a wired network. First, there is the required assurance of adequate radio connectivity. Ideally, each node should have good connectivity with at least two other nodes, especially if the node in question is mobile. Path or route redundancy is essential in this case. Irregular terrain and the lack of adequate sites often make multiple connectivity a tedious and difficult task, particularly when trying to minimize the number of nodes required to meet the coverage requirements [KLEI 78]. Second is the question of adequate channel bandwidth, as limited by multipath (see Sec. 12.1.4). Some sites, such as in urban areas, are prone to high multipath and therefore low data rates. Finally, there is external noise. Since one cannot always control the noise environment, sites are sometimes located to avoid propagated noise.

12.4.3 Network Dynamics and Mobile Terminals

Since one of the virtues of radio is the ability to communicate with mobile units, a packet radio network should be able to deal with a node's entrance to, exit from, and movement within the network. If provided adequately, this capability can then accommodate the gain or loss of *any* node and, furthermore, intelligently reconfigure the network to compensate for the change.

To accomplish this adaptation requires the dedication of some part of the network resource to assess the current network state and to communicate the required alterations. In the PRNET, control of individual PRUs is accomplished

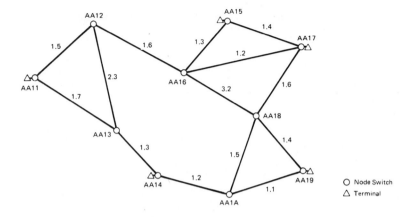

TABLES A, B, C FOR PR-AA18 ONLY

A. NEIGHBOR TABLE

NODE ID	DELAY
AA16	3.2
AA17	1.6
AA19	1.4
AA1A	1.5

B. ROUTING TABLE

TERMINAL	DELAY VIA			
NODE ID	AA16	AA17	AA19	AA1A
AA17	4.4	1.6	4.4	4.6
AA19	7.8	4.6	1.4	2.6
AA11	6.3	5.9	6.7	5.7
AA14	6.1	5.7	3.7	2.7
AA15	4.5	3.0	5.8	6.0

C. OPTIMUM ROUTING TABLE

TERMINAL NODE ID	HOP ADDRESSEE	DELAY
AA17	AA17	1.6
AA19	AA19	1.4
AA11	AA1A	5.7
AA14	AA1A	2.7
AA15	AA17	3.0

Figure 12.18. Routing procedure in a network with distributed control: network schematic and an example of tables contained in the switching node.

through the station-to-PRU protocol mentioned in the preceding section. Assessment of the state of the PRNET is vested in a variety of network measurements using special packets and dedicated processes within the PRU microcomputer. Only those special packets used to measure effective radio connectivity (a combination of radio connectivity and congestion) will be discussed in this section.

It is easiest to portray the dynamics of PRNET topology by first describing the initialization procedure shown in Fig. 12.19. An underlying tenet of this procedure is that no PRU may forward a packet until it has been labeled; that is, recognized by a controlling node (station) as a defined network element. Once labeled, the node can forward packets to whoever is specified in the packet header. As indicated, certain packets, called *repeater-on-packets* (ROPs), are initiated at regular intervals by *all* PRUs (nodes) for reception by all other nodes within one-hop range. After reception by that first node, the packet, with some information about who received it, is forwarded automatically to the station as a normal data packet. These ROPs become

PACKET RADIO NETWORK INITIALIZATION
(Simple Hierarchical Net)

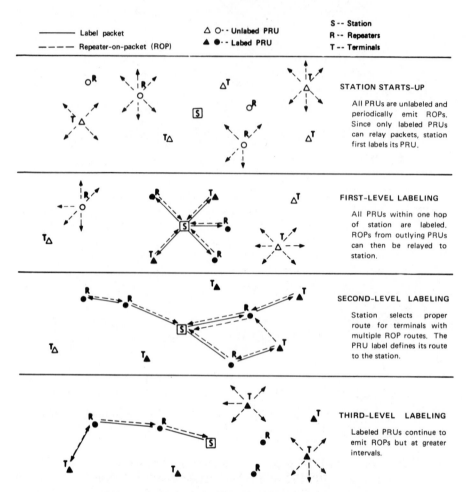

Figure 12.19. Packet Radio Network initialization.

the initial basis for radio connectivity tables. Since many radio links are not bidirectional, ROPs traveling in both directions between a node pair are needed to verify both entries in a connectivity matrix. When a PRU is first turned on and has not been incorporated into the network (i.e., labeled), the ROP interval is short, once every few seconds. After labeling, the unit continues to radiate ROPs, but at a much reduced rate, to provide updates to the connectivity matrix.

Once the network is labeled, this ROP technique displays one disadvantage in an area of high connectivity; that is, a single ROP from a single node can create a small flood of traffic at the station(s) [MINO 79B]. This on-rush can tie up the station computer for undesirably long periods. To avoid this flood and to gain a more accurate assessment of connectivity, an alternative scheme has been implemented. Each node can simply count the number of normal transmissions it receives from each neighbor (adjacent node) during a given period. Periodically, each node then transmits a data packet containing these accumulated counts plus its own transmit count over the same interval. These data are received by all neighbors and are used by them to estimate radio connectivity locally. The results are transmitted to the station(s). This technique reduces the number of administrative packets the station must handle, and hopefully, each packet is now based on more data. If no regular information packets are transmitted during an interval, each node generates a number of so-called local ROPs (LROPs) that terminate after one hop. These LROPs assure a minimum estimate of radio connectivity.

Thus both normal and special traffic can be used to estimate radio connectivity. If connectivity with a given node degrades over predefined intervals to an unacceptable level, steps can be taken to eliminate that node from the network. Conversely, if a new node appears, its presence is automatically announced to its neighbors via some type of ROP. They, in turn, notify the station, which then labels the new node. The only significant differences between this ability to handle time-varying fixed nodes and mobile terminals are the appropriate time constants for measurement and notifications of distress.

Because of the methodology described above, no special distinction is given to mobile terminals in the PRNET at the present time. All nodes exchange ROPs with their neighbors and the connectivity assessment applies uniformly to all. But since the connectivity can change much more rapidly for mobile nodes, each node is also given the ability to emit a distress packet if its connectivity fails abruptly. The sequence is as follows: Each packet the mobile node is attempting to transmit is repeatedly tried on the assigned route a preset number of times. If that series fails, an alternate route is attempted a preset number of times. Should that fail, the mobile node then emits a distress packet requesting, in effect, a new route. The distress packet is forwarded to the station(s) via all available means and the station(s) quickly responds with a new route, based on the present connectivity matrix or perhaps on the route to the station(s) of the distress packet itself. All this happens very quickly and a person at a mobile terminal may not even be aware of a hand-off to another repeater.

12.4.4 Measurements

Measurements are made in the PRNET for two reasons: to observe whether the network is functioning properly, and to characterize the network. We shall discuss here only the first, because it is the one that is oriented toward network operation.

Necessary to the successful operation of a complex system is some means to monitor its performance. This monitoring may be tied directly to the controlling elements of the network for the automatic or manual regulation of network functions, or it may be fed back to the user, who may then either adapt or complain to the network operations center. The point of the feedback is to optimize network performance in some global, local, or priority sense. In a packet-switched network this often means achieving small delays at a reasonable throughput. This criterion normally means routing through the smallest number of hops, provided that none of the nodes are extremely busy, or directly controlling the flow of packets at various points in the network, particularly the access points. Several mechanisms are possible to monitor parameters that relate to performance measures such as delay and throughput [TOBA 77B]. These mechanisms are listed in Tab. 12.5.

The *cumstats* (cumulative statistics) listed in Tab. 12.5 are collected over a known time and therefore become rate statistics. From these the "busyness" of any given node can be examined to determine if it can qualify as a node in a new route. A portion of the cumstats in a subnet node are associated with a *neighbor table*. That is, each PRNET node tabulates the number of successful packet receptions it has had from each of its immediate (one-hop) neighbors during the preceding interval (as described in the preceding section). These data, together with the total number of transmissions each node has made during the same interval, are used to calculate the transport success of all hops within the subnet. Ultimately, a link quality parameter is calculated based on a combination of signal level plus the expected congestion at the receiving node based on the measurements described above. This parameter becomes a measure of the present value of that link to network operation. From these data the likelihood of a packet being successfully transported over a given link can be estimated. Then, over several tandem links, not only can a new candidate route be selected, but the impact of that route on adjacent nodes can be estimated as well. This

Table 12.5. *Mechanisms for PRNET Measurements.*

Measurement Parameter	Location of Measurement	Purpose of Measurement
Nodal cumstats— network activity as viewed from a subnet node	Within a node in the subset	Total number of transmissions, receptions, both successful and unsuccessful; includes transmissions beyond successful one
Terminal cumstats— network characteristics as viewed from an attached terminal	Within an attached terminal or terminal interface	Total number of transmissions, retransmissions, receptions, and delay distributions
Snapshots— network activity at a given instant as viewed from a subnet node	Within a node of the subnet	Condition of packet buffers in various subnet nodes at a given instant
Pick-up-packets— network activity as viewed by a given packet in transit	Along a specified series of a subnet nodes and including and devices	Accumulates the packet route and delay at each node

Source: [TOBA #76B].

impact is an important part of route selection and is a unique consequence of broadcast radio.

If at a given moment a new route cannot be found with the information described above, subsequent action can be taken to help control the flow of data into the net. Thus a network control facility can adjust (limit or expand) data flow through any node on the basis of measured data. When trying to limit data flow it is usually most efficient to limit it at its source, in this case the entry node to the network.

The rate or interval of measurement is also important. Obviously, measurement intervals greater than those needed to portray topological change (nodal movement) accurately are of no value in network management [MINO 79A].

12.5 IMPORTANT NEEDS

In this final section we discuss a few subjects that still challenge the designers of packet radio networks. The list is not intended to be exhaustive, simply suggestive.

12.5.1 Definition of Network "Goodness"

It took a good bit of abstraction and cleverness to define a limit on the information-carrying capacity of a communication link or channel. Shannon's capacity theorem, however, has become a standard against which to compare various modulation and coding techniques [SHAN 48]. Networks have no less a need for a definition of goodness, but it is not necessarily capacity alone. (Recall capacities with attendant delays were shown in Fig. 12.4 for a simple multiple-access network.) One metric could be the excess delays in packet delivery; that is, delays beyond stated thresholds. Although such a number could be used in a comparison of very specific networks, it falls short as a broader-scale criterion about networks in general.

To be useful, the metric should apply to a broad range of DRNs. To ensure this universality, it may be necessary to isolate the subnet and define the metric on the sources alone, as in looking at their aggregate ability under equilibrium conditions to offer traffic to the network. Even then there remains the question of whether the method can be sufficiently general to permit flexibilities, such as certain sources having preferential offering rates compared to others, or avoiding the nonlinearities of the network's performance being dependent on the relative values of separate sources. Perhaps the metric should be restricted to that class of traffic offering rates that result in a linear system; that is, any increase in offering rate at any source results in a corresponding increase in the aggregate network throughput without an increase in delay. That definition may be too restrictive, since delay is often a "soft" requirement.

The metric should be defined such that it can be meaningfully evaluated by simulation, direct observation, or if the subnet were sufficiently simple, by analytical techniques. Packet radio networks are particularly difficult to model since there are not only interdependent effects stemming from network utilization and multiple access, but the broadcast nature of the network makes that interdependence more complete than is typically found in wired networks [LEIN 80]. Of course, there will still remain a myriad of other, often subjective values of any network, such as redundancy, adequacy of interfaces to other networks, and ultimately cost.

12.5.2   Various Costs of an Area-Coverage DRN

At the outset of this chapter it was claimed that if normal land-mobile radio voice channels were replaced by data channels whose direct information rate were equivalent, perhaps 30 or more such data channels could occupy the same spectrum as one 25-kHz voice channel. This increase in spectral efficiency will become more and more compelling as the demand for mobile services increases. The disadvantage in switching to data is the potentially more expensive terminal, which would require a form of display or even hard copy. The radio itself will almost certainly become cheaper than a corresponding land-mobile voice radio, even though the stability requirements will increase if only narrowband (100 to 200 Hz) assignments were issued.

Wideband multiple-access systems such as Packet Radio have not yet been considered for commercial application because they are (1) potentially more expensive than their narrowband counterpart (due mainly to the spread-spectrum modulator/demodulators) and (2) are less spectrally efficient for other than highly intermittent traffic [BERR]. The unit cost, assuming high-volume production, of the present experimental packet radio is estimated at about $5000 each. This is considerably more than the present land-mobile radio but is also more elaborate than necessary for commercial use. A comprehensive study of the costs of new forms of land-mobile radio, both to the user and the impact on the limited spectral resource available, is much needed.

12.5.3   Demand Assignment

Packet-switched networks are designed for the efficient movement of data from sources with a high peak-to-average offering rate. Packet radio is no exception. From time to time, however, there may be a need to move substantial amounts of data, such as a large file or even high-rate digitized voice. This type of traffic is called stream traffic and may require different transport protocols than, say, intermittent computer traffic. For example, voice data need not have the reliability of computer data, but it must not encounter delays greater than a fraction of a second. When there are multiple data needs in a single network, efficient use of the network may require that a user negotiate a throughput rate, a delay characteristic, and perhaps a reliability. In return, the network tries to achieve this reliability, delay, and throughput in the route assigned to the new user. The conditions for that specific connection (one or more routes) are then valid until the connection is closed and the resource returns to the network pool.

This concept of demand assignment is made possible by intelligent switches and may also require some global network knowledge or centralized control. In any case it marks a very significant trend in network design and operation.

12.5.4 Broadcast Protocols

An exciting feature of packet radio networks has been their broadcast nature. That is, any given transmission is heard by all nodes within one-hop range. Such broadcast capability naturally leads to multipoint routing. Rather than dispatching the same packet to multiple nodes serially, it is possible, with the appropriate routing technique, to reach all destination nodes with one "ripple" of the packet through the network. Even this type of "routing on the ripple" is not difficult to do once a minimum spanning tree centered about the originating nodes can be deduced [DALA 77]. What is difficult is making the broadcast routing mechanism reliable, that is, providing the positive acknowledgments from various destinations without their being delivered serially.

This capability is desperately needed in certain types of network conferencing. Although reliability may not be needed in, say, voice conferencing, it is needed in data conferencing.

12.5.5 End-to-End Encryption in Packet Radio Systems

Encryption as used here is defined as the capability to deny an adversary the ability to read network transmissions even if he or she could acquire them. It does not apply to methods used simply to deny awareness of the radio signal, as in spread-spectrum modulation, or access to it, as might be the case in bit-by-bit code switching [KAHN 78].

Encryption has traditionally been implemented on a link basis. This means physically protecting all nodes and distributing to them, via an independent channel, a key that allows the two ends of the link to communicate privately. Message-switched networks such as AUTODIN I have this type of equipment.

With the introduction of packet-switched networks and flexible, dynamic routing of submessage units, the concept of encryption should change somewhat. Packet switching, particularly as it involves mobile terminals, is much better matched to ETE encryption, leaving the subnet flexible and free of the need for physical security. Thus, as packet switching evolves, ETE encryption is receiving greater attention. This technique requires the text of a given message to be encrypted at the source and that no other encryption occurs regardless of the path through the network. It may also mean, however, that the packet header, containing address, routing, and other information, will remain in the clear because intermediate nodes may have no encryption/decryption capability. This encryption-free header permits an adversary to recreate the network topology from simply listening to header data; the text portion of the packet is still secure. Packet networks can, of course, employ both ETE and link encryption to maintain security of the entire packet.

One conceivable obstacle to performing such "traffic analysis" on a packet-switched network with only ETE encryption could be the use of public-key encryption systems [DIFF 76]. These systems permit the public dissemination of an encryption key by an intended recipient, but once a message is encrypted using this key, no one except the recipient can decrypt it, including the sender. These systems could conceivably be employed by the individual nodes in a packet-switched network to limit or entirely exclude the acquisition of header information by an interceptor. (If a PRU itself is captured, more but still limited information might become available to the intruder, depending on the encrypting procedure used.)

Two public-key inplementation concepts come to mind. The first treats all the packet header the same as far as encryption/decryption is concerned. A given node receives a packet intended for it: one, that is, whose header is encrypted in its own public key. That node also knows the public key of its neighbors and can therefore handle the packet as prescribed by the header, encrypting the entire header using the appropriate key for the next node along the route. Directed alternate routing and acknowledgments can be sent similarly.

The second concept uses public keys mainly in the route portion of the header. With the exception of the source and destination IDs, which could be encrypted in the public key of the end node, much of the remainder of the header would be in the clear or perhaps a common network-wide code. The source, knowing the route, would encrypt each segment of the route in the key appropriate to each corresponding node. However, to be able to obtain packet identification and to recognize whether to forward the packet or not, some of the header has to remain in a common code. In this instance knowledge of the exact route may be denied interior nodes and thus alternate routing would be more difficult. Nevertheless, the critical route portions of the header would be protected and selective routing could be accomplished via the key sequence.

One problem with such concepts, however, is that addresses in most networks would not normally require more than 16 bits. Encrytping that short a field would not offer much challenge to one who wants to decrypt such header data.

12.5.6   Some Remaining Tasks

In conclusion, a number of opportunities exist in packet radio design, opportunities not yet all fulfilled. Some of these are addressed in [KAHN 78]. Multiple-station operation is now being implemented and tested in the Packet Radio progam. Obviously, a network with only one control node is vulnerable, so a multiple-station solution is necessary.

Single point vulnerability can also be countered using totally distributed control. This approach has been implemented in networks such as the ARPANET, and has just been demonstrated on the packet radio network.

Another interesting potential for packet radio networks is transmitter power control. What advantages accrue if a node intelligently adjusts (tailors) its power for each transmission? Improved network capacity? Privacy? Radio connectivity measurements described earlier could be made with varying power levels. Then, armed with the knowledge of the minimum power required for one node to access another, the controlling node (station) could prescribe each power level along the route as part of the route assignment. To the extent that these powers were minimum, this action would result in less network self-interference and therefore greater capacity.

Because the present PRNET uses line-of-sight transmissions, it has difficulty under certain terrain conditions such as forests and rugged mountains. On the other hand lower frequencies, capable of offering less constrained propagation, offer severe bandwidth limitations. To be able to use transmission media appropriate to each link within a network, a media-independent node is needed. The intelligent part of a switching node can use some of its resources to assess the characteristics of the channel and controlling nodes can become aware of such conditions in route assignments. Thus a network with a common intelligent nodal core but with heterogeneous transmission media could be adapted to a wide variety of terrain conditions.

Finally, there is the speech application. Applying real-time digitized voice to a packet-switched network may violate the important requirement for intermittent traffic. Attempts are being made to create network capacity and discipline that are not inimical (in delay) to voice [DASI 80, NILS 80, SPIL 80]. That work continues.

ACKNOWLEDGMENTS

Work on the DARPA Packet Radio Network has been the combined effort of many organizations and people. Led by DARPA, the following organizations had significant input: Bolt, Beranek and Newman; Network Analysis Corporation; Rockwell International; SRI International; and UCLA. Input from SRI colleagues John Leung, Ron Kunzelman, and Keith Klemba is especially appreciated.

REFERENCES

ABRA 70   Abramson, N., "The Aloha System—Another Alternative for Computer Communications," *AFIPS Conf. Proc.*, Vol. 37, FJCC, 1970, pp. 695–702.

BELL 79   "Special Issue on Advance Mobile Phone Service," *Bell Syst. Tech. J.*, Vol. 58, No. 1, 1979.

BERR   Berry, L.A., and E. J. Haakinson, "Spectrum Efficiency for Multiple Independent Spread-Spectrum Land-Mobile Radio Systems," Report 78-11, National Telecommunications and Information Administration.

BIND 75   Binder, R., N. Abramson, F. F. Kuo, A. Okinaka, and D. Wax, "ALOHA Packet Broadcasting—A Retrospect," *NCC Proc.*, Vol. 144, May 1975, pp. 203–215.

BOOR 80   Boorstyn, R. R., and A. Kerslenbaum, "Throughput Analysis of Multihop Packet Radio," *IEEE 1980 Int. Conf. Commun.*, Vol. 13.6/1-6 June 1980, Sec. 13.6, pp. 1–6.

BURC 75 Burchfiel, J.R., R. Tomlinson, and M. Beeler, "Functions and Structure of a Packet Radio Station," *NCC Proc.,* Vol. 44, May 1975, pp. 245–251.

CERF 74 Cerf, V. G., and R. E. Kahn, "A Protocol for Packet Network Intercommunications," *IEEE Trans. Commun.,* Vol. COM-22, May 1974, pp. 637–648.

CERF 78 Cerf, V. G., and P. T. Kirstein, "Issues in Packet-Network Interconnection," *Proc. IEEE,* Vol. 66, No. 11, 1978, pp. 1386–1408.

CLAR 68 Clarke, R. H., "A Statistical Theory of Mobile Radio Reception" *Bell Syst. Tech. J.,* Vol. 47, July 1968, pp. 957–1000.

COX 71A Cox, D.C., "Doppler Spectrum Measurements at 91 MHz over a Suburban Mobile Radio Path," *Proc. IEEE,* Vol. 59 (Tech. Corres.), June 1971, pp. 1017–1018.

COX 71B Cox, D. C., and D. O. Reudink, "Dynamic Channel Assignment in High Capacity Mobile Communications System," *Bell Syst. Tech. J.,* Vol. 50, July–August 1971, pp. 1833–1857.

COX 72A Cox, D. C., "Delay-Doppler Characteristics of Multipath Propagation at 910 MHz in a Suburban Mobile Radio Environment," *IEEE Trans. Antennas Propag.,* Vol. AP-20, September 1972, pp. 625–635.

COX 72B Cox, D. C., and D. O. Reudink, "Dynamic Channel Assignment in Two-Dimensional Large-Scale Mobile Radio Systems," *Bell Syst. Tech. J.,* Vol. 51, September 1972, pp. 1611–1630.

DALA 77 Dalal, Y., "Broadcast Protocols on Packet-Switched Computer Networks," Ph.D., thesis, Stanford University, Digital System Laboratories Technical Report No. 128, April 1977.

DASI 79 DaSilva, J. S., and S. Mahmoud "Capacity Degradation of Packet Radio Fading Channels," *IEEE ACM Proc. 6th Data Commun. Symp.,* November 1979, pp. 96–101.

DASI 80 DaSilva, J. S., J. B. Mercado, and S. Mahmoud, "Packet Speech for Land Mobile Channels, *IEEE 1980 Int. Zurich Semin. Digital Commun.,* Vol. E4/1-6, March 1980, Sec. E4, pp. 1–6.

DIFF 76 Diffie, W., and M. E. Hellman, "New Directions in Cryptography," *IEEE Trans. Inf. Theory,* Vol. IT-22, No. 6, November 1976, pp. 644–654.

DIXO 76 Dixon, R. C., "Spread Spectrum Systems," in Wiley, New York, 1976.

FRAL 75A Fralick, S. C., and J. C. Garrett, "Technological Considerations for Packet Radio Network," *NCC Proc.,* Vol. 44, May 1975, pp. 233–243.

FRAL 75B Fralick, S., et al., "Digital Terminals for Packet Broadcasting," *NCC Proc.,* Vol. 44, May 1975, pp. 253–262.

FRAN 75 Frank, H., I. Gitman, and R. M. Van Slyke, "Packet Radio System—Network Considerations," *NCC Proc.* Vol. 44, May 1975, pp. 217–231.

FREN 70 Frenkiel, R. H., "A High-Capacity Mobile Radiotelephone System Model Using a Coordinated Small-Zone Approach," *IEEE Trans. Veh. Technol.,* Vol. VT-19, May 1970, pp. 173–177.

FCC 68 "In the Matter of the Carterfone Device in Message Toll Telephone Service, Docket 16942 and 17073," *FCC Rep. Second Ser.,* Vols. 13, 14, 1968, p. 423.

FCC 71 "In the Matter of Policies and Procedures for Consideration of Applications to Provide Specialized Common Carrier Service in the Domestic Public

Point-to-Point Microwave Radio Service and Proposed Amendment to Parts 21, 43 and 61 of the Commission's Rules (Docket 18920), First Report and Order on Docket 18920," *FCC Rep. Second Ser.*, Vol. 29, 1971 p. 879.

FCC 76   "FCC Application of Satellite Business Systems," Vol. 2, Federal Communications Commission, Washington, D.C., 1976.

FCC 80   "Xerox Corporation Petition for Rulemaking, before the Federal Communications Commission, November 16, 1978 and Comments of Xerox Corporation," Federal Communications Commission, January 1980, in reference to Gen. Docket No. 79–188, RM-3247.

GANS 72   Gans, M. J., "A Power-Spectral Theory of Propagation in the Mobile Radio Environment," *IEEE Trans. Veh. Technol.*, Vol. VT-21, February 1972, pp. 27–38.

GITM 74   Gitman, I., R. M. Van Slyke, and H. Frank, "On Splitting Random Access Broadcast Communication Channels," *Proc. 7th Hawaii Int. Conf. Syst. Sci., Subconf. Comput. Nets,* January 1974.

GITM 75   Gitman, I., "On the Capacity of Slotted ALOHA Networks and Some Design Problems," *IEEE Trans. Commun.*, Vol. COM-23, March 1975, pp. 305–317.

GITM 76A   Gitman, I., R. M. Van Slyke, and H. Frank, "Routing in Packet Switching Broadcast Radio Networks," *IEEE Trans. Commun.*, Vol. COM-24, August 1976, pp 926–930.

GITM 76B   Gitman, I., "Comparison of Hop-By-Hop and End-To-End Acknowledgment Schemes in Computer Communication Networks," *IEEE Trans. Commun.*, Vol. COM-24, November 1976, pp. 1258–1262.

GRIE 79   Grieco, D. M., and W. C. Fifer, "Signal Processing for a Packet Radio on a Multipath Environment," *IEEE Natl. Telecommun. Conf.*, Washington, D.C., Vol. 2, November 1979, p. 25.

GRON 80   Gronemeyer, S. A., "Packet Radio for Mobile Communications," *IEEE/SAE Proc. 30th Annu. Conf. IEEE Veh. Soc.*, Dearborn, Mich., September 1980.

JACO 78   Jacobs, I. M., R. Binder, and E. V. Hoversten, "General Purpose Packet Satellite Networks," *Proc. IEEE,* Vol. 66, No. 11, 1978, pp. 1448–1467.

JAKE 67   Jakes, W. C., Jr., and D. O. Reudink, "Comparison of Mobile Radio Transmission at UHF and X-Bands," *IEEE Trans. Veh. Technol.*, Vol. VT-16, October 1967, pp. 10–14.

KAHN 75   Kahn, R. E., "The Organization of Computer Resources into a Packet Radio Network," *NCC Proc.*, Vol. 44, No. 000, May 1975, pp. 177–186.

KAHN 77   Kahn, R. E., "The Organization of Computer Resources into a Packet Radio Network," *IEEE Trans. Commun.*, Vol. COM-25, No. 1, 1977, pp. 169–178.

KAHN 78   Kahn, R. E., S. A. Gronemeyer, J. Burchfiel, and R. Kunzelman, "Advances in Packet Radio Technology," *Proc. IEEE,* Special Issues or Packet Communication Networks, Vol. 66, No. 11, 1978, pp. 146–1496.

KLEI 74   Kleinrock, L., and F. Tobagi, "Carrier Sense Multiple Access for Packet Switched Radio Channels," *ICC Proc.*, June 1974, pp. 21B-1 to 21B-7.

KLEI 75B   Klein, T. J., "A Tactical Packet Radio System," *NTC Proc.*, New Orleans

Vol. 75, December 1975.

KLEI 75A Kleinrock, L., and F. Tobagi, "Random Access Techniques for Data Transmission over Packet Radio Channels," *NCC Proc.* Vol. 44, May 1975, pp. 187–201.

KLEI 75C Kleinrock, L., and F. Tobagi, "Packet Switching in Radio Channels: Part I. Carrier Sense Multiple Access Modes and Their Throughput-Delay Characteristics," *IEEE Trans. Commun.*, Vol. COM-23, December 1975, pp. 1400–1416.

KLEI 77 Kleinrock, L., and M. Scholl, "Packet Switching in Radio Channels: New Conflict-Free Multiple Access Schemes for a Small Number of Data Users," *ICC Proc.*, 1977, pp. 22.1-105 to 22.1-111.

KLEI 78 Kleinrock, L., and J. Silvester, "Optimum Transmission Radii for Packet Radio Networks of Why Six Is a Major Number," *IEEE Natl. Telecommun. Conf.*, Birmingham, Ala., Vol. 1, 4.3/1-5, December 1978, Sec. 4.3, pp. 1–5.

KLEI 80 Kleinrock, L., and M. O. Scholl, "Packet Switching in Radio Channels: New Conflict-Free Multiple Access Schemes," *IEEE Trans. Commun.*, Vol. COM-28, No. 7, 1980, pp. 1015–1020.

KUNZ 78 Kunzelman, R. C., "Status Report on the ARPA Packet Radio Experiment Network," *IEEE Proc.*, San Francisco, Vol. COMPCON, February 28–March 3, 1978, pp. 157–160.

LAWS 78 Lawson, B. R., "Testbed for Evaluation of Packet Radio Man Army Tactical Corps," *IEEE EASCON Proc.*, Vol. 2, September 1978, pp. 215–217.

LEIN 80 Leiner, B. M., "A Simple Model for Computation of Packet Radio Network Communication Performance," *IEEE Trans. Commun.*, Vol. COM-28, No. 12, 1980, pp. 2020–2023.

LEUN 79 Leung, J. K., SRI International Private communication, 1979.

MCQU 78 McQuillan, J. M., and V. G. Cerf, "Tutorial: A Practical View of Computer Communications Protocols, IEEE Catalog No. EHO 137-0, *IEEE Service Center,* Piscataway, N.J. 1978.

MINO 79A Minoli, D., and I. Gitman, "Monitoring Mobile Packet Radio Devices," *IEEE Trans. Commun.*, Vol. COM-27, No. 2, 1979, pp. 509–517.

MINO 79B Minoli, D., "Packet Radio Monitoring via Repeater-on-Packets," *IEEE Trans. Aerosp. Electron. Syst.*, Vol. AES-15, No. 4, July 1979, pp. 466–473.

MOTO 73 "The Dynatac Concept and the 900 MHZ Mobile Radio Band," Motorola (April 1973) Technical Report submitted to the FCC related to Docket No. 18262.

NIEL 75 Nielson, D. L., "Microwave Propagation and Noise Measurements for Mobile Digital Radio Application," in (Stanford Research Institute, Menlo Park, Calif., January 1975) SRI Packet Radio Note No. 4., SRI Project Report.

NIEL 77 Nielson, D. L., "Microwave Propagation Measurements for Mobile Digital Radio Application," *IEEE Trans. Veh. Technol.*, Vol. VT-27, No. 3, September 1977, pp. 117–132.

NILS 80 Nilsson, A., W. Chou, and C. J. Graff, "A Packet Radio Communication

System Architecture in a Mixed Traffic and Dynamic Environment," *IEEE/ NBS Proc. Comput. Networking Symp.*, December 1980, pp. 51–66.

OKAM 65   Okamura, Y., et al., "Field Strength Measurements and Its Variability in VHF and UHF Land Mobile Radio Services," in *Communication Channels: Characterization and Behavior,* B. Goldberg, ed., IEEE Press, New York, 1965.

OSSA 64   Ossanna, J. F., Jr., "A Model for Mobile Radio Fading Due to Building Reflections: Theoretical and Experimental Fading Waveform Power Spectra," *Bell Syst. Tech. J.,* Vol. 43, November 1964, pp. 2935–2971.

PARK 80   Park, K. Y., "Global Packet Radios Using Low Altitude Satellites," *IEEE 1980 Natl. Telecommun. Conf.,* Vol. 70.5/1-5, December 1980.

PETE 72   Peterson, W. W., and E. J. Weldon, Jr., *Error-Correcting Codes,* 2nd ed., MIT Press, Cambridge, Mass., 1972.

PORT 71   Porter, P. T., "Supervision and Control Features of a Small-Zone Radiotelephone System," *IEEE Trans. Veh. Technol.,* Vol. 20, August 1971, p. 75.

REUD 72   Reudink, D. O., "Comparison of Radio Transmission at X-Band Frequencies in Suburban and Urban Areas," *IEEE Trans. Antennas Propag.,* Vol. AP-20, July 1972, p. 470.

ROBE 72   Roberts, L. G., "Extension of Packet Communication Technology to a Hand-Held Personal Terminal," *Proc. AFIPS,* Vol. 40, pp. 292–298 (1972 Spring Joint Computer Conference).

ROBE 73   Roberts, L. G., and B. D. Wessler, "The ARPA Network," in *Computer-Communication Networks,* N. Abramson and F. Kuo, eds., Prentice-Hall, Englewood Cliffs, N.J., 1973, pp. 485–500.

ROBE 78   Roberts, L. G., "The Evolution of Packet Switching," *Proc. IEEE,* Vol. 66, No. 11, 1978, pp. 1307–1313.

ROBE 80A   Roberts, J. A., and T. J. Healy, "Packet Radio Performance over Slow Rayleigh Fading Channels," *IEEE Trans. Commun.,* Vol. COM-28, No. 2, 1980, pp. 279–286.

ROBE 80B   Roberts, J. A., "Concepts for a Low-Altitude Satellite Packet Radio Network," *IEEE 1980 Int. Conf. Commun.,* Vol. 9.1/1-4, June 1980, Sec. 9.1, pp. 1–4.

SCHI 70   Schiff, L., "Traffic Capacity of Three Types of Common-User Mobile Radio Communication System," *IEEE Trans. Commun. Technol.,* Vol. COM-18, No. 1, February 1970, pp. 12–21.

SCHU 60   Schulter, H., Jr., and W. A. Cornell, "Multiarea Mobile Telephone System," *IEEE Trans. Veh. Commun.,* Vol. 9, May 1960, pp. 49–53.

SHAN 48   Shannon, C. E., "A Mathematical Theory of Communication," *Bell System Tech. J.,* Vol. 27, July and October 1948.

SHOC 79   Shoch, J. F., and L. Stewart, " Interconnecting Local Networks via the Packet Radio Network," *IEEE/ACM Proc. 6th Data Comm. Symp.,* November 1979, pp. 153–158.

SPAU 72   Spaulding, A. D., "The Determination of Received Noise Levels from Vehicular Statistics," *IEEE 1972 NTC Rec.,* Vol. 72, 1972.

SPIL 80   Spilling, P., and E. J. Craighill, "Digital Voice Communications on the Packet Radio Network," *IEEE 1980 Int. Conf. Commun.*, Vol. 21.4/1-21, June 1980, Sec. 21.4, pp. 1–2.

TOBA 75   Tobagi, F., and L. Kleinrock, "Packet Switching in Radio Channels: Part II. The Hidden Terminal Problem in Carrier Sense Multiple-Access and the Busy-Tone Solution," *IEEE Trans. Commun.*, Vol. COM-23, December 1975, pp. 1417–1433.

TOBA 76A   Tobagi, F., "Packet Switching in Radio Channels: Part III. Polling and (Dynamic) Split-Channel Reservation Multiple Access," *IEEE Trans. Commun.*, Vol. COM-24, No. 8, 1976, pp. 832–844.

TOBA 76B   Tobagi, F., S. Lieberson, and L. Kleinrock, "On Measurement Facilities in Packet Radio Systems," *NCC Proc.*, Vol. 45, 1976, pp. 589–596.

TOBA 77A   Tobagi, F., and L. Kleinrock, "Packet Switching in Radio Channels: Part IV. Stability Considerations and Dynamic Control in Carrier Sense Multiple Access," *IEEE Trans. Commun.*, Vol. COM-25, October 1977, pp. 1103–1119.

TOBA 77B   Tobagi, F., "Performance Analysis of Packet Radio Communication Systems," *IEEE Natl. Telecommun. Conf.*, Vol. 1, December 1977, pp. 12:6-1 to 12:6-7.

TOBA 78A   Tobagi, F., and L. Kleinrock, "The Effect of Acknowledgment Traffic on the Capacity of Packet-Switched Radio Channels," *IEEE Trans. Commun.*, Vol. COM-26, June 1978, pp. 815–826.

TOBA 78B   Tobagi, F., "Analysis of Slotted ALOHA in a Centralized Two-Hop Packet Radio Network," *Proc. 7th IEEE Comput. Soc. Int. Conf.*, Vol. COMPCON Fall '78, September 1978.

TOBA 80A   Tobagi, F. A., "Slotted Aloha," *IEEE Trans. Commun.*, Vol. COM-28, No. 2, 1980, pp. 196–207.

TOBA 80B   Tobagi, F. A., "Analysis of a Two-Hop Centralized Packet Radio Network. Part II Carrier Sense Multiple Access," *IEEE Trans. Commun.*, Vol. COM-28, No. 2, 1980, pp. 208–216.

TURI 72   Turin, G. L., "A Statistical Model of Urban Multipath Propagation," *IEEE Trans. Veh. Technol.*, Vol. VT-21, February 1972, pp. 1–9.

YOUN 52   Young, W. R., Jr., "Comparison of Mobile Radio Transmission at 150, 450, 900, and 3700 MHz," *Bell Syst. Tech. J.*, Vol. 31, November 1952, pp. 1068–1085.

13

Local Networks

DAVID C. WOOD
The MITRE Corporation
McLean, Virginia

13.1 INTRODUCTION

Just as packet switching dominated research in computer networks in the early 1970s, local networks have been the focus of research activity in the late 1970s and early 1980s. Moreover, commercial local network products are rapidly appearing in the marketplace. Packet-switching networks such as ARPANET evolved from the need to provide nationwide access to large time-sharing systems. However, with the availability of low-cost minicomputer and microcomputer systems, nationwide access is no longer necessary for simple computation, but is required for data access or unique processing capabilities.

The proliferation of minicomputers and microcomputers has led to the need to interconnect these with all the terminals within a building or campus, so that any terminal may potentially access any system. In addition, access may be needed to any local large host computers, as well as to the outside world via a gateway to a packet-switching network. Moreover, word-processing stations can share a common network to communicate with other devices, such as printers and mass memory. The objective of this chapter is to explain the alternative approaches to local networks and to describe representative example local networks.

A local network is characterized by a maximum distance between any two devices of at most a few kilometers. This limit results in some instances from signaling distance limitations, and in other instances from efficiency considerations. A practical limit to a local network is often the boundary within which cable can be privately installed without the use of common-carrier facilities. However, even these limits can be circumvented by use of a private microwave, infrared, or atmospheric laser link.

An early example of a local ring network was the Distributed Computer System at the University of California, Irvine [FARB 73]. Another milestone was the publication of the original Ethernet description in 1976 [METC 76]. The pace of local network developments accelerated in the late 1970s with the availability of microprocessors. The report of the workshop on local area networking held at the National

Bureau of Standards in August 1977 includes descriptions of about a dozen local network projects [COTT 78]. Further networks are reported in the proceedings of the Local Area Communications Networks Symposium held in May 1979 [MEIS 79]. An article by Freeman and Thurber identifies about 40 local networks [FREE 79]. An extensive annotated bibliography on local networks has been produced by Shoch [SHOC 79C]. A proliferation of commercial local network products arrived on the marketplace beginning in 1981.

13.1.1   Reasons for Local Networks

There are many possible motivations for a local network, and the applications requirements in a particular organization will influence the choice of networking approach. The justification for a local network is most obvious in a multiple computer environment. The same terminal can be used to access all the computers, instead of having two terminals, side by side, each hard-wired to a different computer, as is sometimes the case today. As well as economizing on terminals, the local network can simplify the user interface by providing a standard log on procedure. The local network provides the same resource-sharing potential as long-haul networks, such as transfer of files containing programs, data, and so on. Word-processing systems can also be connected, so that the same terminals used to access general-purpose computers can also be used for document preparation.

Even when only a single computer is to be interconnected with terminals, there are numerous compelling arguments for planning a local network. An important motivation can be a transition strategy to a future system. Imagine a large computer system with many terminals used for numerous applications. The computer system is obsolete and the organization is faced with the ordeal of converting operational applications to a replacement system. By installing a general-purpose local network with the old system, the new system can then be added to the same network. Terminals can access both systems during the transition period while applications are moved over.

Another reason for a local network is an expansion strategy: even though there is only one computer system now, there may be more in the future. A related reason is to provide vendor independence. A number of computer vendors (e.g., DEC, Datapoint, Prime) have their own local network architectures, often as part of their distributed processing systems. Although these vendor-unique systems offer convenient features and simplicity for the user, they also lock the user into that vendor's equipment.

When a local network is designed for a building, cable or other transmission media will be laid systematically throughout the building. This provides flexibility for adding terminals or computers anywhere in the building, with data communications access being provided in a manner similar to electrical power and telephone outlets. Such a planned installation avoids running a cable through the building each time a new terminal is added, and eliminates the resulting "spaghetti" near the computer.

The local network can also result in an increase in the number of terminals accessing a computer. Instead of hard-wiring each terminal to an asynchronous multiplexer or similar terminal interface, the same number of ports can be shared on a contention basis only by the active terminals. More flexibility still can be obtained with a software demultiplexed packet–mode interface to the computer, which avoids the rigid limitation of physical ports. A high-speed interface of this type can enable CRT terminals to be operated at higher speeds, such as 19.2 kbps, than can be supported by the conventional terminal interface. Moreover, the character-at-a-time load on the computer caused by terminal handling can also be reduced.

One of the most promising applications of local networks is in the area of office automation and information systems. Intelligent terminals will become increasingly powerful, with built-in office applications such as word processing, document storage, electronic mail, and calendar management. Local networks that interconnect these terminals will be needed to support transfer of documents between terminals and to high-speed printers, transfer of electronic messages, and so on. Further, local networks can support the interconnection of heterogeneous computers and terminals. The network can provide the necessary conversion between incompatible equipment using techniques such as virtual terminal protocols.

Finally, local networks can provide for the local distribution of data from long-haul data networks. Multiple local computers and terminals can share a common access point or gateway to the long-haul network.

13.1.2   Local Network Requirements

The technical requirements for a local network depend on the applications to be supported and the motivations discussed above. Requirements may range from the need to tie together two dozen 300-bps terminals with two computers, to the provision of shared access among several processors to a common data base. Although a local network optimized for a particular application could be designed, a more viable product is one that satisfies a range of needs even though it may exceed some minimum requirements.

A general-purpose local network suitable for both terminal-to-computer and computer-to-computer applications should be capable of meeting the following quantitative requirements:

- Interconnection between hundreds of terminals of various types and tens of computers, ranging from microcomputers to large systems scattered throughout a building or a collection of buildings
- The ability to support local terminal to host communications with terminals operating up to at least 19.2 kbps, including terminal virtualization by mapping characteristics for various terminals and computers
- The ability to interface terminals to the network inexpensively (e.g. not more than several hundred dollars per terminal)
- The ability to support local computer-to-computer communication with effective data rates in the order of several hundred thousand bits per second or even a megabit per second

- The ability to interface computers via high-speed multiplexed interfaces capable of supporting many virtual connections
- The ability to minimize the impact on computers by using interface protocols, such as X.25
- Access to remote resources via gateways to other networks

Solutions to some of these requirements are well understood, while others are the subject of continuing research and development.

Virtualization of terminal characteristics involves the same principles that have been used successfully for start–stop terminals on long-haul networks, such as in the ARPANET Telnet [DAVI 77] and in CCITT Recommendation X.3 [CCIT 81]. Since local networks usually operate at hundreds of kilobits per second or higher, attaining high-speed computer-to-computer communication should be straightforward given appropriate higher-level protocol implementations, but few experimental data have been reported.

Today, the cost of interface devices for attaching terminals to experimental networks is typically in the range $600 to $1000 per terminal; this is high compared to current terminal prices. However, this cost is expected to drop to several hundred dollars per terminal when interfaces are produced in quantities based on standards implemented in large-scale integration (LSI) technology.

The requirement to support many terminal connections across a computer interface, as well as a high-speed data rate, usually presents a cost–benefit trade-off. The simplest approach to implement for connecting a computer to a local network is for the network to appear to the computer as a group of asynchronous terminals. However, this limits the utility of the network to terminal-to-computer applications. For computer-to-computer applications, higher-speed interfaces are required. Direct memory access (DMA) interfaces are most desirable from the host viewpoint because they allow a block of memory to be transferred with a single command, thereby minimizing host impact.

The requirement to minimize the impact on host computers of network interfacing software requires the use of appropriate interfacing protocols. In the past, the complexity of network software to be developed for hosts has limited growth of network use. The increased availability of software for standard network protocols such as X.25 and the Transmission Control Protocol (TCP) [DARP 80A] will simplify host interfacing. However, more needs to be understood about the overhead of such software [BUNC 80].

Interconnection of local networks to long-haul packet networks is being addressed in a number of experiments involving ARPANET and using the Internet Protocol [DARP 80B]. They include Xerox's Ethernet [SHOC 79A], the Laboratory for Computer Science network at MIT [CERF 78], and Mitrenet [WOOD 79]. Research issues include the protocol level of the gateway between the local network and long-haul network, and the performance impact on the local network of using generalized protocols designed for internetworking. However, the interconnection of local networks to public data networks is not yet possible; problems to be solved include addressing and end-to-end acknowledgments.

It should be recognized that some local networks are designed for more special-purpose requirements than those stated above. For example, an individual vendor's approach to distributed processing will preclude the connection of other vendors' equipment. Rather than interconnecting computers and terminals, some local networks are more like an expansion of a computer system, connecting multiple processors and peripherals such as disks.

13.2 DESIGN APPROACHES

In meeting some or all of the local network requirements identified above, various design alternatives are available. Several approaches exist which are really no different from approaches for connecting the same devices if they were much farther apart.

The switched telephone network can be used to provide circuit-switched communications between terminal and computer, or computer and computer. Modems are required, of course, and the data rate is limited to that obtainable over voice-grade circuits. Moreover, any pair of devices required to communicate must be compatible.

A message-switching or packet-switching approach can be used, with a mini-computer switch being the central node to which all devices are connected in a star network. The weakness of this approach is its unreliability; if the central switch is down, all communications are lost. Also, since all traffic is processed by software in the switch, the switch capacity will be exceeded if there are too many computers and terminals. Then several interconnected switches can be used, just as in a long-haul network. This has the advantage of using off-the-shelf packet switching nodes, but is probably not the most economical approach.

Other approaches are specific to a local network environment since they take advantage of its unique attributes. A local network generally encompasses a limited geographical area, such as a building or campus, with the distance between computing elements being several kilometers or less. Privately installed transmission facilities are employed, rather than common-carrier services, resulting in very much higher transmission speeds, typically several megabits per second.

Since local networks capable of easily interconnecting heterogeneous computers and terminals are not yet an off-the-shelf product, an organization perceiving the need for a local network is faced with a large number of choices. Until adequate commercial products are available, hardware and software skills will be needed to adapt and interface equipment.

The major design parameters for a generalized local network are the following:

Topology
Transmission medium
Signaling mode
Access method

Data rate

Interfacing device

Type of interfaces

13.2.1 Topology

Many existing computer networks are dedicated to providing remote access to a centralized computer facility from many terminals scattered over a wide geographical area. Such centralized or star networks may be one-level, with terminals on multipoint lines radiating from the central facility, or two-level, with terminals connected to regional concentrators, which in turn are linked to the central site.

For switched long-haul data communications, involving interactions between many pairs of subscribers, packet switching has emerged as the dominant technology. Packet-switching networks employ a distributed network of nodes so that packets of data flowing between many subscriber pairs can dynamically share the expensive wideband leased long-distance telephone circuits between the nodes.

Some of the constraints that influence network design are alleviated when distances are very short. For example, privately installed transmission facilities can provide high bandwidth relatively inexpensively over short distances. Consequently, expensive and complex switching nodes are not needed to minimize circuit distance.

Local networks are generally confined to the following *topologies*: star, ring or loop, and bus (see Fig. 13.1). The *star* has a central node and any number of appendages. One example of a star network would be a network front end (NFE) interfacing one or more hosts and many terminals to a long-haul network. Failure of the NFE or the central node of a star network affects the entire network. Another example of a star local network is a digital private branch exchange (PBX). These support

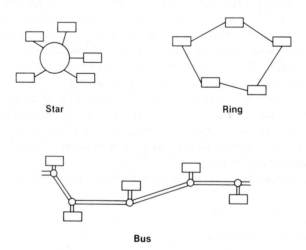

Star   Ring

Bus

Figure 13.1. Local network topologies.

circuit-switched communications for voice and data with data rates of 9600 bps, and more recently, up to 56 kbps. Apart from the data-rate limitation, another disadvantage is the high initial cost. A general disadvantage of star configurations is the dependency on the central controlling node. In terms of reliability (i.e., decreased dependence on a single entity), the other architecures are more promising.

A *ring or loop* architecture is simply a set of computing elements inserted in a closed transmission medium. The computing elements are active devices: they receive incoming data from the previous element in the loop, remove data for subscribers connected to that element, receive data for transmission from subscribers, and transmit data to the next loop element. The control can be centralized, with the loop channel having a primary control node, or distributed, with all nodes having equal status. The Distributed Computer System (DCS) at the University of California, Irvine, was an early example of a local ring network [FARB 73]. Other examples of a ring architecture are the LCS net at MIT [CLAR 78] and the Cambridge Ring [WILK 79]. For a definitive account of various loop-type networks, see [LIU 78] and [PENN 79].

A *bus* architecture is a set of computing elements attached to a shared transmission channel. The transmission medium may be a linear bus or dendritic (i.e., branched like a tree). When the transmission medium is a cable (e.g., ribbon, coaxial, or optic fibers) this architecture is commonly called a *cable-bus*. Broadcast transmissions propagate the length of the medium and are received by all other elements. Thus the elements themselves are passive, in contrast to the active elements in a loop network.

Bus architectures are predominant among the local network products appearing in the commercial marketplace. The bus appears advantageous to the loop in a large building; branches can be used to serve multiple floors and wings, yet the maximum distance between two points remains short enough that propagation delay does not affect performance.

13.2.2 Transmission Medium

Common choices for the physical *transmission medium* include twisted-wire pairs and coaxial cable. Both are inexpensive and can be installed easily in a building; coaxial cable has the potential for higher data rates. Microwave radio or even atmospheric laser links may be used to extend a local network for greater distances. Recently, fiber optics has become a candidate for the transmission medium, with the potential for gigabit data rates.

13.2.3 Signaling Mode

The *signaling mode* or transmission scheme used to transmit the data on the transmission medium may in general be digital or analog. In the case of digital transmission, a baseband or pulsed signal is transmitted and may be regenerated by repeaters if necessary. Analog transmission, also referred to as *broadband,* involves the modulation of some carrier signal and the possible use of amplifiers. Broadband signaling allows the 300-MHz capacity of coaxial cable to be used for other applications, such as off-the-air or closed-circuit television, as well as for multiple data channels, by frequency-division multiplexing. The data rate on an individual broadband channel is usually less than with baseband, but the potential aggregate data rate is greater with broadband. Broadband signaling is more expensive, because of the cost of the modems, on the order of $500.

13.2.4 Access Method

The *access method* determines which device has access to the transmission medium at any instant. Access may be determined by a polling scheme, as in multipoint lines, by a token that grants permission to transmit, or by various contention mechanisms. Contention schemes are widely used in local networks having a bus architecture. Token schemes are usually found in loop networks.

   Contention schemes allow a large number of low-duty cycle devices to share a broadcast channel using random-access techniques. The first random-access broadcast network using a radio channel was the ALOHA system at the University of Hawaii. Using a strategy that has come to be known as *pure ALOHA,* messages were transmitted as desired, and unacknowledged messages were retransmitted [ABRA 70]. For a large number of independent devices with packet arrival rates approximating a Poisson distribution, it has been shown that the maximum efficiency of the channel is $1/2e$ or 18%.

   The channel utilization can be increased by synchronizing the start of packet transmissions with a central clock, so that packets that collide will do so completely. Known as *slotted ALOHA,* this scheme increases the maximum efficiency to $1/e$ or 37%.

   A further refinement, known as *carrier-sense multiple-access* (CSMA), is to listen to the channel before transmitting, so as to avoid collisions. If the channel is idle, the packet is transmitted immediately. However, if the channel is busy, several actions can be taken [KLEI 75]. In a *nonpersistent* CSMA, retransmission of the packet is rescheduled according to some delay distribution; after the delay, the channel is sensed again and the process repeated. In a *1-persistent* CSMA protocol, the sender waits for the channel to go idle (i.e., persists on transmitting) and then transmits the packet immediately. Of course, if two or more senders are waiting for the channel to go idle, they will all transmit simultaneously and a collision will occur. Therefore, the *p-persistent* CSMA protocol randomizes the starting time of waiting packets between the two extremes noted above according to a parameter p, the probability that a ready packet persists. The various CSMA protocols can produce a maximum channel efficiency in the range 60 to 80%, depending on the ratio of propagation delay to packet transmission time. The nonpersistent CSMA attains a higher throughput than the 1-persistent CSMA for the same parameters.

A final refinement is to have the sender listen to the channel while transmitting so as to detect collisions immediately. Known as CSMA with *collision detection* (CSMA-CD), and also as *listen while talk* (LWT) [HOPK 79], this protocol ensures that transmission of colliding packets can be stopped immediately so as not to waste time on the channel. CSMA-CD has emerged as a common choice in bus networks such as Ethernet. The efficiency of this protocol depends on the ratio of the time to detect collisions to the average packet transmission time, and is typically over 90% [TOBA 79].

A *token* is a special signal that is passed round the network. A node may only transmit when it receives the token. Token schemes have a more predictable delay than do contention schemes, but require additional complexity to guard against single points of failure, such as loss of the token.

Control of access to the transmission medium may be either centralized or distributed. Centralized control is more often employed with time-division or reservation access methods, with a central controlling node managing time slots. On the other hand, use of contention access methods usually implies that control is distributed among all nodes equally.

13.2.5 Data Rate

The *data rate* will be influenced by other design parameters, such as the transmission medium, signaling mode, and interface units. The data rate on coaxial cable may range from hundreds of kilobits per second up to several megabits. Use of optical fibers has the potential for gigabit data rates. The actual throughput attainable between two devices on the network may be considerably less than the data rate of the transmission medium, depending on the access method, protocols, and speed of the interfacing units.

13.2.6 Interfacing Device

The *interfacing devices* or units interconnect various types of user equipment to the transmission medium at access points or nodes. Conceptually, the interfacing device can be considered in two parts: one part is communications technology dependent, the other part is communications technology independent. The dependent part implements the access and control mechanisms for the particular transmission medium, such as CSMA-CD. The independent part provides the mechanisms for enabling communication between the various user devices (computers or terminals) and the network. This part usually provides datagram or virtual circuit protocols, and possibly virtual terminal protocols. The capability of this part, such as its speed and the protocols it provides, determines to a great extent the functionality of the network. Most interface units are microprocessor based.

The interfacing device may be implemented as a stand-alone component, as is usually the case with vendor independent local networks such as Sytek and Ungermann-Bass, or integrated into terminals and other equipment, as is the case with vendor-unique systems such as Xerox's Ethernet. A further physical separation of components is possible, into a media access unit, such as the transceiver which is clamped to the coaxial cable and performs the baseband signaling in systems such as Ethernet, and the controller, which implements the various protocols (see Fig. 13.2).

13.2.7   Type of Interfaces

The *type of interfaces* provided by the interfacing device determines the user devices that can be directly connected to the network. Direct attachment of asynchronous terminals requires RS-232-C, or the newer RS449, interfaces and appropriate software to handle connection establishment and data transfer. For a terminal to access various host computers through the network, terminal support functions need to be provided along the lines of the ARPANET Telnet [DAVI 77] and CCITT Recommendation X.3 [CCIT 81]. These functions include speed conversion, flow control, code conversion, mapping of the break function, control of echoing, and device-specific functions such as the insertion of padding characters to provide carriage return delay.

Various options are possible for computer interfaces and determine the functionality that the network provides the computer. The simplest approach is for the interfacing device to emulate asynchronous terminals and to use an asynchronous port on the computer for each terminal connection. However, this limits use of the network for that computer to terminal access. For greater capabilities and improved performance, a multiplexed packet–mode interface can be supported, in which data from many terminal connections is carried over the same physical interface. With

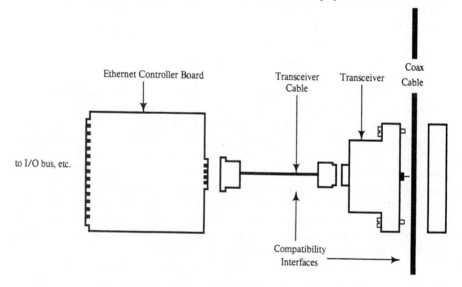

Figure 13.2. Typical local network implementation.

appropriate operating system software, such an interface can support process-to-process communication between processes in the computer and remote processes in other computers on the network.

The nature of the physical interface will depend on the particular computer, but could be serial or parallel. Moreover, it could cause an interrupt in the computer for each character, or it could allow a block of data to be transferred per computer interrupt using direct memory access.

13.3 EXAMPLES OF LOCAL NETWORKS

The networks described in this section provide examples of various ways of combining the design parameters discussed above. The networks described represent the key research developments of the late 1970s upon which are based many of the commercial products entering the marketplace in the early 1980s. The characteristics of the local networks described in this section are compared in Tab. 13.1

13.3.1 Cambridge Ring

The digital communication ring at Cambridge University in England is designed to provide a high-speed communications path between computers and other devices in the laboratory [HOPP 78, WILK 79]. The interfacing devices, called *stations,* are connected in a ring topology (see Fig. 13.3). The transmission medium consists of two twisted pairs, except for one link, which uses an optical fiber. A four-wire modulation scheme is used, using baseband signaling, giving a raw data rate of 10 Mbps. The signal is regenerated by repeaters in each station, which may be up to 200 m apart.

A packet consists of a destination byte, a source byte, and two information bytes, together with a few control bits, for a total length of 37 bits. Packets make a complete circuit of the ring and are marked at the destination as having been copied or rejected. When a station is ready to transmit, it fills the first empty packet to come to it; when the packet returns the station marks it as empty, but may not refill it. Instead, it passes downstream. This prevents one station from hogging the ring to the exclusion of others.

The delay at each station is approximately 1½ pulse intervals (i.e., 1.5×10^{-7} sec). Only two packets are being carried in the ring at any time. A unique station, called the *monitor station,* is used to set up the slot structure at startup and to provide error detection facilities. Computers are connected to the stations via an access box that can provide higher-level protocols.

13.3.2 Distributed Computer System

The Distributed Computer System (DCS) is a local network which was designed and implemented at the University of California, Irvine, beginning in 1971 [FARB 73,

Table 13.1. *Local Networks.*

	Network									
	Cambridge Ring	*DCS*	*DCLN*	*Ethernet*	*Hyper-channel*	*MIT—LCS*	*Mitrenet*	*NBS Network*	*CBX*	*Local Net 20*
Organization	Cambridge University	University of California, Irvine	Ohio State University	Xerox	Network Systems Corp.	MIT	MITRE	National Bureau of Standards	Rolm	Sytek
Date operational	1978	1971	1977	1976 (experimental), 1980	1976	1979	1976	1978	1980	1980
Topology	Ring	Ring	Ring	Tree	Bus	Ring (or tree)	Tree	Tree	Star	Bus
Transmission medium	Twisted pair, optical fiber	Twisted pair	Twisted pair	Coaxial cable	Coaxial cable	Twisted pair	Coaxial cable	Coaxial cable	Twisted pair	Coaxial cable
Signaling mode	Digital	Digital	Digital	Digital	Digital	Digital	Analog	Digital	Digital	Analog
Access method	Token	Token	Shift register insertion	Contention	Contention	Token/contention	Contention	Contention	Circuit switched	Contention
Data rate	10 Mbps	2.3 Mbps	1 Mbps	10 Mbps	50 Mbps	1 Mbps	1 Mbps	1 Mbps	Up to 19,200 bps	128 kbps

Table 13.1 *(cont.)*

	Network									
	Cambridge Ring	DCS	DCLN	Ethernet	Hyper-channel	MIT–LCS	Mitrenet	NBS Network	CBX	Local Net 20
Interface device	Station	Ring interface	Loop interface	Transceiver, work-station	Adapter	Local network interface	Bus interface unit	Terminal interface equipment	Data terminal interface	Packet communications unit
Type of interfaces	Computer	Computer	Computer	Intelligent terminal, computer	Computer peripherals	Terminal, computer	Terminal, computer	Terminal	Terminal	Terminal

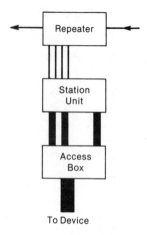

Figure 13.3. Cambridge ring network.

FARB 78]. DCS provides a general-purpose time-sharing system distributed among a number of minicomputers connected in a ring communications system.

The design goals of the system include the provision of a reliable fail-soft service at a relatively low cost. This was achieved by a distributed organization of hardware, software, and system control.

The DCS hardware system is a collection of system components, primarily minicomputers, connected to a digital communication ring by devices called ring interfaces. This communication ring serves as a unidirectional information path operating at 2.3 Mbps over twisted pairs.

The DCS software is process oriented. All activities are carried out by processes, interacting via the sending and receiving of messages. These messages are addressed to the destination process by name rather than by physical hardware address. A message from one process addressed to another is first placed onto the ring. As the message arrives at each ring interface, the interface compares the destination process with a list of all processes active in the attached computer using a 16-name associative memory. If the indicated process name is present, the interface attempts to copy the message into the computer memory. Whether the process addressed is present or not, the message continues around the ring to the interface where it originated, where the message is removed from the ring.

Access to the ring is controlled by a token, a special bit pattern which circulates continuously around the ring [MOCK 77]. When a ring interface has a message to put on the ring, it waits for the token, and transmits the message followed by the token.

The current system comprises a ring with five ring interfaces, each attached to a minicomputer (Lockheed Sue or Varian 620I). To the minicomputers are connected terminals, printers, and disks. Each computer has a resident software system called the *nucleus* which provides for the scheduling of processes and the transmission and reception of messages. All other system functions, such as resource allocation, device input–output, and file system services, are provided by separate processes which can execute on any processor. User-level support tools typical of a time-sharing system are provided.

A number of failure detection and recovery mechanisms are incorporated on DCS. The distribution of hardware, software, and control among the components of the network provides redundancy and, in most instances, fail-soft behavior.

13.3.3   Distributed Loop Computer Network

The Distributed Loop Computer Network (DLCN) has been designed and implemented as a research project at the Ohio State University [LIU 78]. The initial network consists of six nodes, interconnecting large computers, minicomputers, and microcomputers. The loop network consists of a high-speed digital communication channel using twisted pairs arranged in a closed loop.

Computers are attached to the loop by a device called a *loop interface*. The loop interface receives incoming messages, and either accepts them for delivery to the local subscribers or transmits them to the next interface. The interface contains buffer space used for message input and output to the subscriber. The interface is implemented using AM2900 series chips, and includes three AM2901 microprocessor slices and 4K 8-bit words of random-access memory.

The transmission scheme used on the loop is a distributed control protocol known as a *shift-register insertion scheme* for the transmission of multiple variable-length messages. Incoming messages from the loop are temporarily buffered when necessary to allow the insertion of messages originated by the local subscriber. Messages are variable length with 80 bits of header, including framing, source and destination interface and process address, and a 16-bit CRC.

A Distributed Double-Loop Computer Network (DDLCN) is being implemented as a successor to the DLCN [LIU 79]. It consists of a double-loop structure to provide fault tolerance not present in a single-loop system.

13.3.4   Ethernet

Ethernet is a local area network developed jointly by Digital Equipment Corporation, Intel Corporation, and Xerox Corporation. It uses coaxial cable in a branching nonrooted tree with baseband signaling at 10 million bps to interconnect up to 1024 stations with a maximum station separation of 2.5 k.

The original experimental Ethernet was implemented at the Xerox Palo Alto Research Center in 1975 [METC 76]. That version interconnected Xerox Alto terminals with various computers using signaling at 2.94 Mbps.

The commercial version of the Ethernet is documented in the specification published jointly by DEC, Intel, and Xerox [DIGI 80]. That specification is intended as a reference document to further the use of Ethernet as a standard for local area networks. Ethernet is used to interconnect Xerox office information system products such as workstations, print servers, and file servers, which have been introduced since 1980. The devices interconnected via Ethernet all support a set of higher-level protocols developed by Xerox [XERO 81A, XERO 81B] based on the Pup protocol architecture used with the experimental Ethernet [BOGG 80].

A typical implementation of the Ethernet consists of a controller, which performs most of the protocol functions, and a transceiver, directly adjacent to the coaxial cable. The controller may be implemented in a station, such as a Xerox workstation, or stand-alone, as with some compatible products from other vendors. The controller is connected to the transceiver by a transceiver cable consisting of four twisted pairs.

The Ethernet specification encompasses the data link layer and the physical layer. The data link layer consists of the carrier-sense multiple access with collision detection protocol used for link control, and a message protocol which defines the framing, addressing, and checksum used in the message format. The physical layer specifies the physical characteristics of the coaxial cable, the configurations, and the signaling. A cable configuration consists of segments of coaxial cable, up to 500 m in length, joined by repeaters. A maximum of two repeaters are allowed in the path between any two stations. A large-scale configuration is illustrated in Fig. 13.4. Baseband signaling on the cable is performed at 10 Mbps using Manchester phase encoding. Up to 100 transceivers may be connected to a cable segment. Placement of transceivers is restricted to regular 2.5 m intervals along the cable, indicated by marks, to ensure that signal reflections from the transceiver do not add in phase to a significant degree.

Other vendors have developed Ethernet-like products compatible with the Ethernet specification. The Net/One system from Ungermann–Bass, Inc., includes Network Interface Units which connect terminals and computers to an Ethernet-compatible coaxial cable (see Fig. 13.5). The Z80A-based Network Interface Unit Mode 1 has four serial ports and two parallel interfaces.

13.3.5 Hyperchannel

Hyperchannel is a commercial product of Network Systems Corporation [THOR 75 THOR 80]. It is designed to provide very high data rate communications between multiple processors and peripherals (disks, tapes, etc.) for applications such as shared data bases in a large multicomputer site (see Fig. 13.6).

Hyperchannel uses coaxial cable in a bus topology. Transmission is at 50 million bps. A combination of CSMA contention protocol and fixed priority assignment for each node is employed. The interfacing devices, known as *adapters,* are used to attach computers to the cable; no provision is made for attaching terminals directly. The adapters, which cost upward of $30,000, interface with channels on the computers, by emulating known devices such as disk drives. When heterogeneous hosts are connected to the network, any conversion of codes must be performed by the hosts.

Hyperchannel is noteworthy as the first commercial product for vendor-

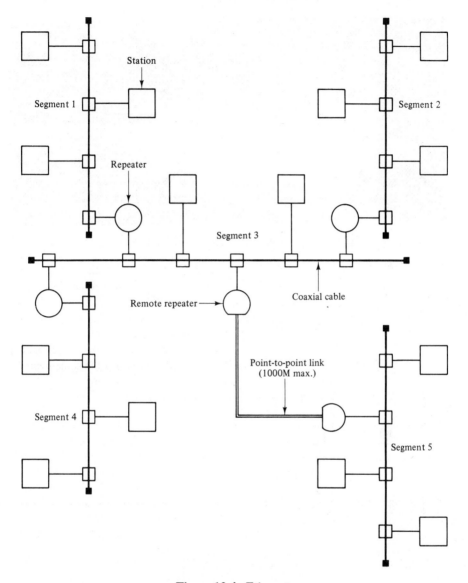

Figure 13.4. Ethernet.

independent local networks. However, it is intended primarily for connecting processors with shared peripherals.

13.3.6   MIT Laboratory for Computer Science Network

The MIT Laboratory for Computer Science (LCS) has developed a local area network which will serve the needs of the laboratory and is expected to form the

Figure 13.5. Ungermann–Bass network interface unit.

basis of an eventual campus-wide network [COTT 78]. The objective of the LCS network is to provide an intercommunication capability between minicomputers, microcomputers, and large-scale systems within the laboratory, and to provide a vehicle for research in distributed computing.

In conjunction with the developers of the Distributed Computer System, a Local Network Interface (LNI) has been developed which can be used for either a ring network or an Ethernet [FARB 77, MOCK 77]. By presenting the same logical

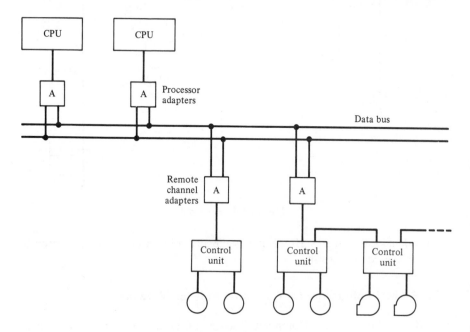

Figure 13.6. Hyperchannel.

interface to a host, the design allows the same basic interface hardware to be used with either network topology, with only minor modifications to the control structure and internal data flow. An initial ring version of the LNI, designed to run at 1 Mbps, was being tested in 1978. The LNI has been designed so that it will be capable of implementation on a single LSI chip.

Eventually, the LCS network is expected to be composed of a number of subnetworks, some using Ethernet technology and others using ring technology, all using identical protocols, and sharing a single address space. The LCS network will be connected to ARPANET and is likely to employ the Transmission Control Protocol (TCP) internet protocol.

13.3.7 Mitrenet

Mitrenet is a cable bus system developed by the MITRE Corporation using standard community antenna television (CATV) coaxial cable and microprocessor-based bus interface units (BIUs) to connect subscriber computers and terminals to the cable in a local network. Mitrenets are installed at MITRE in Bedford, Massachusetts, and in McLean, Virginia, as well as a number of government sites, including the Walter Reed Army Medical Center in Washington, D.C., and the U.S. House of Representatives [DEMA 76, DOLB 77, NAYL 78].

The basic architecture of the cable bus comprises two parallel coaxial cables, one inbound and the other outbound (see Fig. 13.7). This architecture takes advantage of the well-developed unidirectional CATV components. A BIU connects a subscriber device to the inbound and outbound cable system, transmitting on the inbound cable and receiving on the outbound cable. The BIU accepts data from the subscriber, buffers the data until the channel is free, and then transmits the data as an addressed packet. The BIU also scans each packet on the bus for its own address. If the packet is intended for the subscriber, the BIU reads the complete packet from the channel into the buffer, and then clocks the data to the subscriber device at the proper data rate.

The cable bus uses carrier-sense multiple-access with collision detection (CSMA-CD). No subscriber starts a transmission unless the channel is, to the best of the subscriber's knowledge, not in use. Once a transmission has started, the subscriber listens on the receive channel to its own transmission to detect a collision caused by another subscriber also transmitting. An earlier cable bus system at MITRE known as MITRIX, employed time-division multiple-access, in which time slots were assigned permanently or on demand by a central controller [WILL 74].

Mitrenet uses analog radio-frequency (RF) transmission, in contrast to the digital baseband transmission used in Ethernet. Coaxial cable is capable of effectively transmitting analog signals in the frequency range 5 to 300 MHz. The BIUs contain RF modems which modulate a carrier signal to transmit the digital information. Most Mitrenets operate at a data rate of 1 million bps, which occupies about 2 MHz of bandwidth, although earlier systems operated at 307.2 kbps. The remainder of the 300 MHz can be used to carry many parallel channels on the same cable using various

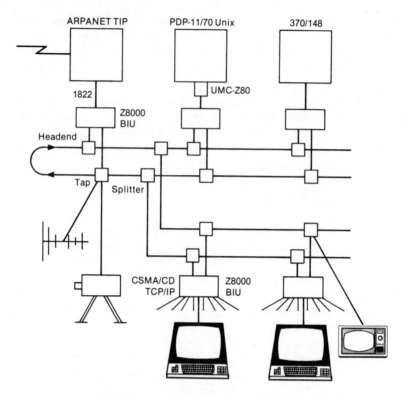

Figure 13.7. Mitrenet configuration.

frequencies. Installed Mitrenets carry one or more digital channels; video, including off-the-air television signals and closed-circuit television signals; FM radio, and voice telephone.

The bus interface units have evolved with microprocessor technology. The earliest BIUs, built in 1977, contain a Mostek 6502A microprocessor and connect one terminal to the cable. A Z80-based version, built by Digital Communications Corporation, contains two serial ports. A Z8000-based BIU, built by Reaction Instruments, Inc., has either three serial ports and one parallel port (see Fig. 13.8), or eleven serial ports. The protocols implemented in the Z8000 BIU include, in addition to CSMA/CD, the Department of Defense standard Transmission Control Protocol (TCP) and Internet Protocol (IP). Thus the BIU supports full internetwork communications between the local network and other interconnected networks supporting TCP/IP.

13.3.8   National Bureau of Standards Network

The National Bureau of Standards (NBS) has developed a stand-alone microprocessor-based device known as a Terminal Interface Equipment (TIE), which can be used

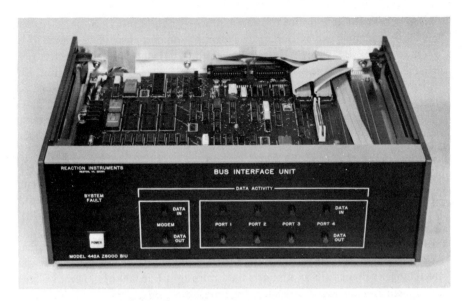

Figure 13.8. Mitrenet bus interface unit.

to interface a wide range of existing terminals and computers to an Ethernet-like contention-based cable system [CARP 78]. The NBS network uses baseband transmission at 1 Mbps on coaxial cable in a branched-tree topology.

The TIE consists of one network board and from one to eight user boards, packaged together in a cage with power supply and other components. Each user board supports one asynchronous interface to a terminal or computer port at speeds up to 9600 bps. Each user board has a MCS6512 microprocessor with 2K to 8K bytes of read-only memory (EPROM) and 2K bytes of random-access memory (RAM). The TIE is connected to the coaxial cable by a tap which contains a line receiver, line driver, and collision detector.

As in Ethernet, transmission on the cable is broadcast using carrier-sense multiple-access with collision detection. Packets on the cable contain up to 128 bytes of data, and include a 16-bit address and a 16-bit checksum. The TIEs support a virtual circuit protocol, enabling a terminal connected to a TIE to establish a connection with a terminal or computer connected to another TIE. An operational network containing about 50 TIEs was being installed late in 1979.

13.3.9   Rolm CBX

Digital private branch exchanges (PBXs) which have provided voice communications both within an office and, through outside lines, to the commercial telephone network, are being upgraded to also support data. PBXs represent a circuit-switched approach to local networks.

The Rolm Computerized Branch Exchange (CBX) supports both voice and switched data communications for asynchronous data up to 19,200 bps. A voice telephone is connected by one twisted pair of standard telephone wiring to an interface in the CBX where the voice is digitized. A data terminal is connected by an RS-232 interface to a nearby Data Terminal Interface (DTI), shown in Fig. 13.9, which in turn is connected by two twisted pairs of telephone wiring to a data line interface in the CBX. The DTI can be up to 5000 ft. from the CBX. A call is established by pushing a toggle on the DTI, to request service, and typing an appropriate command on the terminal. Automatic queueing is provided when the called number is busy.

The CBX contains a time-division multiplexed (TDM) bus operating at 7.3 Mbps. Each digital voice connection occupies 192,000 bps. Each voice connection time slot on the bus can be used to carry up to 40 data calls using a submultiplexing scheme unique to the Rolm system. The cost of an installed system for voice and data is approximately $1000 per termination.

Other PBX vendors include Northern Telecom and Datapoint. Northern Telecom's SL-1 supports data rates up to 9,600 bps; Datapoint's Information Switching Exchange (ISX) supports data rates up to 56,000 bps. The ISX has a distributed architecture in which terminals are connected to remote switching units, which in turn are joined to a central control unit. Most PBXs support only asynchronous communications, and do not support any protocol conversions, thus requiring the communicating devices to be compatible.

PBXs present a practical alternative for local networks with modest data-rate requirements. They are generally used for voice as well as data. Disadvantages include the high initial cost and the lack of gateways to packet-oriented networks.

Figure 13.9. Rolm data terminal interface.

13.3.10   Sytek

Sytek is one of the first commercial broadband local area networks. Their LocalNet 20 product, introduced in 1980, provides communications between terminals and host ports over 128 kbps data channels using CSMA/CD. Their microprocessor-based interface units, called Packet Communication Units, contain frequency agile modems that can be digitally tuned to any of 20 frequency channels within a 6 MHz channel group. Interchannel bridges are available to transfer packets between channel groups.

Sytek operates with standard CATV cable components using a branching tree topology. The system is normally used with a single cable mid-split system, although dual cable systems are supported as an option. The Packet Communication Units transmit on a channel in the frequency range of 70 to 106 MHz, and receive on a channel in the range 226.25 MHz to 262.25 MHz. At the headend of the branched tree, a frequency translator shifts the inbound transmissions up by 156.25 MHz. Models of the Packet Communication Units support either two or eight RS-232 ports for attaching to terminals or host ports. The data range on each port is individually selectable within the range of 300 bps to 19.2 kbps.

The LocalNet 40, introduced in 1982, performs signaling at 2 Mbps. It will support high speed host interfaces, such as to a DEC Unibus.

13.4   TECHNICAL ISSUES

The example local networks described in the preceding section are mostly experimental systems in research environments. In about 1981, products based on these systems began to appear in the marketplace. However, the commercial marketplace is in its infancy and improvements are needed in a number of technical areas for vendor-independent local networks to be widely accepted. These issues are the subject of this section.

13.4.1   Terminal Interfacing

One of the attractions of a local network is the ability to connect terminals directly to the network so that they may be plugged in anywhere within a building and may access any computers on the network. The problem is doing this in a cost-effective manner.

With the experimental networks described previously, and early commercial products, the interfacing cost per terminal is typically in the order of $600 to $1000. Since CRT terminals cost less than that, and their cost continues to drop rapidly, the cost of interfacing must drop substantially for local networks to be economically attractive.

Several approaches are possible. One possibility is to have several terminals which are close together share an interfacing device, similar to a cluster controller. In this way, the fixed cost of power supply and packaging is spread among more terminals. The optimum number of terminals per interface will depend on terminal distribution and the processing power of the microprocessor used in the interface, but will likely be in the range of two to eight terminals.

The processing power needed in the interface to support several terminals can be achieved either by using multiple microprocessors, such as one each per terminal and one for the network, or by using a single more powerful microprocessor, such as the newer 16-bit microprocessors.

Although a stand-alone interfacing device will always be needed for dumb terminals, with certain types of terminals the interface could be incorporated in the terminal. This is possible with terminals that have space for a user-supplied board to be inserted.

Standards organizations are attempting to establish standards for local network communications, encompassing access methods such as carrier-sense multiple-access with collision detection, and cable signaling methods. When these efforts are successful, large-scale integration (LSI) chips implementing these functions will be developed and will be incorporated in terminals by vendors.

In addition to providing access to the transmission medium, a terminal interfacing device must support the establishment of virtual circuits and the management of terminal characteristics. Thus the terminal interface is similar to the packet assembler/disassembler (PAD) function, and for scroll-mode terminals must support features similar to X.3 and a command language similar to X.28 used in long-haul networks.

Connecting more sophisticated page-oriented terminals to networks has long been a problem because of the absence of a standard virtual terminal protocol for features such as screen addressing and function keys. One of the applications of local networks will be to interconnect different types of word processing and office automation equipment. Thus development of virtual terminal protocols for word-processing equipment will be required.

13.4.2 Computer Interfacing

Most experimental local networks interface to only one or two types of host computers. Usually, this is done by connecting to the same serial asynchronous ports to which terminals are normally connected. This is fine if the network is only to be used for terminal-to-computer access. However, computer-to-computer applications require a higher-speed interface. This usually requires hardware and software tailored to the particular computer. The problem is in the effort required to develop high-speed interfaces for each type of computer, and in the overhead the networking software makes on the host computer.

One of the limitations in the growth of packet-switched networks was the effort required to develop network interfacing software. The adoption of X.25 as an international standard has greatly reduced that problem. Similarly, at the hardware interfacing level, the absence of any high-speed interface standard led to the development of the asynchronous bit serial interface (ABSI) used to connect host computers to ARPANET [BOLT 78]. The high-level data link control (HDLC) now provides a suitable standard communications interface.

The high transmission speeds of local networks, hundreds of thousands or millions of bits per second, in contrast to the 56-kbps communications circuits widely used in long-haul packet-switched networks, demand much higher-speed computer interfaces. Options include the use of serial synchronous communications as well as high-speed parallel interfaces.

A 16-bit parallel interface, such as a general-purpose program controlled interface to a minicomputer, provides a theoretical maximum operating speed in the range 250 to 500 kbps. A further benefit of this kind of interface is that it provides control handshaking signals which can be used for flow control between the computer and interfacing device. A disadvantage is that it results in an interrupt per character in the host computer software.

The ideal computer interface is to use direct memory access (DMA), which can provide high speed (in the low-megabit range) without the overhead incurred on the host computer by an interrupt per character. The ease of providing a DMA interface to the local network will depend on the particular computer. For example, for PDP-11s, a Z80-based device known as the UMC from Associated Computer Consultants operates as an intelligent peripheral on the Unibus. The Z80 can read and write directly to the PDP-11 memory, and can be programmed to communicate with the local network interfacing device.

Standards organizations are beginning to recognize the need for a standard high-speed computer interface that can be used to connect to local networks. Agreement on such a standard and its acceptance by computer vendors would make the development of local networks very much easier.

13.4.3 Performance

With most experimental local networks used mainly for terminal-to-computer communications, performance has not been a major concern. However, before local networks can effectively support computer-to-computer communications, significant performance improvements are needed.

Although the data signaling rates employed on local networks range from several hundred kilobits per second to several megabits per second, the effective point-to-point transfer rate between two computers on the network is usually only a fraction of that. With an early version of Mitrenet, a point-to-point data rate of 36 kbps was obtained with a system operating at 307.2 kbps [HOLM 79]. Thus it would appear that an effective transfer rate of 10 to 15% of the signaling rate is not uncommon. What are the reasons for this difference?

Contributing factors include protocols, microprocessor speed, and interface limitations. Protocols can limit bandwidth if, for example, an acknowledgment must be received for one packet on a virtual circuit before other packets can be sent. A small maximum packet size results in less efficient use of the transmission medium with CSMA/CD [SHOC 79B], and a lower throughput for the interfacing device.

The speed of the microprocessor in the interfacing device limits the rate at which data can be handled. Finally, the nature of the hardware interface to the host computer has a major impact. An interface that results in interrupts for each character will be significantly slower than a DMA interface.

Improvements are possible in all these areas. As more experience is gained, protocols will be optimized for local networks. For example, because of the low delay within the network, acknowledgments must be sent promptly. Newer 16-bit microprocessors will provide substantially more powerful interfacing devices.

13.4.4 Security and Privacy

In packet-switching networks, privacy is handled largely by checking that two subscribers belong to a common community of interest before allowing a virtual circuit to be established between them. Similar checks can be made by the interfacing devices which connect subscribers to a local network.

For greater security, packet-switching networks employ link encryption between nodes and on subscriber access circuits. However, packets must be in the clear as they pass through a node so that header information can be accessed to determine routing. Thus the node software must be trusted and verified.

Since local networks are generally broadcast, no examination is made of the packet between source and destination. However, since all packets pass by all interfacing devices, at least portions of the software in the interfacing devices must be verified. Software to be verified includes address detection and security-level validation. This is much less than the amount of software that would require verification in a general-purpose packet switch.

To separate data streams and provide protection against traffic analysis, headers as well as messages may be encrypted. Traffic entering the local network can be encrypted using the Data Encryption Standard, which is available in high-speed chips able to accommodate the local network data rate. In the future it is likely that public-key distribution methods will be available, permitting dynamic key modification.

13.4.5 Protocols and Standards

Various protocols are necessary for the orderly exchange of information across computer networks. Standard protocols avoid new implementations whenever a new interconnection occurs. The International Organization for Standardization (ISO) Open Systems Interconnection Reference Model provides a seven-layer framework for the protocols encountered in a network [ISO 82]. Standards currently exist only for the lowest three levels, at the network interface, exemplified by X.25 for interfacing to packet-switching networks (see Tab. 13.2).

In the case of local networks, standards activity has focused on the two lowest levels: the physical layer and the link layer. Publication of the Ethernet specification is intended to encourage its acceptance as a de facto standard. That specification

Table 13.2. *Protocol Comparison.*

ISO Seven-Layer Model	CCITT Adopted Standards	IEEE Proposed Local Network Standard	Xerox Ethernet	Mitrenet
Application				
Presentation	X.3, X.28, X.29		Courier	
Session				
Transport			Sequenced Packet	TCP, IP
Network	X.25 packet level		Internet Datagram Protocol	
Data Link	HDLC	Logical Link control	CSMA/CD	CSMA/CD
Physical	X.21 bis (RS-232-C)	CSMA/CD or Token bus or Token ring	Baseband coax	Broadband coax

defines, at the physical layer, the physical characteristics of the coaxial cable, the topology as a branching nonrooted tree, and the baseband signaling at 10 Mbps using Manchester phase encoding. At the link layer, the specification defines the CSMA/CD access protocol and the message protocol for framing, addressing, and checksums.

An IEEE local network standards committee has also focused on the two lowest levels. The proposed standard under development in 1982 includes three basic options: CSMA/CD on a bus, token access control on a bus, and token access control on a ring. Within each of these, there are further options as to signaling (baseband or broadband), type of cable (coax or twisted pair), modulation technique, and data rate (ranging from 1 Mbps to 20 Mbps).

A benefit of these standards activities will be the resulting availability of integrated circuits implementing the standard protocols, thereby reducing the cost of devices to interface to local networks. Chips implementing the Ethernet specifications are expected to be available in 1982 or 1983.

Most local networks will not remain stand-alone; rather, they will be interconnected to a long-distance network. Thus the local network will have to support internetworking and be compatible with the transport-level protocols required by the long-distance network. A fundamental choice is the extent to which the established protocols for long-distance networks are used in the local network, and the resulting protocol level required in the gateway which interconnects the local network to the long-distance network.

A gateway could operate at the datagram level, handling each packet as a self-contained entity and unrelated to other packets. Alternatively, the gateway could handle virtual circuits, preserving the sequence of packets and ensuring that a reliable data stream is passed from one network to another. In the case of the public data networks using X.25, virtual circuits are managed at the network interface level; thus the gateway must keep track of each virtual circuit. An adequate addressing scheme for internetworking will also be required.

In the Department of Defense protocol structure, virtual circuits are managed on an end-to-end basis [FOSS 79]. The internet protocol [DARP 80B] provides a datagram service for the delivery of a packet through an interconnected system of networks, such as long-distance packet networks, local networks, packet radio, and satellite networks. Thus the gateway between networks operates at the datagram level, and virtual circuits are handled on an end-to-end basis by the Transmission Control Protocol (TCP) [DARP 80A].

Local networks are likely to suffer from the same lack of higher-level protocol standards that has inhibited the use of packet-switching networks [MCQU 79]. Most local networks are used to provide access from asynchronous terminals to computers, as is often the case with long-distance networks. Connection of more sophisticated terminals, such as page mode and data-entry terminals, will be limited until appropriate virtual terminal protocols have been defined by ISO and subsequently implemented. Similarly, computer-to-computer applications, such as file transfers between dissimilar hosts, will await standards. Until then, effective exchange of information will be primarily between a single computer vendor's equipment, using that vendor's proprietary higher-level protocols, such as IBM's SNA, Digital's DECnet, and Xerox's Network Systems protocols.

Early local networks, based on 8-bit microprocessors, have usually been limited to supporting terminal to host access within the local network. The generation of 16-bit microprocessors will allow standard network protocols, such as X.25 and TCP, to be implemented in local network interfacing devices at low cost. This will provide users with the capability of communicating with other local and distant devices without requiring extensive network software in the user's equipment.

13.5 CURRENT STATUS AND FUTURE DIRECTIONS

Commercial local network products began to appear in the marketplace prolifically in 1981. The marketplace can be divided into two classes: those vendors who are primarily producing computers and office automation systems; and those vendors who are producing just a communications system. In the first class, the local network is just a part of the product, is fully integrated into devices such as workstations, and uses the vendor's own protocols. Examples of such systems are Apollo, Datapoint, Wang, and Xerox.

In the second class, the local network is a vendor-independent communications system for tying together heterogeneous computers and terminals, and usually consists of stand-alone microprocessor based interfacing devices supporting standard interface protocols such as RS-232 or X.25. Examples of such systems are Contel, Sytek, and Ungermann-Bass.

Another distinctive class of local network is the PBX, which is suitable for terminal-to-computer requirements. The cost per terminal connection is comparable to the other approaches, although it is usually not practical to start with a small configuration because of the minimum PBX needed.

For large local network installations with many hundreds of terminals, the dominant cost is for the connection or interfacing device for each terminal. This cost can be expected to drop to several hundred dollars, comparable to a low-speed modem, as standards are adopted and implemented in integrated circuits. Newer and more powerful microprocessors may enable an interfacing device to support a cluster of terminals, thereby sharing the cost of packaging and power supply over several terminals.

Terminals will be connected to the interfacing devices using RS-232 and similar standards. However, computers will require physical connection via either high-speed serial communications interfaces, or direct memory access. At the software level, the anticipated widespread availability of X.25 make it a likely choice for multiplexed, packet-mode interfaces.

Local networks will not operate in isolation. An important consideration will be the interconnection of the local network to a long-haul packet switching network via a gateway.

ACKNOWLEDGMENTS

The author gratefully acknowledges the contribution of Steven F. Holmgren and Anita P. Skelton to ideas and portions of the material included in this chapter. The assistance of Cathy McDonald in the preparation of the text is gratefully appreciated.

REFERENCES

General (Secs. 13.1, 13.2, and 13.4)

ABRA 70   Abramson, N., "The Aloha System—Another Alternative for Computer Communications," *AFIPS, Fall Joint Comput. Conf.* 1970, pp. 695–702.

BOLT 78   Bolt Beranek and Newman, Inc., "Specifications for Interconnection of a Host and an IMP", *BBN Tech. Rep. No. 1822,* May 1978 (revised).

BUNC 80   Bunch, S.R., and J.D. Day, "Control Structure Overhead in TCP," *Proc. Trends Appl.: 1980, IEEE/NBS,* pp. 121–127.

CCIT 81   CCITT, "Recommendation X.3: Packet Assembly/Disassembly Facility (PAD) in a Public Data Network," Yellow Book, Vol. VIII, International Telecommunications Union, Geneva, 1981.

CERF 78   Cerf, V.G., and P.T. Kirstein, "Issues in Packet-Network Interconnection," *Proc. IEEE,* November 1978, pp. 1386–1408.

CLAR 78 Clark, D.D., K.T. Pogran, and D.P. Read, "An Introduction to Local Area Networks," *Proc. IEEE,* November 1978, pp. 1497–1517.

COTT 78 Cotton, I.W., "Local Area Networks," *Nat. Bur. Stand. Spec. Publ. 500-31,* April 1978.

DARP 80A Defense Advanced Research Projects Agency, "DOD Standard Transmission Control Protocol," January 1980.

DARP 80B Defense Advanced Research Projects Agency, "DOD Standard Internet Protocol," January 1980.

DAVI 77 Davidson, J., et al., "The ARPANET Telnet Protocol: Its Purpose, Principles, Implementation, and Impact on Host Operating System Design," *Proc. 5th Data Commun. Symp.*, September 1977.

FARB 73 Farber, D. J., et al., "The Distributed Computing System," *Proc. IEEE COMPCON*, February 1973, pp. 31–34.

FOSS 79 Fossum, R.R. and V. G. Cerf, "Communications Challenges for the 80s," *Signal*, October 1979, pp. 17–24.

FREE 79 Freeman, H. A., and K.J. Thurber, "Issues in Local Computer Networks," *Proc. Int. Commun. Conf.*, June 1979, pp. 20.3.1–20.3.5.

HOLM 79 Holmgren, S. F., A. P. Skelton, and D.A. Gomberg, "FY79 Final Report: Cable Bus Applications in Command Centers," MTR-79W00383, The MITRE Corporation, McLean, Va., October 1979.

HOPK 79 Hopkins, G. T., "Multimode Communications on the MITRENET," *Proc. MITRE/NBS Local Area Commun. Network Symp.*, May 1979, pp. 169–176.

ISO 82 ISO/TC97/SC16, "Open Systems Interconnection Basic Reference Model," Draft International Standard 7498, February 1982. Previous Draft. Published in *ACM SIGCOMM Comput. Commun. Rev.*, April 1981.

KLEI 75 Kleinrock, L., and F.A. Tobagi, "Packet Switching in Radio Channels: Part 1. Carrier Sense Multiple-Access Modes and Their Throughput-Delay Characteristics," *IEEE Trans. Commun.*, Vol. COM-23, No. 12, 1975, pp. 1400–1416.

LIU 78 Liu, M. T., "Distributed Loop Computer Networks," in *Advances in Computers*, Vol. 17, Academic Press, New York, 1978, pp. 163–221.

MCQU 79 McQuillan, J.M., "Local Network Technology and Lessons of History," *Proc. MITRE/NBS Local Area Commun. Network Symp.*, May 1979, pp. 191–196.

MEIS 79 Meisner, N. B., Ed., *Proc. MITRE/NBS Local Area Commun. Network Symp.*, May 1979.

PENN 79 Penney, B. K., and A. A. Baghdadi, "Survey of Computer Communications Loop Networks," *Comput. Commun.*, Part 1, August 1979, pp. 165–180; Part 2, October 1979, pp. 224–241.

SHOC 79A Shoch, J., and L. Stewart, "Internetwork Experiments with the Bay Area Packet Radio Network," Xerox Palo Alto Res. Center Tech. Rep.

SHOC 79B   Shoch, J. F., and J. A. Hupp, "Performance of an Ethernet Local Network: A Preliminary Report," *Proc. MITRE/NBS Local Area Commun. Network Symp.*, May 1979, pp. 113–123.

SHOC 79C   Shoch, J. F., "An Annotated Bibliography on Local Computer Networks," Xerox Palo Alto Res. Center Tech. Rep., SSL-79-5, October 1979.

TOBA 79   Tobagi, F.A., and B.V. Hunt, "Performance Analysis of Carrier Sense Multiple Access with Collision Detection," *Proc. MITRE/NBS Local Area Commun. Network Symp.*, May 1979, pp. 217–244.

WOOD 79   Wood, D.C., S.F. Holmgren and A.P. Skelton, "A Cable-Bus Protocol Architecture," *Proc. 6th Data Commun. Symp.*, November 1979, pp. 137–146.

Examples of Local Networks (Sec. 13.3)

Cambridge Ring (Sec. 13.3.1)

HOPP 78   Hopper, A., "Data Ring at Computer Laboratory, University of Cambridge, in Local Area Networking," *Natl. Bur. Stand. Spec. Publ. 500-31*, April 1978, pp. 11–16.

WILK 79   Wilkes, M. V., "The Cambridge Digital Communication Ring," *Proc. MITRE/NBS Local Area Commun. Network Symp.*, May 1979.

Distributed Computer System (Sec. 13.3.2)

FARB 73   Farber, D. J., et al., "The Distributed Computing System," *Proc. IEEE COMPCON*, February 1973, pp. 31–34.

FARB 77   Farber, D. J., "The ARPA Local Network Interface," *Proc. EASTCON 1977*, pp. 14-3A to 14-3C.

FARB 78   Farber, D. J., "The Design of the Distributed Computer System," unpublished paper.

MOCK 77   Mockapetris, P. V., M. R. Lyle, and D. J. Farber, "On the Design of Local Network Interface," *Proc. IFIP 1977*, Toronto, pp. 427–430.

Distributed Loop Computer Network (Sec. 13.3.3)

LIU 78   Liu, M. T., "Distributed Loop Computer Networks," in *Advances in Computers*, Vol. 17, Academic Press, New York, 1978, pp. 163–221.

LIU 79   Liu, M.T., et al., "System Design of the Distributed Double-Loop Computer Network (DDLCN)," *Proc. 1st Int. Conf. Distributed Syst.*, Huntsville, Ala., October 1979, pp. 95–105.

Ethernet (Sec. 13.3.4)

BOGG 80   Boggs, D.R., et al., "Pup: An Internetwork Architecture," *IEEE Trans. Commun.*, April 1980, pp. 612–624.

DIGI 80   Digital Equipment Corporation, Intel Corporation, and Xerox Corporation, "Ethernet Specification," September 1980.

14

Computer Networks:
A Survey

DAVID C. WOOD
The MITRE Corporation
McLean, Virginia

14.1 INTRODUCTION

A computer network has been defined as an interconnected group of independent computer systems that communicate with one another and share resources such as programs, data, hardware, and software [PETE 71]. Computer networks have proliferated rapidly, from a few research networks in the early 1970s, to public data networks in many major countries providing international service. The purpose of this chapter is to describe representative major networks, identifying and contrasting their designs and characteristics. These example networks illustrate how the various components of computer communications may be integrated to form a total network.

For the purposes of this survey, three types of computer networks will be distinguished:

1. Remote-access networks
2. Public data networks
3. Private computer networks

Remote-access networks are designed to provide terminal access from a wide geographic area, generally to a particular host computer. They may not be strictly within the definition of computer networks given above, but several examples are included since they represent the most common type of private data communication network. Such networks are used by the vendors of time-sharing and remote batch computing services to provide national or even international access to their facilities. They are also used to provide access to a central system in applications such as airline reservations, banking, and stock quotation.

Public data networks, often employing packet switching, are designed primarily to provide a cost-effective communications service to a wide variety of subscribers. These networks are usually operated by a common carrier, while the connected computers and terminals may belong to many different subscribers.

Private computer networks include resource-sharing and mission-oriented networks, and often comprise more than just a data communications system. The ARPANET is such an example, with siginificant host capabilities, such as file transfer and message services, in addition to the packet-switching communications sub-network.

This chapter contains descriptions of networks in each of the three categories. Criteria for inclusion of a network are that it be a major example of its type or that it represent a significant advance in the state of the art, that it be in operation or an advanced stage of implementation, and that adequate documentation on the network be available in the open literature.

14.1.1 History

One of the earliest computer communications systems was the SAGE air defense system in the 1950s [EVER 57]. During the 1960s, computers were introduced in telegraphic message-switching systems to replace manual operations using torn punched paper tape. Examples of such automated message-switching systems are AUTODIN I [PAOL 75] and SITA [CHRE 73]. As commercial time-sharing systems became widespread in the late 1960s, many communication networks were established using concentrators to reduce the cost of remote access. Surviving examples of these remote-access networks are INFONET [TENK 74] and the GE Information Services network [MCCA 78].

Initial conceptual work on networks and distributed communications is ascribed to Baran [BARA 64]. The first and most famous packet-switched network, which has had a major influence on the evolution of computer communications, is the ARPANET, developed by the Defense Advanced Research Projects Agency in the United States. Proposed in 1966 [MARI 66, ROBE 67], and in operation since 1969, the network comprises a packet-switched data communications subsystem and a collection of host computers which together make up a resource-sharing network. The packet-switched local network developed during the same period as ARPANET at the National Physical Laboratory in the United Kingdom addresses the same fundamental issues, but on a small scale [DAVI 67, SCAN 69]. An early survey of computer networks, conducted in 1971, examined 10 networks, most of them in the research environment [PETE 71]. The evolution of packet switching has been described by Roberts [ROBE 78].

The early 1970s saw an increasing number of experimental packet-switching networks, some of them developed by common carriers [WOOD 75]. In 1975, Telenet began operation as the first public packet-switched data network. Since then, the focus has increasingly been on public networks and the adoption of international standards to facilitate their use. The evolution of some of the major networks is illustrated in Fig. 14.1.

1970

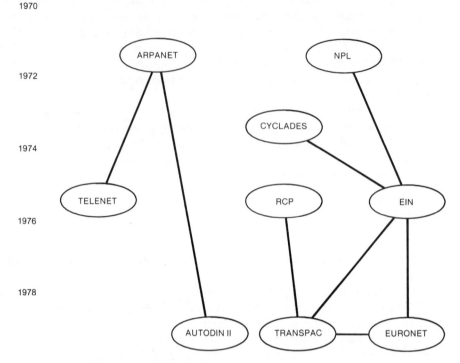

Figure 14.1. Evolution of packet-switching networks

14.1.2 Definition of Characteristics

Computer networks vary considerably in their design and the facilities they offer to users. The characteristics are defined here and used subsequently in the survey.

The *objective* of a network is an important consideration; it could be for research and experimentation, or it could be to provide an economical data communications service. Any *membership* qualifications for joining the network must be satisfied. Networks may be *private* or *public*. Private networks are restricted to a closed community, such as an organization or a research community with common interests. Public networks are operated by a common carrier as a service.

The type of *switching technique* employed may be packet switching, message switching, circuit switching, or some combination or variation of them. Packet switching is the most widely used. Two *types of service* are possible in packet-switching systems: datagram and virtual circuit. In a *datagram* service, each packet is transmitted and delivered in the communications system independent of any other packet; in particular, each packet must be sent with a full address, packets may be delivered out of the sequence in which they were sent, and missing and duplicate packets may not be detected. In a *virtual circuit* service, a call is set up between two subscribers (computers or terminals) by an exchange of packets, and the packet-switching system takes responsibility for delivering packets belonging to the call in sequence and with high reliability. Alternatively, the virtual circuit functions, if required, can be provided in a host computer or interfacing device external to the packet-switching communications system.

Performance characteristics of a network include delay and throughput. *Delay* is the time from the acceptance of a packet or message by the network until its delivery. *Throughput* is the effective data transfer rate in bits per second. Delay is important for interactive applications, whereas throughput is of interest for file transfers.

Major features of the communications network include the type of computers used and architecture of the switching *nodes,* the *topology* in which the nodes are connected, the *capacity* (i.e., data rate) of the communications lines between nodes, the *routing* scheme used to transmit data from source to destination, and the *message* or *packet size.*

Various options are possible for the *computer interface* between host computers and the communications system. One approach is *emulation,* in which the switching node, or an interfacing device, causes the network to appear as devices known to the host, usually asynchronous terminals. Another approach is a *packet-mode* interface, in which packets are exchanged between the host and the packet switch. The emulation approach, while avoiding changes to the host software, limits use of the network to the functions performed by the devices being emulated. A packet-mode interface, with appropriate software in the host, can provide a general interprocess communication facility suitable for performing resource sharing and such services as file transfer.

Terminal interfaces may be provided to allow the connection of terminals to the network or to an interfacing device. Asynchronous terminals are usually supported; synchronous terminals are supported less frequently.

The *capabilities* supported by the network may include terminal-to-computer, computer-to-computer, or terminal-to-terminal communication. The *applications* supported in the host computers may be network independent, or may include network services such as file transfer and message service.

14.2 REMOTE-ACCESS NETWORKS

Remote-access networks are centralized or star networks in which remote access to one central system is possible from many terminals. The network may be one-level, with terminals connected via multipoint lines directly to the central system. Alternatively, the network may be two-level, with terminals connected to concentrators, and the concentrators in turn connected to the central system.

The reason for accessing the central system may be because of some unique data stored there, or to obtain time-sharing services. Systems providing access to data include airline reservations, banking, and stock quotation. These are usually transaction-oriented applications involving a query and a response. Generally, the terminals are connected via multipoint lines using polling.

With the advent of large time-sharing systems in the late 1960s, remote-access networks were created to provide economical access from a wide population of remotely located and widely dispersed user terminals of various types to a cluster of host computers. Such networks may also be used to provide remote batch service. These networks are designed to operate at a high level of reliability and communications efficiency. Basically, these networks are hierarchical, using concentrators to reduce communication line costs between terminals in the various cities served and the central computer complex. The larger networks have more than one host computer location, resulting in a distributed network topology. Dial-in access is often provided for subscribers to access their local concentrators. Examples of this type of network are INFONET, CYBERNET, and the GE Information Services network.

14.2.1 INFONET

INFONET is designed, implemented, and operated by Computer Sciences Corporation (CSC) to provide a remote computing service to commercial customers, including U.S. government agencies [TENK 74, COLL 76]. The network, which has been in operation since 1970, allows user terminals from all locations in the United States, Mexico, and Western Europe to access any CSC host located at Beltsville, Maryland; Oakbrook, Illinois; El Segundo, California; Dallas, Texas; and Toronto and Calgary, Canada (see Fig 14.2). Hosts providing time-sharing and batch services consist of Univac 1108's and 1100/80's operating the Computer Sciences Teleprocessing System (CSTS) and IBM 370/168's running MVS.

INFONET utilizes a virtual circuit-switching technique using concentrators. An optimum routing path based on least cost in terms of network delay is determined and established upon terminal log-on. The path remains fixed throughout a session, from terminal log-on to log-off. Should the path be disrupted because of a link or node failure, a new path would be established to reroute the traffic.

There are about 45 communications nodes, of two types, both using Comten-20 hardware. Terminal Remote Communications Concentrators (RCCs) are scattered at strategic locations to support terminals and are connected directly by high-speed trunks to switching RCCs at the host location which route incoming data to the designated host computer. A typical terminal RCC is capable of supporting 90 low-speed terminals, 16 high-speed terminals, and one or more high-speed trunks. A terminal RCC is connected to one or more switching RCCs, usually with a 19.2-kbps link employing a biplexer and two 9.6-kbps circuits. DDS circuits are used where available, as well as some domestic and international satellite circuits. The switching RCCs are interconnected, creating a distributed network structure. Transmission between terminal RCCs and switching RCCs is in variable-length blocks up to 256 bytes long. From 1 to 10 segments of data from different users may be assembled in one block, together with error control information.

The network interfaces with the Univac hosts via the Communication Terminal Module Controller and appropriate software incorporated with CSTS. The

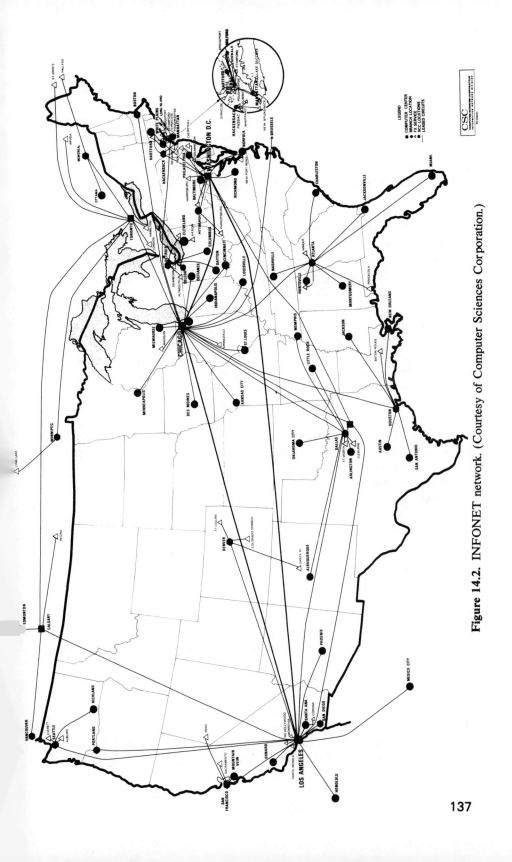

Figure 14.2. INFONET network. (Courtesy of Computer Sciences Corporation.)

137

interface to the IBM host is via the IBM 3705 Communication Controller or its plug-compatible replacement; the Terminal Emulation Interface between the 3705 and RCC makes the terminal connected at some remote location appear to the host as if the host is directly connected to the terminal.

Asynchronous terminals supported include 110- to 300-bps ASCII terminals, 134.5-bps IBM 2741 terminals, and 1200-bps ASCII terminals. IBM 2780 and compatible synchronous terminals operating at 2000 to 4800 bps are supported, including Data 100 terminals used as remote bulk terminals in each branch office. These terminals include a card reader and line printer and are used primarily to provide remote printing. Rotary groups are provided for each class of terminals for dial-in access, and dedicated access circuits are utilized for subscriber bulk terminals with connect times on the order of several hours per day. In cities with lesser traffic volumes, multiplexers with dial-in ports are used, and are connected to a terminal RCC. Toll free dial-in access is provided in 121 cities.

INFONET provides terminal-to-computer capabilities to provide access to time-sharing services. The CSTS operating system developed by CSC for the Univac 1100 Series computers supports a wide range of program development tools and programming languages. The terminal RCC converts all incoming terminal code to a standard eight-level ASCII to relieve the host computer of this function.

The INFONET service is designed such that 85% of user responses to simple interactive tasks will occur within 2 sec and 95% of users responses will occur within 3 sec. Communication delay in the network is on the order of 10% of the total response or about 100 to 300 msec. Under high network load, the terminal RCC temporarily reduces the effective speed of bulk terminals so as to give preference to interactive terminals. INFONET carries an estimated load of 500 million characters per day. A high degree of reliability within the INFONET communication network has been attained through a combination of subsystem design efforts and operational considerations. Overall communication network reliability, as measured from terminal RCC to host computer, is 99.8%.

14.2.2 NASDAQ

The NASDAQ system is a communications network operated by the National Association of Securities Dealers to enable brokers and financial institutions to obtain up-to-the-minute information on over-the-counter (OTC) stock prices and indices. Terminals in over 600 offices are connected via regional concentrators to the NASDAQ central processing complex in Trumbull, Connecticut (see Fig. 14.3).

The inquiry terminals located in a brokerage office are directly connected to an on-site terminal controller referred to as the Over-the-Counter Control Unit (OCU). Each OCU provides limited buffering and message formatting for the terminals. The OCU is in turn connected to a regional concentrator via a 1600-bps full-duplex multipoint line. The regional circuit can support up to 32 OCUs and is controlled in a polled fashion by the regional concentrator. Data are transmitted in an asynchronous manner.

Figure 14.3. Simplified diagram of the NASDAQ system. Double lines indicate trunk lines. (Courtesy of NASDAQ, Inc.)

The regional concentrators are located in Atlanta, Chicago, New York, and San Francisco. The concentrators are Honeywell DDP-516 computers: three in New York and one in the other cities, together with a backup unit at each location. Each concentrator facility has two diverse-routed trunk lines between the facility and the central processing complex, a Univac 1100/22 multiprocessor. The trunks from the New York concentrator operate at 50 kbps; the trunks from the other concentrator sites comprise a 7.2-kbps analog leased circuit and a 9.6-kbps digital circuit. Data are transmitted on the trunk circuits in a synchronous manner.

The concentrator polls each of its regional circuits independently. Each concentrator can support up to 40 regional circuits. A scheduled poll selector routine continuously solicits queries from each line unless inhibited by a special control message from the central processing complex. A poll message invites an OCU to transmit a query message stored in its buffer. If no query message is ready, the OCU responds with a single-character reply. Another OCU is polled, and so on, until a query message is received. Polling on that line then stops until the query has been transmitted to the central processing complex, at which time polling is resumed. When another message is found on that line, it is transmitted to the concentrator, but is held there until the response to the first message is received back at the concentrator. During the transmission of the reply message, polls may be nested within the text of the reply until another query is received. The system handles about 1.5 million transactions a day, with a peak of 80 transactions per second.

The original concentrators are being replaced by newer concentrators which will perform additional functions. To relieve the central processing complex of handling all data-base inquiries, a subset of the data bases will be stored at concentrator sites. Subscriber inquiries to the local data base will be serviced by the concentrator. Quotation changes and inquiries for security information not contained at the local data base will be relayed to the central facility. The new system will also support unsolicited traffic destined for subscriber equipment and allow subscriber use of terminal equipment other than NASDAQ terminals. The Atlanta concentrator will be closed and the New York concentrators will be relocated to Trumbull, Connecticut.

14.2.3   Navy Federal Credit Union

The Navy Federal Credit Union (NFCU) has a communications network to support remote access for an on-line teller system from its 18 branches across the United States to an IBM 370/158 computer at its Vienna, Virginia, headquarters. The system uses IBM's Systems Network Architecture (SNA) to control both IBM 3270 display terminals and IBM 3600 banking terminals in the branch offices. The 3270 terminals are used for data-entry applications such as loans and new accounts, and for inquiries. The 3600 banking terminal keyboards, displays, and printers are used by tellers for on-line transactions. The network is typical of those used in commercial applications.

The network utilizes four full-duplex lines between the central computer site and the remote locations. Three of these lines are multipoint 2400-bps circuits and one is a point-to-point 2400-bps Westar satellite line. At each remote location, the line serves an IBM 3276 controller, which in turn supports one or more display terminals at the location. At some remote locations, the line also serves an IBM 3601 controller, which supports the banking terminals. Synchronous Data Link Control (SDLC) is used on the links; the controllers on the multipoint links are polled in rotation by the IBM 3705, which front-ends the IBM 370.

An entirely different link control procedure, known as the 3600 Banking Loop Discipline, is used between the 3601 controller and the 3600 banking terminals [IBM 77]. Several banking terminals are connected in a closed loop to the 3601 controller. Data are transmitted unidirectionally round the loop. Each terminal regenerates the data and passes them on to the next terminal. Each NFCU 3601 controller supports local or local and remote loops: a local loop at the same office, which operates at 4800 bps, and remote loops at distant offices connected by dedicated 2400-bps lines. Under the loop discipline, data are transmitted to one or more terminals at a time in 306-bit frames.

A significant amount of applications processing is performed in the 3600 controllers. Communication between applications software in the 3600 controllers and in the 370 is managed by SNA. For reliability, dial backup is available from the 3600 to the 370 for end-of-the-day transmission if the leased line is down. As is often the case with multipoint circuits, local and long distance sites are mixed on the same circuit so as to obtain interstate tariffs for all circuits.

NFCU also uses a message switch typical of older communication systems. Messages are relayed to and from over 40 overseas offices, as well as to a number of

U.S. locations. A minicomputer connected to the IBM 370 receives messages over various low-speed circuits, performs code conversion, and forwards the messages to the IBM 370 by emulating a display terminal control unit. Output messages are delivered over the appropriate circuit.

Twelve leased point-to-point teletype circuits are operated at 50 or 75 baud. Two of these circuits terminate in torn tape hubs, where messages are forwarded to the ultimate destination. A 75-baud teletype circuit to Hong Kong connects to a message switch there, which in turn serves 17 offices around the Pacific. Two 50-baud Telex lines, equipped with automatic dialing and answering equipment, are used for messages to and from low-volume U.S. branches.

14.3 PUBLIC DATA NETWORKS

Data communications has always relied heavily on the use of the voice telephone network. Some of the disadvantages of this system for data communications are the limited choice of data rates available, particularly for switched service; the cost, especially for low data rates; and the error rate. Users building their own communications networks have used computing equipment such as multiplexers or concentrators to make more efficient use of the data rates available and to perform error control.

Two new types of public data networks have evolved in recent years to serve the unique needs of data communications. One type is the all-digital transmission services, such as AT&T's Dataphone Digital Service (DDS), the Canadian Dataroute, and the former Datran network. These provide a choice of data rates at appropriate costs, and much improved error rates. DDS and Dataroute initially provided only leased service, but are adding switched service. Datran was the first to offer switched digital service. Digital transmission systems are described in other chapters.

The other type of new public data networks are those employing packet switching. These use leased analog or digital common carrier circuits together with minicomputer packet-switching nodes to provide not only flexible data rates and end-to-end error control, but also other features such as interoperability between incompatible terminals and computers. In the United States, these services are provided by value-added carriers such as Telenet and Tymnet; in other countries, the Postal Telephone and Telegraph administrations (PTTs) are building public packet-switched networks such as Datapac and Transpac [KELL 78].

As a result of initiatives from these carriers, the International Telegraph and Telephone Consultative Committee (CCITT) has established standards for the user interface to these networks. Recommendation X.25, first adopted in 1976, specifies the interface between a host computer and a packet-switching node for computers operating in the packet mode [CCIT 81A]. At the data link control level, X.25 uses the High-level Data Link Control (HDLC) procedure, which has been standarized by the International Organization for Standardization (ISO) [ISO 79].

To allow start–stop terminals to utilize a public switched network, an interface device to handle these terminals, known as a packet assembler/disassembler (PAD), has been defined. The features of the PAD and the way it interacts with the terminal and packet-mode hosts on the network have been standardized by CCITT in Recommendations X.3, X.28, and X.29 [CCIT 81B, CCIT 81C, CCIT 81D].

Almost all new public data networks being developed conform to these standards, and earlier networks are being converted, such as Telenet and the public networks in the United Kingdom and Spain. The CCITT has also defined in Recommendation X.75 international internetworking procedures for interconnecting public packet-switching networks [CCIT 81E].

A number of public data networks are described in this section. A comparison of their characteristics appear in Tab. 14.1.

14.3.1 Datapac

Datapac is a public packet-switching network operated by the TransCanada Telephone System [CASH 76; CLIP 76; MCGI 77; MCGI 78; RYBC 77; RYBC 78A, B; RYBC 80; SPRO 80; TWYV 76; YOUN 76]. The network has been commercially available since 1977, and by 1978 consisted of 10 switching nodes serving 57 Canadian cities (see Fig. 14.4).

Datapac provides virtual circuit service between subscribers. Each node consists of an SL-10 Data Network Processor manufactured by Northern Telecom

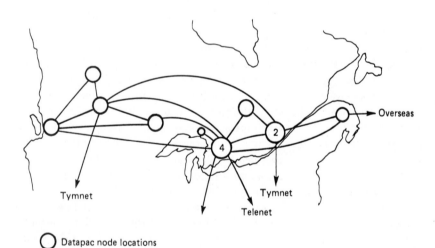

○ Datapac node locations

Note: 55 cities served by Datapac (not shown)

Figure 14.4. Datapac network. (Courtesy of The Computer Communications Group, TransCanada Telephone System.)

Table 14.1. Public Data Networks.

					Network			
	Datapac	EPSS	Infoswitch	Telenet	Transpac	Tymnet
Country	Canada	U.K.	Canada	U.S.	France	U.S.
Date operational	1977	1977	1978	1975	1979	1976
Switching technique	Packet	Packet	Packet/circuit	Packet	Packet	Packet
Type of service	Virtual circuit	Virtual circuit	Virtual circuit	Virtual circuit	Virtual circuit	Virtual circuit
Node processor	Northern Telecom SL-10	Ferranti Argus 700E	Seimens EDX	Prime 200 TP-4000	CII MITRA 125 CP50	Varian
Number of nodes	10	6	4	8 (multiple switches)	12	300
Cities served	57	3	56	81	25	125
Trunk speed	56 kbps	48 kbps	56 kbps	56 kbps	72 kbps	9.6 kbps
Routing	Fixed	Fixed	Fixed	Fixed	Fixed	Fixed
Packet size (bits)	2048	2040	?	1024	1024	528
Host interface	X.25	Nonstandard	Similar to X.25	X.25	X.25	X.25 planned
Terminal interface	Asynchronous	Asynchronous	Asynchronous, synchronous	Asynchronous, synchronous	Asynchronous	Asynchronous, synchronous

Limited. This unit is a multiprocessor machine utilizing a variable mixture of functional processors, arranged on a common bus structure. The nodes are interconnected by 56-kbps trunks from the Dataroute digital network [HORT 74]. All nodes are doubly connected for high reliability. A distributed routing control method is used. Each node contains a routing table which is updated according to messages exchanged between the nodes. This method is intended to cope with failure conditions, but it is not intended to reflect dynamic traffic patterns. Two priorities are provided: the maximum data field lengths of data packets are 128 bytes for priority service and 256 bytes for normal service.

There are two classes of subscriber interfaces to Datapac. The first provides access for computers and intelligent terminals using a packet mode interface. The second class provides access for non-packet mode terminals. The packet mode interface, called the Standard Network Access Protocol (SNAP), conforms to CCITT Recommendation X.25. It provides for multiple virtual circuits over a synchronous interface which initially may be up to 9.6 kbps.

Under the non-packet mode interface, terminals are connected to Datapac by what are called Network Interface Machines (NIMs), which correspond to packet assembler/disassemblers (PADs) defined by CCITT. Initially, asynchronous terminals operating at 110 to 300 bps have been supported according to an Interactive Terminal Interface (ITI), which corresponds to a subset of CCITT Recommendations X.3, X.28, and X.29. The NIM allows the terminal to communicate with a host computer connected to the network by an X.25 interface. Directed by commands from the terminal, the NIM performs virtual call establishment and clearing. During data transfer, the NIM assembles data received from the host and transmits the data to the terminal. The operation of these functions depends on the values of a set of internal variables called NIM parameters. About 13 NIM parameters are supported.

X.25 interfaces have been developed for various hosts. Higher-level protocols at the host provide for the exchange of control information and data between the host and a NIM according to X.29. As an example, IBM 360/370 hosts are interfaced using the Datapac Modified Emulation Program (DMEP), a software package for the IBM 3704/5 communications controllers developed by Cambridge Telecommunications Inc. (CTX) of Bedford, Massachusetts. DMEP adds the logic necessary to interface the 3704/5 to Datapac, that is, support for X.25 and X.29. To the 360/370, the terminals connected through Datapac appear as if they were directly connected through the 3704/5.

Most use of Datapac is for terminal-to-host communications. However, computer-to-computer communication is also possible given appropriate higher-level protocols. Since May 1978, Datapac has been interconnected with Telenet and Tymnet, allowing both terminal-to-host traffic, where the terminal is in either network, and host-to-host traffic.

The delay objective for the network is an average network transit delay of 0.48 sec for normal packets and 0.26 sec for priority packets. The throughput objective is that the throughput of a virtual circuit is limited only by the speed of the access lines.

14.3.2   Experimental Packet-Switched Service

The British Post Office (BPO) Experimental Packet Switched Service (EPSS) came into operation in 1977 for a minimum experimental period of 2 years. The aims of the experimental service are to enable the BPO to gain experience with such a service, to determine whether to include packet switching in future data services, and to enable customers to assess the usefulness of packet switching, as well as its technical and economic viability [HADL 74]. During the experimental period, use of EPSS is limited to about 35 organizations, which are participating in the experiment with a total of 27 computers and 150 terminals [BURG 76].

EPSS provides a virtual circuit service. Even though the BPO was one of the joint submitters of the X.25 proposal to CCITT in 1975, EPSS does not conform to X.25 since implementation began in 1973. In 1978, the BPO awarded a contract to Plessey for a full-scale public packet-switching network conforming to X.25. Telenet is a major subcontractor, providing the packet switch hardware and software.

EPSS consists of three Packet Switching Exchanges (PSEs), located in London, Manchester, and Glasgow (see Fig. 14.5). Each PSE consists of one or more autonomous Packet Switching Units (PSUs): three at London, two at Manchester, and one at Glasgow [HADL 78]. Thus EPSS is really a six-node network. The PSUs comprising a PSE are fully interconnected by a 384-kbps interprocessor link. Multiple 48-kbps links interconnect PSEs. The PSU is based on the Ferranti Argus 700E minicomputer. The London PSUs employ duplicated processors, providing a hot standby. Alternative power supplies are also provided at each PSE.

Each PSU has a capacity of four 48-kbps ports serving hosts or trunks, eight ports serving hosts at 2400 bps or 4800 bps, and 21 ports serving asynchronous terminals at 110 bps or 300 bps. Each PSE has dual 1-Mbyte drums, which are used for the storage of statistical and accounting information.

EPSS employs an alternative routing strategy [GARD 76]. Each node contains a routing table, which shows for each ultimate destination node, the first choice of outgoing route, as well as a secondary choice if this link is congested. Each PSU is a separate node for routing purposes. The contents of the routing tables are based on a minimum-hop philosophy and are static while a node is operational, being altered only by manual intervention.

EPSS handles packets having a maximum data field size of 255 bytes (2040 bits). Packets between a host and node have a header of 12 bytes during call setup and 5 bytes subsequently. Packets transmitted between PSEs have an additional 11 bytes of control information called Main Network Addition [NEIL 75A]. Closed user groups are supported.

The packet mode interface between a host computer and a node uses a unique link-level protocol for error control and acknowledgment [NEIL 75B]. Only one packet may be transmitted, after which an acknowledgment must be received. However, packets can be transmitted and received simultaneously. Two options are available. In the standard protocol, the host and PSE establish byte synchronization,

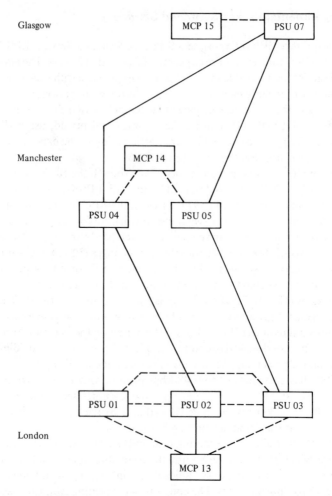

Figure 14.5. EPSS network configuration. PSU, packet-switching unit; PSE, packet-switching exchange; MCP, monitor control point. Dashed line, processor interconnection channels; solid line, inter-PSE trunks. (Courtesy of the British Post Office.)

and the PSE measures the loop delay of the line. High throughput is achieved by returning, at the earliest possible time, the 3-byte acknowledgment to a packet received, even if this means interrupting a packet already in transmission. Since the loop delay seen by the PSE line interfacing equipment is always a fixed number of bytes for each particular subscriber, the packet reception process can be suspended one loop delay after transmission of the last byte of a packet and the acknowledgment removed from the incoming packet. This transmission protocol has been implemented in a special hardware device, the transmission control unit. In the simplified protocol option, the acknowledgment is not transmitted until the packet under transmission is completed, avoiding the need to measure the loop delay and establish loop synchronization.

The packet level of the host interface protocol is similar conceptually to X.25, involving call setup, data exchange, and call clearing phases. Logical channel numbers are known as labels.

Asynchronous terminals may access a PSE via leased or dial-up lines. Dialing out to a terminal is also possible. The packet assembly/disassembly function is performed by a part of the PSE known as a Virtual Packet Terminal (VTP) [NEIL 75C]. A log-on procedure is required from dial-in terminals.

A standard file transfer protocol for use with EPSS has been specified. EPSS has been interconnected to ARPANET via a gateway at University College, London [HIGG 78].

14.3.3   Infoswitch

Infoswitch is a public data network operated by CNCP Telecommunications, one of the two nationwide competing common carriers in Canada (the other being TCTS, the operator of Datapac). CNCP Telecommunications is a cooperative arrangement between the telecommunications departments of the two major railways in Canada, Canadian National Railways and Canadian Pacific Limited.

Infoswitch is a unique hybrid circuit-switching and packet-switching data communications network [CARL 76, HUBE 80, WOOD 78]. The network commenced public service in 1978 with initial nodes in Vancouver, Edmonton, Toronto, and Montreal (see Fig. 14.6). Infoswitch provides three distinct services, known as

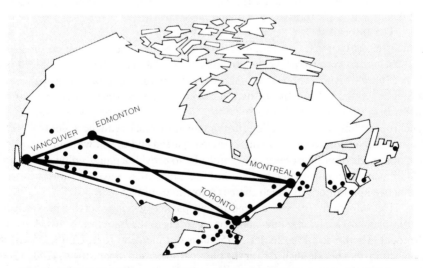

Figure 14.6. Infoswitch network. (Courtesy of CNCP Telecommunications.)

Infoexchange, Infocall, and Infogram. Infoexchange is a digital circuit switching service. Infocall and Infogram are virtual call services based on packet switching. However, in the Infocall service, the network carries out the packetizing functions, whereas in the Infogram service, the subscriber uses a packet mode interface to the network.

The Infoswitch nodes are based on Seimens System EDX hardware and software. The hardware consists of a PDP-11 for the central processor and Seimens-developed communications hardware for line terminators and communications controllers. The central processor is required throughout a packet-switched call and during the establishment of a circuit-switched call. However, once established, a circuit-switched call requires only the communications hardware and places no load on the central processor. For reliability, the switches operate with a full hot standby.

The trunks between the Infoswitch nodes are 56-kbps digital circuits utilizing Infodat, the leased digital data service offered by CNCP Telecommunications since 1974 [CARL 75]. Initially, the circuit-switching service utilizes individually derived circuits dedicated to the speed of the customer. However, a dynamic multiplexing technique is planned which will enable the selection of the desired bandwidth from a 56-kbps trunk at the time of call establishment. Infoswitch utilizes fixed routing per call with predetermined alternate routes.

The Infoexchange service can be used by both computers and terminals. A digital circuit-switched connection is established using a call setup procedure taking less than 1 sec. Either asynchronous (110 to 1200 bps) or synchronous (1200 to 9600 bps) transmission can be used both during the call setup and data transfer phases. Addressing and control information generated by the user's terminal or computer is carried over the data channel without the use of external addressing devices. The speed and link protocol of the two connected users must be identical since the network has no interaction with the data. Infoexchange is intended for applications such as remote job entry, file transfer, and digital facsimile.

The Infocall service can also be used by both computers and terminals. For asynchronous terminals operating at 110 to 1200 bps, the network performs the packetizing according to packet length and control characters defined at subscription time. Multiple asynchronous terminals can communicate simultaneously with a host computer connected via the Infogram packet mode interface. For synchronous subscribers operating at 1200 to 9600 bps, the network packetizes the user's entire synchronous link frame, including start- and end-of-block sequences, control codes, and error-detection codes. The entire frame is passed end to end without interpretation or modification. The objective of Infocall is to provide a plug-to-plug-compatible replacement for circuit-switching or leased lines. Infocall is suited for transaction and interactive applications in which there is a low intermittent data flow.

The Infogram service is an end-to-end packet-switching service in which the user implements a packet mode interface according to the Infogram Network Access Protocol. The protocol resembles X.25 but is not identical to it. Up to 255 virtual connections can be established over the physical access link operating at 1200 to 9600 bps between the host computer and the network. Asynchronous Infocall data and synchronous Infogram data can both be carried on the same access link using separate virtual connections.

Optional features in all three services include abbreviated addressing using one or two characters instead of a full seven-digit address, and host line service in which a connection is set up without any need for addressing. When the called party is busy, an automatic retry may be invoked in the circuit mode, and a camp-on feature provides the equivalent capability in the packet mode. Other features are a collective number group, like a rotary, in which a single number is assigned to a series of terminals or computer ports, closed subscriber groups, and reverse charging.

A single subscriber termination of Infoswitch is able to operate in either the circuit or packet mode. Call setup requires less than 1 sec in both the circuit-switching and packet-switching modes. All network signaling utilizes the packet mode. During data transmission, each switch causes a delay of one octet in the circuit mode and approximately 150 msec in the packet mode.

14.3.4   Telenet

GTE Telenet is the first public packet-switching network in the United States, having begun operation in 1975 [ROBE 75, ROBE 77]. It provides a virtual circuit service primarily for terminal-to-host communications, with local dial-in access available in 81 cities within the United States in mid-1978 (see Fig. 14.7). Computers connected to Telenet are also accessible by users in 18 countries as of 1978, including Canada, Mexico, and most Western European countries. Except for Canada, this international service is initially limited to access to U.S. computers from overseas terminals.

Initially, Telenet used Prime 200 minicomputers as the packet-switching nodes. These are similar to the Honeywell H-516's and H-316's used in ARPANET, but were a more cost-effective choice at the time of the initial Telenet design. The topology of Telenet is a two-level hierarchy: a top-level net of packet-switching nodes, with time-division multiplexers used to extend service to other cities. The top-level network, which consisted of eight nodes in 1978, has a high connectivity of four, resulting in high reliability and low delay. Each node is itself a highly interconnected configuration of on average seven packet-switching minicomputers.

In 1977, Telenet began installing a new family of packet-switching nodes, called Telenet Processors (TPs) [NEWP 77, OPDE 78, WEIR 80]. Developed by Digital Communications Corporation in conjunction with Telenet, the new series is based on an expandable multimicroprocessor architecture, and can be configured as host or terminal interfacing devices as well as packet switches. Each microprocessor, a MOS Technology 6502A, has its own local memory as well as access to a main memory to facilitate the exchange of information. The microprocessors are used both in line processing units (LPUs), which handle between four and eight communications lines, and in central processing units (CPUs), which are used to control the entire system. A TP may contain up to 60 LPUs and 2 CPUs. A dual bus architecture with dual memory banks is provided to achieve the desired redundancy goals. An arbitrator controls access to the memory from either bus.

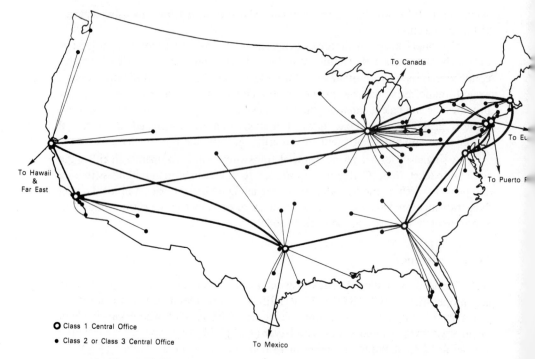

To Canada

To Eu

To Hawaii
&
Far East

To Puerto R

○ Class 1 Central Office

● Class 2 or Class 3 Central Office

To Mexico

Figure 14.7. Telenet network. (Courtesy of GTE Telenet Communications
Corporation.)

A variety of computer interfacing options are available. For packet mode
interfaces, X.25 is gradually replacing the original Telenet host interface, from which
it is descended [TELE 75A]. X.25 host software interfaces available include those for
IBM 360/370 systems, Univac 1100 Series systems, and PDP 11s operating under
RSX 11M. The IBM 360/370 package is installed in the 3704/3705 communication
controller; the Univac package is installed in the mainframe; the PDP 11 package is
implemented as a device driver under the RSX 11 operating system. All allow access
to the host from all terminals supported on the network. The PDP 11 interface also
supports host-initiated connections .

A terminal emulation host interface is also available, using a Telenet Access
Controller (TAC) at the packet-switch site, which makes the network appear to a host
as a number of asynchronous terminals [OPDE 76]. A multiplexer is usually located
at the host site to multiplex the separate connections between the host and the switch.
The newer TP 2200 provides a more efficient terminal emulation host interface. It is
located at the host site and supports up to 480 asynchronous host ports at speeds from
75 to 9600 bps, while using X.25 to communicate with the Telenet packet switch. The
smaller TP 1000 supports up to 14 asynchronous host ports operating at speeds of 75
to 300 bps. Alternatively, the TP 1000 can be used to concentrate a few asynchronous

terminals at a user's remote location and provide an error-controlled link to the network.

Terminal interfaces are supported for asynchronous terminals at speeds up to 1200 bps using dial-in facilities. Parameters are used to control the operation of each terminal port [TELE 75B]. The parameters are a superset of those specified for the packet assembler/disassembler (PAD) in CCITT Recommendations X.3, X.28, and X.29. Multiplexers or TP 1000s are used to provide terminal access in cities not served by a packet switch.

Most use of the network is to obtain economical terminal access to centralized computer systems. Subscribers are approximately equally divided between two general classes: corporations and government agencies, which utilize the network for intraorganization data applications; and commercial data processing and data-base service firms, which utilize the network to provide nationwide and international terminal access to computer-based services offered to their own customers [ROTH 78]. Closed user groups are supported.

The average end-to-end delay through the network is 160 ms. The unavailability seen by hosts on single access lines is reported as averaging 0.17%. The average unavailability of a switch port is less than 0.02%.

14.3.5 Transpac

Transpac is a public packet-switching network in France which came into operation early in 1979 [BLEV 80, DANE 76, GUIL 78, PICA 80]. It is being developed by the French company SESA. Research in packet switching has been conducted by the French PTT since 1971, involving the development of an experimental network called RCP (Réseau à Commutation de Paquets), which has been in operation since 1975 [BACH 76].

The initial Transpac network was planned to consist of 12 packet-switching nodes, with an additional 13 access points for low-speed terminals, equipped with time-division multiplexers (see Fig. 14.8). These numbers are expected to double by 1980.

Transpac offers a virtual circuit service, including both permanent and switched virtual circuits as specified by CCITT Recommendation X.25. At subscription time or at each virtual call setup, the subscriber can select reverse call charging, maximum throughput category, and adherence to a closed user group.

The packet-switching nodes comprise two kinds of hardware components: control units and switching modules. The control units are CII MITRA 125 minicomputers which perform call setup and clearing, and node control. The switching modules, CP 50 units from TRT, a subsidiary of Philips, are special-purpose processors using Intel 8080 microprocessors for line-handling and packet store-and-forwarding [KELL 78]. A node is designed to include two control units and up to 32 switching modules, which communicate with each other by means of a data bus. For high reliability, the node includes a standby control unit and data bus, as well as duplicates for most hardware components of the switching modules. The throughput

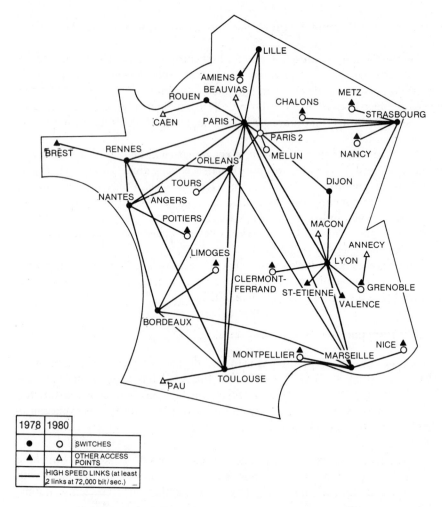

1978	1980	
●	○	SWITCHES
▲	△	OTHER ACCESS POINTS
—		HIGH SPEED LINKS (at least 2 links at 72,000 bit/sec.)

Figure 14.8. Transpac network. (Courtesy of Transpac.)

of the initial nodes will vary from 100 to 500 kbps, with possible expansion up to several Mbps. Additional minicomputers are used for network supervision and accounting in a few local control points, and in a national network management center. The initial configuration has each node connected to three other nodes. Moreover, internode trunks consist of at least two independent 72-kbps lines following different physical routes, but controlled on a shared basis by a multiline procedure [JAME 78]. Several lines in parallel operate as a single data link; loss of some of the lines reduces throughput but does not cause loss of data.

Transpac employs fixed routing per call. That is, at the establishment of a virtual circuit, an appropriate route is chosen through the nodes according to a routing algorithm involving the load of different routes. Then all the packets involved in that virtual circuit take the same route through the network. The multiline procedure means that failure of a line does not require setup of a new route. Packets are limited to a maximum length of two packet sizes, 32 bytes or 128 bytes, depending on the throughput category selected.

Host computers are interfaced to Transpac in accordance with CCITT Recommendation X.25 for packet mode interfaces. Initially, Transpac will use the X.25 level 2 original Link Access Protocol (LAP A) which is not fully consistent with HDLC. Asynchronous terminal access is available using the packet assembler/disassembler (PAD) function in accordance with CCITT Recommendations X.3, X.28, and X.29. Host access circuits may operate up to 48 kbps; terminal access circuits are supported up to 1200 bps for dedicated circuits and 300 bps for dial-in ports.

Transpac has defined an end-to-end message protocol (or transport protocol) for use on top of X.25 [BERT 78A, B; PONC 78]. The end-to-end message protocol provides users (programs or terminals) with the following services: addressing of users, connection between users, and communication between users. Addressing users (processes or terminals) is a hierarchical function consisting of two levels: the Transpac subscriber number of the equipment connected to the network; and the address of the user internal to the subscriber. Connection between users is effected by setting up a virtual circuit using the X.25 call establishment and disconnection procedures. Communication between users is completely based on the virtual circuit mechanism offered by X.25, and includes fragmentation/reassembly, error control, flow control, and interrupt facilities. Since users may transmit messages that exceed the packet size, these are fragmented before transmission to Transpac and reassembled on receipt, making use of the More Data indicator in X.25 to identify the end of a message. End-to-end error control is optional, and may be selected when the connection is established, depending on the nature of the application. Flow control and transmission of interrupts are based on the mechanisms in X.25.

Two virtual terminal protocols using the end-to-end message protocol have also been defined. One is for screen-type interactive terminals; the other is for remote batch terminals. Both have been implemented using a SFENA-DSI CO/ORDINATEUR 500 minicomputer as a front end to IBM 370 systems. The front end maps the virtual terminal protocols so as to emulate IBM 3270 and IBM remote batch terminals.

Transpac is expecting both interactive and remote batch users. The service availability announced for Transpac, at the customer port on a node, is over 99.99%.

14.3.6   TYMNET

TYMNET[1] is a communications network which was originally designed by Tymshare to provide customer access to its own time-sharing service, beginning in 1971 [KOPF 77, RADW 80, RIND 76, TYME 71]. Under the joint-usage provision allowed by the FCC, capacity on the network was shared with other organizations. Since 1976, TYMNET has been a value-added network providing a public data communications

---

[1]TYMNET is a registered trademark of TYMSHARE Inc.

service, and now offers international access from Canada and most Western European countries (see Fig. 14.9).

TYMNET provides a switched virtual circuit service using a form of packet switching. However, TYMNET has some significant differences from other conventional packet-switched networks. In particular, a packet transmitted between adjacent nodes may contain data belonging to several virtual circuits.

The original nodes were Varian 620I minicomputers. The network has evolved to include the Varian 620L/100 and the Varian 73. In 1978, by which time the network had grown to about 300 nodes, a microprocessor based node, the TYMNET II "engine" was introduced [TYME 78]. There are several types of node, each serving different functions. One type is the TYMSAT, used to interface low-speed and remote batch terminals. A second type is the base, which contains the interfaces to TYM-

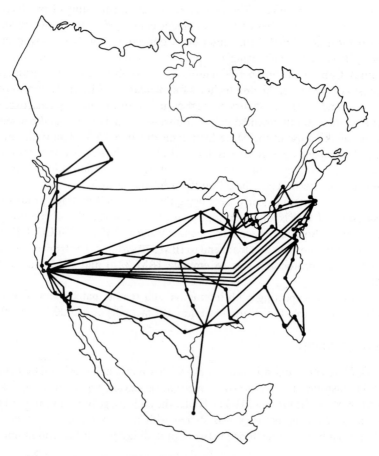

Figure 14.9. TYMNET network. (Courtesy of TYMSHARE.)

SHARE's host computers. A third type is the TYMCOM, used to interface to a broader variety of hosts.

The nodes are interconnected by leased voice-grade lines, operating at data rates of 2400 to 9600 bps. The nodes are fairly highly interconnected, with up to 16 internode trunks connected to a node. The average virtual circuit traverses about three internodal links.

TYMNET uses a fixed routing per call with centralized control [RIND 77]. When a terminal user wishes to establish a connection to a host, the request is forwarded to a network supervisor which assigns an optimal path to connect the terminal to the desired host. The optimal path is a function of the line speed between nodes, the number of links to be traversed, and the loading of each link. The nodes along the selected path are notified of the virtual circuit. Connections are usually completed in 2 to 7 sec. The supervisor runs in an Interdata 7/32.

A hierarchy of four supervisors are available, each capable of taking over if the active supervisor fails. It takes about 2.5 min. for the replacement supervisor to determine the current topology of the network and status of virtual circuits, by querying each node in turn. Existing virtual circuits are not effected, but new virtual circuits cannot be established during the takeover period, which occurs only once a week on average.

Each internode line is capable of supporting a fixed number of channels. When a route is established by the supervisor, one channel on each link traversed is assigned to the virtual circuit. Exclusive use of that channel, and of buffers at each end, are reserved for the duration of the circuit. About 40 virtual circuits for low-speed terminals may be carried on one 2400-bps line. The channels are serviced in a round-robin fashion, and data belonging to several channels may be combined in one physical packet for transmission to the next node. Depending on the size of the logical records being transmitted, data from 1 to 20 channels may be combined in one packet, the maximum size of which is 528 bits. A node-to-node flow control scheme called "backpressure" is used, in which each node informs its neighbor nodes every half-second on which channel to permit data to flow. If a buffer exceeds some threshold, the node informs the neighbor node or host to stop sending data on that path until further notice. No end-to-end flow control is provided, but if, for example, the pipeline from a host to a terminal fills up, the backpressure could propagate all along the path from the terminal to the host. No end-to-end acknowledgment is provided in the network itself. The techniques above all serve to minimize the line overhead consumed by routing information, framing characters, flow control, acknowledgments, and so on [KOPF 77, RIND 76].

Host interfaces are of three kinds. The simplest is an asynchronous interface where the network appears as a bank of asynchronous terminal ports. There is a synchronous interface using bisync, with software in the host front end to make the network appear to the host as asynchronous terminals. Interfaces in which the host software is modified to know about the network are used mainly with Tymshare hosts. Terminal interfaces supported by the TYMSAT include asynchronous terminals from 110 to 1200 bps, and synchronous terminals of the 2780 and 3780 variety.

TYMNET was designed primarily as a terminal-to-host network. In addition to customer's computers, TYMSHARE's XDS-940, PDP-10, and IBM 370 computers are connected to the network. Host-to-host connections and host-to-terminal connections (dial out) are also possible.

14.4   PRIVATE COMPUTER NETWORKS

Private computer networks are described in this section; they often consist of more than simply a data communications service. This category includes resource-sharing networks, such as ARPANET, designed to facilitate the sharing of host resources, in which the data communications is just one component. It also includes mission-oriented networks designed for a specific application, such as EURONET. Characteristics of the networks are compared in Tab. 14.2.

14.4.1   ARPANET

The best known and most documented network is the ARPANET. It was originally built to demonstrate the concept of packet switching and to provide a mechanism for the sharing of expensive and specialized computer facilities at ARPA-sponsored research sites around the country [ROBE 70, ROBE 73].

The initial network was implemented in 1969-70 and an effective resource sharing service began in 1971. The network grew rapidly over the next few years to about 60 nodes; in recent years it has expanded to about 100 nodes (see Fig. 14.10). By 1975, the network had evolved from a research and development emphasis to an operational service, and responsibility for its operation was transferred to the Defense Communications Agency.

The ARPANET is intended to be used solely for the conduct of or in support of official U.S. government business. It is used for data communications and resource sharing by Department of Defense (DoD) users, by non-DoD government agencies, and by contractors sponsored by government agencies [DCA 78]. The network spans the United States and extends to Hawaii, Norway, and England.

In addition to its operational use as a data communications service, the network is also employed in various ARPA-sponsored research projects. High-level protocols are being developed to link specific applications across a resource-sharing network. Examples include a network graphics protocol and a network voice protocol [SPRO 78.]

The ARPANET has been interconnected with other types of packet networks, including satellite networks, packet radio networks, and local area networks [JACO 77, JACO 78, KAHN 78, CLAR 78]. The Transmission Control Protocol (TCP) has been developed as a host-to-host protocol for use across these different networks in conjunction with the Internet Protocol [DARP 80A, B].

ARPANET is the prototypical packet-switching system, providing fundamen-

Table 14.2. *Private Computer Networks.*

	ARPANET	AUTODIN II	CYCLADES	EIN	EURONET	SITA
				Network		
Country	U.S.	U.S.	France	Europe	Europe	Worldwide
Date operational	1971	1981	1975	1976	1979	1969
Switching technique	Packet	Packet	Packet	Packet	Packet	Message
Type of service	Virtual circuit	Datagram	Datagram	Datagram	Virtual circuit	Message switched
Node processor	Honeywell 316/516, Pluribus	DEC PDP-11/70	CII MITRA 15	CII MITRA 15	CII MITRA 125 CP 50	Philips DS-714, Univac 418
Number of nodes	60	8	7	5	4	9
Cities served	25	?	?	5	9	2000 terminals
Trunk speed	50 kbps	56 kbps	?	9.6 kbps	48 kbps	9.6 kbps
Routing	Adaptive	Adaptive	Adaptive	Adaptive	Fixed	Fixed
Packet size (bits)	1008	5300	?	?	1024	1920
Host interface	Nonstandard "1822"	Nonstandard "SIP"	Terminal emulation	X.25		Bisync
Terminal interface	Asynchronous	Asynchronous	Asynchronous, synchronous	Asynchronous, synchronous	Asynchronous	Polling

157

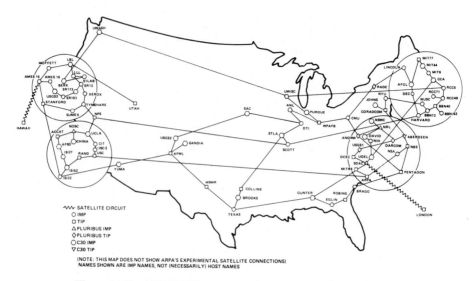

SATELLITE CIRCUIT
IMP
TIP
PLURIBUS IMP
PLURIBUS TIP
C30 IMP
C30 TIP

(NOTE: THIS MAP DOES NOT SHOW ARPA'S EXPERIMENTAL SATELLITE CONNECTIONS)
NAMES SHOWN ARE IMP NAMES, NOT (NECESSARILY) HOST NAMES

Figure 14.10. ARPANET geographic map, April 1982. (Courtesy of Bolt, Beranek and Newman, Inc.)

tally a virtual circuit service. There is an optional datagram service which is used by specific research applications.

The packet-switching nodes, known as Interface Message Processors (IMPs), were originally Honeywell 516 and 316 minicomputers [HEAR 70, MCQU 72]. Each of these IMPs can support up to four hosts and up to four trunk lines to other IMPs (but not more than seven hosts plus lines). About half of the nodes are Terminal Interface Processors (TIPs), originally a Honeywell 316 with a multiline controller, which can accommodate up to three hosts and 63 terminals [ORNS 72]. A few of the nodes are Pluribus IMPs, a multiprocessor system designed for higher throughput capacity, modularity in size, and redundancy for improved reliability [HEAR 73, ORNS 75]. Beginning in 1981, the nodes are being replaced by BBN C/30 switches.

The nodes are interconnected by 50-kbps leased lines. Satellite circuits are used for the overseas links. Each node is connected to a minimum of two other nodes for reliability; some nodes are connected to three or four other nodes. The node-to-node protocol uses a 24-bit checksum.

ARPANET employs a distributed adaptive routing algorithm [MCQU 77]. Under the original routing algorithm, in use until 1979, each node maintained a table used to determine the output line on which to transmit a packet for each possible destination. A packet was directed along the path for which the total estimated transit time to the destination was smallest. The routing table was updated every two-thirds of a second based on information exchanged by neighboring IMPs. In the new algorithm, each node maintains a data base describing the delay on each network line [MCQU 79]. Using this data base, each node computes the minimum delay path to all other nodes using an algorithm called *shortest path first.* Each node periodically measures the delay along its outgoing lines and broadcasts this information to all other nodes in the network for use in updating the data bases.

A message sent from a host to an IMP may be up to 8095 bits in length. Within the network, the message is split into packets, each up to 1008 bits long, which are routed independently through the network, possibly by different routes. At the destination node, the packets are reassembled to form the original message before it is transmitted to the destination host. This distinction of message and packet size occurs only in ARPANET and packet-switching networks closely derived from it. The rationale for the two sizes is that the larger message size reduces the overhead on hosts, whereas the smaller packet size is needed for low delay within the network [CROW 75, MCQU 75]. However, most other packet-switching networks have adopted a single maximum packet size for use both from host to node and within the network; the most common maximum packet size is about 2000 bits.

Most hosts are located within 2000 feet of the IMP and are connected by a cable using an asynchronous bit-serial interface (ABSI), sometimes referred to as an 1822 interface for the Bolt Beranek and Newman report, which contains the specifications [BBN 78]. Each bit is passed across the interface via a Ready For Next Bit/There's Your Bit handshake procedure. This technique permits the bit rate to adjust to the speed and word length of a variety of hosts; the interface typically operates at 100 kbps. A host connected to an IMP by a communications line and modems requires a Very Distant Host (VDH) interface which provides error checking. This has been replaced by the HDLC Distant Host (HDH) interface using HDLC error checking.

Terminals connected to the TIP may be either hard-wired or dial-in. The TIP supports primarily asynchronous terminals, and performs the packetizing, permitting terminals to access hosts elsewhere on the network.

ARPANET has served as the forerunner for a variety of host-level services and the protocols needed to support them. Most capabilities are built on top of the standard host-to-host protocol, which provides interprocess communication between processes in different computers. The implementation of the host-to-host protocol in a host is known as a Network Control Program (NCP) [CARR 70, FEIN 78]. The most widely used network capability is Telnet (for Telecommunications Network), which permits terminals connected to a host or TIP to access remote hosts [DAVI 77]. Other widely implemented network capabilities are the file transfer protocol and network mail. Current research-oriented use of the network includes packetized voice and interconnection with other networks, both packet switching as well as satellite, packet radio, and local cable-based networks.

The ARPA Network Control Center (NCC), operated by Bolt Beranek and Newman in Cambridge, Massachusetts has evolved over the years into a sophisticated capability for maintaining the nationwide IMP communications subnetwork from a central location with very high reliability. Functions of the NCC include new software distribution over the network, remote software diagnosis, remote fault diagnosis of hardware, and collection of traffic statistics [MCKE 75].

ARPANET has been subject to extensive performance measurement [KLEI

76, KLEI 77]. The original design goal of less then one-half second end-to-end delay has been met. The throughput rate for file transfers ranges between 8 and 20 kbps, depending on the number of nodes between the two hosts [WOOD 75].

14.4.2 AUTODIN II

AUTODIN II is a packet-switching network developed by the Defense Communications Agency to meet the data communications needs of the U.S. Department of Defense [STAT 77]. The network provides long-distance data communications within the United States for computer systems supporting diverse defense applications such as command and control, logistics, and personnel. The main objective of the network is to provide more economical service for terminal-to-computer and computer-to-computer communications than would occur with the use of separate dedicated networks for each of more than 40 application systems. The 4-node network became operational in 1981. However, in 1982 it was announced that AUTODIN II would be terminated and an ARPANET-based network used instead.

The packet-switched network provides a datagram service, in which each packet entered into the network is handled independently of any other. Packets are not necessarily delivered in the sequence in which they were entered. Interfacing devices at subscriber host locations can be used to provide a virtual circuit service by performing sequencing and other end-to-end control functions. An element of the packet-switching node, the terminal access controller, provides interface functions for terminals.

The network was planned to consist of eight packet-switching nodes within the United States (see Fig. 14.11). Each node comprises a cluster of DEC PDP 11/70 computers organized in three main elements: switch control module, terminal access controller, and line control modules. The basic packet-switching function is performed by the switch control module which consists of one or more PDP 11/70s. The interfacing of terminals is performed by the terminal access controller (TAC), which also consists of one or more PDP 11/70s. Line protocol handling and demultiplexing functions are performed by the line control modules, which consist of DEC line termination units and KMC-11 programmable microprocessors. Each node includes a standby processor which is capable of taking over for any failed element. The nodes are modularly expandable, with a throughput of from 0.5 to 2.5 Mbps.

The packet-switching nodes are highly interconnected, initially using 56-kbps digital circuits. The average number of links traversed from source node to destination node is 1.2. Packets are of variable size, up to a maximum of about 5300 bits.

Host computers are attached to the network by a datagram interface provided by a packet-mode protocol known as the Segment Interface Protocol (SIP) [SEVC 77]. A modified version of the Advanced Data Communications Control Procedures (ADCCP) link protocol with a 32-bit CRC is used. ADCCP is the American National Standards Institute (ANSI) equivalent of HDLC [ANSI 79]. Several options are available for implementing the host interface. A Multiple Channel Control Unit (MCCU) at the host site implements the SIP and other higher-level protocols in a

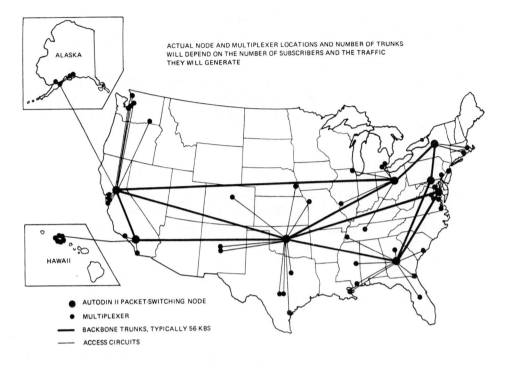

ACTUAL NODE AND MULTIPLEXER LOCATIONS AND NUMBER OF TRUNKS
WILL DEPEND ON THE NUMBER OF SUBSCRIBERS AND THE TRAFFIC
THEY WILL GENERATE

ALASKA

HAWAII

● AUTODIN II PACKET-SWITCHING NODE
• MULTIPLEXER
── BACKBONE TRUNKS, TYPICALLY 56 KBS
── ACCESS CIRCUITS

Figure 14.11. Representative AUTODIN II configuration. (Courtesy of the Defense Communications Agency.)

DEC PDP 11/34 and emulates devices known to the host, usually asynchronous terminals. Alternatively, the SIP can be implemented in the host or its communications front end. Virtual circuits are established and managed according to a Transmission Control Protocol (TCP), which is implemented in the TAC, MCCU, or directly in the host. TCP provides end-to-end error control, acknowledgments, and flow control, as well as the capability for process-to-process communications. TCP has been adopted as a standard host-to-host protocol for all Department of Defense packet-switching networks [DARP 80A].

The terminal access controller portion of the node provides interfaces for various asynchronous and synchronous terminals, connected via dial-up or dedicated lines. A terminal-to-host protocol (THP) is used to permit various types of terminals to communicate with diverse hosts. The THP is based on the concept of a network virtual terminal with negotiated options.

The network will support terminal-to-computer, computer-to-computer, and computer-to-terminal traffic. Since AUTODIN II will carry classified traffic at various security levels, numerous techniques are employed to ensure that subscriber data are not compromised [BERK 77]. Link encryption is used on all internode trunks and on access circuits from classified subscribers. The architecture of the packet-switching node employs security kernel technology based on the "MITRE model" to assure that the security requirements are met by the node software [BELL 73].

The performance specification for AUTODIN II indicates that a packet carrying interactive traffic will be delivered with an average delay of one-tenth of a second. For bulk computer-to-computer traffic, a throughput rate of 75% of the lower access circuit speed will be attainable. The availability of communications between a pair of subscribers will be 99% for single-homed subscribers. For dual-homed subscribers (i.e. subscribers connected to two nodes), the availability will be 99.95%.

14.4.3 CYCLADES

CYCLADES is a packet-switching network linking heterogeneous computers in universities and research centers in France (see Fig. 14.12). Its main objective has been to promote and coordinate research in heterogeneous computer networks. Since 1975, CYCLADES has provided an operational service, and is used by universities and government [POUZ 73, POUZ 75, ZIMM 77].

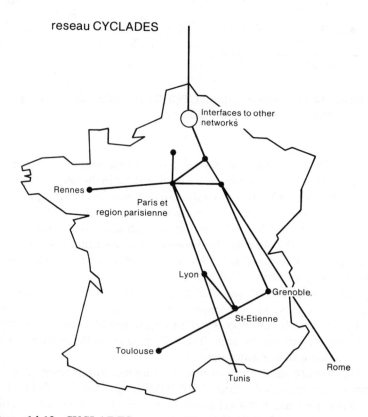

Figure 14.12. CYCLADES network. (Courtesy of European Informatics Network.)

The packet-switching system, called CIGALE, provides its users with a datagram service. An end-to-end transport protocol is implemented in host computers and provides an interprocess communication facility called the transport service [ZIMM 75].

The packet-switching nodes of CIGALE are CII MITRA 15 minicomputers. The network consists of seven nodes connected in a distributed topology. CIGALE provides no end-to-end flow control, error control, or sequencing. CIGALE uses a combination of logical, hierarchical, and general addressing. A hierarchical address space is used whereby a host belongs to the region indicated by its name. However, within that region, a logical address is used which does not correspond to a physical node or port. General addresses are used for those exceptions for which a regional address is unacceptable.

Adaptive routing is performed in CIGALE based on the regular exchange of routing information between the nodes.

Host interfaces are standard binary synchronous line control procedures. This has enabled hosts to be connected without any changes in existing hardware and operating system.

Terminals are not connected directly to the packet-switching nodes. However, a terminal concentrator or minihost has been developed based on the same MITRA 15 minicomputer.

Services available on CYCLADES include remote access to time-sharing services, remote batch, and file transfer. Efforts are under way to extend terminal access from asynchronous terminals to synchronous terminals with such features as formatted screen and protected zones.

14.4.4 DECnet

DECnet is the collective name for the set of software products which extend various Digital Equipment Corporation (DEC) operating systems so they may be interconnected with each other to form computer networks. DECnet is included in this survey because it represents a general network architecture; a specific example of a network using DECnet is given at the end of this section. DECnet implementations across various Digital computer systems conform to a framework defined in the Digital Network Architecture (DNA). The objective of DECnet is to provide a modular and layered set of network software components which can be used to configure networks of Digital computers for remote terminal communication, resource sharing, and distributed processing [WECK 76A, B; WECK 80; CONA 76].

DECnet software operates across the range of DEC hardware and operating systems, including PDP-11 systems running under RT, RSX-11S, RSX-11M, RSX-11D, and RSTS/E operating systems, PDP-10 and DEC system-10 systems running under TOPS-10 operating systems, and PDP-8 systems running under RTS/8 operating system. Each system is considered a node within DECnet, irrespective of whether it functions as a host executing application programs, a concentrator controlling terminals, or switch routing messages, or any combination thereof. DECnet systems can be configured using simple point-to-point communications, or in distributed topologies with switching nodes much like a packet-switching network. Irrespective of the configuration, the DECnet software provides a virtual circuit service which can be used by various applications services.

DNA consists primarily of three layers of communications protocols. The functional interfaces between the protocols are well defined, and each protocol implementation is modular enabling subsets to be used where appropriate. This layering also minimizes the effort needed to connect to other networks. The three layers of protocol are the data link control protocol, the logical link and routing protocol, and application protocols.

The data link control protocol uses the Digital Data Communications Message Protocol (DDCMP). DDCMP provides error control for the reliable transmission of blocks of data over a communication link. DDCMP is similar conceptually to HDLC, except that it is byte oriented whereas HDLC is bit oriented. DDCMP can also be used over parallel links.

The next layer is the Network Services Protocol (NSP). It provides a general mechanism for process-to-process dialogue by establishing a logical link between processes, controlling the data flow on the link, and managing the disconnection of the link. The process-to-process communication enables communication between objects such as terminals or files represented by processes. NSP provides for connection to specific processes or to generic function processes representing a service. On each logical link, NSP guarantees delivery of data, guarantees message sequencing, and provides a flow control mechanism to prevent buffer deadlocks. Thus NSP is analogous to the host-to-host protocols used on packet-switching networks. NSP also has a single message transfer service, analogous to a datagram facility.

The routing function is also performed by NSP, directing messages from source node to destination node. The routing algorithm itself is separate from NSP and resides in a user-level process in each node for ease of change.

The application layer within DNA provides various user or function specific services in a location-independent fashion. One such protocol is the Data Access Protocol (DAP) for obtaining I/O device and file services within the network [PASS 77]. DAP enables files to be accessed by the user remotely in the same way that they are accessed locally. It provides both access of records in remote files, as well as the transfer of files. To permit file access independent of the characteristics of each file system in a heterogeneous network, files and devices are accessed via common generic functions which are translated locally into functions specific to each system.

An example of a network employing DECnet is a service-order system developed by a telephone company, Saskatchewan Telecommunications [HOCK 78, LOVE 79]. The network is a star configuration with a PDP-11/70 network controller in the Regina headquarters and PDP-11/34s in Regina and each of seven remote district offices. All computers use the DEC RSX-11M real-time operating system. The system's DECnet software facilitates file transfer, data transfer, and interprocessor communications. It also supports downline loading. Application software and maintenance routines are downline loaded from the network controller site to the district computers. District disk files of service orders are transferred to the headquarters in Regina for further processing at the end of each working day. A district office also has access to peripherals and files at the network controller or at other district offices.

14.4.5 European Informatics Network

The European Informatics Network (EIN) was established by an international agreement in 1971 [BARB 74]. It is a research network with the objectives of facilitating research in computer networking, permitting resource sharing between research centers, and providing a model for public data networks. There are 11 signatories to the agreement: France, Germany, Italy, Netherlands, Norway, Portugal, Sweden, Switzerland, United Kingdom, Yugoslavia, and Euratom [EIN 78].

All signatories contribute equally to a common fund that has covered the development of a packet-switching node and management of the project [BARB 76]. The packet-switching node was developed by an international consortium headed by Logica of the United Kingdom and SESA of France. Signatories may elect to purchase, install, and operate a packet-switching node. Five signatories have done so, and a five-node packet-switching network has been in operation since 1976 with nodes in France, Italy, Switzerland, the United Kingdom, and at Euratom. The respective locations of the nodes are the Institute de Recherche d'Informatique et d'Automatique (IRIA) near Paris, the Centro Rete Europea di Informatica (CREI) in Milan, the Eidgenossische Technische Hochschule in Zurich, the National Physical Laboratory (NPL) near London, and the European Communities Joint Research Center (JRC) at Ispra, Italy. Several secondary centers are attached to packet-switching nodes by leased lines, and associated centers may access the network through the public switched telephone networks (see Fig. 14.13).

EIN employs packet switching and provides a datagram service between subscriber computers. Other features, such as packet sequencing and delivery confirmation, are optional. The nodes are CII Mitra 15 minicomputers [PONC 76]. The nodes form a distributed network, with six 9600-bps leased lines interconnecting the five nodes. An adaptive routing algorithm is used. Initially, each node functioned as a partial network control center, but a separate network control center has subsequently been added at NPL [BARB 78B].

Most host computers are interfaced to the nodes by various front-end minicomputers which implement an end-to-end protocol known as the transport station protocol. The transport station provides a choice of two levels of service: a datagram service known as *lettergram mode*, and a virtual circuit service known as *liaison mode*. Terminals are not connected directly to the nodes, but must access the network via host computers or the interfacing minicomputers. Experimentation is taking place with a virtual terminal protocol which can support either scroll-mode terminals or page-oriented terminals.

When Euronet became operational, it replaced the communications subnetwork of EIN. A multimicroprocessor adaptor was developed to be used between an

Figure 14.13. EIN network. (Courtesy of European Informatics Network.)

existing EIN subscriber or an existing EIN node, and an X.25 public network [ANDR 80, BARB 78A]. The EIN project ended in 1980.

14.4.6 Euronet

Euronet is a packet-switched network established by the Commission of the European Economic Community (EEC) to enable terminals located in the nine member countries to gain access to data bases holding scientific, technical, and socioeconomic information [DAVI 75, DAVI 78, KELL 78, KELL 80]. The packet-switched network is being provided jointly by the nine Postal Telephone and Telegraph (PTT) administrations of the EEC countries. The French PTT, acting on behalf of the EEC PTTs, contracted for the development and supply of the network with a multinational consortium of companies, one from each EEC country, headed by SESA of France and Logica of the United Kingdom. The packet switches are based on those used in Transpac, which is also being developed by SESA.

The initial network, opened in 1979, consists of four packet-switching nodes, in London, Frankfurt, Paris, and Rome. Remote-access facilities are provided by multiplexers in Amsterdam, Brussels, Copenhagen, Dublin, and Luxembourg. A Network Management Center is located in London (see Fig. 14.14).

Euronet is a private network in that it is being established on behalf of the EEC Commission, which will determine the hosts to be connected to the network. However, terminal access is expected to be publicly available to any user who makes an access agreement with an individual PTT. Although initially the network will cater solely to the needs of the EEC Commission, it is expected that subsequently it will be

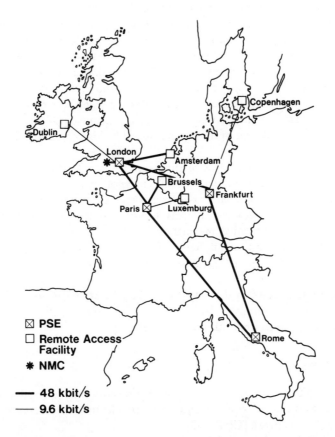

Figure 14.14. Euronet. (Courtesy of the British Post Office.)

used by the PTTs to carry other types of traffic for other users. The network may evolve to become the basis for a European public data network linking national networks being developed by the individual PTTs.

Euronet will provide a virtual circuit service. Both permanent virtual circuits and virtual calls will be offered.

The packet-switching nodes are based on the hardware and software being developed for Transpac, using the Mitra 125 control units and CP50 switching modules. Most components of the node are duplicated for reliability. The same fixed routing system is used as in Transpac. Internode trunks operate at 48 kbps, with multiplexers connected via 9600-bps circuits.

Host computers use CCITT Recommendation X.25 with leased circuits at data rates from 2400 bps to 48 kbps. Link access protocol version LAP A is used initially. Asynchronous terminal access is available over leased circuits up to 1200 bps and via the public switched telephone network up to 300 bps. Terminal access is provided by a packet assembler/disassembler facility in the packet-switching nodes according to CCITT Recommendations X.3, X.28, and X.29.

These protocols have been extended to include a facility known as Network User Identification (NUI). Terminals using the public switched telephone network to access Euronet are required to provide an NUI code or password, which is used for charging purposes for the Euronet virtual call. Access to the network for both hosts and terminals is provided by national public data networks as soon as they exist.

Announced tariffs consist of a volume charge of 10 French francs (about U.S. $2.25) per kilosegment independent of distance (one segment is 64 octets), and a duration charge based on the data rate of the calling terminal [DAVI 78]. National access charges for leased lines or dial-up access will be in accordance with national practice.

It is expected that initially the predominant traffic will be calls originated by terminals to access host computers, usually in another country. Some 27 host computers offering about 100 data bases have been identified for connection to the network. Data bases will cover such areas as agriculture, environment, medicine, space, economics, and legislative information.

The initial configuration will have about 55 X.25 host ports and about 300 terminal ports, of which about 225 will be dial-up. The network should have a 99.7% availability.

In the future, access to the network is likely to expand to other European countries outside the community. Interconnection with public data networks in the United States and Canada may also be expected.

14.4.7 SITA

SITA (Société Internationale de Télécommunications Aéronautiques) is a nonprofit cooperative organization of over 200 airlines. It provides to its members a worldwide message-switching network [CHRE 73].

The network comprises a high-level network of message switches and a collection of concentrators known as satellite processors (see Fig. 14.15). There are nine message switches, located in Amsterdam, Beirut, Frankfurt, Hong Kong, London, Madrid, New York, Paris, and Rome. These are highly interconnected by 9600-bps leased circuits. The maximum distance between any two nodes is three links. There are 24 satellite processors, each connected to one message switch by a 2400- or 4800-bps circuit.

The message switches are Philips DS-714 or Univac 418 computers. About 24 airline reservation computers are connected to the various message switches, by 2400-or 4800-bps circuits. The satellite processors are Raytheon 704/706, Raytheon RDS 500, or Thomson Houston 4020 Systems. They act as concentrators of airline teleprinter traffic and controllers of airline CRT terminals. About 2000 CRT terminals of various types are supported by polling procedures.

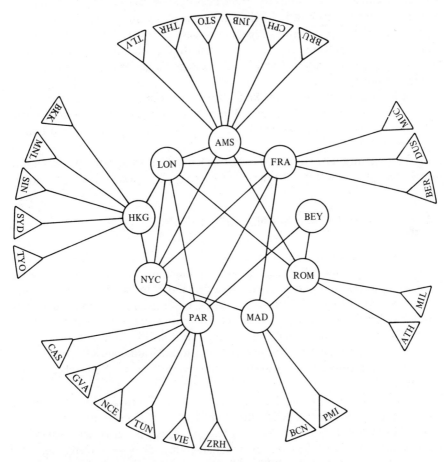

Figure 14.15. SITA automatic network (August 1977). Circle, high-level center (9); triangle, satellite processor or medium-level center (24). (Courtesy of SITA.)

The SITA network carries two main types of traffic: conversational and telegraphic. The *conversational traffic* (Type A) comprises queries/responses for reservations. A query is generated at a CRT in an airline office, transmitted to a satellite processor and sent through the network to the parent reservations computer. There the query is processed, a response is generated, and sent back to the CRT. The response time required for this transaction is 3 sec.

The *telegraphic traffic* (Type B) consists of administrative messages. These may be one-way single or multiaddressed messages, destined to and generated by airline teleprinters or computers. The transmission time requirement for these messages is on the order of several minutes. The network provides stringent security for such messages, guaranteeing against loss or duplication.

Messages entering a message-switching node are segmented into blocks of a maximum length of 240 characters. The blocks of a message are reassembled at the destination switch. Blocks are switched in core memory during transit through an intermediate node. For integrity, Type B messages are stored on drums at the source node until an acknowledgment is received from the destination node that they have been delivered. Reassembly of multiblock messages is performed on drums at the destination node.

A fixed routing scheme is used; all blocks between a pair of nodes follow the same path. All other nodes are informed when a node observes a change in the status of the links to which it is connected. Alternate fixed routes are selected according to preestablished priorities.

For high availability, each message switch includes a standby processor and duplicate drums. Downtime of a message switch is not to exceed 2 hours per month.

14.5   CURRENT STATUS AND FUTURE DIRECTIONS

Public packet-switching networks are now operational in many countries. The adoption of X.25 and subsequent recommendations by CCITT is facilitating the interconnection of these public networks. As demand from users has increased, most computer vendors have provided X.25 software as a standard part of their operating systems. A demand for X.25 software resulted in Europe from the growth of Euronet. In the United States, AT&T's initial announcement in 1978 of its Advanced Communications Service (ACS) led further credibility to X.25, although ACS was delayed and eventually replaced by the Advanced Information Systems/Net1, scheduled for introduction in 1983.

The research community both in Europe and the United States has continued on a separate path from the X.25 approach adopted by the carriers. The research community favors datagram services, whereas the carriers prefer virtual circuits. The broadening of X.25 in 1980 to encompass datagrams will not completely solve the problem, for it is likely to result in implementation of incompatible datagram and virtual circuit subsets. Continued refinement of the protocols can be expected to enhance their reliability and to improve performance.

The architecture of packet-switching systems is expected to evolve to a more hierarchical organization. Multimicroprocessor systems will be used increasingly as switching nodes to take advantage of the cost effectiveness of microprocessors, and the improved reliability offered by full redundancy of components [ROBE 77].

More sophisticated applications of computer networks can be expected to emerge. With the trend to distributed processing, the existence of the communications network will become transparent, and remote access to resources will become more commonplace, such as the remote file access provided by DECnet. Some observers predict that digitized voice will become a significant part of the traffic carried by packet-switching systems in the more distant future. Computer vendors will support increasing capabilities for networking between their own systems using their own network architectures and protocols. For a long time, computer-to-computer applications between heterogeneous systems, such as file transfer and electronic mail, have been limited to research communities, such as ARPANET. This is primarily due to the absence of higher level protocol standards. However, approval by ISO of protocol standards at the transport and session level is expected in 1982-83, and for various presentation level services such as file transfer by 1984. When these are widely implemented, by the late 1980's, open systems interconnection using computer networks will become widespread.

ACKNOWLEDGMENTS

The author is grateful to the representatives of the various networks surveyed for providing information on their respective networks. Thanks are also extended to Carla Cotterill for assistance in researching references, and to Cathy McDonald for preparation of the text.

REFERENCES

Introduction (Sec. 14.1)

BARA 64   Baran, P., et al., "On Distributed Communications," Rand Corporation Series of 11 reports, 1964.

DAVI 67   Davies, D. W., K. A. Bartlett, R. A. Scantlebury, and P. A. Wilkinson, "A Digital Communication Network for Computers Giving Rapid Response at Remote Terminals," *ACM Symp. Oper. Syst. Principles*, Gatlinburg, Tenn., October 1967.

EVER 57   Everett, R. R., C. A. Zraket, and H. D. Benington, "SAGE: A Data Processing System for Air Defense," *Eastern Joint Comput. Conf.*, 1957, pp. 148–155.

MARI 66   Marill, T., and L. G., Roberts, "Towards a Cooperative Network of Time-Shared Computers," *Proc. AFIPS Fall Joint Comput. Conf.*, 1966.

MCCA 78   McCalley, R. D. and K. J. Barrett, "Network Design Allows Diverse Gear Access to Host," *Data Commun.*, February 1978.

PAOL 75   Paoletti, L. M., "AUTODIN," in *Computer Communication Networks*, North-Holland, Amsterdam, 1975, pp. 345–372.

PETE 71   Peterson, J.J. and S.A. Veit, "Survey of Computer Networks," The MITRE Corporation, Washington Operations, MTR-357, September 1971.

ROBE 67   Roberts, L. G., "Multiple Computer Networks and Intercomputer Communication," *ACM Symp. Oper. Syst. Principles*, Gatlinburg, Tenn., October 1967.

ROBE 78   Roberts, L. G., "The Evolution of Packet Switching," *Proc. IEEE*, November 1978, pp. 1307–1313.

SCAN 69   Scantlebury, R. A., "A Model for the Local Area of a Data Communication Network—Objectives and Hardware Organization," *Proc. ACM Symp. Data Commun.*, October 1969.

WOOD 75   Wood, D.C., "A Survey of the Capabilities of 8 Packet Switching Networks," *Proc. NBS/IEEE Symp. Comput. Networks: Trends Appl.*, June 1975, pp. 1–7.

Remote-Access Networks (Sec. 14.2)

INFONET (Sec. 14.2.1)

COLL 76   Collard, J. C., P. A. Tenkhoff, "INFONET: The Evolution of a Network," *Proc. 3rd Int. Conf. Comput. Commun.*, Toronto, August 1976, pp. 261–267.

TENK 74   Tenkhoff, P. A., "The INFONET Remote Teleprocessing Communication Network—Design, Performance, and Operation," *Proc. Int. Conf. Comput. Commun.*, August 1974, pp. 401–412.

Navy Federal Credit Union (Sec. 14.2.3)

IBM 77   "IBM 3600 Finance Communication System Common Carrier Facility Specifications Guide," Ref GA272811-1, March 1977.

Public Data Networks (Sec. 14.3)

CCIT 81A   CCITT, "Recommendation X.25: Interface Between Data Terminal Equipment (DTE) and Data Circuit Terminating Equipment (DCE) for Terminals Operating in the Packet Mode on Public Data Networks," Yellow Book, Vol. VIII, International Telecommunications Union, Geneva, 1981.

CCIT 81B   CCITT, "Recommendation X.3: Packet Assembly/Disassembly Facility (PAD) in a Public Data Network," Yellow Book, Vol. VIII, International Telecommunications Union, Geneva, 1981.

CCIT 81C   CCITT, "Recommendation X.28: DTE/DCE Interface for a Start-Stop Mode Data Terminal Equipment Accessing the Packet Assembly/Disassembly Facility (PAD) in a Public Data Network Situated in the Same Country," Yellow Book, Vol. VIII, International Telecommunications Union, Geneva, 1981.

CCIT 81D   CCITT, "Recommendation X.29: Procedures for the Exchange of Control Information and User Data Between a Packet Assembly/Disassembly Facility (PAD) and a Packet Mode DTE or Another PAD," Yellow Book, Vol. VIII, International Telecommunications Union, Geneva, 1981.

CCIT 81E   CCITT, "Recommendation X.75: Terminal and Transit Call Control Procedures and Data Transfer System on International Circuits Between Packet-Switched Data Networks," Yellow Book, Vol. VIII, International Telecommunications Union, Geneva, 1981.

ISO 79   International Organization for Standardization, "Data Communication—High Level Data Link Control Procedures," IS3309, IS4335, IS6159, and IS6256, Geneva, 1979.

KELL 78   Kelly, P. T. F., "Public Packet Switched Data Networks, International Plans and Standards," *Proc. IEEE*, November 1978, pp. 1539–1549.

Datapac (Sec. 14.3.1)

CASH 76   Cashin, P. M., "Datapac Network Protocols," *Proc. 3rd Int. Conf. Comput. Commun.*, Toronto, August 1976, pp. 150–155.

CLIP 76   Clipsham, W. W., F. E. Glave, and M. L. Narraway, "Datapac Network Overview," *Proc. 3rd Int. Conf. Comput. Commun.*, Toronto, August 1976, pp. 131–136.

HORT 74   Horton, D. J., and P. G. Bowie, "An Overview of Dataroute: System and Performance," *Conf. Rec. Int. Conf. Commun.*, Minneapolis, June 1974, pp. 2-13 to 2-17.

MCGI 77   McGibbon, C. I., and H. Gibbs, "Datapac—A Phased Approach to the Introduction of a Public Packet-Switched Network," *Proc. IFIP 1977*, pp. 509–513.

MCGI 78   McGibbon, C. I., H. Gibbs, and S. C. K. Young, "Datapac—Initial Experiences with a Commercial Packet Network," *Proc. 4th Int. Conf. Comput. Commun.*, Kyoto, Japan, September 1978, pp. 103–108.

RYBC 77   Rybczynski, A.M., and D.F. Weir, "Datapac X.25 Service Characteristics," *Proc. 5th Data Commun. Symp.*, Snowbird, Utah, September 1977, pp 4–50 to 4–57.

RYBC 78A   Rybczynski, A. M., D. F. Weir, and I. M. Cunningham, "Datapac Internetworking for International Services," *Proc. 4th Int. Conf. Comput. Commun.*, Kyoto, Japan, September 1978, pp. 47–56.

RYBC 78B   Rybczynski, A. M., P. N. Smith, and J. M. Marsh, "The Role of Standards in the Support of Character Mode DTEs on Datapac," *Can. Inf. Process. Soc. Conf.*, Edmonton, May 1978.

RYBC 80   Rybczynski, A. M., J. D. Palframan, and A. Thomas, "Design of the Datapac X.75 Internetworking Capability," *Proc. 5th Int. Conf. Comput. Commun.*, Atlanta, October 1980, pp. 735–740.

SPRO 80   Sproule, D., and M. Unsoy, "Transit Delay Objectives for the Datapac Network," *Proc. 5th Int. Conf. Comput. Commun.*, Atlanta, October 1980, pp. 685–692.

TWYV 76   Twyver, D. A., and A. M. Rybczynski, "Datapac Subscriber Interfaces," *Proc. 3rd Int. Conf. Comput. Commun.*, Toronto, August 1976, pp. 143–149.

YOUN 76   Young, S. C., and C. I. McGibbon, "The Control System of the Datapac Network," *Proc. 3rd Int. Conf. Comput. Commun.*, Toronto, August 1976, pp. 137–142.

Experimental Packet-Switched Service (Sec. 14.3.2)

BURG 76   Burgess, M. J., and J. A. Lockwood, "Experimental Packet-Switched Service: The Customers and Their Packet Terminals," *P.O. Electr. Eng. J.*, July 1976, pp. 122–126.

GARD 76   Gardner, A. J., and K. N. Sandum, "Experimental Packet-Switched Service: Routing of Packets," *P.O. Electr. Eng. J.*, January 1976, pp. 235–239.

HADL 74   Hadley, D. E., and D. W. F. Medcraft, "Experimental Packet-Switched Data-Transmission Service: Network Design and Implementation," *P.O. Electr. Eng. J.*, July 1974, pp. 88–94.

HADL 78   Hadley, D. E., and B. R. Sexton, "The British Post Office Experimental Packet Switched Service (EPSS)—A Review of Development and Operational Experience," *Proc. 4th Int. Conf. Comput. Commun.*, Kyoto, September 1978, pp. 97–102.

HIGG 78   Higginson, P. L., and Z. Z. Fisher, "Experiences with the Initial EPSS Service," *Proc. Eurocomp*, May 1978, pp. 581–600.

NEIL 75A   Neil, W., M. J. Spooner, and E. J. Wilson, "Experimental Packet-Switched Service: Procedures and Protocols: Part 1. Packet Formats, Facilities and Switching," *P.O. Electr. Eng. J.*, January 1975, pp. 232–239.

NEIL 75B   Neil, W., M. J. Spooner, and E. J. Wilson, "Experimental Packet-Switched Service: Procedures and Protocols: Part 2. Transmission Procedures," *P.O. Electr. Eng. J.*, April 1975, pp. 22–28.

NEIL 75C   Neil, W., M J. Spooner, and E. J. Wilson, "Experimental Packet-Switched Service: Procedures and Protocols: Part 3. Operation of Asynchronous Terminals," *P.O. Electr. Eng. J.*, July 1975, pp. 110–117.

Infoswitch (Sec. 14.3.3)

CARL 75   Carleton, G. F., J. F. Pincosy, and R. M. Davies, "Infoswitch and Infodat," *Proc. World Telecommun. 1975*, pp. 2.3.8.1–2.3.8.8.

CARL 76   Carleton, G. F., "Infoswitch—A Public Nationwide Data Network in Canada Provided by CNCP Telecommunications," presented at *NTG Group Conf.*, Baden-Baden, West Germany, February 1976.

HUBE 80   Huber, J. F., "EDX—A Uniform System Architecture for Circuit, Packet, and Message Switching," *Proc. 5th Int. Conf. Comput. Commun.*, Atlanta, October 1980, pp. 195–201.

WOOD 78   Woodin, G. K., "Infoswitch—How to Use It," *Can. Inf. Process. Soc. Conf.*, Edmonton, May 1978.

Telenet (Sec. 14.3.4)

NEWP 77   Newport, C. B., and P. Kaul, "Communications Processors for TELENET's Third Generation Packet Switching Network," *IEEE EASCON-77 Rec.*, September 1977, pp. 8-2A to 8-2K.

OPDE 76   Opderbeck, H., "The Performance of a Terminal Emulation Interface to a Packet-Switched Data Network," *Proc. 3rd Int. Conf. Comput. Commun.*, Toronto, August 1976, pp. 452–459.

OPDE 78   Opderbeck, H., J. H. Hoffmeier, and R. L. Spitzer, "Software Architecture for Microprocessor Based Packet Network," presented at the *AFIPS Natl. Comput. Conf.*, Anaheim, Calif., June 1978.

ROBE 75   Roberts, L. G., "Telenet: Principles and Practice," *Proc. Eurocomp 1975*, pp. 315–329.

ROBE 77   Roberts, L. G., "Packet Network Design—The Third Generation," *Proc. IFIP 1977*, pp. 541–546.

ROTH 78   Rothschild, L. F., and T. Unterberg, "Telenet Corporation Prospectus," June 1978.

TELE 75A   Telenet Communications Corporation, "Host Interface Specification," November 1975.

TELE 75B   Telenet Communications Corporation, "Interactive Terminal Interface Specification," September 1975.

WEIR 80   Weir, D. F., J. B. Holmblad, and A. C. Rothberg, "An X.75 Based Network Architecture," *Proc. 5th Int. Conf. Comput. Commun.*, Atlanta, October 1980, pp. 741–750.

Transpac (Sec. 14.3.5)

BACH 76   Bache, A., L. Guillou, H. Layec, B. Lorig, and Y. Matras, "RCP, The Experimental Packet-Switched Data Transmission Service of the French PTT: History, Connections, Control," *Proc. 3rd Int. Conf. Comput. Commun.*, Toronto, August 1976, pp. 37–43.

BERT 78A   Berthomieu, D., J. Basset, and J. Rascol, "Example of User Protocols to Access the TRANSPAC Network," *Proc. Comput. Network Protocols*, Liège, 1978, pp. C6-1 to C6-6.

BERT 78B   Berthomieu, D., J. Basset, and J. Rascol, "An Experiment on Terminal Interfacing to IBM Computers through the X.25 French Public Network TRANSPAC," *Proc. Eurocomp 1978*, pp. 1009–1022.

BLEV 80   Blevanus, J., and G. Mitaut, "The Use of X.75 in the Transpac International Gateway," *Proc. 5th Int. Conf. Comput. Commun.*, Atlanta, October 1980, pp. 723–728.

DANE 76   Danet, A., R. Despres, A. LeRest, G. Pichon, and S. Ritzenthaler, "The French Public Packet Switching Service: The TRANSPAC Network," *Proc. 3rd Int. Conf. Comput. Commun.*, Toronto, August 1976, pp. 251–260.

GUIL 78   Guilbert, J.-F., "TRANSPAC—Marketing Issues in a Public Packet Network: Impact on Users, Network, and Service Development," *Proc. Eurocomp 1978*, pp. 1027–1049.

JAME 78   Jamet, B., "A Multiline Data Link Control Procedure," *Proc. 4th Int. Conf. Comput. Commun.*, Kyoto, September 1978.

KELL 78   Kelly, P. T. F., "The Telecommunications Network for EURONET," *P.O. Electr. Eng. J.*, January 1978, pp. 208–216.

PICA 80   Picard, P., "Business Planning for a Data Network: The Transpac Example," *Proc. 5th Int. Conf. Comput. Commun.*, Atlanta, October 1980, pp. 664–669.

PONC 78   Poncet, F., and P. Allaire, "Message Exchange Protocol for TRANSPAC and EURONET Network Management," *Proc. Comput. Network Protocols*, Liège, 1978, pp. C4-1 to C4-8.

TYMNET (Sec. 14.3.6)

KOPF 77   Kopf, J., "TYMNET as a Multiplexed Packet Network," *Proc. AFIPS Natl. Comput. Conf.*, 1977, pp. 609–613.

RADW 80   Radwin, M. S., "Tymnet's Advanced Communications Technology and Recent State-of-the-Art Service Introductions," *Proc. 5th Int. Conf. Comput. Commun.*, Atlanta, October 1980, pp. 113–118.

RIND 76   Rinde, J., "TYMNET I: An Alternative to Packet Switching Technology," *Proc. 3rd Int. Conf. Comput. Commun.*, Toronto, August 1976, pp. 268–273.

RIND 77   Rinde, J., "Routing and Control in a Centrally Directed Network," *Proc. AFIPS Natl. Comput. Conf.*, 1977, pp. 603–608.

TYME 71   Tymes, L., "TYMNET—A Terminal Oriented Communication Network," *Proc. AFIPS, Spring Joint Comput. Conf.*, 1971, pp. 211–216.

TYME 78   Tymes, L., and J. Rinde, "The TYMNET II Engine," *4th Int. Conf. Commun.*, Kyoto, September 1978, pp. 109–114.

Private Computer Networks (Sec. 14.4)

ARPANET (Sec. 14.4.1)

BBN 78   Bolt Beranek and Newman, Inc., "Specification for the Interconnection of a Host and an IMP," *BBN Tech.* Rep. No. 1822, May 1978 (revised).

CARR 70   Carr, C. S., S. D. Crocker, and V. G. Cerf, "Host–Host Communication Protocol in the ARPA Network," *Proc. AFIPS Spring Joint Comput. Conf.*, 1970, pp. 589–597.

CLAR 78   Clark, D. D., K. T. Pogran, and D. P. Reed, "An Introduction to Local Area Networks," *Proc. IEEE*, November 1978, pp. 1497–1517.

CROW 75   Crowther, W. R., et al., "Issues in Packet Switching Network Design," *Proc. AFIPS Natl. Comput. Conf.*, 1975, pp. 161–175.

DARP 80A   Defense Advanced Research Projects Agency, "DOD Standard Transmission Control Protocol," January 1980.

DARP 80B   Defense Advanced Research Projects Agency, "DOD Standard Internet Protocol," January 1980.

DAVI 77   Davidson, J., et al., "The ARPANET Telnet Protocol: Its Purpose, Principles, Implementation, and Impact on Host Operating System Design," *Proc. 5th Data Commun. Symp.*, Snowbird, Utah, September 1977, pp. 4-10 to 4-18.

DCA 78   Defense Communications Agency, "ARPANET Information Brochure," revised March 1978.

FEIN 78   Feinler, E., and J. Postel, "ARPANET Protocol Handbook," Network Information Center, SRI International, January 1978 (revised).

HEAR 70   Heart, F. E., et al., "The Interface Message Processor for the ARPA Computer Network," *Proc. AFIPS Spring Joint Comput. Conf.*, 1970, pp. 551–567.

HEAR 73   Heart, F. E., et al., "A New Minicomputer/Multiprocessor for the ARPA Network," *Proc. AFIPS Natl. Comput. Conf.*, 1973, pp. 529–537.

JACO 77   Jacobs, I., et al., "CPODA—A Demand Assignment Protocol for SATNET," *Proc. 5th Data Commun. Symp.*, November 1977, pp. 2-5 to 2-9.

JACO 78 Jacobs, I. M., R. Binder, and E. V. Hoversten, "General Purpose Packet Satellite Networks," *Proc. IEEE*, November 1978, pp. 1448–1467.

KAHN 78 Kahn, R. E., S. A. Gronemyer, J. Burchfiel, and R. C. Kunzelman, "Advances in Packet Radio Technology," *Proc. IEEE*, November 1978, pp. 1468–1496.

KLEI 76 Kleinrock, L., W. E. Naylor, and H. Opderbeck, "A Study of Line Overhead in the ARPANET," *Commun. ACM*, January 1976, pp. 3–13.

KLEI 77 Kleinrock, L., and H. Opderbeck, "Throughput in the ARPANET— Protocols and Measurement." *IEEE Trans. Commun.*, Vol. Com-25, No. 1, 1977, pp. 95–104.

MCKE 75 McKenzie, A. A., "The ARPA Network Control Center," *Proc. 4th Data Commun. Symp.*, Quebec City, October 1975, pp. 5-1 to 5-6.

MCQU 72 McQuillan, J. M., et al., "Improvements in the Design and Performance of the ARPA Network," *Proc. AFIPS Fall Joint Comput. Conf.*, 1972, pp. 741–754.

MCQU 75 McQuillan, J. M., "The Evolution of Message Processing Techniques in the ARPA Network," Infotech State of the Art Report, 1975. Reprinted in J. M. McQuillan, and V. G. Cerf, *A Practical View of Computer Communications Protocols*, IEEE Computer Society, New York, 1978.

MCQU 77 McQuillan, J. M., and D. C. Walden, "The ARPA Network Design Decisions," *Comput. Networks*, Vol. 1, 1977, pp. 243–289.

MCQU 79 McQuillan, J. M., I. Richer, and E. Rosen, "An Overview of the New Routing Algorithm for the ARPANET," *Proc. 6th Data Commun. Symp.*, November 1979.

ORNS 72 Ornstein, S. M., et al., "The Terminal IMP for the ARPA Computer Network," *Proc. AFIPS Spring Joint Comput. Conf.*, 1972, pp. 243–254.

ORNS 75 Ornstein, S. M., and D. C. Walden, "The Evolution of a High Performance Modular Packet-Switch," *Int. Conf. Commun.*, San Francisco, June 1975. Reprinted in J.M. McQuillan, and V.G. Cerf, *A Practical View of Computer Communications Protocols,* IEEE Computer Society, New York, 1978.

ROBE 70 Roberts, L. G., and B. D. Wessler, "Computer Network Development to Achieve Resource Sharing," *Proc. AFIPS Spring Joint Comput. Conf. 1970*, pp. 543–549.

ROBE 73 Roberts, L. G., and B. D. Wessler, "The ARPA Network," in *Computer-Communications Networks*, N. Abramson and F. F. Kuo, eds., Prentice-Hall, Englewood Cliffs, N.J., 1973.

SPRO 78 Sproull, R. F., and D. Cohen, "High-Level Protocols," *Proc. IEEE*, November 1978, pp. 1371–1386.

WOOD 75 Wood, D. C., "Measurement of User Traffic Characteristics on ARPANET," *Proc. 4th Data Commun. Symp.*, Quebec City, Canada, October 1975, p. 9–2.

AUTODIN II (Sec. 14.4.2)

ANSI 79 "Advanced Data Communications Control Procedures," American National Standards Institute X3.66, 1979.

BELL 73 Bell, D. E., and L. J. LaPadula, "Secure Computer Systems: A Mathematical Model," ESD-TR-73-278, Vol. II, November 1973.

BERK 77 Berkheiser, E. W., P. C. Baker, and R. Capaldo, "Security Architecture for AUTODIN II," *Proc. Natl. Telecommun. Conf.*, 1977, pp. 37:4-1 to 37:4-6.

SEVC 77   Sevcik, P. J., "AUTODIN II Subscriber Access Protocols and Interfaces," *Proc. Natl. Telecommun. Conf.*, 1977, pp. 37:6-1 to 37:6-6.

STAT 77   Stathopoulos, A., and H. F. Caley, "The AUTODIN II Network," *Proc. IEEE EASCON 1977*, pp. 8-1A to 8-1J.

CYCLADES (Sec. 14.4.3)

POUZ 73   Pouzin, L., "Presentation and Major Design Aspects of the CYCLADES Computer Network," *Proc. 3rd Data Commun. Symp.*, November 1973, pp. 80–87.

POUZ 75   Pouzin, L., "The CYCLADES Network—Present State and Development Trends," *Proc. IEEE/NBS Symp. Comput. Networks: Trends Appl.*, Gaithersburg, Md., June 1975, pp. 8–13.

ZIMM 75   Zimmerman, H., "The CYCLADES End to End Protocol," *Proc. 4th Data Commun. Symp.*, Quebec City, Canada, October 1975, pp. 7-21 to 7-26.

ZIMM 77   Zimmerman, H., "The CYCLADES Experience—Results and Impacts," *Proc. IFIP*, Toronto, August 1977, pp. 465–469.

DECnet (Sec. 14.4.4)

CONA 76   Conant, G. E., and S. Wecker, "DNA: An Architecture for Heterogeneous Computer Networks," *Proc. 3rd Int. Conf. Comput. Commun.*, Toronto, August 1976, pp. 618–625.

HOCK 78   Hockings, B., "Distributed Network Speeds Orders," *Telephony*, November 6, 1978, pp. 32–39.

LOVE 79   Loveland, R. A., and C. W. Stein, "How DECnet's Communications Software Works," *Data Commun.*, January 1979, pp. 49–65.

PASS 77   Passafiume, J. J. and S. Wecker, "Distributed File Access in DECnet," *Proc. 2nd Berkeley Workshop Distributed Data Manage. Comput. Networks*, Berkeley, Calif., May 1977.

WECK 76A   Wecker, S., "The Design of DECNET—A General Purpose Network Base," *ELECTRO/76*, Boston, May 1976.

WECK 76B   Wecker, S., "DECNET: A Building Block Approach to Network Design," *Natl. Telecommun. Conf.*, Dallas, November 1976.

WECK 80   Wecker, S., "DNA: The Digital Network Architecture," *Proc. IEEE Trans. Commun.*, Vol. COM-28, No. 4, 1980, pp. 510-526.

European Informatics Network (Sec. 14.4.5)

ANDR 80   Andreoni, G., G. M. Kacin, and D. L. A. Barber, "Use of EIN Microprocessor Units for Network Performance Measurements," *Proc. 5th Int. Conf. Comput. Commun.*, Atlanta, October 1980, pp. 679–684.

BARB 74   Barber, D. L. A., "Progress with the European Informatics Network," *Proc. Int. Conf. Comput. Commun.*, August 1974, pp. 215–220.

BARB 76   Barber, D. L. A., "A European Informatics Network: Achievement and Prospects," *Proc. 3rd Int. Conf. Comput. Commun.*, Toronto, August 1976, pp. 44–50.

BARB 78A   Barber, D.L.A. R. Kalin, and C. Solomonides, "An Implementation of the

X.25 Interface in a Datagram Network," *Proc. Comput. Network Protocols*, Liège, 1978.

BARB 78B Barber, D.L.A., "The EIN Project: The End of the Beginning," *Proc. 4th Int. Conf. Comput. Commun.*, Kyoto, Sepember 1978, pp. 33–38.

EIN 78 "The European Informatics Network in Spring 1978," *EIN Rep. 78/005*.

PONC 76 Poncet, F., and C. S. Repton, "The EIN Communications Subnetwork Principles and Practice," *Proc. 3rd Int. Conf. Comput. Commun.*, Toronto, August 1976, pp. 523–531.

EURONET (Sec. 14.4.6)

DAVI 75 Davies, G. W. P., "The EURONET Project," *Proc. Eurocomp*, 1975, pp. 229–239.

DAVI 78 Davies, G. W. P., J. Y. Gresser, P. T. F. Kelly, and J. R. Thomas, "The EURONET Telecommunication and Information Network," *Proc. 4th Int. Conf. Comput. Commun.*, Kyoto, September 1978, pp. 189–194.

KELL 78 Kelly, P. T. F., and E. J. B. Lee, "The Telecommunications Network for EURONET," *P.O. Electr. Eng. J.*, January 1978, pp. 208–216.

KELL 80 Kelly, P. T. F., "EURONET DIANE—A European Harmonization Project," *Proc. 5th Int. Conf. Comput. Commun.*, Atlanta, October 1980, pp. 658–663.

SITA (Sec. 14.4.7)

CHRE 73 Chretien, G. J., W. M. Konig, and J. H. Rech, "The SITA Network," *Proc. Comput. Commun. Networks Conf.*, University of Sussex, England, September 1973.

Current Status and Future Directions (Sec. 14.5)

ROBE 77 Roberts, L. G., "Packet Network Design—The Third Generation," *Proc. IFIP 1977*, Toronto, pp. 541–546.

15

Internetworking

LOUIS POUZIN
Centre National d'Etudes des Télécommunications
Issy les Moulineaux, France

15.1 INTRODUCTION

The development of computers created the need to use them from remote sites. Using telephone lines and remote terminals was a first step in distributing data processing services. Later, the development of higher-speed and reliable packet-switching networks introduced the possibility of interconnecting a large number of computers and terminals [ROBE 70]. Concurrently, the need to achieve interworking between equipments and systems of different makes has brought about conventions for exchanging data, which are known as protocols [POUZ 78]. However, protocols are specific to closed communities, as they have developed mostly within research environments. Data communications are now becoming commonplace in industrialized countries, and computers are turning into a mass market. Thus building networks, and networks of networks, appears as a natural temptation. Joining a network, or interconnecting existing networks, are bound to be everyday problems of the 1980s, until overall standardization perhaps takes over. Nevertheless, existing systems will remain long after new standards are promulgated. Thus we can safely predict a long life for internetworking.

This chapter intends to emphasize practical aspects of internetworking. However, too many practical recipes turn into a hodgepodge if they are not placed into a proper methodological approach. Hence the following organization.

Section 15.2 gives typical examples of internetworking problems. Solutions are only sketched, as the purpose of this section is to illustrate the diversity of the subject and the spectrum of possibilities opened to a designer.

Section 15.3 introduces concepts evolved for building networks. The key structure is a set of layered protocols, which handle specific communication and control functions. This structure is fundamental for understanding network architectures. It is now adopted without exception by computer manufacturers.

Section 15.4 discusses heterogeneity in data processing systems. History and user needs contribute to a certain degree of diversity. Even with a comprehensive set of standards there would be software packages designed for specific purposes. Thus one should not expect that interconnection problems will ever disappear totally.

Section 15.5 presents models of basic internetworking problems. The reader is warned that models do not convey much information on implementation. They only purport to help in the analysis of a practical problem of interconnection. It is interesting to note that there are a very small number of basic situations, which apply to all problems encountered so far.

Section 15.6 is a tool kit. All specific technical problems encountered in converting from one protocol to another are discussed separately, with most common solutions or compromises identified through experience. Some of these problems are: naming, error and flow control, and interrupts. Perfect conversions are often impossible, but various techniques yield acceptable constructions.

Section 15.7 describes a few additional problems pertaining to routing, that is, the choice of a physical route for data traveling through interconnected networks.

Section 15.8 outlines real-life examples of internetworking solutions. They illustrate some of the techniques presented in the preceding sections.

Section 15.9 is a summary of existing standards related to internetworking. Although they are limited in their application, they may alleviate some development work in the future.

Section 15.10 reviews remaining unsolved problems, which fortunately are not yet common in practice. As a whole, most technical problems are now understood and may be handled satisfactorily. On the other hand, the major barrier to internetworking will become increasingly political. Jurisdictional restrictions to systems interconnection are replacing technical hurdles [COMP 79].

15.2   TYPICAL EXAMPLES

To illustrate the diversity of interconnection problems, some typical cases are presented next.

15.2.1   Interconnection of Two Star Networks

A *star network* is a central computing facility accessed from a set of terminals. We might also call this a network of terminals. Interconnecting two networks of this kind usually means providing access to services of one computer from terminals attached to the other computer (Fig. 15.1).

Practical examples of this type of internetworking appear quite spontaneously when a single organization operates two or more computers dedicated to different

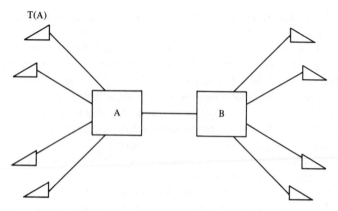

T(A)

Figure 15.1. Interconnection of two star networks.

services (e.g., one offers data-base query, another document preparation). Users of both services could dial successively whichever computer they need if they are allowed dial-in access to both systems and if all terminals are supported by both computer systems. Otherwise, they would have no other choice than having two dedicated terminals, unless the two computer systems are interconnected in some way.

A way for a terminal on computer A, say T(A), to access services on computer B, is to request A to establish a logical path from T(A) to B. From there on T(A) would appear as a terminal attached to B. In this mode, A is said to be *logically transparent* because it somehow becomes invisible to the user on T(A).

A physical link controlled by appropriate transmission convention is necessary between A and B so that they can exchange data in a reliable manner. In addition, A must handle requests from T(A) or B for operating, maintaining, and closing logical paths between T(A) and B. Furthermore, A must perform every chore necessary for translating data, formats, or procedures specific to T(A) into other conventions acceptable by B. Beside its other processing functions, A acts as a *terminal concentrator* as seen from B.

Other functions may also be carried out by A: keeping track of accounting data on the use of B's services from T(A)'s terminals, filtering access to B, providing meaningful diagnostic messages to T(A) when B's services do not respond normally, facilitating recovery, and so on. In this case A is no longer transparent, as it enhances B's services with additional intelligence. A becomes an intelligent terminal concentrator.

As a different example, we may again envision a computer dedicated to data-base query and another to document preparation. However, users could be more sophisticated than previously, because they would like to compose documents in which they would insert information extracted from a data base. Instead of working through separate sessions, with the burden of retyping queried data, it would be more convenient to call the data base in the middle of a document preparation, and to edit the response into the document draft.

In such a case, it is not desired that T(A) accesses B as if it were a terminal on B.

Rather, it is adequate that an application program executing in A be able to access services on B in order to complete its task for T(A). In this mode B is said to be *transparent* because the user on T(A) may think he or she is only using A.

As previously, a physical link is necessary between A and B, with appropriate control. But A only handles requests and responses between its application programs and B. One might say that A acts as a terminal attached to B.

This form of internetworking is used by some airline reservation systems to check on customer credit cards while booking seats.

15.2.2   Interconnection of Two Packet Networks

In its simplest form a packet network is a transmission system carrying packets of data from one computer system to another. Interconnecting two of them usually implies that they should provide together a packet transmission service as if there were only one network (Fig. 15.2).

The successful development of packet networks for data transmission has produced a number of experimental and commercial networks. Each of them links a collection of computer systems, usually with some facilities for attaching terminals, and covers a particular geographical area. For reasons such as international cooperation or marketing strategies, it may appear desirable that services offered by a computer system A attached to network N1 become accessible from computer B attached to network N2.

When the two packet networks N1 and N2 are identical, it may be possible to associate them so that the resulting construction appears as a single network with identical properties. This should not be taken for granted, as networks may be *self-incompatible*; that is, two copies of the same network design may not be able to exchange packets, due to technical peculiarities.

In general, N1 and N2 are different and cannot exchange packets. However, one may think of a black box C (Fig. 15.3) which could act as B's surrogate for N1 and A's surrogate for N2, in relaying packets between N1 and N2. Customarily, such a black box is called a *gateway* [HIGG 75].

The technical description of a gateway cannot be summarized in a few sentences, as it touches on numerous topics, which are covered in subsequent sections.

15.2.3   Interconnection of Two Computer Networks

A computer network consists of a set of data processing systems capable of performing cooperative tasks according to common rules called protocols. Data exchanged

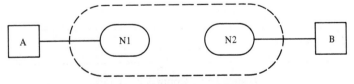

Figure 15.2. Interconnection of two packet networks.

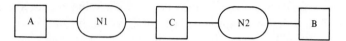

Figure 15.3. Gateway between two packet networks.

between data processing systems are usually carried through a transmission network operating as an autonomous system (Fig. 15.4). Some data processing systems, or possibly all, provide for terminal handling facilities.

Examples of computer networks are ARPANET [ROBE 70] or CYCLADES [POUZ 73], which are the first experimental large-scale implementations. Commercial products based on the same principles are now offered by major computer manufacturers, such as IBM-SNA or DECnet. However, they usually assume rather simple transmission facilities (e.g., leased circuits) rather than a general meshed network of various transmission media.

The major breakthrough brought about by computer networks is distributed processing, the ability to assemble a collection of resources (programs, files, terminals) located on different computers in order to perform a set of coordinated tasks. Putting together a variety of geographically dispersed resources is in itself a complex structure. Interconnecting several computer networks increases complexity due to the large number of potential interactions between all resources.

A restricted mode of association consists in the possibility of establishing bilateral exchanges between some computers. This implies an association of the transmission systems used in each network, plus additional conventions for passing data between designated computers. Such restricted interconnection may be sufficient if there is only a need for exchanging files between some computers.

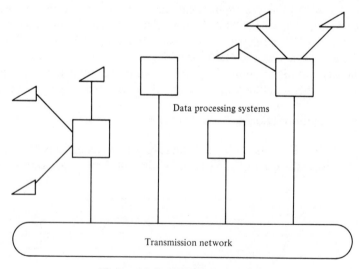

Figure 15.4. Computer network.

A more general case consists in making most data processing services accessible from any terminal on either network. This problem is studied further later.

15.3   NETWORK ARCHITECTURE

Internetworking could be presented as a do-it-yourself craftmanship, which it actually is in many practical instances [LLOY 75]. However, there is much benefit in laying out basic principles, which may be identified in most cases, irrespective of specific implementations [COTT 78, GIEN 79]. Principles do not solve all problems, but they facilitate understanding and help in designing simpler solutions.

The principle of independent layers has been generally accepted as a sound approach in the construction of large systems. In computer networks it was logical to introduce system boundaries between the major distinct functions: what functions and what boundaries are matters for discussion [ZIMM 80]. Networks' standards are presently being studied within the International Standard Organization [ISO 81]. In order to focus on principles, we may use a simple computer network model which appears to be applied in most implementations (Fig. 15.5).

15.3.1   Protocol Layers

A data transmission function is the lower layer. Its purpose is to carry bits from one point to another. Practical implementations use a variety of transmission techniques: permanent or switched circuits, multipoint or broadcast channels, or packet switching.

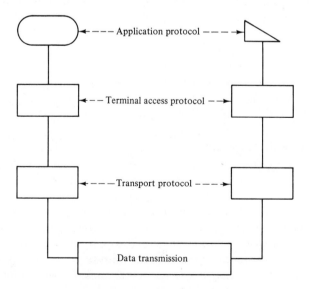

Figure 15.5. Protocol layers.

A transport function is a second layer. Its purpose is to move blocks of data from one process to another. Examples of processes could be an application program running in a computer, a subsystem such as a transaction processor, a terminal handler within a terminal controller, or an interactive package within a personal computer.

The transport function takes care of the constraints associated with the existence of a transmission layer (e.g., error correction, fragmentation into packets, and reassembly into larger blocks). It also provides for additional facilities, such as multiplexing independent streams of data, and flow control between sender and receiver. The transport function operates *end-to-end* so as to provide for the highest guarantee of error free service.

A *terminal access function* is usually a third layer, since the most common form of using computers is from a terminal. The role of this layer is to allow the control of remote terminals through a set of message conventions.

These end-to-end conventions are called *protocols* [POUZ 78] in the network terminology. They make no assumption about local implementations, as long as messages are exchanged with proper formats. Owing to this discipline, it becomes possible to associate heterogeneous systems without putting too many constraints on their design.

In typical implementations terminal and transport protocols are packaged into a *network access method,* which can be located in a front-end minicomputer. On the terminal side, it is located within a remote concentrator, or even microprogrammed within an intelligent terminal.

When data exchange takes place directly between application programs, they may call only on the transport function. This form of association opens the way to *distributed processing*, in which several computer systems are involved simultaneously in the same applications.

15.3.2 Simplified Model

The structure described above may be further simplified and generalized in order to make more apparent the relationship between its various components (Fig. 15.6).

At the highest level, user applications exchange information following the rules of specific user protocols, one of which is a *virtual terminal* protocol, in the frequent case where a terminal works with an application.

All these protocols call on a *transport service,* through a *transport interface,* which takes care of the specific problems associated with transmission: error and flow control, multiplexing, liaison management, and so on.

These functions are implemented in *transport stations* (located within data processing equipments) and exchange information following the rules of a *transport protocol,* which is transparent to higher-level user protocols.

In order to communicate physically, transport stations call on a *transmission service* through a *transmission interface.* The transmission service could be broken down further. But this is not useful, because transmission services are typically offered as independent systems by public carriers or private transmission networks.

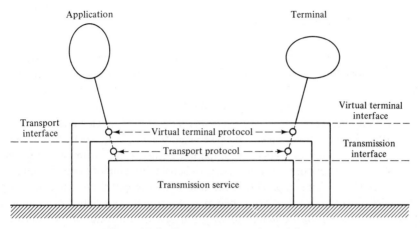

Figure 15.6. Computer network model.

This model points out several aspects:

- Protocols define end-to-end relationships.
- Interfaces define local relationships.
- Protocols at level N are transparent to protocols at level $N + 1$.

It should be noted that this type of structure, where functional levels are carefully delineated, appeared quite recently. It may be observed in ARPANET, CYCLADES, and new products announced by computer manufacturers (DEC, IBM). Previous networks implement all these functions, but their structure is so confused that it is difficult to distinguish elements performing well-defined basic functions.

15.3.3   ISO Model

As a result of an exceptionally fast standardization effort, ISO has adopted a model architecture for *open systems interconnection*. This work, accomplished between 1979 and 1981, has been agreed upon as an International Standard [ZIMM 80].

The model architecture agreed by ISO is a recognition of the approach evolved for building heterogeneous computer networks at the experimental stage. The layering principle is systematically applied as a protective strategy to anticipate evolutions in concepts and technologies.

The ISO model contains seven layers, termed (from the top down): 7, application; 6, presentation; 5, session; 4, transport; 3, network control; 2, link control; and 1, physical interface (see Sec. 15.9.6).

The simplified model, introduced in Sec. 15.3.2, may be considered as a macroscopic view, as it relates quite simply to the ISO model. We have termed Virtual terminal the whole of layers 5 and 6, while layers 1, 2, and 3 are termed Transmission service. This simplification carries no technical implication.

15.4 LEVELS OF COMMONALITY

Computer networks are not yet commonly offered as commercial products. They grew out of user attempts to share costly resources. One major difficulty in implementing networks is to start with a diversity of products, more or less equivalent, but definitely not designed to work in cooperation.

A computer network is *homogeneous* when all of its elements have been designed to be compatible. This is the case when the whole network comes from a single supplier, or when plug-to-plug compatible elements come from other vendors.

A computer network is *heterogeneous* when it is built out of elements that have been designed independently. This is the case when computer systems come from different manufacturers. Heterogeneity may result from the association of equipment which were already installed independently. It may also be a policy of diversification in order to get the best products at the best price.

Computer manufacturers uncover their network armada gradually, and put the emphasis on offering "total" systems. However, a significant number of potential customers balk at the idea of signing away their future in the hands of a single supplier. Thus heterogeneity is to become a market rather than an eccentricity.

Designers of computer networks are faced with the problem of reaching a good compromise between homogeneity and heterogeneity. The layers of protocols introduced earlier appear as a minimum set of common conventions in order to allow the sharing of applications, terminals, and transmission systems. Nevertheless, users would find additional comfort in further levels of commonality between data processing systems.

15.4.1 Access Protocol

For a user, human or automated, a network correspondent may be another user, or most likely an application program, running or sleeping on some other computer. It would be highly desirable to call directly this particular correspondent rather than stepping through a series of specific dial-up and log-in protocols, which are an effective deterrent for untrained users.

15.4.2 Command Language

Any computer user may notice a lot of inconsistencies within command languages at his or her disposal on a single installation. Networks have just placed this odd situation into brighter light, also adding a few more items of their own.

Since it is not conceivable to eliminate abruptly previously available software, any attempt toward more consistency adds another story to a tower of Babel. It is not clear that we can find some realistic approach to tackling this problem. Perhaps we have already passed long ago the point where it was too late.

15.4.3   Network Commands and Facilities

As opposed to the jungle of computer system languages, there are few operational networks, and very few network commands have so far emerged. Thus it should be possible to introduce commonality before it is too late.

15.4.4   Data Management

Every data processing system is equipped with a battery of tools specializing in data base management, file management, text editing, macroprocessors, and so on. Many users prefer writing their own, perhaps because they are overwhelmed by the sheer volume of user manuals. This situation is likely to get worse with heterogeneous networks. Presently, substantial efforts are devoted to the development of tools for the management of distributed data. This is still a research area.

15.4.5   Commonality versus Heterogeneity

Historically, network development started with lower levels of commonality: transmission, transport, and simple terminal access. Gradually, the boundary of commonality progresses upward into application-oriented protocols. In other words, the network model will grow a few more outer layers. However, commonality is not a panacea. In areas closely related to applications, diversity keeps some advantages. Different user populations may require different customizations. Specific solutions may be more economic. Innovation should not be stifled.

15.5   INTERCONNECTION IN PRINCIPLES

In the network model introduced previously, layers are designed so as to allow a large freedom of implementation, as long as the service remains the same as seen from upper layers. This general characteristic of structured systems facilitates in the interconnection of separate networks [GIEN 79].

Indeed, let us take an example of two computer networks in which the virtual terminal protocol and the transport protocol are identical, but using different transmission systems. Then, they may be modeled as in Fig. 15.7. Since protocols apply end to end, terminals attached to one network would access applications in the other network if it were not for the gap between transmission systems. It is clear from this model that the interconnection problem boils down to the interconnection of two different transmission systems, so that messages exchanged in the transport layer be properly routed and delivered to their destination [GIEN 75, DICI 79].

Most internetworking problems may be analyzed in terms of typical basic configurations. A set of basic cases are examined next.

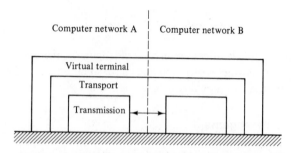

Figure 15.7. Two quasi-identical computer networks.

15.5.1   Substitution of a Layer

A practical situation could be the replacement of a private packet net by a public packet net, all other components remaining unchanged. In the network model a certain layer (L) is replaced with a new one (L1) offering a different interface (Fig. 15.8).

As long as the service provided by L1 is "similar" to the one provided by L, it is feasible to map interface L onto L1 through an interface converter often called a *bridge*. There is no good measure of similarity between L and L1. The complexity of the bridge and the characteristics of the service should be assessed.

When the original and the new service are functionally very different, it is not always clear that a substitution is possible without affecting higher layers: for example, replacing a transmission system using leased or switched circuits by a packet network may require the replacement of higher layers, because transit delays deteriorate their performance.

The foregoing example illustrates the delicate balance designers have to strike when layering a system. In principle, layering is intended to prevent the propagation of modifications throughout the entire system. However, this is effective only to the extent that potential future characteristics have been more or less anticipated. Occasionally, new technologies based on new concepts require major changes in the overall system architecture.

Additional examples of layer substitution are given in Sec. 15.8.

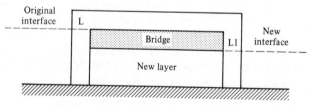

Figure 15.8. Substitution of a layer.

15.5.2   Interconnection within One Layer

A practical situation could be the interconnection of two computer networks with identical protocols, but using different transmission systems, N1 and N2.

In the model one layer is made up of two distinct components (Fig. 15.9). Interfaces with the upper layer may be different, but this is immaterial as long as protocols are identical.

An adapter is necessary between N1 and N2. This is often called a *gateway* [WALD 75]. Typically, gateway functions may be placed in either of two categories:

1. *Mapping.* When entities and functions, within N1 and N2 are in one-to-one correspondence, it may be convenient to map them onto each other (e.g., each message passing from N1 to N2 is reformatted). This is the case when N1 and N2 are two variants of the same design.
2. *Bridging.* In other cases, it is not possible to establish a satisfactory one-to-one mapping. An alternative solution is to cross the obstacle within the next higher layer, which by definition is the same in both computer networks.

Thus the gateway appears to N1 and N2 as a common higher layer (Fig. 15.10). Since the protocol is common, messages passing through the gateway need no further conversion.

15.5.3   Interconnection of Two Similar Networks

It is assumed that networks are built on the same model, and that protocols are "similar." Again similarity is a vague concept. An actual criterion is the complexity of the adaptation.

Interconnecting two similar networks consists in interconnecting each layer separately (Fig. 15.11). Functionally, this would result in as many gateways as there are layers to interconnect. As we have said, a mapping gateway within one layer requires strong similarity; otherwise, a bridging gateway should be in the next higher layer. Thus it may occur that the only layer where similiarity is strong is an outer layer (e.g., the virtual terminal) (Fig. 15.12).

15.5.4   Interconnection of Two Dissimilar Networks

Even when networks are built on the same model, mapping corresponding layers may be too cumbersome. A worse case is networks based on different models, or too

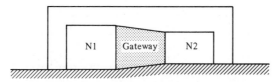

Figure 15.9. Interconnection within one layer.

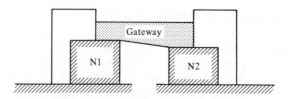

Figure 15.10. Gateway in a higher layer.

intricate to be modeled at all. Then it is not even possible to identify corresponding layers. A solution is to resort to an outer layer that always exists: device handling. Every application program communicates with some kind of real or virtual device: terminal, magnetic tape, file and so on. Thus a gateway may appear as mimicking some device attached to each network (Fig. 15.13). It may be convenient that emulated devices be identical (e.g., a teleprinter), but this is not necessary as long as the gateway ensures a mapping between them.

15.6   MAPPING PROBLEMS

The previous analysis shows that protocol mapping is central to every interconnection problem, as it is always performed in one layer or another. One might imagine that protocols and interfaces could be described formally, so that mapping would become a mechanical process. Actually, this is still a research area [DAY 78]. Mapping uses ad hoc solutions, which are not always very satisfactory. Typical problems encountered are listed below:

> Naming
> Logical path
> Error control
> Flow control
> Interrupts
> Timings
> Dialogue
> Diagnostics
> Supervision
> Accounting

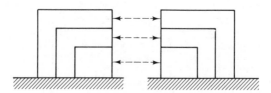

Figure 15.11. Two similar computer networks.

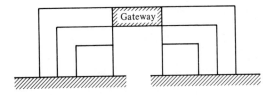

Figure 15.12. Gateway in the virtual terminal layer.

These problems are now briefly examined. Most of them could be the subject of an extensive separate treatment.

15.6.1   Naming

Each computer network design includes some specific naming scheme for identifying sources and destinations of data traffic (hereafter called *entities*).

Typically, there may coexist several name layers (e.g., the transmission network, the network access, and the file system).

In some computer networks, the whole naming scheme is consistent, hierarchical, and results directly from the definition of protocol layers. This may be the case in homogeneous networks. In some other cases, especially heterogeneous computer networks, only the lower layers of protocols apply a minimum consistent naming. Higher layers use specific schemes within each computer system.

Internetworking normally has to deal with heterogeneous naming, at least for some protocol layers. Two typical methods may be used: static mapping or allocation.

Static Mapping

In static mapping, every entity, say b_i, in a network B that should be addressable from a network A is given a name, say a_i, in A's name space (Fig. 15.14). Messages destined to b_j are sent to a_i and delivered to a gateway, which replaces a_i with b_j among other mapping operations.

Two requirements must be met for this method to be applicable.

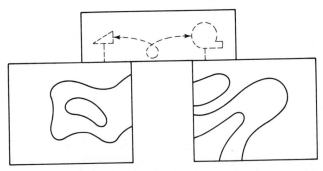

Figure 15.13. Dissimilar networks.

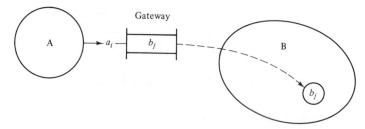

Figure 15.14. Static mapping.

1. The complete set $[a_i, b_j]$ must be defined a priori.
2. It must be possible to deliver to one (or several) gateways messages carrying as many distinct names as there are addressable entities.

The first requirement is usually met as a direct implication of having finite-length names. It might not be the case if names were variable in length, with an almost unbounded name space. There may also be a table space problem if the set $[a_i, b_j]$ is too large to be stored into the gateway memory. If the mapping a_i to b_j can be expressed with an algorithm, the gateway need only execute this algorithm for every passing message. Otherwise, a table is required with as many entries as potentially addressable entities.

The second requirement is met in only some networks. It depends on the ability of the transmission layer to route to the same physical destination messages with different names. ARPANET delivers to the same point all messages with the same host number. CIGALE [POUZ 74B] has a logical name space and can deliver to the same point messages addressed to an arbitrary set of "transport stations." Public networks using the X.25 interface have only one name per physical destination [CCIT 78].

Allocation

In the allocation scheme it is assumed that entities in B addressed from A are in a limited number at any point in time, and that they are used only during well-identified time periods often called *sessions*. This is typical of time-sharing or remote batch operation.

Addressing an entity across network boundaries implies a procedure in which three phases may be identified (Fig. 15.15). In the initial phase A requests the gateway to allocate a name a_i to be used subsequently as a substitute for b_j. *Thereafter, messages sent to a_i are forwarded to b_j by the gateway. Finally, the temporary association (a_i, b_j) is canceled, and a_i may be allocated to another session* [POST 71].

The allocation scheme comes with two requirements:

1. It must be possible to deliver to one (or several) gateway messages carrying as many distinct names as there are simultaneous sessions.
2. Addressing entities across network boundaries requires a multistep procedure.

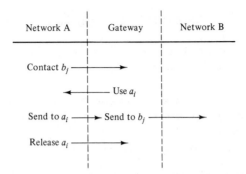

Figure 15.15. Allocation.

As compared to the mapping scheme, the allocation scheme may save table space, if this were a problem. On the other hand, the overhead inherent in the procedure excludes practically any form of data exchange based on independent messages, such as transactions, monitoring, or control. It is also more vulnerable, when the gateway or one of the networks loses track of which a_i and b_j are in correspondence. Nevertheless, the allocation scheme is often used, because many computer systems impose a multistep procedure for logging in, accessing files, and so on. Consequently, the gateway has to keep track of ongoing sessions in any case.

Both methods require the ability to locate several names at the same physical destination (one or several gateways). However, there are ways to circumvent this requirement, if need be. At a given level of protocol, messages are usually parsed into control fields, used by the protocol, and a text field, which may be anything passing transparently through the protocol. Some part of the text field may be turned into a subname interpreted by the gateway.

However, it may be costly or undesirable to use a subnaming technique, if it requires extensive changes in existing systems. A last resort consists in using as many distinct physical destinations as necessary; that is, multiple links are installed between the network and the gateway (Fig. 15.16). Each physical link carries traffic to/from a specific name a_i.

What has been described above applies only to the naming of entities in B as seen from A. If entities in A must become addressable from B, as is usually the case, another independent name mapping scheme is needed from B to A. Indeed, mapping is a unidirectional function. If the B naming scheme is substantially different from the

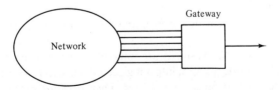

Figure 15.16. Multiple links.

one in A, two different mapping techniques may have to be implemented in the gateway.

When interconnection is anticipated at the design stage, some simple precautions save a great many later complications:

- Provide a large homogeneous hierarchical name space.
- Assign the highest level of a a hierarchical name to a network name.
- Route messages to logical destinations decoupled from physical devices (I/O ports, circuits, etc.). [DALA 81].

The last characteristic solves the problem of locating several names at the same physical destination. Together with the other two characteristics, it allows the delivery to one or more gateways of all messages destined to a "foreign" network. Moreover, B's names may be used directly within messages originating from A, because routing mechanisms in A need only process the network name when the final destination is located outside A. Thus no name mapping is necessary when crossing network boundaries. However, some reformatting is usually necessary, as it is unlikely that the very same message format would apply all the way through.

Such characteristics may be found in CYCLADES. This was not the case in the initial implementation of ARPANET (no network name, messages routed to physical devices), nor is it in public data networks, in which a subscriber number is mapped onto a single physical attachment port.

15.6.2 Logical Link

In practically every computer system some data are moved about in streams. Terminal to process communications are almost always handled on this way. However, there are usually not as many physical channels as data streams. Multiplexing techniques are used to share physical resources between a number of data streams. Mechanisms built for the purpose of handling data streams are given many different names. In this chapter we use the term *logical link*.

Logical links are endowed with specific properties, such as:

- They may be opened and closed, or they may be permanent.
- They may carry data in one direction only, or in two directions, alternately or simultaneously.
- They may offer an additional data path specialized for short messages of higher priority.
- They usually provide for error and flow control mechanisms.

When two networks A and B are interconnected, it becomes necessary to extend a logical link in A, say LL_a, into a logical link in B, as if we were splicing two ropes, or connecting two pipes (Fig. 15.17). Then obvious problems arise when logical links in either network do not exhibit equivalent properties. Some of these problems are examined in subsequent subsections. They illustrate mapping tech-

Figure 15.17. Splicing logical links.

niques, but they are by no means exhaustive. Each interconnection case has to be studied and solved with ad hoc means. When no satisfactory solution can be devised, or when possible solutions are too complex, one must decide that mapping does not work, and look for a more satisfactory solution at a higher level, by way of bridging.

As an example, let us assume that LL_a is bidirectional (as in most networks), while LL_b is unidirectional (as in ARPANET). Two LL_b are needed, and the gateway performs traffic splitting and merging (Fig. 15.18). Opening LL_a in A is interpreted by the gateway as a request to open two LL_b in B, one for each direction. However, we have a problem when opening requests are initiated in B, because the gateway has to convert two LL_b opening requests to only one LL_a request.

If there is a higher-layer protocol in B, such as the initial connection protocol of ARPANET [POST 71], whereby LL_b are always opened by a pair in a predefined manner, the gateway may follow that protocol and yield only one LL_a in A. On the other hand, if no strict rule applies, the only practical alternative for the gateway is to open one LL_a for each LL_b, even though traffic will be unidirectional on each LL_a. Unfortunately, this solution may not be satisfactory for higher-layer protocols in A, which may be designed for the use of bidirectional logical links, without being capable of handling two where they expect only one. In the end, it may become necessary to use different higher-layer protocol when exchanging data between A and B, or to give up mapping at the logical link level.

Some transmission networks based on packet switching require that packets be transmitted over logical links implemented at the lower transmission level. These logical links are usually termed *virtual circuits*. Other packet networks are simply designed to carry independent packets, without the need to use or establish virtual circuits. This kind of transmission service is usually called *datagram*. When interconnecting two transmission networks of either kind, virtual circuits cannot be established across the two networks, because one of them offers no such thing. Two solutions may be envisioned for the transmission service across the two networks. Either make it appear as datagram, or as virtual circuit.

Let us assume that the choice is to offer datagram, because the transport layer can easily adjust to it. Then the situation may be modeled as in Fig. 15.8, in which we want to use a virtual circuit interface L1 in lieu of a hypothetical datagram interface L. A bridge is used to convert the virtual circuit interface into a datagram interface, in order to carry independent packets through network A (Fig. 15.19). Network B needs no bridge, since it is assumed to offer a datagram interface.

Figure 15.18. Uni/bidirectional mapping.

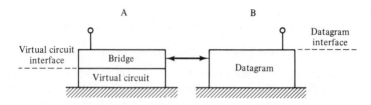

Figure 15.19. Datagram/virtual circuit bridge.

Carrying datagrams over virtual circuits is rather straightforward. Each datagram is transmitted as a single packet, if it can fit into the maximum packet length authorized on virtual circuits. Otherwise, a datagram is fragmented into successive packets and reassembled by the bridge at the other end of a virtual circuit. On the other hand, optimizing the use of virtual circuits may be a tricky problem. Indeed, opening and closing a virtual circuit for every datagram could entail unacceptable overhead in network A. Thus the bridge attempts to maintain opened virtual circuits as long as it expects more datagrams to flow over the same path. Only traffic analysis and simulation can help determine optimum strategies.

In the model of Fig. 15.19, we have not made any assumption on the technical characteristics of virtual circuit and datagram. Thus the very same model applies if we swap names (i.e., if we wish to make a datagram network appear as operating virtual circuits). However, there are technical differences. Packets transmitted over virtual circuits must be delivered in the same order. By definition, a datagram network does not guarantee delivery in the order of transmission. Thus the bridge must implement a reordering protocol over the datagram network. It must also interpret and/or transmit all signaling functions associated with the specific virtual circuit interface to be offered to the next higher layer (e.g., X.25).

15.6.3 Information Quantum

Information exchanged between layers of protocols is always structured. Units exchanged are not just bits, but packets, messages, blocks, items, and so on. Control mechanisms operate on control fields, some of which contain numbers used to identify uniquely a particular piece of information. Numbers are typically assigned sequentially, and they are essential for error or flow control mechanisms [CERF 74].

When mapping a protocol into another, numbers must be translated. There is no simple algorithm, however (e.g., one protocol may handle message numbers, and the other packet numbers). The relationship would be simple if messages always contained the same number of packets. In most cases lengths are variable, and the relationship between two numbering schemes cannot be predicted accurately. Implications will be discussed with error and flow control.

15.6.4   Error Control

Error control comprises two major phases: detection and recovery. Detection is normally performed either by transmitter or receiver or both. An error is detected when some communication protocol is violated (e.g., spurious message, number out of range, etc.).

Some errors are deemed unrecoverable, and consequences are to be handled by a higher-layer protocol. There is usually no difficulty in doing a satisfactory mapping of unrecoverable errors, to the extent that their occurrences are well identified. Such errors are normally signaled with specific messages, which are translated by a gateway.

Error detection and recovery procedures are typically based on acknowledgments and retransmission from a point in past traffic where no error had yet occurred. Thus the two ends of an ongoing data stream must be able to backtrack up to the same safe restarting point. Most protocols use numbering schemes for acknowledgment and backtracking (i.e., message number, packet number, character count, etc.). This is where difficulties arise, because numbering schemes in both networks may not have a well-defined relationship. Ways around that problem are described in subsequent sections.

A common data structure is superimposed on top of existing mismatched protocols. This is usually possible, because higher layers handle information units such as page, transaction, and file. Thus error detection and recovery are pushed into a higher layer, where both ends of a data stream work on the same information quantum, and operate end to end [SHOC 79].

Detection and recovery procedures in each network are decoupled from one another (Fig. 15.20). In lay terms, control on LL_a is terminated in the gateway. Transmitted data are stored into an intermediate buffer, from which they are forwarded over LL_b. As long as the gateway can buffer enough information for the worst case of retransmission, problems evaporate, since there is no need to map recovery protocols any more. There is, however, a major change in functionality, since there is no longer end-to-end control over the total logical link. Transmission integrity relies primarily on the gateway reliability, without any controllable evidence. This form of control is often termed *hop by hop,* or *cascade* [GROS 79].

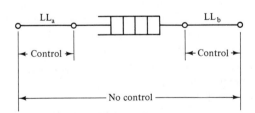

Figure 15.20. Control cascade.

15.6.5   Flow Control

This mechanism allows a receiver to limit the amount of delivered traffic, according to its capability to process or store incoming data. By necessity, flow control operates on some information quantum. Thus one should expect mapping problems similar to those encountered with error control. This is compounded by the fact that most flow control mechanisms used on logical links are intertwined with error control, because they share the same numbering scheme. However, there is some relaxation, as flow control objectives are not strictly defined [POUZ 81]. Rather, they intend to maintain a sufficient amount of delivered traffic without unduly tying up communications resources.

The mapping of flow control may occasionally be straightforward, when protocols are very similar. In most cases the technique used is, as in Fig. 15.20, a cascade of two separate protocols with a buffer in between. Here the buffering problem may be much more constraining than in error control. Indeed, the amount of storage is related to traffic patterns mismatches between two networks. In order to maintain a sufficient flow downstream, it may be necessary to buffer a certain number of information quanta.

The worst case occurs when the upstream portion of the logical link, say LL_a in Fig. 15.20, is lacking flow control (i.e., the receiving end has no way of limiting the amount of incoming data [SHEP 82]. This case is quite frequent, because a popular way of attaching an existing system, without modification to its software, is to use a terminal port, such as a remote batch or interactive terminal. Terminals are usually fed data at a nominal rate depending on their mechanical characteristics (i.e., they are flow controlled from the source of the data stream). Thus a gateway may be confronted with the problem of gobbling up a whole file gushing in at line printer speed, while the outlet is a 300-bps trickle. That is a definition of flash flood. The only cure is enough buffer (i.e., overflow on secondary storage). If such an occurrence is rare, it may be acceptable to throw away excess traffic and go to a recovery procedure, if one exists.

15.6.6   Interrupts

Interrupts are short messages used for signaling, especially when normal operation must be interrupted or resumed. They may be delivered ahead of data sent before them, and they must bypass any blockage due to error or flow control.

If interrupts could be transmitted in very large numbers, it is conceivable that they would have to be submitted to some form of flow control. In practice, protocol designers assume that interrupts may be lost and retransmitted, or that there can only be one outstanding interrupt until it is acknowledged. This obviates the need for more refined error and flow control.

When a logical link with interrupts must be mapped into a logical link without interrupt, several options may be taken:

- Translate an interrupt into a special message in the data stream. This may be sufficient when the transmission system offers a maximum transit delay. Then the interrupt is extracted from data buffered at the receiver end. However, this screening will usually require software adjunction, if interrupts were not expected in the original system.
- Translate an interrupt into a killer packet, which destroys information in transit ahead of itself (e.g., by resetting the logical link). This option is not acceptable as a general solution, but it may do when interrupts are only used as a means to abandon an active process.
- Transmit interrupts as datagrams, when the transmission system offers this service.
- Open a separate logical link for interrupts.

When the two logical links in each network offer an interrupt mechanism, some difficulties may still occur:

- One network carries shorter-length interrupts than the other. Then one may attempt to restrict the use of interrupts to the shortest acceptable length. Or one may split an interrupt into a shorter interrupt, with an extension sent separately in the data stream.
- Acknowledging interrupts may become ambiguous when the two logical links do not apply identical semantics: for example, an acknowledgement generated in a gateway does not mean that the interrupt has been delivered properly to its final destination.

15.6.7   Timings

Communication protocols are protected against deadlocks by timers, which trigger certain emergency or recovery actions when expected messages do not materialize. Values chosen for timeouts are dependent on specific environment characteristics, such as transit delay, response time, or other timings. End-to-end protocols workings are usually sensitive to lower-layer timings, because they affect performance or even integrity. Changing a lower layer, or putting several in cascade may play havoc in the overall timer tuning. Unfortunately, there does not appear to be a methodology for solving timing problems. Exhaustive study by hand, or simulation, are most often applied.

15.6.8   Dialogue

This mechanism boils down to: Whose turn is it to transmit? Modern systems handle this matter in a formal manner, by placing delimiters, or special flags, in the data stream. The initial turn is determined by convention, or contention. Additional features are made available to speed up or force a turn exchange. These conventions constitute a dialogue protocol, which may be built into an application-oriented protocol, such as virtual terminal, file transfer, remote job entry, and so on. Dialogue is handled in the session layer of the ISO model.

Older systems do not generally use such conventions. Turn exchange is determined as a result of message parsing, special character sequences, or as an established custom. All that is highly context sensitive, and in some cases ambiguous. Mistakes do occur when a user keys in data that were not expected at that time.

Mapping a fuzzy turn system into a formal one is generally not feasible. A typical way around this consists of setting a free mode, in which both ends may transmit at any time. Human users are then warned to follow specific conventions, lest they get into unpredictable traps.

15.6.9   Diagnostics

Modern protocols are designed with a set of coded error messages. Mapping an error code into another is often a difficult exercise, because the label attached to an error message is rather vague and does not really tell what is actually causing the error. Some protocols come with a rich variety of error conditions; others are more laconic. There is usually no possible one-to-one mapping. An accepted practice consists in turning error conditions without obvious equivalent into a catchall message, such as: unidentified error, network failure, or some other bland epigram. Of course, error analysis and recovery is then left to the user or a higher-layer protocol.

A worse case is the mapping of a physical device into some other protocol. Typically, output devices are supposed to be monitored by human operators who understand English or whatever language they speak. Thus diagnostics appear as meaningful or meaningless plain text inserted into a data stream, with hardly any obvious separator, except perhaps a new line followed by a few exotic characters. This is, of course, quite intractable in a mechanized environment. The only cure is to sleuth about for expectable diagnostic texts and strip them off data streams. This approach can only work statistically, as there are always unheard-of diagnostics bound to show up some day. On the other hand, mischievous users may have fun producing output that looks just like error messages.

Warning messages, such as "HOST GOING DOWN IN 10 MIN," may slip through totally unnoticed when they originate from a host operator who types what he or she wants. If this is unacceptable, one should map other layers than an interactive terminal.

15.6.10   Supervision

Sophisticated systems are now equipped with a battery of internal supervisory tools exercised through very specific control messages. It is unrealistic to attempt any kind of mapping, as supervision is intimately tied into implementation. Thus as far as supervision is concerned, systems or networks remain disconnected. Even if some border crossing were technically feasible, it is usually opposed by the persons in charge of operation, because they do not want external interference in monitoring, statistics gathering, troubleshooting, reconfiguration phases, and so on. A familiar implication is that no one is in charge of the overall operation of interconnected networks. When users complain, they are often told that the blame is with the other guy. This finger-pointing syndrome is already becoming a standard fixture of public packet networks.

15.6.10.1 Accounting

Technically, accounting (i.e., gathering billing information) could be viewed as an appendage to supervision. However, a minimum of consistency across networks is required, so that traffic exchanged can be accounted for in the same manner on each side of the border. Then commercial strategies may be more difficult to map into one another than accounting data. Some networks bill characters, others bill packets. Some charge for connection set up, some do not. There can only be ad hoc solutions to specific problems.

15.7 ROUTING

Routing is the set of functions in charge of choosing a physical, or sometimes logical, path from a source to a destination. Star-shaped networks need no routing, as there is only one route between two points. When a network includes switching components, there may be several, if not a very large number of potential routes. Choosing one requires some strategy and associated mechanisms.

When two or more networks are interconnected, potential physical routes may increase. Thus existing routing mechanisms may no longer be sufficient [SUNS 77]. In the following sections we examine some typical topologies.

15.7.1 One Gateway

The gateway is the only physical path between two networks (Fig. 15.3). A route from A to B, say R (A, B) is composed of R (A, C) followed by R (C, B). This composition may be called *concatenation* or cascade.

When interconnecting networks an overall routing strategy is usually excluded, either due to technical difficulties, or because networks are operated by separate organizations, or because there does not appear to be any benefit in coupling routing. Thus R (A, C) and R (C, B) remain independent. Routing mechanisms are not affected by interconnection. Delivering messages to an intermediate point (C) is normally achieved as a result of the particular naming scheme adopted for "foreign" destinations (see Sec. 15.6).

By property of recurrence, the same holds true for a daisy chain of networks (Fig. 15.21), or for any topology in which routes go through a fixed sequence of gateways. The path may be unique or it may be predetermined.

Figure 15.21. Daisy chain.

15.7.2 Two Gateways

The topology in Fig. 15.22 suggests that two gateways instead of one are provided for better reliability. This means that when one internetwork path fails, all traffic should use the other path. Another reason might be that more than one gateway is necessary to handle the total traffic. Yet another reason may be route optimization when the two networks overlap geographically.

In any case, an implication is that network A, for example, should be capable of routing traffic to B through gateway C or D, depending on various criteria not necessarily related to the identity of the final destination. Thus routing in A must use more than one physical outgoing port toward entities located in B. This capability comes free when A uses a logical name space decoupled from physical components Otherwise (e.g., in X.25 networks) the route from A toward a particular entity in B will always use the same gateway. Overcoming this deficiency requires the development of a complex name substitution scheme allowing an entity in B to be viewed from A as distinct entities with different names. The name selected for routing from A to B would have to be broadcast to all potential sources, or they would have to search for it. Aside from its complexity, such a scheme would introduce specific protocols applicable to this class of interconnection topologies.

Multiple gateways between two networks are a generalization of this case. The same problems arise as with two gateways. However, there do not seem to be many practical situations requiring multiple gateways.

15.7.3 Meshed Interconnection

Several networks are interconnected so that there are several distinct routes going through different sequences of networks: for example, in Fig. 15.23, R (x, y) may be established through A-B-D, A-D, A-C-D, and so on. This case is likely to become typical for national public networks interconnected through international gateways.

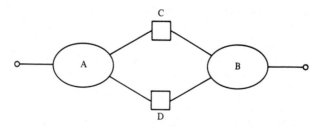

Figure 15.22. Multiple interconnection.

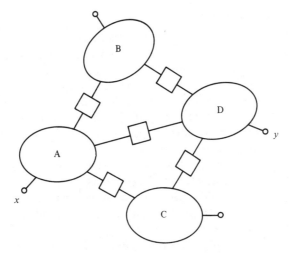

Figure 15.23. Meshed interconnection.

Depending on gateway functionalities and on network similarities, this topology may be viewed through several models, as explained in the following sections.

15.7.3.1 Similar Networks

When all interconnected networks offer a datagram service, gateways may be thought of as passive packet repeaters or translators. As long as naming schemes allow using one physical port for several destinations, packets may be routed to their destination through an arbitrary sequence of networks. The whole set of interconnected networks appears externally as a single datagram network. This approach, which has been termed the Catenet [POUZ 74A], allows an indefinite extension of the number of interconnected networks, and makes the interconnection topology transparent to higher-layer protocols. Thus the topology may be rearranged without affecting users.

Each network must deliver traffic to one or several gateways. If every destination is mapped onto a single gateway, the problem is identical to the one-gateway case (see Sec. 15.7.1). Otherwise, some route selection would be necessary [BOGG 80].

Each gateway must deliver traffic to one or several networks. Here again, it seems that in practice gateways do not perform routing functions, since the path is unique or predetermined.

One might think that the Catenet would apply as well to the other kind of packet interface, virtual circuits à la X.25. Actually, this is not so. Indeed, X.25 contains a mix of end-to-end functions, and local interface functions. As has been shown in Fig. 15.20, cascading end-to-end functions does not yield an end-to-end function. To make the matter worse, X.25 contains explicitly or implicitly optional end-to-end functions, for which national and international carriers make different choices. Thus the end-to-end service resulting from a particular topology is by and large undefined. It has to be determined case by case [GROS 79].

15.7.3.2 *Dissimilar Networks*

When interconnected networks are very dissimilar, gateways become sophisticated converters mapping several layers of protocols, perhaps up to application-
oriented layers such as a virtual terminal. Then one may take the dual view of a set of
gateways interconnected through transmission networks [CERF 78]. Due to gateways heterogeneity and organization independence, no substantial cooperation may
be expected among gateways. Therefore, global optimization of the traffic or end-to-
end functions are not even attempted. The notion of a high-level network using
gateways as switching nodes has not yet materialized.

Since gateways perform higher-layer protocols mapping, the mode of data
transmission is usually some form of virtual circuit. It may be necessary for an
application protocol, or a human user, to step through gateways for establishing a
virtual circuit. Routing is either predetermined or chosen by the user in connecting
successively through each traversed network.

This form of interconnection is presently used between several public packet
networks (Telenet, TYMNET, Datapac).

15.8   INTERCONNECTION IN PRACTICE

This section illustrates some of the techniques presented earlier. It gives short descriptions of several implementation cases.

15.8.1   CIGALE and EIN

These two networks were built as research tools. CIGALE [POUZ 74B] is the packet
network of the CYCLADES computer network in France. EIN [BARB 76] is the
packet network of a European computer network. Both networks are very similar.
CIGALE and EIN are datagram networks. They use the same packet format, but:

- Some network services are different.
- Interfaces and line procedures are different.

Therefore, it is not possible to interconnect directly a CIGALE node and an EIN
node. A gateway has been developed. Its functions are:

- Exchange packets with CIGALE using an ECMA frame and a specific
  line procedure. *Note:* ECMA frames are character oriented. The layout is
  as follows: SYN, SYN, DLE, STX, text, DLE, ETX, checksum, SYN,
  SYN.
- Exchange packets with EIN using an HDLC frame and a specific line
  procedure. *Note:* HDLC frames are bit oriented. The layout is as follows:
  Flag, address, control, text, checksum, flag.
- Filter out or convert requests for network services.

There is no need for name mapping in the gateway, since both CIGALE and EIN use a hierarchical name space containing a network name.

This interconnection makes CIGALE and EIN appear as a single network for packet transmission. It is a perfect application of the Catenet approach.

15.8.2 CYCLADES and Transpac (Fig. 15.24)

At the time this interconnection scheme was devised, the CYCLADES network interconnected more than 20 computers and about 10 terminal concentrators. It used CIGALE for packet transmission. Transpac, the French PTT packet network, was to replace CIGALE by the end of 1979. Transpac offers only a virtual circuit service through an X.25 interface.

In order to use Transpac, computers on CYCLADES were provided with an adapter (a bridge) mapping a datagram interface onto a virtual circuit interface. Bridges are intended for several modes of adaptation:

1. Allow communications between CYCLADES computers (A, B, C) and terminal concentrators (D).
2. Allow communications between CYCLADES computers (A, B, C) and computers attached directly to Transpac through an X.25 interface (E).
3. Allow communications between CYCLADES computers (A, B, C) and terminals attached to Transpac through an X.28 interface (F).

Each mode corresponds to the mapping of a different layer. Mode 1 maps the transmission layer (i.e., datagram/virtual circuit. It is modeled as shown in Fig. 15.8.

Mode 2 maps the transport layer. CYCLADES protocols include explicitly a transport layer. Computers attached directly to Transpac may be provided with only an X.25 interface (i.e., the minimum required). The choice made for the mapping is to consider level 3 of X.25 (the one handling virtual circuits) as a pseudo-transport layer for Transpac computers. Then the mapping applies between CYCLADES logical

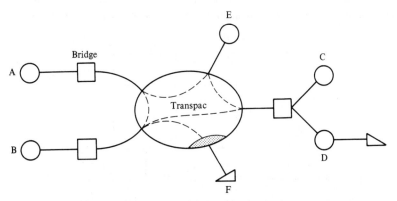

Figure 15.24. CYCLADES and Transpac.

links (called liaisons) and X.25 virtual circuits. The model is shown in Figs. 15.9 and 15.17.

Mode 3 maps the CYCLADES virtual terminal protocol into commands required by X.29, for handling asynchronous terminals through TRANSPAC. The model is as shown in Fig. 15.12.

A diagrammatic representation of the functional layers of the CYCLADES–Transpac bridge is shown in Fig. 15.25.

15.8.2.1 Transmission Layer

When communications take place between CYCLADES gear, only mode 1 is used. Its functions are:

- Exchange "letters" with CYCLADES computers through one of the synchronous line procedures in use.
- Exchange packets with Transpac through an X.25 interface.
- Fragment letters into packet sequences, with appropriate X.25 headers.
- Reassemble packets into letters, and strip off X.25 headers.

Note: A letter is the information quantum in CYCLADES transport stations (0 to 4K octets) [ZIMM 75].

Bridges use permanent or switched virtual circuits. This is a matter for further trade-off. There is only one virtual circuit between any two bridges.

In addition, some modifications are required in existing transport station software, so that they input–output letters rather than CIGALE packets.

No conceptual difficulties arise at this level, because the transmission layer in CYCLADES is assumed to be a simple packet carrier, which does not guarantee the delivery of every packet. Thus transmission integrity still relies on the transport protocol.

15.8.2.2 Transport Layer

The variety of X.25 implemented in Transpac does not contain any end-to-end control functions. It is only a local interface. Consequently, it is not possible to

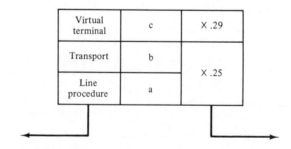

Figure 15.25. CYCLADES–Transpac bridge.

maintain end-to-end control between a CYCLADES computer and a Transpac computer using only X.25. The end-to-end transport protocol terminates in the bridge, and cascades into a virtual circuit, as shown in Fig. 15.20. Therefore, there is no longer a guarantee of transmission integrity through Transpac.

Opening a liaison in CYCLADES translates into opening a virtual circuit in Transpac. Interrupts messages must be limited to 8 bits (due to X.25). There is no mapping error and flow control. Mode 2 acts simply as a buffer between two independent logical links.

15.8.2.3   *Virtual Terminal Layer*

The virtual terminal protocol in CYCLADES consists of coded messages carrying text or control information [NAFF 78A]. It is designed for handling a hypothetical message terminal. Physical terminal handling is delegated to terminal concentrators, so that application programs are unaware of the specific characteristics of the real terminal (half or full-duplex, line length, delays, control keys, etc.).

The X.29 interface consists of packet formats reflecting closely the functions of an ASCII character terminal. The physical characteristics of the terminal are not hidden. On the contrary, they are explicitly visible as a set of 16 parameters, which may take different values.

In order to accommodate a variety of physical terminals, without destroying the principle of virtual terminal, mode 3 of the bridge contains a set of standard parameter values applying to various classes of real terminals.

The mapping between X.29 packet formats and virtual terminal messages is rather straightforward. As mentioned earlier, there is a "turn" problem because there is no dialogue control in X.29. Thus it is assumed that a break character as defined in X.29 indicates a turn exchange. Characters typed by a terminal user when no turn is available are just saved into a buffer, in order to allow typing ahead.

15.8.2.4.   *Summary*

To sum up, the CYCLADES—Transpac bridge is actually three gateways in one box. Each of the modes is exercised for a specific class of adaptation. Users may buy only the modes they need. This example illustrates the case of two networks structured in well-defined layers, but layers are in different numbers (three in CYCLADES, two in Transpac), and they are not functionally equivalent.

15.8.3   CYCLADES and EIN

Both CYCLADES and EIN are heterogeneous computer networks. They are so similar that they may be presented as two successive versions of the same design, with the same set of protocol layers. In Sec. 15.8.1 we outlined the interconnection of the transmission layers, composed of datagram networks. In this section we cover the interconnection of the transport and virtual terminal layers.

Since both networks are quasi-identical, the model in Fig. 15.11 applies. It consists of interconnecting peer layers, independent of each other.

15.8.3.1 Transport Protocols

Both transport protocols are described in [ZIMM 75] and [EIN 76]. Both are practically identical, except that:

- Some control fields are larger in the EIN transport protocol, since the numbering cycle is longer.
- Negotiation of parameters is not implemented in CYCLADES.
- Telegrams (i.e., interrupt messages) are acknowledged in EIN but not in CYCLADES.

The mapping of letter numbers is straightforward, since letters are in one-to-one correspondence. So are messages opening and closing liaisons.

Messages originating from EIN for parameter negotiation are intercepted by the gateway, and answered in a predefined manner. Interrupts acknowledgments sent from EIN are also intercepted by the gateway. Since they consume credits (i.e., the right to send one letter), the gateway returns one credit per acknowledgment, in order to keep the credit status unchanged.

15.8.3.2. Virtual Protocols

Both virtual terminal protocols are described in [NAFF 78A] and [EIN 77]. All messages are in one-to-one correspondence. Differences appear in the coding of some control fields, which are transcoded by the gateway. An odd discrepancy results from a CYCLADES feature allowing a condensed coding of message lengths. Since this feature does not exist in EIN, the letters length may increase when mapping from CYCLADES to EIN. When the new length happens to overflow the maximum length agreed in opening the liaison, an extraneous letter is generated by the gateway. This must be balanced by the gateway taking away one credit from the next EIN allocation.

15.8.4 Front-End Converter

When attaching a computer to a network based on the model in Fig. 15.5, protocols layers have to be inserted somehow between application programs and the transmission network. They could be part of a telecommunication access method integrated with the bulk of the operating system. Actually, this is done by computer manufacturers only for their own products. As manufacturers' protocols are not yet standardized the development of a specific software package for a heterogeneous network would be an expensive one-time investment.

To get around this problem, a most popular way of attaching computers, without altering their native software, consists in building a gateway in the form of a front-end converter (Fig. 15.26). The converter emulates some physical terminal normally supported by a native access method (e.g., TTY's, or a message terminal). Messages exchanged with the emulated terminal are mapped into appropriate virtual terminal messages. The converter also implements all protocol layers necessary to be homogeneous with the overall network conventions [NAFF 78B].

In Fig. 15.26, the layer called network interface is dependent on the specific transmission network to which the gateway is physically connected. It is X.25 in the case of public networks using this standard. It reduces to a synchronous transmission procedure such as HDLC in the case of a datagram network. It could be a contention handling procedure in the case of a local broadcast network such as Ethernet [METC 76].

This form of computer attachment to packet networks has become so popular that many commercial products are available. They emulate the most frequent terminals in the field, mainly TTY's and IBM's. The hardware is typically a multi-microprocessor construction, pipelining messages through the various functional layers.

15.8.5 Procedure Conversion

A typical case of terminal emulation, as in the case described in Sec. 15.8.4, occurs with a multipoint circuit, as shown in Fig. 15.26. Multipoint circuits are normally handled with a synchronous procedure operated in a polling mode. This allows higher speeds and better control than asynchronous circuits used with TTY's.

In polling mode, a master station (the central computer) directs all exchanges by sending messages to all terminals. All of them listen, as nothing prevents signals

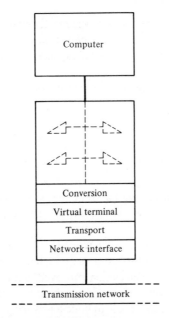

Figure 15.26. Front-end converter.

from being received at all points. However, by convention, only the terminal whose address is in the message executes the specified action. The master station keeps sending messages which must be acknowledged by the addressed terminal within a specified delay. Terminals can only transmit when they are invited. Thus each terminal must be polled frequently enough so that the human user does not have to wait too long. In practice every terminal is polled between twice per second, and every 5 sec.

With a packet transmission network, it would be technically feasible to deliver polling messages to terminals and return their answer. However, transmission delays would increase drastically the cycle period necessary to poll every terminal. In addition, public packet networks charges are volume sensitive, with a minimum charge per packet. Consequently, polling messages are not exchanged through a packet network.

The conversion operated in the gateway consists in decoupling transmission over the (emulated) multipoint circuit and over the logical link to the terminal. Both are joined through a pair of queues in the gateway (one queue for input, one for output).

The input queue is polled by the master station. If a message has already arrived from the terminal, it is transmitted. Otherwise, an EOT (end of transmission) is sent.

Output sent by the master station is stored into the output queue and forwarded to the terminal. In case of buffer saturation in the gateway, a WABT (wait) is returned to the master station.

One may observe that this form of conversion introduces functional changes:

- Acknowledgments received by the master station mean only that a message has been well received by the gateway, not by the terminal.
- Terminals may be operated in full duplex (i.e., inputting while outputting).

Depending on the application environment, these changes may have a positive or a negative effect.

15.9   STANDARDIZATION

It certainly would appear more rational to define standards for a network architecture, protocols, and interfaces. However, one should keep in mind a few realistic observations.

Existing networks will remain alive much longer than their individual components. What makes networks obsolete is neither their components, which can be replaced, nor their protocols, which can be improved, but the services they offer. It is only when pressure builds for new services, which cannot be accommodated on existing systems, that a decision is made to build a new network offering both existing and new services. The life cycle of a network is about 10 years.

Making standards is a lengthy process. Many parties must reach a consensus, and technicalities are a challenge. Bypassing this maturation process leads to clumsy design for which general acceptance and expected life time are reduced.

In practical terms, standardization does not eliminate diversity, and never will. It only weeds out an excess of diversity. Standardization is not an alternative to network interconnection problems, but it may alleviate them.

Although it is often advocated to design systems top-down, standardization progresses bottom-up. This is probably so because it is close to impossible to reach overall agreement on a complete set of standards. Instead, standard committees start with the minimum acceptable by all parties, and that is usually at a low level.

15.9.1   Electrical Interface

Interconnecting two pieces of equipment requires some wiring, physical connectors, and conventions on electrical characteristics. There are many independent industry or military standards for short-distance connections. Long-distance connections are normally established through common-carrier facilities. Thus standards in that area are produced by a common-carrier club, CCITT (Comité Consultatif International Telegraphique et Téléphonique), in which the European state monopolies, or PTTs (Post Telegraph Telephone), exert an overwhelming influence.

Basic CCITT standards for electrical connection are V24 and X.21.

15.9.1.1   V24 Interface

V24 is the electrical and mechanical interface between a data processing terminal and a modem, for speeds up to 20 kbps. Another variant, V35, is required for higher speeds.

Modems work in pairs. They translate digital signals into modulated voice frequencies carried through telephone circuits. Even though intermodem signaling is also standardized, speeds higher than 1200 bps usually require modems of the same make.

15.9.1.2   X.21 Interface

X.21 is an interface designed for public data networks using digital transmission. In addition to electrical and mechanical characteristics, it includes a procedure for establishing and closing switched digital circuits. There is no upper limit on the bit speed.

The initial definition of X.21 dates from 1972. However, very few public digital data networks are operational. Thus the application of X.21 has lagged.

15.9.2   Transmission Procedure

The International Standard Organization (ISO) is a federation of national standardization bodies. Since 1976 they have undertaken the definition of a standard procedure for exchanging data blocks over a circuit. This effort was crowned in 1976 with the adoption of a set of standards for various configurations:

- Point-to-point balanced mode, where both ends have equal capabilities.
- Point-to-point unbalanced mode, where one end is a master station (called a primary), and the other a slave (called secondary).
- Multipoint mode, with one primary and several secondaries.

The generic term used to qualify these standards is HDLC (High-level Data Link Control) [ISO 76, ISO 77]. By the time it was adopted, many higher-levels protocols had sprung up, putting HDLC at a low level. The term "HDLC" is used to mean different levels of standards, not always in a proper sense. It can apply to the framing of the transmitted data blocks, to the data block format, or to the procedure, as will be explained in the following. A pure HDLC standard implementation should apply all these levels. In practice, many implementations are hybrid, as they take only some levels of HDLC.

15.9.2.1 Frame Level

HDLC is intended for the transmission of data blocks, not characters. Due to technical constraints associated with signal processing, it is necessary to introduce clear separations between noise and meaningful signals. This is called *framing*. Separators are special bit sequences which occur at the beginning and at the end of an information block, in order to indicate unambiguously where the meaningful bits are located.

In the HDLC standard [ISO 76], the special bit sequence used as a separator is called a *flag*. Its value is 01111110.

Confusion would definitely arise when transmitting data containing some bit pattern identical to a flag. This is prevented with an additional convention called *bit stuffing*, which preserves data transparency. Whenever five consecutive 1's occur in transmitting data, the transmitter inserts an extraneous 0. Conversely, a receiver drops a 0 following five consecutive 1's. Thus there cannot be any confusion between flags and data. A sequence such as Flag Data Flag is called a *frame*.

The generation of flags and the bit stuffing as well as their recognition are usually done in hardware as part of an I/O adapter.

15.9.2.2 Format Level

Data in between flags are formatted as shown in Fig. 15.27. Field A (8 bits) designates the address of the sending or receiving secondary. Field C (8 bits) contains control information. Field TEXT, if present, contains any bit sequence. Field FCS (16 bits) is a frame-checking sequence (i.e., a cyclical checksum), ensuring with a high probability the bit integrity of the whole frame.

The computation and checking of FCS is usually performed in hardware.

15.9.2.3 Procedure Level

Historically, the term *procedure* has been used to designate the set of rules followed by a transmitter and a receiver for exchanging data over a circuit. More

Figure 15.27. HDLC frame format.

recently, the term *protocol* was coined to designate similar rules in a more general context. These rules include error detection and recovery by retransmission.

The structure of HDLC procedures is based on commands and responses (i.e., coded messages exchanged between a primary and one or several secondaries). Field C in the frame format contains the coding of commands and responses [ISO 77].

Frames transmitted may be numbered or unnumbered. Numbered frames carry a number increasing sequentially. This is used by the receiver to detect missing or duplicate frames. Acknowledgments are numbers indicating that all frames sent with a lower number have been received correctly. The numbering cycle runs modulo 8, but it may be extended to 128.

Unnumbered frames are used for additional functions, such as resetting, initialization, or signaling.

HDLC procedures are usually implemented in software, or microprograms. There are some expectations that a chip will appear on the market.

15.9.2.4   Independent Application

HDLC framing, format, and procedure may be applied independently: for example, HDLC formatted blocks may be framed with the character sequences used over the last decade in conjunction with BSC procedures, while the procedure used could be specific. Thus the expression "We are using HDLC" calls for more lengthy explanations.

15.9.3   Virtual Circuit Interface

When some common carriers discovered belatedly the potential of packet switching, a hasty standardization effort led in 1976 to a new CCITT interface, called X.25. This interface provides the following functions:

- Establishing and closing virtual circuits
- Transmitting packets over a virtual circuit
- Controlling the flow of packets along a virtual circuit.

A complete description of X.25 may be found in CCITT documents [CCIT 77A]. In line with CCITT standards, X.25 does not specify how two user equipments exchange packets through a public network. Rather, it specifies how packets are exchanged between user equipment and a public data network.

With this approach, the rules for exchanging packets between two processes linked through a virtual circuit remain undefined. In practice, each carrier implements some specific options, which may be applied by its own subscribers. Linking two subscribers of the same network requires a careful matching of their options, unless they agree to have identical implementations. Linking two subscribers of different networks requires a specific study and depends on the way carriers convert options into one another [UNSO 81].

Much propaganda has emanated from some PTTs to spread the belief that X.25 is the solution to the reliable interconnection of any data equipment. This is not substantiated by fact.

15.9.4 ASCII Terminal Interface

The major attraction of public data networks is that tariffs are lower than those of switched or leased circuits for low-speed transmission. Therefore, standards have been defined for the attachment of asynchronous terminals, up to 2400 bps. The digital circuit interface is X.20; the virtual circuit interface is X.28.

Asynchronous terminals transmit characters (5 to 8 bits) framed with start and stop signals. X.4 defines the bit speed, format, and framing of characters. The human procedure for establishing and closing switched digital circuits is X.20.

Two terminals using X.20 and X.21 may call each other and exchange characters.

The attachment of an ASCII terminal to a virtual circuit requires a terminal handler, which converts an asynchronous character stream into X.25 packets. The terminal handler, called a PAD (packet assembler/disassembler), is part of public packet networks. In order to adapt to different terminals' characteristics, 16 parameters may be set by the human terminal user. The definition of these parameters are given in X.3. The command language available to the user for parameter setting, virtual circuit establishment, and packet transmission, is defined in X.28.

An ASCII terminal is usually in conversation with an interactive system on a computer attached through X.25. This latter standard is insufficient, because more functions are required to interact with a PAD for parameter setting and reading, and identification of the human user requests. They reflect in terms of packets the functions available to the terminal user. The corresponding standard is X.29.

15.9.5 Internetworking Standards

This area is still underdeveloped. The world of public transmission facilities is split roughly into three major techniques: telephony, digital circuit, and virtual circuit. All three are circuit oriented. Thus it appears tempting to build data paths out of segments based on different techniques, when the need arises. This is not implemented presently.

Telephone access to a virtual circuit network is the most common internetwork facility. The user must dial a phone number giving a connection to an asynchronous port on a PAD. Thereafter, the user may establish a virtual circuit by typing a command on a keyboard. However, there is no dial-out facility from a virtual circuit into the switched telephone system.

In anticipation of a futuristic world where every subscriber of any network could connect to any other subscriber of another network, a standard numbering plan has been standardized by CCITT as X.121 [CCIT 78]. It provides for the numbering of national data networks, with a hierarchical name space. Potentially, there is provision for dialing out into the telephone or Telex networks to reach a called subscriber.

After X.25 was defined, it turned out that another interface was desirable to interconnect X.25 networks. This additional interface, called X.75, is applied only between public networks. It is not available to private networks that would like to interconnect with public ones.

X.75 specifies how X.25 packets are presented at an internetwork boundary [CCIT 77B]. Since X.25 is a menu rather than a specification, each network is responsible for mapping its own options into X.75 terms. There is much similarity between X.75 and X.25. On one hand, X.75 does not offer options related to a subscriber interface. On the other hand, networks exchange additional information related to billing and routing.

15.9.6   OSI Standards

ISO has undertaken an ambitious program for standardizing an open system architecture (OSI). This work is carried out within TC97/SC 16. The goal is to define a set of layers with their associated protocols so as to make possible the interconnection of heterogeneous systems, without resorting to ad hoc adaptations.

The model agreed on [ISO 81] comprises seven layers. The top layer (7) is defined as being the user application. Below it are six functional layers:

6. *Presentation*. Pertaining to the handling of data structures.
5. *Session*. In charge of the management of logical connections between user applications. Standards agreed in 1983 are IS 8326 and 8327.
4. *Transport*. To present a unified and reliable service for transporting data. Standards agreed in 1982 are IS 8072 and 8073.
3. *Network*. Routing and signaling, such as the virtual circuit level of X.25.
2. *Procedure*. Management of a physical link to a transmission network.
1. *Physical*. Physical and electrical interface.

15.9.7   Proposed Standards

In anticipation of the ISO work, a number of professional organizations put forth proposals. The best known forum in which network experts work out some degree of international consensus is represented by IFIP working groups within the Technical Committee on Data Communications (TC.6).

The working group WG 6.1 has proposed.

- A datagram format
- A transport protocol

- A virtual terminal protocol
- A file transfer protocol

These proposals are backed by experiments in internetworking which establish their feasibility and provide some insight into performance parameters.

15.10 CONCLUSIONS

In this chapter we have presented methods and techniques for interconnecting networks, at various levels of services: transmission, transport, and virtual terminal. Numerous variations have been implemented and work almost to satisfaction. Practical solutions have been found for all major needs. There are, however, some remaining mismatches, for which no definite solution may be devised. This reflects a fundamental aspect of today's protocols. They were designed and implemented as natural objects, without formal definition. Natural objects cannot always be made totally equivalent.

In the future we can expect a further surge of new problems brought about by organizational requirements or newer technologies.

- Routing and flow control within interconnected networks are global problems for which solutions are yet to be determined. Little research has been done to date. A primary cause may be attributed to the lack of pressure for studying practical situations. Most organizations running networks tend to look at each other as competitors, or strangers at best. They do not favor interconnection schemes that would expose their inner workings or internal traffic patterns. They are not willing to become dependent on other networks' behavior. Nevertheless, they will, for the same reasons as air traffic control bodies have done so.
- Supervision is another area where a much higher degree of coupling would be necessary to achieve a good grade of service. However, well-established finger-pointing traditions within PTTs are not likely to improve very fast.
- Security has generally been neglected. A significant research and engineering effort would be necessary to work out practical schemes. However, cryptography is progressing steadily.
- Above the basic protocol levels, devoted primarily to communications, internetworking implies distributed applications with associated problems of distributed control, reliability, consistency, and so on. Research has been very active in this area since 1975. New developments and experiments are becoming available.
- Communications protocols of the past decade were based on logical links between two entities. New technologies used in local networks, radio, and satellites are based on an intrinsic broadcast technique which has not been fully explored functionally. New models of communication protocols

should be invented in the next few years with their corresponding problems of insertion within an existing environment [ELDE 81].
- The rapid transition to digital signals is spreading in telephony and image transmission. Integrated systems are already being developed by industry. It is clear that internetworking will become significantly more complex in such an environment.

Digital processing and computer systems are pervading continuously expanding fields of applications. As a result, communications between human organizations tend increasingly to be mediated through computers. Thus the functional requirements and the level of sophistication involved in interconnecting systems are likely to expand further.

REFERENCES

BARB 76   Barber, D. L. A., "A European Informatics Network—Achievement and Prospects," *Proc. ICCC*, Toronto, August 1976, pp. 44–50.

BOGG 80   Boggs, D., et al., "Pup: An Internetwork Architecture," *IEEE Trans. Commun.*, Vol. COM-28, No. 4, 1980, pp. 612–624.

CCIT 77A   CCITT, "Recommendation X.25—Interface between DTE and DCE for Terminals Operating in the Packet Mode on Public Data Networks," Orange Book, Vol. VIII.2, International Telecommunications Union, Geneva, 1977.

CCIT 77B   CCITT, "Recommendation X.75—Terminal and Transit Call Control Procedures and Data Transfer System on International Circuits between Packet Switched Data Networks," SG VII, Temp. Doc. 207-E, International Telecommunications Union, Geneva, 1977.

CCIT 78   CCITT, "Recommendation X.121—International Numbering Plan for Public Data Networks, SG VII, Temp. Doc. 186-E, International Telecommunications Union, Geneva, April 1978.

CERF 74   Cerf, V. G., and R. E. Kahn, "A Protocol for Packet Network Interconnection," *IEEE Trans. Commun.*, Vol. COM-22, May 1974, pp. 637–648.

CERF 78   Cerf, V. G., and P. T. Kirstein, "Issues in Packet Network Interconnection," *Proc. IEEE*, Vol. 66, No. 11, 1978, pp. 1386–1408.

COMP 79   Special Issue on Computer Networks and Date Protection Law, *Comput. Networks*, Vol. 3, No. 3, June 1979.

COTT 78   Cotton, I. W., "Computer Network Interconnection," *Comput. Networks*, Vol. 2, No. 1, February 1978, pp. 25–34.

DALA 81   Dalal, Y. K. and R. S. Printis, 48-bit Absolute Internet and Ethernet Host Numbers. *ACM-IEEE 7th Data Comm. Symp.*, Mexico City, October 1981, pp. 240–245.

DAY 78   Day, J., "A Bibliography on the Formal Specification and Verification of Computer Network Protocols," *Proc. Comput. Networks Protocols Symp.*, Liège, February 1978, p. 3.

DICI 79   Diciccio, V., C. Sunshine, J. A. Field, and E. G. Manning, "Alternatives for

Interconnection of Public Packet Switching Data Networks," *ACM–IEEE 6th Data Commun. Symp.*, Pacific Grove, Calif., November 1979, pp. 120–125.

EIN 76   *European Informatics Network*: An End-to-End Protocol for EIN, EIN/76/003, NPL, London, January 1976.

EIN 77   European Informatics Network Proposal for a Scroll-Mode Virtual Terminal, EIN/CCG/77/02, NPL, London, February 1977.

ELDE 81   Elden, W. L., "Gateways for Interconnecting Local Area and Long Haul Networks," *Proc. Local Networks Distributed Office Syst.*, London, ON-LINE ed., May 1981, pp. 391–406.

GIEN 75   Gien, M., J. Laws, and R. Scantlebury, "Interconnection of Packet Switched Networks: Theory and Practice," *Eurocomp*, London, ONLINE ed., September 1975, pp. 241–260.

GIEN 79   Gien, M., and H. Zimmermann, "Design Principles for Network Interconnection," *ACM–IEEE 6th Data Commun. Symp.*, Pacific Grove, Calif., November 1979, pp. 109–119.

GROS 79   Grossman, G. G., A. Hinchley, and C. A. Sunshine, "Issues in International Networking," *Comput. Networks*, Vol. 3, No. 4, September 1979, pp. 259–266.

HIGG 75   Higginson, P. L., and A. J. Hinchley, "The Problems of Linking Several Networks with a Gateway Computer," *Eurocomp*, London, September 1975, pp. 452–466.

ISO 76   International Organization for Standardization, "High Level Data Link Control—Frame Structure," IS 3309, 1976.

ISO 77   International Organization for Standardization, "High Level Data Link Control—Elements of Procedures," IS 4335, 1977.

ISO 79   International Organization for Standardization, "Reference Model of Open Systems Interconnection," ISO/TC97/SC16/N227, June 1979, p. 181.

ISO 81   International Organization for Standardization, "Reference Model of Open Systems Interconnection," ISO/DIS 7498, April 1981.

LLOY 75   Lloyd, D., and P. T. Kirstein, "Alternative Approach to the Interconnection of Computer Networks," *Eurocomp*, London, September 1975, pp. 499–518.

METC 76   Metcalfe, R. M., and D. Boggs, "Ethernet: Distributed Packet Switching for Local Computer Networks," *Commun. ACM*, Vol. 19, No. 7, 1976, pp. 395–404.

NAFF 78A   Naffah, N., "High Level Protocol for Alphanumeric Data Entry Terminals," *Comput. Networks*, Vol. 2, No. 2, May 1978, pp. 84–94.

NAFF 78B   Naffah, N., and H. Zimmermann, "Protocol Converters and User Interface in the CYCLADES Network," 3rd Berkeley Workshop Distributed Data Manage. Comput. Networks, Berkeley, Calif., August 1978.

POST 71   Postel, J. B., "Official Initial Connection Protocol," NIC-7101, June 1971, p. 5.

POUZ 73   Pouzin, L., "Presentation and Major Design Aspects of the CYCLADES Computer Network," *ACM–IEEE 3rd Data Commun. Symp.*, November 1973, pp. 80–87.

POUZ 74A	Pouzin, L., "A Proposal for Interconnecting Packet Switching Networks," *Eurocomp*, London, May 1974, pp. 1023–1036.
POUZ 74B	Pouzin, L., "CIGALE—The Packet Switching Machine of the CYCLADES Computer Network," *IFIP Congr.*, Stockholm, August 1974, pp. 155–159.
POUZ 78	Pouzin, L., and H. Zimmermann, "A Tutorial on Protocols," *Proc. IEEE*, Vol. 66, No. 11, 1978, pp. 1346–1370.
POUZ 81	Pouzin, L., "Methods, Tools, and Observation on Flow Control in Packet-Switched Data Networks." *IEEE Trans. on Comm.*, Vol. COM-29, April 1981, pp. 413–426.
ROBE 70	Roberts, L. G., and B. D. Wessler, "Computer Network Development to Achieve Resource Sharing," AFIPS–SJCC, May 1970, pp. 543–549.
SHEP 82	Shepherd, D., and P. Corcoran, "A Gateway Development System." *Microprocessors and Microsystems*, Vol. 6, No. 1, January 1982, pp. 21–24.
SHOC 79	Schoch, J., "Packet Fragmentation in Inter-network Protocols," *Comput. Networks*, Vol. 3, No. 1, February 1979, pp. 3–9.
SUNS 77	Sunshine, C. A., "Interconnection of Computer Networks," *Comput. Networks*, Vol. 1, No. 3, January 1977, pp. 175–195.
UNSO 81	Unsoy, M. S., and T. A. Shanahan, "X.75 Internetworking of Datapac and Telenet." *ACM–IEEE 7th Data Commun. Symp.*, Mexico City, October 1981, pp. 232–239.
WALD 75	Walden, D. C., and R. D. Rettberg, "Gateway Design for Computer Network Interconnection," *Eurocomp*, London, September 1975, pp. 113–128.
ZIMM 75	Zimmermann, H., "The CYCLADES End-to-End Protocol," *ACM–IEEE 4th Data Commun. Symp.*, Quebec City, October 1975, pp. 7.21–7.26.
ZIMM 78	Zimmermann, H., and N. Naffah, "On Open Systems Architecture," *Proc. ICCC*, Kyoto, September 1978, pp. 669–674.
ZIMM 80	Zimmermann, H., "The ISO Model of Architecture for Open Systems Interconnection," *IEEE Trans. Commun.*, April 1980, pp. 425–432.

16

Packet, Circuit, and Virtual Circuit Switching

MARIO GERLA
Computer Science Department
University of California,
Los Angeles, California

16.1 INTRODUCTION

Early computer communications were supported by dedicated, point-to-point circuits. The typical configuration consisted of a star topology with the main computer at the center, connected to a number of local and remote terminals and peripheral devices. In the mid-1960s, however, the advancement of computer technology and the increased complexity of computer applications led to the evolution of data processing from a centralized to a distributed organization with data bases and software programs distributed over several smaller computers at different sites rather than concentrated in a single super machine.

This geographical distribution of resources made it necessary to build communications networks that permit each device to be connected to any other device in the system. Having ruled out the fully interconnected, point-to-point topology solution as generally being non-cost effective, network designers turned to switched solutions that would permit better utilization of the communication facilities without compromising the integrity and quality of data transmissions.

Since the mid-1960s, the data-switching technology has undergone a constant evolution under the increasing pressure of demanding users and sophisticated applications on the one side, and the availability of a rapidly advancing minicomputer and microprocessor technology on the other. In this chapter we trace this evolution. We review a number of data-switching techniques, we investigate the reasons for their development, and we establish criteria for the selection of one or the other of these techniques to meet given user requirements.

Before discussing one by one the specific switching techniques, it is appropriate to describe briefly the various phases of the data-switching evolution in recent years.

EVOLUTION OF DATA SWITCHING
TECHNIQUES

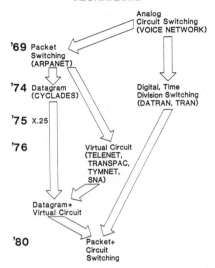

Figure 16.1. Evolution of data switching techniques.

This historical background will be helpful in understanding the differences and similarities existing among various techniques (see Fig. 16.1).

Before the mid-1960s the only switching technology available was the analog circuit switching technology used in the public voice network. Data, therefore, were initially switched through the voice network. Major drawbacks of this mode of operation were, however, the long setup delay, the lack of line error recovery, the inefficient use of the facilities by bursty users, and the speed selection limitation.

In the late 1960s, ARPANET was developed under government sponsorship to overcome the limitations of analog switching [HEAR 70, ROBE 70]. The result was the packet-switching technology, which is described in detail in Sec. 16.2. ARPANET was a major success and served as the model for a large number of private and public networks in the early 1970s.

In the view of some researchers, however, the ARPANET packet protocol was still too close to the circuit-switching approach. The network, for example, was required to set up a virtual connection from entry to exit node for each user session request. An effort to move any remaining notion of circuit (or better, virtual circuit) to the user level culminated in the *pure packet* or *datagram* protocol implemented in the French Network CYCLADES in 1974 [POUZ 73]. The communications subnetwork of CYCLADES, called CIGALE, is implemented as a basic transport medium offering as a sole service the transfer of individual packets from entry to exit point. No end-to-end error protection, resequencing, or reassembly is provided within the network.

While the research community was perfecting the definition and implementation of the datagram protocol, the business and public carrier environments started exploring the possibility of a standard network access protocol that would permit any computer or intelligent terminal to talk to any network by means of a single software and hardware interface. A design effort sponsored by CCITT produced in 1976 the X.25 recommendation for access to a packet network [CCIT 76]. The X.25 protocol, in sharp contrast with the datagram protocol, specifically required the network to set up a virtual circuit for each user session, and to use the virtual circuit facility for address identification and flow control.

After the approval of X.25 as the official international standard, virtually all packet networks (public and private) started the development of X.25 interfaces to provide X.25 service to their customers. Since the X.25 standard applies only to the network access segment, the network manufacturers still had considerable freedom in internal (node-to-node) protocol design. Some manufacturers, as the Canadian Datapac, for example, chose to retain a datagram-switching protocol inside the network [RYBC 77]. Other manufacturers opted for an all-out X.25 implementation in which a network path is set up in advance for each user session and data are transferred along the path using a hop-by-hop X.25 protocol. The latter implementation, most commonly known as *virtual circuit switching,* was followed by the majority of the public carriers including GTE-Telenet [ROBE 75], Transpac [DANE 76], and Euronet [DAVI 76].

As an improvement on the datagram protocol, the X.25 virtual circuit protocol introduced a number of safeguards and protection measures within the network which were particularly appealing to the public carriers. One well-recognized disadvantage of the X.25 protocol, however, was the delay incurred in setting up virtual calls. This delay, generally on the order of seconds, precluded the use of the X.25 protocol for one extremely important application: inquiry/response. To overcome this limitation, and under the pressure of the datagram lobby, the CCITT organization later approved a proposal for the combination of the datagram and virtual circuit switching schemes in an expanded X.25 standard interface [SEVC 78, FOLT 80].

While packet-switching protocols were refined and standardized, the circuit-switching world was experiencing a parallel evolution. Time-division switching was introduced in the early 1970s as a new, more efficient form of circuit switching [CHEN 75]. Time-division switching eliminated some of the drawbacks of analog switching: it offered a broad selection of circuit speeds (while voice-grade speed only was available in analog voice networks), it drastically reduced call setup times, and it improved network monitoring and control.

With the improvements introduced by time-division switching, the circuit-switched network approach became again attractive for a number of data users. In particular, it became attractive for users interested in high-data-rate, batch transfer applications, who saw little advantage in the segmentation of their files into small packets to be delivered individually through the network. Circuit switching also gained support from users heavily committed to a synchronous protocol environment (e.g., BSC or SDLC), who opted for the transparent (although perhaps less efficient) circuit-switched solution rather than engaging in the development of X.25 software and hardware interfaces for all of their host and terminal devices.

The circuit-switched option became even more attractive in the late 1970s when new potential applications appeared on the horizon: digitized voice, facsimile, and video. In a modern, automated office environment, voice, video, and fax communications requirements are as important as data requirements. Therefore, the possibility of merging all of these requirements into a common integrated network received immediate attention. It soon became obvious, however, that neither packet nor circuit protocol alone could satisfy the combination of such diverse applications, with their extremely different delay and bandwidth requirements. Therefore, the only possible solution was the combination of packet and circuit switching in a common, integrated network architecture. Development of integrated switching architectures was carried out successfully in both research [COVI 75] and industrial [GERL 78A] environments.

Looking back to Fig. 16.1, we observe that the history of modern data switching starts in the mid-1960s with the contraposition of packet and circuit switching as diametrically opposite disciplines, and gradually evolves in the following 15 years toward an integration of selected features from the packet- and circuit-switching technology into a common, integrated architecture.

In this chapter we study this evolution and its causes. We start by classifying switching schemes in Sec. 16.2. In Sec. 16.3 we discuss datagram switching and place particular emphasis on the limitations of the datagram protocol, which motivated the development of a new switching technique, virtual circuit switching. This new technique is then described in Sec. 16.4, with ample reference to existing implementations. The inadequacies still existing in the virtual circuit scheme are examined in Sec. 16.5, and the integrated packet- and circuit-switched approach is presented as a possible solution to such problems. A number of integrated network architectures are reviewed, and integrated network control issues are addressed. Section 16.6 offers some concluding remarks on the data-switching evolution that occurred in recent years, and some views of the advances in switching technology that we may witness in future years.

16.2   MULTIPLEXING AND SWITCHING TECHNIQUES

To understand and place the switching alternatives of a distributed network in a proper perspective, we must first understand the alternatives available for the multiplexing of several users on a physical link. The multiplexing function is a fundamental component of the switching protocol.

Protocol is here defined as a set of conventions followed by two or more parties in order to maintain the coordination and synchronization necessary to accomplish a common goal. In a link protocol, for example, the goal is the efficient and reliable transfer of data over a link. In a switching protocol, the goal is to relay data through a multihop network to the desired destination.

Consider the situation depicted in Fig. 16.2: several users connected to switch A transmit data (intermittently) to users connected to switch B. A and B are linked by a communications line with appropriate modems at each termination. The switch is a processor whose memory and processing capabilities depend on the multiplexing and

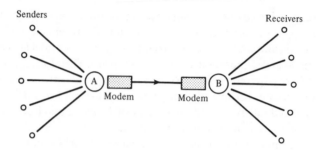

Figure 16.2. Multiplexed line configuration.

switching technique implemented. The *multiplexing protocol* may be defined as the protocol that permits the combination of data from multiple senders on the same communication link. The protocol has the capability of separating the different data streams at the receiving end.

Now consider a multinode network, as shown in Fig. 16.3. In a multinode network the *switching protocol* is the protocol responsible for the transport of user data from the origin to the desired destination. Since several user data streams generally coexist on each network link, the switching protocol must be able to distinguish these streams at each intermediate node (multiplexing function), and it must forward each stream to the proper output link (switching function). Using this very simplified representation of a data network, the switching protocol may be viewed as a combination of a multiplexing function and a switching function. Section 16.2.1 reviews the various alternatives available for the implementation of these functions.

16.2.1 Multiplexing Techniques

16.2.1.1   Frequency-Division Multiplexing (FDM)

In FDM, trunk bandwidth is subdivided into a number of channels of smaller bandwidth values. This subdivision is generally fixed and does not vary in time. A user desiring to transmit data must wait until a channel of appropriate bandwidth becomes free. The channel is then assigned to the user for the entire duration of the session. At the receiving end, the different data streams are separated using analog filters.

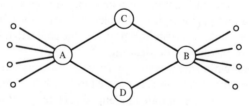

Figure 16.3. Multinode network.

16.2.1.2   Time-Division Multiplexing (TDM)

In TDM, a fixed time interval, called a *frame*, represents the basic cycle of the multiplexed scheme. The frame is subdivided into time slots, and each slot is allocated to a particular data source. In a simple time-division multiplexer using character interleaving, each slot corresponds to a single character time on the high-speed link. In more elaborate schemes, the slot may be sufficiently large to contain the maximum-size block transmitted by the user (see, for example, the slotted frame of a multiple-access satellite channel [KLEI 78]).

Each device multiplexed on the channel is assigned a number of slots in the frame proportional to its speed. Since different devices (with different speeds) may be multiplexed at different times on the same multiplexer, there is the possibility of periodically reconfiguring slot subgroupings and assignments to match the device requirements. Since slot assignment within the frame is known to both transmitter and receiver, the transfer of data is accomplished with no need for explicit addressing. At the transmit side, incoming user data are buffered until the occurrence of the next slot belonging to that user. To minimize buffering requirements it is necessary to distribute user slots as uniformly as possible within the frame.

16.2.1.3   Statistical Time-Division Multiplexing (STDM)

The drawback of the TDM scheme is that bandwidth is wasted when a data source is not 100% active (since slots are assigned to sources for the entire duration of the session). To overcome this inefficiency, a more flexible type of time-division multiplexing was developed, statistical-time division multiplexing (STDM) [CHU 69]. As in the TDM scheme, incoming characters from all sources are enclosed in a frame. However, the size of the slot assigned to each source varies dynamically depending on traffic activity. If the source is idle, the slot may be reduced to an "absence" flag, or it may, in some cases, be completely suppressed. If the source is active, the slot contains all the characters that arrived since the last frame, up to a maximum slot size whose value will depend on the specific STDM implementation. The effect of this scheme is to allocate bandwidth proportionally to user demands, avoiding waste caused by idle users and achieving high channel utilization even in very bursty traffic environments.

Many implementations of the STDM concept are possible. The general scheme is shown in Fig. 16.4. In all implementations, the frame assembler periodically (say, every T seconds) scans the input buffers and constructs a frame with contributions from some (or all) users. The frame is then placed on the channel queue awaiting transmission (note: a queue may build up if the aggregate input rate temporarily exceeds the line speed). At the receiver side, frames are disassembled in the same sequence as they were assembled by the transmitter, and user slots are delivered to the corresponding destinations. Sequencing of the frames on the link is provided so that the data are delivered in sequence to each destination.

Differences among the various implementations may arise in regard to the following features:

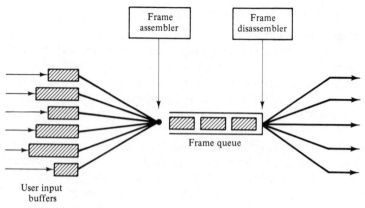

Figure 16.4. General STDM scheme.

A.   *User identification within the frame*

Users may be identified by the position of their slot in the frame (as in TDM). In this case, all users must always be represented in the frame. If a user has nothing to send, his or her slot will reduce to an "absence" flag, indicating that there is no useful data in that slot. The absence flag is represented by 1 bit in the TRAN System [KLEI 76], and typically by 2 bits in the CODEX System [VAND 76]. Another scheme for identifying users within the frame consists of adding an explicit ID to the user data. The explicit ID solution implemented by TYMNET [RIND 76] permits the suppression of the absence flag and the organization of the users in the frame in an arbitrary order. This is achieved at the expense of more overhead (an 8-bit ID number) for each active user.

B.   *Frame-size limitations*

If the frame assembler collects at each pass all the data present in the input buffers, the frame size may become arbitrarily large in a large-population, bursty traffic environment. To prevent this from happening, most schemes place some limitations on the maximum frame size and, possibly, on the slot size allowed to each individual user. Given these constraints, it may happen that the frame is completed before all the users have been given attention. The next frame may then resume the scan where the previous frame stopped; or, alternatively, it will restart from the top of the user list. Different implementations will use different size constraints and different scanning policies. In TYMNET [RIND 76], there is a limit on the maximum frame size (= 528 bits) as well as on the individual slot size, and scanning is resumed in a round-robin fashion.

C.   *Error recovery*

In most implementations, error recovery at the frame level is provided by an ARQ protocol implementing error detection and frame retransmission upon failure to receive a positive acknowledgment. TRAN, CODEX, and TYMNET all use error recovery schemes inspired to the HDLC or SDLC protocol. A specialized STDM scheme implemented by TRAN, however, does not include error recovery for synchronous traffic [TRAN 79]. The rationale behind this decision was to simplify the switch design by moving the error recovery procedures up to a higher level.

In summary, the common feature of all STDM techniques is to scan the user buffers periodically and to combine the data present in the buffers into a frame (this frame is sometimes referred to as *composite* or *compound* packet). The advantages of this strategy, with respect to TDM, are the improved line efficiency in a bursty user environment and the added error protection (if the ARQ option is exercised). The price paid to obtain these advantages is represented by an increased buffering requirement, a queueing delay, and some loss of *transparency*. In this chapter transparency is approached from the point of view of the communication processor (in this case the multiplexer/demultiplexer). Its operation is transparent if it does not have to understand the protocol structure that regulates each user data stream; in particular, it does not have to interpret the controls and commands of the protocol, nor recognize special characters or bit patterns.

The main advantage of transparency is the independence of the processor design from the specific user protocol implementation. The TDM processor is obviously transparent to user protocols. The STDM processor is transparent to asynchronous traffic; for synchronous traffic, it must recognize and suppress the idle characters (or idle flags) which fill the gap between data blocks in the input stream, and it must reinsert the idle characters (or flags) in the output stream. Since the idle fill pattern varies from protocol to protocol, this requirement leads to a protocol-dependent STDM processor design.

16.2.1.4   Packet Multiplexing

In the packet multiplexed scheme the data from each source are transported in private packets (rather than in composite packets, as in the STDM scheme). Constraints may be placed on packet size, depending on the specific implementation (in ARPANET, for example, the maximum number of information bits in a packet is 1008 bits [HEAR 70]). Each packet is individually protected by an error detection and retransmission scheme; and it contains sufficient information (in the header) to identify the sending and receiving party.

Two different packet-switching protocol implementations exist: the datagram and the virtual circuit implementation. In the *datagram* implementation, each packet carries in the header the full address of origin and destination (typically, the port ID numbers). The receiver, upon verifying that the packet was received correctly, checks the destination port ID and delivers the packet accordingly. In the *virtual circuit* implementation, whenever two users want to communicate with each other, a full-duplex logical channel (called a virtual circuit) is first established. A logical channel ID number is assigned to the user pair, and this ID number is carried in the header of all the packets exchanged between the pair. Tables mapping ID numbers into full origin and destination port addresses are implemented in the entry and exit switches. In addition to this abbreviated addressing feature, the virtual circuit scheme also provides for the sequencing of packets within each session (i.e., packets are numbered sequentially and are delivered to the destination in order). When the session terminates, the virtual circuit is "closed" (i.e., the maps at the sending and receiving station are erased and the channel ID number is freed for future reuse by another connection). This configuration, in which virtual circuits are opened and closed depending on demands, is called the *switched* virtual circuit configuration. A virtual circuit may also be permanently assigned to a user pair, in which case it is called a *permanent* virtual circuit.

The packet scheme (both in the datagram and the virtual circuit version) offers the dynamic channel assignment benefits already found in the STDM scheme. As a further advantage over the STDM scheme, the packet scheme permits more freedom and flexibility in the design of the priority structure among different users, thus allowing lower delay for high-priority users, who do not have to wait for the construction of the composite frame before transmission. On the other hand, line overhead is generally higher than in the STDM scheme since each packet carries full address and CRC information. Furthermore, some of the transparency features of the STDM scheme are lost in the packet scheme. For instance, in an asynchronous input, the processor must recognize special control characters (e.g., carriage return) that trigger the formation of a new packet.

Finally, in comparing virtual circuit and datagram performance, we observe that virtual circuit introduces set up delay and address map overhead, but reduces line overhead once the connection is established (because of abbreviated addressing), and maintains sequencing. For these reasons, virtual circuit is more appropriate for long sessions with steady data flow, whereas datagram is more efficient for short sessions of the inquiry/response type.

16.2.2   Switching Techniques

As we mentioned before, the switching protocol presupposes the capability to separate the individual data streams multiplexed on a common link. The implementation of the underlying multiplexing function generally determines also the choice of the switching scheme to be used in the network. Consequently, there is an almost perfect parallelism between multiplexing techniques and switching techniques.

16.2.2.1   Analog Circuit Switching

This is the traditional switching technique used in analog voice switched networks. The underlying multiplexed scheme is an FDM scheme which subdivides each trunk into a number of parallel voice-grade channels. At call setup time, physical connections are established between incoming and outgoing channels at each intermediate node in the path. The route is generally selected using fixed routing tables stored in the nodes. The series of channels that form the path is completely dedicated to the user pair for the entire duration of the session and is released only upon session termination.

16.2.2.2   Digital (Time-Division) Circuit Switching

The digital switching technique assumes an underlying time-division structure in which user data are transported on each trunk in a time-division multiplexed frame. At call setup, a network path is determined following an appropriate routing policy (which may be fixed or dynamically updated). On each trunk along the path, a number of frame slot positions are assigned to the connection, and maps are set up at each intermediate node specifying how data should be transferred from incoming slots to outgoing slots (see Fig. 16.5). As a result, a circuit of fixed bandwidth is assigned to the connection for the entire duration of the session, and is released only upon user request.

Digital switching has several advantages over analog switching in a data communications environment. Among these are the flexibility of selecting bandwidth values in a very wide range (typically from 100 bps to 56 kbps), and lower setup delay.

16.2.2.3   Statistical Time-Division Switching

Statistical time-division switching is the natural extension of statistical time-division multiplexing. At call setup time, a path is established for each user connection. During the data transfer phase, user data are multiplexed on each trunk using statistical time-division multiplexing (i.e., data from the various connections traversing the trunk are combined in a "composite" frame as discussed in Sec. 16.2.1.2). At each intermediate node, the composite frame is disassembled and user data are buffered in FIFO transit buffers (one buffer per connection). On output, each trunk periodically scans the buffers for the connections that are routed through it and combines the data present in the buffers into a composite frame. The association of transit buffers and output trunks defines the route of each connection and is established at connection setup time. At the termination end, user data are routed to the corresponding host or terminal output channel upon disassembly of the frame.

The main advantage of statistical time-division switching over conventional time-division switching is better line efficiency. The main drawbacks are higher end-to-end delays and higher storage requirements due to queueing at the intermediate nodes.

**DIGITAL CIRCUIT SWITCHED NETWORK:
BASIC TIME DIVISION SWITCHING STRUCTURE**

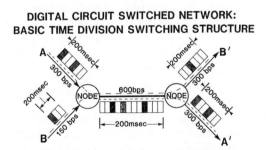

Figure 16.5. Time-division switching.

16.2.2.4 Packet Switching

In the packet-switching scheme user data are transported from source to destination in the form of packets, each packet traveling independently through the network in a store-and-forward mode. We again distinguish between two types of packet switching: datagram and virtual circuit.

In the datagram version, each packet header contains the full source and destination address and any additional information necessary to handle the packet properly at each intermediate node (e.g., packet priority, type, etc.). The route is chosen at each intermediate node by reading a routing table which indicates the best output trunk to each destination. Since routing tables are updated periodically, packets in the same session may follow different paths. Sequencing, therefore, is not maintained in the network, but must be provided at the user level.

In the virtual circuit version a "virtual" circuit must be set up from source to destination before user data can flow. A network path is selected and a unique ID is assigned to the connection at call setup time. More generally, different paths may be chosen for the two directions of a full-duplex connection; and a different ID may be assigned to each hop along the path, together with a map associating incoming and outgoing IDs at each intermediate node. The use of a different ID for each hop simplifies the problem of selecting unique IDs throughout the network.

After the connection is established, data packets may be exchanged between the end users. These packets need to carry only the connection ID number in the header. The ID number is inspected at each intermediate node, and is indexed into a table that will provide the outgoing link and (if necessary) the new ID number.

Packets within a virtual circuit are sequenced, thus eliminating the need for reassembly at the user level (as required in datagram networks). Each virtual circuit can be individually flow controlled, giving the network the opportunity to allocate resources fairly among the various users (whereas in a datagram network flow control does not distinguish between different user sessions).

16.2.2.5 "Generalized" Virtual Circuit Switching

The analogy between some of the virtual circuit switching features and the features of time-division and statistical time-division switching (i.e., the call setup procedure, the sequencing of data within each connection, and the use of fixed paths) suggests a more general definition of the virtual circuit switching concept. Essentially, there is a continuum of solutions between the conventional TD switching scheme and the virtual circuit switching. In conventional TD switching the frame time is fixed, and is synchronized over all trunks by a master clock. Slots within each frame are allocated to users at setup time.

In statistical TD switching, one or more of these requirements are relaxed. Frame slots are no longer fixed: rather, they are dynamically allocated to users. Frame size may vary from frame to frame depending on load fluctuations. Users may be identified within the frame by an explicit ID (rather than by their frame positions, as in the TD scheme). Furthermore, the frame may be error protected by a link protocol.

In its most advanced form (as implemented, for example, in Tymnet) the statistical TD switching scheme closely resembles the virtual circuit switching scheme, providing sequencing, selective flow control, user identification by ID number rather than by full source/destination address, and fixed path routing. The only significant differences are, for statistical TD switching, the combination of several user segments in the same frame (composite packet concept) and the periodic construction of the frame, collecting user data "on the fly" from the user input buffer. In contrast, the virtual circuit scheme generally transports the user message in one or more individual packets, which are asynchronously created based on demands.

Although these differences have some impact on network performance (as discussed in later sections), the elements in common are so numerous that they justify the definition of a "unified" class of data switching techniques known as virtual circuit switching (VCS). The distinguishing features of VCS are the following:

- "Virtual circuit" setup prior to transmission
- Fixed path (established at call setup)
- Dynamic sharing of bandwidth on the trunks along the path
- Sequencing of user data within each virtual circuit
- Selective flow control
- Identification of user data within the network by means of an ID number (explicit; or implicitly defined by position) rather than full source/destination address

16.3 THE DATAGRAM PROTOCOL AND ITS LIMITATIONS

It is fair to say that the datagram protocol has up to recently dominated most of the experimental and operational network scene. All the ARPA-sponsored research networks (ARPANET [HEAR 70], SATNET [KLEI 78], and PACKET RADIO NET [KAHN 77]) use some form of datagram scheme. Among the commercial networks, SITA, a worldwide airline reservation network [KRON 75], and DATA-PAC, the Canadian public network [RYBC 77], to mention just a few, implement the datagram concept.

In parallel with the development of these experimental and commercial systems based on the datagram concept, extensive performance studies were carried out to determine packet switching cost effectiveness in different traffic environments. The unanimous finding was that, although the datagram technology is ideal for interactive type communications among computers and/or intelligent, synchronous terminals, it may not be the most efficient solution for other types of requirements: file transfers, asynchronous terminal support, and real-time traffic (e.g., facsimile or digitized voice). Furthermore, the studies showed that datagram, while providing efficient utilization of bandwidth resources at nominal loads, required a battery of rather sophisticated flow and congestion control techniques to achieve fair bandwidth allocation and congestion prevention during peak loads.

These inefficiencies and limitations of the datagram protocols have motivated researchers and manufacturers to investigate alternative data transport protocols, generally based on some kind of integration of datagram, virtual circuit, and circuit-switching technologies.

This section provides a literature survey of the most significant proposals and developments aimed at correcting specific datagram problems. It describes the various steps of the evolution from datagram protocols to virtual circuit and integrated protocols.

16.3.1 Asynchronous Terminal Support

Asynchronous terminal handling creates two fundamental problems in a packet network. The first problem is the significant nodal processing overhead introduced by the assembly of incoming characters into packets. In the ARPANET TIP, for example, the character-handling activity imposes major limitations on nodal throughput [ORNS 72]. The second problem is the substantial line overhead generated by packets containing only a few characters. To reduce line overhead, the entry node may, in some applications, delay packet construction until several characters have been received [OPDE 76]. This, however, may lead to unacceptable message delays. Other ad hoc schemes are discussed in [OPDE 76].

A general solution to the asynchronous terminal problem is the installation of a specialized front-end processor to remove the terminal support burden from the switch. This solution, however, may not be the most cost effective unless the processor serves other purposes besides network access (e.g., protocol conversion, formatting, distributed data-base managements, etc.).

If the only requirement is the transfer of data between asynchronous terminals and computer ports, without intermediate "value-added" services, a more cost-effective solution to asynchronous terminal support is the statistical multiplexing technique described in Sec. 16.2.1.3. In the statistically multiplexing scheme, line overhead is typically much smaller than in conventional packet formats. Furthermore, nodal processing overhead is reduced since fewer packets (frames) are created, and message delay is improved since characters are transmitted "on the fly" upon arrival to the entry switch, without buffering the message, as required in some packet protocol implementations.

16.3.2 Transparency to Nonstandard Protocols

The connection of user devices to a conventional packet network requires the existence of software interfaces translating user protocols into network protocols. If the entire user population complies with a common standard protocol (e.g., X.25), only one interface is required, making the interface problem economically tractable. Today's large private data networks, however, often result from the superposition of different applications, each application retaining its own terminals, host computers, and protocols, and representing practically a closed users' group. It is not uncommon in these networks to find terminals and cluster controllers polled remotely from the host with a BSC protocol, which coexist with asynchronous terminals and HDLC or SDLC synchronous devices.

The protocol interface problem is even more dramatic in public networks, where services must be provided to a large customer population with very diversified equipment, applications, and protocols.

While recognizing that the compliance with a standard access protocol (e.g., X.25 for hosts and intelligent terminals, with the PAD (packet assembler/disassembler) extension for nonintelligent terminals) is, in the long term, the most desirable solution, we must cope in the interim with the chaos of existing, incompatible protocols [SAND 76]. The packet network approach, providing separate interfaces (either in the switch or in the front-end processor) for the various protocols, is often too costly. A more cost-effective solution is therefore protocol transparency.

In the transparent mode of operation, the network forwards the incoming data stream to the destination along a physical (or virtual) path preestablished at connect time, with no need for inspection or alteration of the underlying protocol and control structure.

The most straightforward way of providing transparency is circuit switching. The drawback of circuit switching is, of course, the loss of bandwidth efficiency in the presence of bursty traffic. A more efficient solution to transparency is the statistical time-division multiplexing scheme, which transmits only the information characters (in sequence and, optionally, with intermediate error control) to the destination.

16.3.3   File Transfers

The most efficient connection for the transmission of files and, more generally, for long messages between two remote devices operating at the same speed is the circuit-switched connection. Several studies have investigated the critical parameters (e.g., message length, transaction frequency, etc.) which influence the trade-offs between packet and circuit switching [ITOH 73, MIYA 75, KUMM 76]. Among the criteria used in the comparison were line overhead and delay, where circuit-switched delay included connection setup time. Most of the studies place the critical message length between 1000 and 10,000 bits, depending on channel utilization and other network parameters. Below the critical length, packet is more cost effective; above it, circuit switching is the better option.

Experimental findings tend to confirm the theoretical predictions. In ARPANET, for example, a coast-to-coast file transfer traversing 10 intermediate nodes will rarely exceed 5 kbps even in lightly loaded network conditions, in spite of the 50 kbps line facilities! The throughput limitation in this case is due mainly to the inefficient match between host protocols and packet network delays. If a circuit-switched connection were possible through ARPANET, a file transfer could be accomplished in one-tenth of the time, utilizing the same host protocols.

These observations suggest that an integrated packet and circuit structure is probably the best solution for a mix of interactive and batch traffic [MIYA 75, PORT 76].

16.3.4   Digitized Speech

In most private networks voice and data requirements coexist next to each other. Traditionally, the two requirements have been satisfied with separate networks: a PBX-based switched network for voice, and a dedicated packet- or circuit-switched network for data. Recent advancements in vocoder technology, however, have made it possible to generate digitized speech of acceptable quality at rates as low as 2.4 kbps. These new capabilities open the door to various alternatives for the integration of data and digitized speech in a common digital network [GITM 78]. One possible alternative is packetized voice, which consists of packetizing the incoming voice stream into packets of proper size, and of delivering these packets through the network in a datagram mode. If packetized voice quality is acceptable, this integration is very attractive since it takes advantage of the speech on–off statistics, and provides bandwidth savings of up to 50% (with respect to a separate circuit-switched network implementation for speech) [GITM 78].

The critical problem of this integration is the sensitivity of voice to network delays. To maintain the quality of the conversation at an acceptable level, the network must maintain end-to-end delays below a given threshold, and must preserve the original time gaps between voice packets. The latter requirement can be satisfied by absorbing eventual delay fluctuations in the destination buffer, at the expense of an additional (fixed) delay. Unfortunately, the datagram protocol during peak loads tends to introduce large, random gaps between consecutive packets, especially if origin and destination are separated by several network hops. The gap fluctuation range depends on the number of hops, the volume of interfering traffic, the circuit error rate, the frequency of the dynamic rerouting decisions, and the tendency of the routing procedure to generate loops.

Another problem in using the datagram protocol for digitized speech is the fact that voice packets should be kept quite small (on the order of 100 bits, say) to reduce both average delays and the dispersion of delays, a feature required for good voice transmission [FORG 77]. Small packet size leads to large line overhead if the standard packet header (168 bits in ARPANET) is used.

To overcome these problems, alternative approaches to standard packet switching have been proposed for digitized voice. Among the leading alternatives, a proposal by Forgie and Nemeth [FORG 77] suggests a "packetized" virtual circuit approach in which routes are established on a per call basis as in a conventional circuit-switched network, and calls are blocked when trunk utilization reaches a critical threshold. The approach differs from circuit switching, however, in that voice packets travel along the path in a store-and-forward manner, and trunk bandwidth is statistically shared among all connections.

Coviello and Vena propose a Slotted Envelope Network (SENET) scheme to handle the voice–data mix [COVI 75]. This scheme is essentially a hybrid scheme combining packet and statistical TD switching in which a fixed-size slotted frame (envelope) multiplexes voice and data packets on each trunk. Voice connections are established in a circuit-switched manner by preassigning frame slots along a fixed path from origin to destination, while packets travel on dynamically selected routes utilizing at each hop data slots as well as "silent" voice slots. The SENET scheme is described in more detail in Sec. 16.5.2.

Both proposals, although somewhat different in nature, indicate that a virtual circuit–switched type connection for voice (with unused capacity reassigned to data traffic) is to be preferred over a datagram approach.

16.3.5   Fairness in Bandwidth Sharing

One of the requirements in a data network is that each user receive an amount of network resources (in particular, an amount of bandwidth) proportional to his or her traffic demands. Depending on the network implementation, bandwidth allocation could be either fixed (i.e., obtained via circuit switching) or statistical (i.e., provided in a statistical sense between the entry and the exit node).

In a light-load situation, all users are granted the requested bandwidth. In a heavy-load situation, not all requests can be satisfied; therefore, some congestion control procedure is invoked to prevent additional traffic from entering the network and to distribute the limited bandwidth resources fairly among the current users.

In datagram networks, although a large variety of flow and buffer control mechanisms have been proposed, designed, and implemented, bandwidth allocation fairness is still an open problem. Simulation has shown, for example, that connections between neighbor nodes tend to capture a larger share of network resources than do connections traversing several intermediate nodes, defying the fairness provisions of the end-to-end flow control mechanisms [CHOU 76]. Other examples of buffer monopolization effects in packet networks are described in [GERL 80].

This situation of unfairness and, more generally, inability to guarantee a given throughput/delay performance to the user is of concern in private and, more important, in public networks, where some user groups may demand a constant grade of service regardless of the load in the network. In packet networks, these performance-sensitive users are generally assigned a higher priority. The design of the priority structure, however, becomes complex if there are several user groups with different grade of service requirements. Furthermore, in a multilevel priority implementation, the requirements of intermediate priority levels may not be met unless some flow control is exercised on the higher levels.

A fail-safe solution to unfairness is to offer private, dedicated bandwidth to those users who require a constant grade of service. This can be accomplished efficiently in an integrated packet and circuit network, where the customer can choose between a packet service of lower cost but higher risk of performance degradation, and a dedicated bandwidth service, more costly but more protected. These conclusions were reached by Port et al. in [PORT 76].

The drawback of dedicated bandwidth is inefficiency. A better compromise between efficiency and service guarantee is offered by virtual circuit switching. Although virtual circuit switching does not guarantee bandwidth, it does permit rejection of a new connection request when the connection is likely to congest the network; and it permits selective reduction of input traffic in order to distribute resources fairly when the network becomes heavily loaded.

Circuit switching and virtual circuit switching are therefore attractive alternatives to datagram switching for users who require bandwidth guarantee and, more generally, performance assurance. The criterion to be used in the choice is the trade-off between efficient bandwidth sharing and service guarantee. Sections 16.4 and 16.5 describe techniques for the implementation of bandwidth assurance, flow control, and fairness in virtual circuit networks and hybrid packet and circuit networks.

16.4   VIRTUAL CIRCUIT SWITCHING

In discussing the drawbacks of the datagram protocol, the virtual circuit protocol was mentioned as one of the possible solutions to correct some of those drawbacks. Here we examine the pros and cons of the virtual circuit implementation in more detail. We begin by reviewing the main characteristics of a virtual circuit implementation. These are:

1. "Virtual circuit" establishment prior to transmission
2. Fixed path
3. Dynamic bandwidth sharing along the path
4. User block identification within the network by means of ID number rather than by full source/destination address

It should be mentioned that the literature is rich in comparative evaluations of datagram versus VC protocol schemes. For a few years this topic was the center of a rather heated controversy between supporters and opposers of X.25, the packet network access protocol standard proposed by the CCITT committee [CCIT 76]. Unfortunately, political considerations have often prevailed over technical arguments [POUZ 74], so that many of the studies reveal strong bias in one direction or the other. An additional element of confusion was the fact that the X.25 standard is, properly speaking, a protocol for the *multiplexing* of packets on the network access trunk, rather than a true *switching* protocol for the transport of packets throughout the network. Therefore, some of the conclusions of those studies cannot be applied to a general virtual circuit switching protocol, which, according to our definition, is a protocol involving all the trunks along the path, not only the access trunks.

In the following sections we attempt to give a fair appraisal of the virtual circuit switching protocol as defined in this chapter.

16.4.1   Advantages of the Virtual Circuit Protocol

The main advantages of the virtual circuit protocol (as opposed to the datagram protocol) are the *reduction of header overhead* and the *improved controllability* of user data flow by the network.

Within each trunk of a VC network each user block is identified by a unique ID number. The size of the ID field will depend on the number of virtual circuits that can be simultaneously multiplexed on the trunk. In a VC implementation that uses X.25 on each intermediate trunk, the ID field is 12 bits long (i.e., 4096 distinct virtual circuits) [CCIT 76]. In the TYMNET virtual circuit implementation, each connection is identified by an 8-bit logical record number (i.e., up to 256 distinct connections) [RIND 76]. These overhead figures are in sharp contrast with the 64 bits of the ARPANET header (containing source and destination information) [HEAR 70], and the 160 bits of the TCP internet protocol header, to which other 160 bits of TCP transport protocol header are then added [POST 80]. The header overhead reduction is dramatic, and has a major impact on line efficiency, especially in interactive traffic environments characterized by short packet lengths (say, a few characters per packet) [ROBE 75].

The second major advantage of the VC protocol is the capability to control the flow on individual circuits. This is achieved by controlling the number of buffers used by each virtual circuit at each intermediate node along the path. If buffer utilization exceeds a specified threshold, this is a symptom that there is some congestion somewhere downstream in the virtual circuit; therefore, the flow on that virtual circuit is stopped temporarily until the congestion is cleared. This flow control philosophy is implemented in Transpac [SIMO 79] and TYMNET [RIND 79]. In a datagram network, on the other hand, when a host becomes congested, or when a cross section of the network becomes saturated, no attempt is made to reduce selectively the flow on the user connections that are responsible for the congestion. Rather, trunk queues are allowed to grow up to a certain threshold, and beyond this threshold *all* the traffic is stopped indiscriminately. This is a potential cause of unfair and inefficient use of the resources.

In some applications, traffic rates on user connections can be predicted with reasonable accuracy. In this case, the VC protocol will not only *detect* and *resolve*, but also *prevent* network congestion by accepting a virtual call only if sufficient bandwidth resources are available within the network. This concept is used in the packetized virtual circuit (PVC) network proposed by Forgie et al. for a digitized speech application [FORG 77]. The ability to prevent congestion is particularly critical in voice applications (and, more generally, in real-time applications) since heavy queueing delays due to congestions may cause loss of information and, possibly, disruption of a connection.

Another advantage of virtual circuit switching is the prevention of loops. It is well known that the dynamic routing procedures most commonly implemented in datagram networks may cause, under unfavorable circumstances, temporary looping of packets [NAYL 76]. Looping in datagram networks may be avoided using sophisticated algorithms, at the expense, however, of higher overhead and slower response to traffic pattern changes [GALL 77]. In the virtual circuit network looping cannot occur, since packets follow a fixed path chosen at setup time.

16.4.2 Disadvantages of the Virtual Circuit Protocol

The improved controllability and lower line overhead of the VC protocol do not come free. We will see that the price is *higher memory overhead* and *reduced resource sharing efficiency*.

The higher memory overhead derives from the fact that at each intermediate node along a virtual circuit we have to store a context block with the essential parameters for that circuit. As a minimum, we store the virtual circuit ID number and a pointer to the next node on the path. In addition, we may store a count of packets sent (P_s) and packets acknowledged (P_r), a pointer to a buffer area dedicated to that virtual circuit, and other parameters specifying the type of traffic (e.g., interactive data, batch transfer, digitized voice), the priority, and the flow control thresholds. Context blocks must be stored in main memory, since they must be inspected and modified within milliseconds for each packet transaction. The amount of main memory available at each network processor thus sets an upper limit on the number of simultaneous virtual circuits that can be handled.

The fixed path restriction prevents the use of dynamic routing. This, of course, may cause some loss in efficiency when the network is lightly loaded. In fact, the transmission of a file, say, on multiple parallel paths, could substantially reduce a total file transmission time. To overcome this problem, one may actually come up with mechanisms for multipath virtual circuits [ROBE 78]. The increased complexity of these schemes, however, may very well offset the gain in efficiency.

Apart from the loss of efficiency, a (probably more serious) problem of fixed path routing is the vulnerability to line and node failures. When an element (link or node) fails, a new path must be established for each virtual connection involving that element. This implies the updating of a large number of context blocks in a relatively short interval, if we wish to make the recovery transparent to the user and thus avoid loss of data on the virtual circuits. In many virtual circuit implementations, the automatic route recovery was found to introduce excessive load on lines and processors, and therefore the responsibility of recovering from route failures was moved up to the user. When a link or node along the path fails, the user is disconnected, and must therefore request a new connection and retransmit the data that were lost because of the failure. In datagram networks equipped with an adaptive routing procedure, user packets are automatically rerouted on alternate paths when a failure occurs. (Packets, however, may still be lost when a node fails, thus again requiring error recovery at the user level.)

Another potential cause of reduced efficiency is the dedication of buffer resources along the virtual circuit. If n VCs have monopolized the buffer pool of a given processor, the $(n + 1)$st connection may be refused even if all the n VC's are presently idle. The network will, of course, assign buffers to connections based on some average and peak traffic expectancy, but some temporary starvation of buffers will be difficult to avoid [MANN 78].

From the response-time performance point of view, the most severe handicap of VC is the requirement of a call setup phase (for nonpermanent connections) before actual data can be transmitted. This initial delay (which can be several seconds in some networks) is perfectly acceptable in some applications (e.g., file transfer, digitized voice) but many preclude the use of virtual circuit switching for other applications (e.g., inquiry/response).

16.4.3   The Best of All Worlds: Combination of VC and Datagram Protocols

A qualitative analysis of the pros and cons shows that the VC protocol is more cost effective than the datagram protocol for any application that meets the following conditions:

1.   An initial call setup delay of a few seconds is acceptable.
2.   The duration of the session is considerably longer than the call setup time.
3.   The average data flow rate within the session is sufficiently high to justify the dedication of virtual circuit resources (context blocks, buffers, etc.) along the path for the entire duration of the session.

It is easy to verify that many of the applications currently supported by computer communications networks (i.e., interactive terminal-to-computer sessions, terminal-to-terminal sessions, interactive graphics, file transfers) satisfy these conditions. Among the future applications, digitized voice and facsimile appear to be particularly well suited for virtual circuit communications.

Only one major application is definitely not compatible with the virtual circuit protocol, and this is the transaction-oriented, inquiry/response, terminal-to-computer traffic.

If we consider a typical transaction environment, where a terminal sends every few minutes a query to a remote data base and expects a response within seconds, we easily recognize that setting up a virtual call for each query would lead to an unacceptable delay. Furthermore, a permanent virtual circuit between terminal and remote data base may represent an excessive cost (in terms of memory overhead) compared with the actual data rate. Consequently, the datagram approach is the preferred solution for a transaction environment.

A cost-effective coexistence of transaction requirements and other applications is possible with a *hybrid datagram and virtual circuit* network. To improve network efficiency, the virtual circuit component itself may be implemented as a combination of private packet protocol (for synchronous users) and composite packet protocol (for asynchronous users).

The protocol integration poses substantial technical problems, which are discussed in Sec. 16.4.5. A short-term solution is not difficult to come by, however, since a basic datagram service already exists within each VC network: namely, the protocol used to transport call request packets from origin to destination. The call request packet, in fact, contains source and destination address information and several other parameters typically found in a datagram header; this information is used to index the routing tables stored at each node along the path and to select the next leg of the path to destination. Thus a datagram facility is readily created within a VC network by permitting user packets to ride fake call request packets. This "piggyback" solution has in fact been chosen by CCITT for the integration of virtual circuit and datagram facilities within X.25 [FOLT 80].

16.4.4   Virtual Circuit Network Implementations

With the general acceptance of X.25 as the standard protocol for access to packet networks, most private and public networks are now providing (or are planning to provide) an X.25 virtual circuit-type connection between user device (or DTE, data terminating equipment) and the network processor (or DCE, data communications equipment), with the possible addition of the datagram service as an option. While the trends for *network access* (and interconnection) implementations are converging toward the virtual circuit scheme, the choice between the datagram and the virtual circuit for the *internal transport* mechanism is still divided between the datagram and the virtual circuit alternative. The internal transport protocol is, of course, transparent to the user, who sees only the X.25 network access interface. The decision is thus entirely in the hands of the manufacturer and the network manager, who must choose the most cost-effective solution for the given traffic environment.

An example of datagram transport protocol (with X.25 as an access protocol) is offered by Datapac, the Canadian public data network [RYBC 77]. Examples of virtual circuit transport protocol are Telenet [ROBE 77, OPDE 78, NEWP 77], Transpac [DANE 76, SIMO 79], and TYMNET [RIND 76, RIND 79, KOPF 77]. In the remainder of this section we describe and compare the virtual circuit implementations in these three networks.

16.4.4.1   Telenet

Telenet is a public data network serving more than 100 cities in the United States and abroad. The first version of Telenet, in the early 1970s, was a close replica of the ARPANET model, with an internal datagram structure. The second version of Telenet, developed in 1978 [OPDE 78], uses a virtual circuit scheme based on the X.25 protocol. The X.25 protocol is used in two different ways: (1) as a standard network interface to connect users to the network, and (2) as an internal interface between nodal processors [OPDE 78]. An end-to-end virtual circuit connection in Telenet is established by connecting in series a number of X.25 segments, one segment for each intermediate link. The use of X.25 (instead of another virtual circuit protocol) for internal communications was motivated by reasons of software efficiency (the X.25

interface had to be provided for access network anyway). The route of an incoming call is selected at each hop from routing tables which are periodically updated from the Network Control Center, and which provide for several alternate paths to each destination. Periodic updating and alternate paths permit adjustments to failures, topological changes, and network load pattern [WEIR 80]. In the present implementation, the route of each virtual circuit is fixed at call setup time. However, an automated route recovery scheme is currently being planned. This scheme will automatically select an alternate route if the original route fails. The present scheme requires circuit reinitialization by the user after a failure. Plans for providing multiple paths for each virtual connection are also considered [ROBE 77]. Multiple-path routing will improve the efficiency of the transport mechanism, but will also introduce some complications, one of which is the necessity to resequence packets travelling on different physical paths within the same virtual circuit.

16.4.4.2   Transpac

Transpac is the French public data network, administered by the French PTT. The network became operational in 1979, with 12 nodes, and was scheduled to grow to a size of 50 to 100 nodes by 1985. The network architecture is a virtual circuit architecture based, like Telenet, on the X.25 protocol for network access as well as for internal link operations [DANE 76]. The distinguishing features of Transpac are its routing and flow control policies [SIMO 79].

Routing in Transpac is centralized. A Network Control Center (NCC) collects from each node periodic reports on average number of connections, estimated traffic on each connection (i.e., traffic declared by the users at connection setup time), measured traffic, and buffer utilization. Based on these reports, the NCC computes the optimal paths from each node to each destination, and distributes to all the nodes a set of routing tables which implement such paths. Each node will then route an incoming call based on the routing table instructions and on local load measurements (i.e., some local adaptivity is added to the central control to permit rapid response to traffic fluctuations and to eventual component failures).

Flow control is distributed, and is exercised by each node independently. The inputs to the control are the number of virtual circuits allocated on each outgoing trunk, the estimated traffic requirement on each virtual circuit, and the buffer utilization.

The virtual circuit traffic requirement is estimated by each node from the throughput declared by the user at call setup time, and from actual traffic measurements. When the aggregate estimated traffic on a trunk exceeds a safety threshold, an incoming call is rerouted to other trunks. If no feasible trunk is available, the call is refused.

In spite of this careful (and conservative) bookkeeping of allocated bandwidth vis-à-vis available bandwidth, congestion may still develop because of unexpected bursts or component failures. To prevent congestion, each node constantly monitors buffer utilization and takes the following actions:

1.   If buffer utilization exceeds threshold S_0, no more calls are accepted by the node.
2.   If buffer utilization exceeds threshold S_1, traffic is slowed down on the existing virtual circuits, by delaying the acknowledgments to the neighboring nodes (selective flow control).
3.   If buffer utilization exceeds threshold S_2, some virtual circuits are disconnected, following some predefined priorities.

This rather conservative mechanism of preallocation of network resources (in a statistical sense) before call setup is part of the Transpac philosophy to offer to the user a service with guaranteed throughput and delay performance, a property obviously very appreciated in a public network. This approach, of course, has raised some criticism, since dedication of resources, even in a statistical sense, always implies restrictions on the sharing of such resources, leading to inefficiencies in network operation [MANN 78, POUZ 76].

16.4.4.3   Tymnet

TYMNET is a public data network serving more than 300 cities in the United States and abroad. The transport scheme is a virtual circuit scheme based on the statistical multiplexing and switching concept [RIND 76]. At call setup time, each virtual circuit is assigned a fixed path throughout the network. On intermediate trunks, the data are transported in error-protected frames using a link protocol similar to HDLC. Each frame combines ("multiplexes") the data of all the virtual circuits. Each circuit is represented by a logical record consisting of an 8-bit logical record number, an 8-byte count and as many bytes as specified in the byte count (see Fig. 16.6).

The logical record number has only local significance and is used to identify uniquely a virtual circuit within the trunk. The virtual circuit from end to end is defined by a series of logical record numbers, one for each intermediate trunk. Permuter tables provide the necessary mapping between incoming and outgoing virtual circuits at each intermediate node [RIND 76].

Routes in TYMNET are computed and implemented by the network control center, called Supervisor. The Supervisor continually evaluates the best routes (based on hop distance and loading criteria) from each source to destination. When a new connection is requested, the originating node informs the Supervisor, which then selects and implements the path through the network (i.e., it selects logical record numbers and sets up permuter table entries at all intermediate nodes). After the path is established, the Supervisor informs source and destination node that data transmissions can begin.

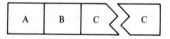

Figure 16.6. TYMNET logical record. A, 8-bit logical record number; B, 8-bit byte count; C, data field.

Thus, TYMNET routing policy is entirely centralized. Transpac and Telenet policies represent a compromise between a centralized and distributed approach, with centralized route computation, but distributed route implementation (i.e., each node chooses the next leg on the path from local routing table). It is worth mentioning that a distributed routing implementation with local routing tables installed at each node is particularly interesting when the datagram option is desired. In this case, datagrams can simply be routed using the local tables. If no tables exist, as in TYMNET, the datagram option involves substantial complications and costs.

Flow control in TYMNET (as in all virtual circuit networks) is done on a per virtual circuit basis. The particular mechanism used, called *backpressure*, is a simplified version of the *credit* scheme. In the general credit scheme, the sender transmits n packets and then stops until the receiver grants the permission (or credit) to send another group of n packets. If the receiver wishes to slow down the sender because its buffers are congested, it may simply delay the return of the credit until the congestion has been cleared. In the backpressure scheme, a bit vector, called a backpressure vector, is periodically (every half second) sent by a node to each neighbor. Each bit in the backpressure vector represents the credit for one of the virtual circuits multiplexed on the trunk. If the bit is one, the sender can transmit n more characters on that virtual circuit; if the bit is zero, the virtual circuit is blocked. The value n varies from circuit to circuit according to the speed of the sending device. A node will turn the backpressure bit to zero whenever the backlog of characters in the corresponding virtual circuit exceeds a given threshold. Thus, if congestion develops at an intermediate node along a virtual circuit path, flow control selectively propagates upstream from the congested area back to the source and temporarily stops new inputs on the virtual circuit until the congestion is cleared.

16.4.5   Open Issues

Virtual circuit switching is a fairly recent technology, and poses many issues that have not yet been satisfactorily resolved. The following sections outline some areas that require further investigation.

16.4.5.1   Routing

The routing policies implemented in existing virtual circuit networks are all based on the principle of routing an incoming call on the "shortest" path, where the "length" of a path is a function of number of hops and link utilization. This has been the principle traditionally used also in datagram networks. In virtual circuit networks, however, because of the more predictable user traffic behavior (the data rate on a virtual connection tends to be relatively steady in time; and users often declare the expected throughput at call setup time), it is possible to improve the shortest path routing method by introducing the concept of "available bandwidth" on each trunk. The available bandwidth is defined as the trunk capacity minus the current average flow. For each call request, the routing algorithm should then search for the shortest path which has *sufficient available bandwidth* to satisfy the new call request. If there is no sufficient bandwidth on any single network path, a number of alternatives are possible:

1.   The call is refused.
2.   The call is accepted, but flow control is exercised so that the user input rate does not exceed the available bandwidth.
3.   Multiple paths are assigned to the call so that the aggregate available bandwidth meets the request.

A routing algorithm based on available bandwidth is outlined in Sec. 16.5.3.

Multiple path routing is another important issue for further study. One of the critical points here is the trade-off between the additional complexity (i.e., computation of alternate paths, resequencing problems, etc.) and the gain in bandwidth efficiency.

Finally, a routing issue that is now receiving considerable attention is the automatic route recovery after failures. Recovery from failures is one of the strong selling points of datagram networks; it is clear that virtual circuit networks must offer an efficient solution to this problem if they are to maintain their competitive edge.

16.4.5.2   Flow Control

The virtual circuit architecture offers substantial advantages over the datagram architecture from the point of view of flow control and network congestion protection. It would be erroneous, however, to believe that virtual circuit networks are free of deadlock. An easy way to prevent deadlocks would be the dedication of buffers to each virtual circuit at each intermediate node. This solution, however, seems to be too costly for most applications. More efficient mechanisms of the type proposed for datagram networks must be investigated [RAUB 76, GIES 78].

16.4.5.3   Datagram Option

The implementation of a datagram option which bypasses the virtual call setup procedure is also an important issue that deserves further work. We have seen the implications of the routing scheme on the feasibility of transporting datagrams within a virtual circuit network and have seen how centralized routing schemes (such as the TYMNET scheme) may present difficulties in this regard.

Additional problems may arise in the flow control implementation, since datagram traffic is not as easily controllable as virtual circuit traffic. If datagram service is offered as a low-priority (and therefore low-cost) service with respect to virtual circuit, a straightforward solution may be to discard datagrams when congestion occurs, and rely on higher-level protocols for retransmissions.

Finally, an important operational issue that must be resolved after the successful implementation of the datagram option is the efficient use of the option itself. Which applications should use VC, and which datagram? Should the user choose, or should the network impose the service? Qualitatively, we know that transaction-type traffic should use datagram; and, we know that virtual circuit is preferable in congestion-prone environments. There are, however, many borderline cases which require a quantitative evaluation and justify a systematic study of this issue.

16.5   INTEGRATED PACKET AND CIRCUIT SWITCHING

16.5.1   Why Integrated Switching?

As we mentioned in Sec. 16.2, one of the drawbacks of the "complete sharing" philosophy in the datagram scheme was the lack of throughput and delay guarantee to individual users. There are applications (e.g., nonbuffered facsimile, high-quality digitized voice, interactive graphics) in which the user is willing to give up the cost advantages and the error protection features offered by pure packet switching to obtain a high degree of bandwidth assurance. In this respect, virtual circuit switching represents a step in the right direction, since by permitting the individual flow control and if necessary the refusal of user connections, it avoids trunk overloading and therefore reduces mutual user interference. Still, the bandwidth guarantee provided by virtual circuit switching is statistical in nature, and it depends on the predictability of traffic requirements on each virtual circuit, on the effectiveness of the selective flow control scheme, and the capability of monitoring trunk utilization and bandwidth availability throughout the network.

An absolute (as opposed to statistical) throughput and delay guarantee can be obtained only via circuit switching (i.e., by allocating to each user a circuit of given bandwidth for the entire duration of the session). The use of circuit switching, of course, introduces blocking, a problem that did not exist in datagram networks. We presume, however, that the user wishing a high-performance guarantee prefers to be blocked and denied service (and asked to retry later) rather than being given instant, but inadequate service. High service assurance is not the only motivation for circuit switched implementations. Many other reasons, such as the capability to partition network bandwidth among different user groups and applications, the improved transparency, and the higher switch throughput efficiency, justify the circuit-switched choice.

The selection of the best switching scheme, however, becomes more complicated in *mixed-media* environments, including applications ideally suited to circuit switching (i.e. nonbuffered facsimile) as well as applications that require the packet switching service (e.g., inquiry/response systems). Neither a pure packet nor a pure circuit network can efficiently satisfy all the requirements. Both services must therefore be provided. The dilemma, then, is between *segregation* and *integration* of P/S and C/S modes.

In the segregated case, two entirely independent networks are provided: one for P/S users and one for C/S users. This generally implies separate switches, separate trunk facilities, separate access facilities, and separate network control procedures [PORT 76]. (Indeed, some trunk sharing may be possible if multiple trunks are available between switching sites, so that trunks can be dynamically reassigned based on relative utilization.) Separation in general means duplication of hardware and software facilities and very limited sharing of trunk bandwidth, thus leading to high implementation and operation costs.

In the integrated approach, a single switch performs both P/S and C/S functions, and a single trunk multiplexes both C/S and P/S traffic. In addition, some network control procedures (e.g., routing) may be shared between the two modes, and common network access interfaces may be provided to both P/S and C/S users [PORT 76]. In principle, integration offers potential switch cost savings with respect to the segregated approach since it permits the sharing of common modules (e.g., trunk and line interface modules, call establishment and connection control modules, measurement and monitoring modules, etc.) and common procedures (e.g., diagnostic, billing, etc.) [JENN 76]. It also offers trunk savings, since the network operator can more easily shift bandwidth resources to adapt dynamically to changing demands. Furthermore, if a common access interface is provided, the user would have the flexibility of choosing from time to time the most efficient switching technique depending on the specific application he or she is running.

The integrated switch technology is still a fairly recent technology. In fact, an efficient integrated switch design requires a distributed, multiprocessor architecture in which specialized, heavy-duty tasks (e.g., switching of characters from input to output frames) are implemented with independent processors [JENN 76]. It was only in recent years that distributed architectures have become economically feasible, due to the advances in microprocessor technology and in multiprocessor system integration [ENSL 77].

In the following sections we first describe some of the implemented (or proposed) integrated packet and circuit schemes and address the issue of control (e.g., routing, flow control, etc.) in such networks. We then evaluate the benefits that can be gained with integration, and review some published analytical and simulation models assessing the integrated network performance as a function of various system parameters. Finally, we identify a set of issues requiring further study.

16.5.2   Integrated Network Architectures

The simplest (and most common) integrated network implementation consists of a digital circuit-switched network in which the portion of trunk bandwidth not used by circuit traffic is allocated to packet traffic [GERL 78A]. This implementation creates a packet subnetwork (within the original network) with topology equivalent to the original topology and with link capacities equal to the excess trunk capacities. Since excess trunk capacities vary in time according to circuit-switched demands, the packet subnetwork has time-varying trunk speeds. Recalling that data in a digital switched network are transported on each trunk in time-division, character-interleaved frames, the character slots that are not used for circuit traffic are therefore made available to packet traffic.

"Circuit" character slots (i.e., slots assigned to circuit-switched connections at call setup time) and "packet" character slots are processed differently at each interme-

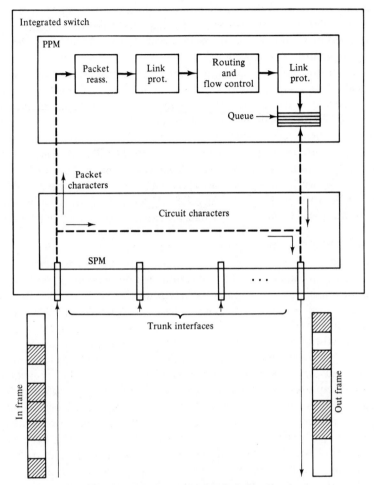

Figure 16.7. Integrated switch functions.

diate switch: namely, the incoming frame is inspected first by the SPM (switch processor module). Incoming circuit slots are then mapped directly by the SPM into appropriate slots of outgoing trunks, as specified by the circuit routing map established at call setup time (see Fig. 16.7). Incoming *packet* characters, on the other hand, are extracted from the frame and are delivered to a PPM (packet processing module), where conventional packet functions (i.e., packet reassembly, link protocol, flow control, routing, and transfer to an outgoing packet queue) are performed.

The use of two separate processors (i.e., SPM and PPM) is motivated by throughput efficiency considerations. The SPM is an extremely fast but rather unsophisticated processor, whose only task is transferring characters from incoming slots to outgoing slots. The PPM, on the other hand, processes incoming data at a much lower rate (on a packet basis rather than on a character basis), but must perform several sophisticated operations on each processed packet. If the PPM were responsible also for the circuit-switching function (i.e., if it were interrupted by each incoming character), the processor overhead would become extremely high and throughput efficiency would drop dramatically.

A rather straightforward variation of the architecture described above permits us to "modify" the connectivity of the packet subnetwork arbitrarily (and dynamically). Namely, any two nodes that are two or more hops apart in the original topology can be made adjacent to each other in the packet subnet topology by establishing a direct, circuit-switched channel of fixed bandwidth between them. Packets are then transferred directly on this channel. This idea of creating dedicated end-to-end "pipes" for packet traffic was first conceived and implemented by TRAN. In the TRAN network one pipe is created for each source destination pair and is called PACUIT link, where PACUIT = PACKET + CIRCUIT, to stress the fact that each pipe is an end-to-end circuit on which data are carried in the form of packets [GERL 78A].

The PACUIT implementation has merits as well as disadvantages. One obvious disadvantage is the fact that the fixed allocation of bandwidth to each PACUIT pipe precludes dynamic bandwidth sharing between packet and circuit traffic, as well as sharing among traffic packets from different source/destination pairs (some degree of sharing is actually possible by slowly "modulating" PACUIT bandwidth according to relative traffic demands, as discussed in Sec. 16.5.3).

Among the benefits of PACUIT we may mention the fact that traffic controllability and fairness are improved, since each source/destination pair is individually flow controlled, and competition for common bandwidth is tightly regulated. This avoids unfair capture of bandwidth by a few users, and permits giving better throughput assurance to individual user sessions [GIES 78]. Second, switch processing load is dramatically reduced by circuit switching the traffic through the network rather than reassembling each packet at each intermediate node [FOSC 78]. Third, the establishment of a direct PACUIT pipe between source and destination permits the transport of asynchronous traffic through the network transparently and efficiently using conventional statistical multiplexing techniques available for point-to-point connections. In the TRAN architecture, for example, asynchronous traffic is handled with end-to-end PACUIT links controlled by a statistical multiplexing protocol of the type described in Sec. 16.2.2.3 [GERL 78A]. A similar scheme is used to support asynchronous traffic in the Codex system [VAND 76].

In the integrated implementation described so far it was assumed that circuit traffic is handled transparently at each switch: namely, for the entire duration of the circuit-switched session, input character slots are mapped into output slots regardless of whether data or idle characters are transmitted on the circuit. No attempt is made to reassign temporarily unused circuit slots to packet traffic. If we now assume that the switch has the additional capability to detect the presence or absence of data in each individual circuit that traverses it, we can clearly expect substantial bandwidth savings (at the expense, of course, of additional switch complexity). An integrated packet and circuit technique exploiting this principle was implemented in SENET (Slotted Envelope NETwork) [COVI 75].

In SENET, data on each trunk are carried in frames called *envelopes*. These envelopes are transmitted synchronously on all trunks, as frames are in a time-division switched network. As a difference from conventional time-division switching, however, the envelope structure is subdivided into segments (rather than character slots), each segment carrying all the data for a specific channel (see Fig. 16.8) (i.e., the data characters for each channel are grouped into a single segment rather than being interleaved with other channels throughout the frame). A movable boundary separates Class I data (i.e., circuit-switched channels) from Class II data (i.e., packets). Each circuit-switched channel is assigned a fixed position in the envelope at connect time. Character slots, however, are not assigned permanently to each channel; rather, the presence or absence of data is detected and idle characters are suppressed: namely, a circuit-switched channel that is temporarily idle will be represented in the envelope by an "absence" flag. This permits dynamic adjustment of the boundary between Class I and Class II traffic, and the reassignment of any temporarily unused circuit-switched bandwidth to packet traffic. To implement the movable-boundary feature, the envelope must, of course, be completely assembled in the switch before transmission. This is in contrast with the "on-the-fly" disassembly and reassembly of frames made possible by the time-division framing scheme.

The main advantage of the SENET technique with respect to the conventional character-interleaved time-division scheme is the improvement in bandwidth sharing. This improvement is particularly significant when the circuit-switched traffic is bursty. It is not a coincidence that SENET was designed to support digitized speech characterized by the alternation of active (i.e., talking) periods and silence (i.e., listening) periods. Furthermore, the talking periods consist of a sequence of talk spurts sepa-

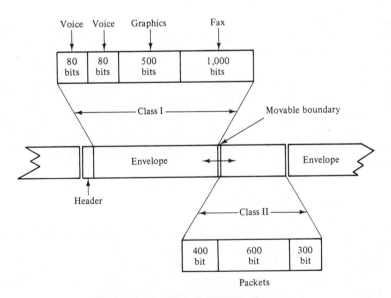

Figure 16.8. Slotted envelope format.

rated by short pauses. In the original SENET design, the envelope size was chosen to be sufficiently small (i.e., 10 msec) so as to allow bandwidth recovery not only during the silence periods, but also during the short pauses.

The increased bandwidth efficiency of the SENET scheme does not come without drawbacks. In particular, the penalties are: higher latency delay, since at each intermediate node circuit traffic is delayed on the average by a half envelope interval; higher line overhead (each envelope segment must carry some header information to permit the receiving node to demultiplex the envelope properly); and higher switch complexity (because of the busy/idle detection requirement, circuit-switched traffic processing in SENET involves more sophisticated functions than does the time-division framing scheme). Quantitative performance results for SENET are presented in Sec. 16.5.4.

Several other integration schemes have been proposed, most of which bear close similarity to the digital switching scheme or the slotted envelope scheme [MCAU 78, ROSS 78]. In contrast to these techniques, a rather original approach is taken in the "cut-through" scheme described in [KERM 79]. In this scheme, all the trunks in the network are subdivided into subchannels of equal capacity. Each user message opens (and closes) its own circuit-switched path while traveling through the network (i.e., the header of the packet sets up a circuit-switched connection at each intermediate node, so that the remainder of the packet is transferred through the node "on the fly," without reassembly). If blocking occurs because no free subchannels are found at some intermediate hop, the message is completely reassembled at that intermediate node and completes its journey through the network in a store-and-forward fashion using a packet protocol. Packed and circuit protocol integration is achieved, therefore, not only within the same network, but also within the same message!

Cut-through switching offers potential advantages with respect to both packet and circuit switching. On one hand, it eliminates the reassembly and buffering delay of packet switching at light load; on the other hand, it eliminates the call setup delay of conventional circuit switching. These advantages are confirmed by numerical results obtained in a wide range of traffic and network environments [KERM 79]. From the implementation point of view, cut-through switching technology is more complex and costly than the integration schemes described previously. In view of continuing technological advances and decreasing hardware costs, however, the cut-through scheme, as well as other more sophisticated integration schemes, appear to be worth further investigation.

16.5.3 Integrated Network Control

In the preceding section we described techniques for physically subdividing trunk bandwidth in order to create two separate packet and circuit subnetworks. In this section we concern ourselves with the control procedures that are necessary to manage these subnetworks. We recall that the three fundamental control functions that must be provided in a data communications network are:

1. Routing
2. Flow and congestion control
3. Failure detection

The control of packet networks (of both datagram and virtual circuit type) has been the object of very extensive research and experimentation efforts in the past decade, leading to a broad gamut of alternative schemes. Research on circuit-switched network control schemes has also been very active. In particular, the adoption of CCIS (Common Channel Interoffice Signaling) techniques has enormously expanded the range of possible controls in circuit networks, by routing signaling and control messages on a separate store-and-forward subnetwork.

Given the existence of well-established control procedures for both packet and circuit modes, a possible solution to integrated network control consists of the implementation of separate controls for packet and circuit subnetworks. Separate controls are not very desirable, however, for the following reasons. First, the line and processor overhead is doubled, since each set of controls requires a separate set of routines and data structures at each node, and introduces a separate exchange of control messages between modes. Second, the sharing of resources between packet and circuit services is generally neither efficient nor fair, since control decisions are not coordinated nor based on consistent network status information. The following example shows how lack of coordination may lead to biased network operation in favor of circuit users. Suppose that circuit-switching controls only know about the circuit-switched bandwidth allocated on each trunk and have no information on the packet-switched traffic volume carried in the network. Under these assumptions, incoming circuit requests will be accommodated until trunk bandwidth is totally allocated to circuit-switching, while packet traffic is progressively reduced, and eventually even completely cut off from the network. This mode of operation is clearly unfair. It may also be not cost effective, since packet customers tend to use bandwidth resources more efficiently (and therefore generate more revenue) than do circuit customers.

These drawbacks can be avoided with an integrated control policy which uses common network information to implement routing, flow control, and failure detection and recovery procedures. The integration of node and/or link failure detection and reporting procedures does not present particular problems, since hardware failures are clearly independent of the transport mechanism (packet or circuit) used. The integration of routing and flow control procedures, on the other hand, is not so straightforward since packet and circuit goals do not always coincide. In fact, the objective of packet routing is to find the minimum delay path, whereas the objective of circuit routing is to find a path that has sufficient residual bandwidth to accommodate a given circuit request. Similarly, the objective of packet flow control is to prevent throughput degradation, unfairness, and deadlocks due to buffer overallocations and overflows, whereas the objective of circuit-switching flow control is to avoid throughput degradation, unfairness, and deadlocks due to uncoordination in bandwidth allocation.

Although the arguments in favor of control integration are very convincing, numerous technical difficulties arise in this integration, so that a complete, well-established approach to unified packet and circuit control does not yet exist. To simplify matters, some proposals postulate that circuit traffic automatically has priority over packet traffic [COVI 75]. This assumption, although justified in some applications, would lead to exactly the kind of unfairness described earlier. Another approach would be to assume that the bandwidth is a priori partitioned between packet and circuit services (i.e., fixed boundary). This assumption simplifies the controls, but it leaves no room for bandwidth sharing.

In the remainder of this section we describe a novel (though as yet untested) approach to routing and flow control in hybrid packet and circuit networks. The proposed method allows full bandwidth sharing, and it does not postulate higher priority of circuit traffic over packet traffic. An additional merit of this method is the fact that it is based on distributed computation and is, therefore, robust to link and node failures.

The nucleus of the hybrid control is represented by a relatively simple bandwidth routing algorithm reported in [GERL 78B] and [GERL 79]. The goal of the algorithm is to compute for each node pair in the network a set of paths ranked by increasing length (i.e., number of intermediate nodes) and increasing residual bandwidth (i.e., amount of bandwidth on the path available for carrying additional traffic). As a result of this computation, which is carried out in a distributed fashion, each node will possess a set of paths to each destination with corresponding length and available bandwidth. Considering the example in Fig. 16.9, node 1 will store the following paths to destination node 2:

1.   Path 1–2; length = 1; available bandwidth = 2
2.   Path 1–3–2; length = 2; available bandwidth = 6
3.   Path 1–3–4–2; length = 3; available bandwidth = 9

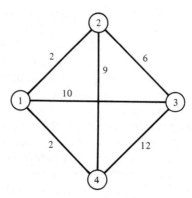

Figure 16.9. Bandwidth routing example. Link labels represent residual bandwidth (both directions).

This information is used by the source node to route an incoming call request on the most cost-effective path. In the example of Fig. 16.9, an incoming circuit-switched request of 1 unit of bandwidth from source 1 to destination 2 would be routed directly on trunk (1, 2); while a request for 8 units would be routed on path 1-3-4-2.

The algorithm that computes all the paths (ranked by increasing length and increasing bandwidth) is described in [GERL 78B]. Here, we present a simplified version of the algorithm, which computes only two paths: the shortest path and the maximum bandwidth path.

We assume that each node periodically monitors the average bandwidth U in use on each outgoing trunk. Clearly,

$$U = U_c + U_p$$

where U_c = aggregate circuit-switched bandwidth

U_p = average packet-switched bandwidth

The average available bandwidth B is then given by

$$B = C - U$$

where C is the trunk capacity.

The available bandwidth $b(q)$ on path q is defined as the smallest value of B over all the trunks on path q:

$$b(q) = \min_{i \in q} B_i$$

The algorithm is based on the periodical exchange of information between nodes, and on local table updating at each node based on the information received from the neighbors. Two independent modules can be identified: the shortest path module and the maximum bandwidth module.

The *shortest path module* computes the shortest path to each destination and the bandwidth available on such path. The module requires the following set of tables at each node $i (i = 1, \ldots, N)$: (1) routing vector RV_i, where $RV_i(j)$ is the next leg on the shortest path to destination j; (2) bandwidth vector BV_i, where $BV_i(j)$ is the available bandwidth on the shortest path to j; (3) hop vector HV_i, where $HV_i(j)$ is the number of hops on the shortest path to j.

Periodically, say every few seconds, each node i broadcasts the vectors BV_i and HV_i to all its neighbors. On receiving these vectors, node i, say, will proceed to the updating of its tables as follows:

$$HV_i(j) \leftarrow \min_{n} [HV_n(j) + 1]$$

where n spans the set of neighbors of node i. If n' is the neighbor that minimizes the hop distance to j, then

$$\text{BV}_i(j) \leftarrow \min[\text{BV}_n'(j), B_{in}']$$

where n spans the set of neighbors of node i. If n' is the neighbor that minimizes the hop distance to j, then

$$\text{BV}_i(j) \leftarrow \min[\text{BV}_n'(j), B_{in}']$$

When node i is first brought up in the network (or is reinitialized after a failure), its tables are initialized as follows:

$$\text{RV}_i(j) = j; \quad \text{BV}_i(j) = 0; \quad \text{HV}_i(j) = \infty; \quad \text{V for all } j \neq i$$

and

$$\text{RV}_i(i) = i; \quad \text{BV}_i(i) = \infty; \quad \text{HV}_i(i) = 0$$

It can be easily shown that repeated application of the vector exchange and update procedure drives the tables to their steady-state values after a finite number of steps, which is typically on the order of the network diameter.

The *maximum bandwidth module* has the objective of finding the path with maximum available bandwidth between each node pair. The module uses the vectors MRV, MBV, and MHV, which have the same structure and definition as in the shortest path module (except for replacing the term "shortest path" with the term "maximum bandwidth path"). Table updates (at node i) are carried out as follows:

$$\text{MBV}_i(j) \leftarrow \max_n \; [\min(\text{MBV}_n(j), B_{in})]$$

for n spanning the set of neighbors of node i. If n' is the neighbor that maximizes the bandwidth from i to j, then

$$\text{MHV}_i(j) \leftarrow \text{MHV}_n'(j) + 1$$

and

$$\text{MRV}_i(j) \leftarrow n'$$

Initialization and convergence behavior of the maximum bandwidth algorithm are identical to those of the shortest path algorithm.

Given that each node has up-to-date knowledge of the shortest path and maximum bandwidth path to each destination, we explain next how this information can be used for hybrid packet- and circuit-switched routing and flow control.

The routing procedure consists of three distinct routines applied to datagram, virtual circuit, and circuit switching, respectively. All routines use the same data structure.

A datagram packet is routed along the shortest path until the queue length on an intermediate node exceeds a predefined threshold Q_{max}. From this point on, the datagram is routed on the maximum bandwidth path. Notice that this scheme achieves efficient alternate routing without the looping and oscillation problems observed in previous datagram networks [NAYL 76]. Looping is precluded by the fact that both shortest path and maximum bandwidth path are loopless by definition.

For a virtual circuit connection, the route is chosen to match the average data rate that is expected on this connection. The average rate is either specifically declared by the user, or is determined by the network entry node on the basis of previous measurements. Three cases are possible:

1. If the average rate is less than the bandwidth available on the shortest path, the shortest path is chosen.
2. If the average rate is larger than the shortest path bandwidth but smaller than the bandwidth available on the maximum bandwidth path, the latter path is chosen.
3. If the average rate exceeds the maximum available bandwidth, the connection request is refused (alternatively, the request may be accepted, after having stipulated with the user that the input rate will be metered and kept below the bandwidth available in the network).

For a circuit-switched connection the routing procedure is identical to that of the virtual circuit connection, except for the fact that the bandwidth request is exactly known in advance and is specifically declared by the user. Furthermore, the connection request is generally rejected if the requested bandwidth exceeds the available bandwidth. Actually, if the user terminal clock is controlled by the network, the terminal effective input rate may be reduced by stopping its clock periodically. Using this clock control strategy, the original bandwidth request may be reduced to a level matching the available network bandwidth.

Flow control is implemented by three procedures which separately control datagram, virtual circuit, and circuit-switched traffic, respectively. These procedures utilize the same set of tables as those used for routing control.

The flow of datagrams into the network (i.e., network access flow control) is regulated on the basis of the value of maximum available bandwidth. Incoming datagrams directed to a given destination are accepted as long as the maximum available bandwidth to such destination is above a given threshold; otherwise, they are rejected and must be resubmitted by the user after timeout. Upon acceptance into the network, datagrams may be further flow controlled by conventional flow control strategies; for example, a limit may be set on the number of datagrams that can be maintained on each internal queue (channel queue limit scheme); or sets of buffers can be reserved for datagrams that have covered a given number of hops (structured buffer pool strategy) [GERL 80].

Virtual circuit calls are flow controlled at the network access point. The average bandwidth requested (either specifically declared by the user, or estimated by the network) is compared with the current maximum available bandwidth. If the request is within the available bandwidth, the call is accepted as it is. If the request exceeds the available bandwidth, the call is rejected and the user is informed of the amount of bandwidth currently available. At this point, the user can resubmit the request specifying that he or she is willing to transmit at a reduced rate (the network would then meter user packets to verify compliance with the reduced acceptance rate); or the user may give up and retry at a later time. However, there are some real-time applications (e.g., digitized voice) [FORG 77] in which operation at a reduced rate would not be acceptable.

Flow control on circuit-switched traffic is applied during the call setup phase. At the entry node, the bandwidth request is compared with the available bandwidth. If the request exceeds the availability, the call is refused. Alternatively, if the terminal clock is controllable from the network (and the user is willing to accept a reduction in transmission rate), the network may "slow down" the terminal by intermittently starting and stopping its clock, so that the effective terminal rate is reduced to a value acceptable by the network.

16.5.4   Integrated Network Performance

Since the concept of integrated network is relatively new, there is no well-established set of performance criteria for the evaluation of integrated networks or their comparison with other schemes. For the individual components of the integrated network, however (i.e., packet and circuit switching), standard measures are available. These are: for a packet net, the average delay under a given traffic pattern; and for a circuit-switched net, the blocking probability under a given traffic pattern. In the packet case, average delay is a cumulative measure which reflects the efficiency of all the internal protocols, such as routing, flow control, link protocols, source–destination protocols, and so on. Similarly, the blocking probability in a circuit-switched network reflects the efficiency of route selection and signaling procedures.

For integrated networks that offer an elastic boundary between the circuit and the packet subnetwork, a candidate set of measures may be the delay for the packet component, the blocking probability for the circuit component, and the capability of sharing resources between the packet and the circuit component by means of dynamic boundary adjustment. Boundary control should be dictated, of course, by traffic volumes as well as performance requirements and relative priorities of the two components.

The analysis of movable-boundary integrated systems is a challenging problem. An elegant analytical solution was found by Fisher and Harris [FISH 76] for the SENET integrated system with movable partition between voice and data components, described earlier in Sec. 16.5.2. In the Fisher and Harris model, a slotted frame is used to carry both voice and data packets. S slots in the frame are reserved to voice, and $N = F - S$ slots are reserved to data, where F is the total number of slots in the frame. Voice is transferred in circuit-switched mode, whereas data are packet switched. Two possible schemes are considered: (1) the *fixed-boundary* scheme, which is performance-wise equivalent to two separate packet and circuit implementations; and (2) the *variable-boundary* scheme, in which silent voice slots are reassigned to data packets. The model permits to evaluate average data packet delay on a single trunk as a function of data load on the trunk. Typical behavior of this system is shown in Fig. 16.10. In this example, the frame has a duration of 10 msec, and is subdivided into 15 slots. The average number of voice packets per frame is five, a constant during the experiment. In order to maintain voice blocking probability below 2%, $S = 10$ slots are reserved to voice traffic. The remaining five slots are assigned to data traffic. With the fixed-boundary scheme, the maximum allowable data load is five packets per frame. This value is increased to 10 packets per frame using the variable-boundary scheme, as shown in Fig. 16.10. A 100% throughput improvement for the data users is therefore achieved by exploiting the dynamic bandwidth-sharing features of the integrated schemes.

Beside the dynamic boundary issue, another feature that is commonly advertised in integrated networks is the capability to modify network connectivity and topology by establishing direct bandwidth "pipes" between source—destination pairs. This feature is offered by the PACUIT scheme in the TRAN network, as described in Sec. 16.5.2, and was independently proposed by Foschini et al. in [FOSC 78]. In assessing the PACUIT technique, a critical trade-off arises between the delay reduction due to the removal of buffering and reassembly needs at intermediate modes, and the reduction of dynamic sharing benefits due to pipelining. An analytical model has

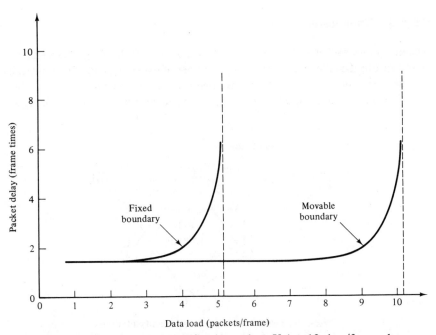

Figure 16.10. Movable versus fixed boundary. Voice, 10 slots/frame; data, 5 slots/frame.

been developed to study this trade-off [GERL 78A, KEYE 78]. The remainder of this section reports on some of the results obtained from this model [GERL 78A].

Consider the six-node network shown in Fig. 16.11. Line speeds are 9.6 kbps. Users are connected directly to the network nodes with 1.2-kbps access lines. Traffic is assumed uniform among all node pairs. Traffic volume and average message length are considered as parameters in this study. Two strategies are examined: the conventional packet-switched strategy and the PACUIT strategy. In the latter, PACUIT links of proper bandwidth are established between all node pairs. For each strategy, average message delay is evaluated as a function of message length and network load. Figures 16.12 and 16.13 show the results obtained for two values of network load, corresponding to 30% and 60% of maximum network capacity, and for message length varying in the range from 32 to 2000 bits. In both cases PACUIT leads to lower delays than packet does. For small message size, the lower delay is due to the lower PACUIT header overhead. For large message size PACUIT and packet overhead is comparable, but PACUIT manages to reduce delays by transmitting messages "on-the-fly" rather than buffering them at each intermediate node as packet switching does.

The superiority of PACUIT over packet performance for a wide range of network and traffic parameters seems to indicate that the lack of dynamic bandwidth sharing in the PACUIT scheme is more than compensated by the integrated switching benefits, namely: reduced header and on-the-fly transmission.

16.5.5   Open Issues

The integrated packet and circuit technology is a recent technology which still poses many unsolved challenging problems. A number of issues currently under investigation were presented and discussed in the previous sections: integrated switch architecture, integrated routing and flow control, and performance evaluation of integrated

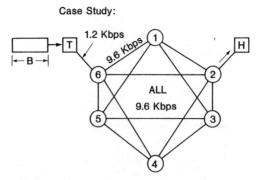

Case Study:

Trunk Bandwidth = 9.6 Kbps   User Speed = 1.2 Kbps
VARIABLES: Message Length B; Network Load

Figure 16.11. Six-node network example.

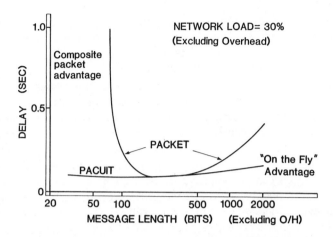

Figure 16.12. Packet versus Pacuit delay comparison (30% load).

networks. Two other important problems that need to be addressed are the dynamic bandwidth allocation and the multilevel network partitioning problem.

Dynamic bandwidth allocation becomes important when the integrated switching facility is used to establish pipes on an end-to-end basis, as in the PACUIT scheme. Each pipe corresponds to a circuit that multiplexes data from one source to one destination. The bandwidth of the pipe is sized according to the traffic volume from source to destination. A static bandwidth allocation would therefore assign bandwidth based on the average source-to-destination requirements. This is generally not the best policy, however, since traffic requirements are bursty in nature. A more effective policy would monitor the instantaneous requirements on all the pipes and would allocate bandwidth in proportion to the actual demands. This policy, called *dynamic bandwidth allocation*, should be implemented with a distributed algorithm

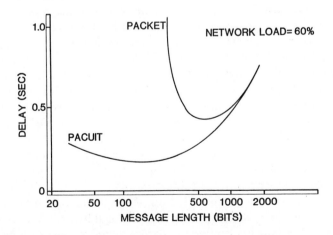

Figure 16.13. Packet versus Pacuit delay comparison (60% load).

(as routing and flow control are) to obtain better reliability and network reaction time. Although good engineering solutions are known for the dynamic bandwidth allocation problem, no general approach has yet been proposed.

Another issue that needs to be addressed is the implementation of large integrated networks. For large packet-switched networks it is customary to propose hierarchical architectures, with a number of regional subnetworks feeding into a backbone network. The need for a multilevel architecture is even more important for integrated networks, especially those employing the PACUIT techniques. For PACUIT systems, the number of PACUIT links increases with the square of the number of nodes, thus leading to an extreme bandwidth fragmentation for large network sizes, which cannot be efficiently handled by any dynamic bandwidth allocation scheme. A possible solution to this problem consists of partitioning a large network into regional networks of more manageable size (say up to 10 nodes) which are interconnected via a backbone network. Full PACUIT link connectivity is maintained only within the regional networks and within the backbone network, respectively. A message between two regions must therefore travel along three separate PACUIT links in series. The challenging (and yet unresolved) problems posed by hierarchical architectures are the optimal network partitioning (into backbone and regional segments) and the development of routing, flow control, and dynamic bandwidth allocation schemes appropriate for this hierarchical environment.

16.6   CONCLUSIONS AND FUTURE PERSPECTIVES

If we look back and analyze the evolution of data switching over the past 15 years, we realize that this evolution was largely the result of the interplay between growing user demands on one side, and communications processor technology advances on the other. In the late 1960s the user demand for a cost-effective data communication capability with low delay and high reliability was satisfied using minicomputer technology and a packet-switching protocol implemented entirely in software. In the following years, user demands for higher bandwidth services covering a broader gamut of applications were met using virtual circuit and, later, integrated packet- and circuit-switched schemes. The cost-effective implementation of the latter schemes relied on multi-microprocessor organizations made possible by the advances in microprocessor technology in the late 1970s [ENSL 77, THUR 77].

This interplay between market requirements and technological advances is likely to last through the 1980s. It is predictable, in fact, that the cost of long-distance communications facilities will steadily increase and the amount of bandwidth available will in some cases (e.g., satellite and radio channels) reach saturation, while the cost of processors and memories will steadily decrease, due to the advances in LSI and VLSI technology. Consequently, the network designer will tend to increase switch sophistication in an attempt to reduce line costs. This will lead to the development of very efficient switching protocols supported by highly modularized switches, with the majority of the functions implemented in hardware and firmware modules. The modularity of the implementation will permit the tailoring of the protocol to specific user requirements, and will facilitate the integration of different schemes.

Next we list some of the issues and requirements that will have major impact on the development of the switching technology in the 1980s.

16.6.1   Transparency

In spite of the universal acceptance of X.25 as the standard network access protocol, it will take some time before all computer manufacturers will offer a standard X.25 interface in their equipment. Until then, users will be faced with the following alternatives: they can either purchase front-end processors for the translation from native protocol to X.25 and then back to native protocol; or in the case of integrated packet and circuit network, they can use the transparent circuit-switched or permanent circuit option with the much simpler X.21 standard interface. There are some trade-offs in this choice. The front-end processor would allow better network line utilization than the circuit-switched solutions, especially if traffic is bursty; it may also provide additional services, such as remote polling of terminals with drastic reduction of polling overhead within the network. The problems with front-end processors, however, are the additional cost and, most important, the difficulty often encountered in emulating accurately and efficiently a native protocol in an external machine. Transparency is therefore a factor that will attract users to integrated packet and circuit networks for many years to come.

16.6.2   New Applications

New applications, such as digitized speech, fax, and image, will have to be supported by the networks of the 1980s. Digitized speech may be carried either in packet-switched, or in circuit-switched, or finally, in virtual circuit-switched mode: there are pros and cons in any of these schemes. The final answer will probably depend on the technology advancements in the 1980s. Fax and image, however, will undoubtedly require a circuit-switched mode of operation. The coming of these new applications will give a very strong impulse to the development of integrated packet and circuit networks.

16.6.3   High-Speed Switching

The growth of the network user population and of the applications in both private and public networks will require switching processors capable of handling 10 Mbps plus traffic volumes. This level of traffic cannot be switched cost effectively using pure packet switching: the amount of processing required to handle each packet quickly drives the size and cost of packet processors to prohibitive limits. Circuit switching, on the other hand, places a much lower load on the processor. A more cost-effective solution to high-speed switching therefore seems to be offered by the combination of packet and circuit switching, where circuit switching is used to transport efficiently and transparently the bulk of the traffic through intermediate modes.

16.6.4   Network Partitioning

In a profitable public network, line speeds are sized so as to achieve line utilization in access of 60 to 70%. This implies that during peak hours some users may get degraded service. This situation may be perfectly acceptable to the majority of the customers, who are willing to suffer an occasional degradation in performance in exchange of a major reduction in cost. Some customers, however, may require (and may be willing to pay for) a steady performance because of the nature of their applications. Traditionally, preferential service to privileged customers was given in the past by assigning higher priorities. In the varied traffic environments that are likely to exist in the 1980s, however, priorities will be inadequate and counterproductive. The only fail-safe solution is offered by integrated networks, which permit permanent allocation of a portion of trunk bandwidth to selected users. In the limit, a user may be able to "lease" a private subnetwork within the public integrated network. Another advantage of network partitioning is the improved network security deriving from the fact that intruders cannot penetrate the subnetwork from foreign devices.

16.6.5   Network Interconnection

Most of the considerations in this chapter were directed to geographically distributed data networks implemented with point-to-point land lines. Two other data network environments have received increasing attention in recent years: local networks [CLAR 78] and satellite networks [JACO 78]. Although very different in many respects, local and satellite networks have in common the capability to offer channels of a very high bandwidth (up to several Mbps). Both local and satellite networks are therefore ideal environments for the development of high-bandwidth applications (e.g., digitized image and fax). If high-bandwidth traffic must be exchanged between local networks far apart, the ideal solution would be to relay it via satellite. However, satellite stations are not available everywhere; therefore, a medium for the access to the satellite must be provided. Furthermore, the satellite channel may not be the most cost-effective solution if the local networks are only a few hundred miles apart. These considerations lead to the requirement for a geographically distributed, land-based data network which can interconnect with both local and satellite network environments and can efficiently transfer high-bandwidth streams. The nature of the applications suggests that the high-bandwidth stream could be best handled in a circuit-switched mode through the network. The need for interconnection of diverse networks is therefore likely to provide a further impulse to the development of integrated packet and circuit networks in the 1980s.

REFERENCES

CCITT 76	CCITT Recommendation X.25, "Interface between DTE and DCE for Terminals Operating in the Packet Mode on Public Data Networks," 1976.
CERF 74	Cerf, V., and R. Kahn, "A Protocol for Packet Network Intercommunications," *IEEE Trans. Commun.*, Vol. COM-22, No. 5, May 1974.
CHEN 75	Chen, F.T., et al., "The DATRAN Network: System Description," *NTC Conf. Proc.*, New Orleans, December 1975.
CHOU 76	Chou, W., and M. Gerla, "A Unified Flow and Congestion Control Model for Packet Networks," *Proc. ICCC '76*, Toronto, August 1976.
CHU 69	Chu, W. W., "A Study of Asynchronous Time Division Multiplexing for Time-Sharing Computer Systems," *Fall Joint Comput. Conf. Proc.*, 1969.
CLAR 78	Clark, D., et al., "An Introduction to Local Area Networks," *Proc. IEEE*, November 1978.
COVI 75	Coviello, G., and P. Vena, "Integration of Circuit/Packet Switching by a SENET (*Slotted Envelope NETwork*) Concept," *Proc. NTC '75*, New Orleans, December 1975.
DANE 76	Danet, A., et al., "The French Public Packet Switched Service: the Transpac Network," *Proc. Int. Conf. Comput. Commun.*, Toronto, August 1976.
DAVI 76	Davies, G. W. P., "Euronet Project," *Proc. 3rd Int. Conf. Comput. Commun.*, Toronto, 1976.
ENSL 77	Enslow, P., "Multiprocessor Organization: a Survey," *ACM Comput. Surv.*, March 1977.
FISH 76	Fisher, M., and T. Harris, "A Model for Evaluating the Performance of an Integrated Circuit- and Packet-Switched Multiplex Structure," *IEEE Trans. Commun.*, Vol. COM-24, No. 2, 1976.
FOLT 80	Folts, H. C., "X.25 Transaction Oriented Features: Datagram and Fast Select," *IEEE Trans. Commun.*, Vol. COM-28, No. 4, April 1980.
FORG 77	Forgie, J., and A. Nemeth, "An Efficient Packetized Voice/Data Network Using Statistical Flow Control," *Proc. ICC '77*, Chicago, June 1977.
FOSC 78	Foschini, G. J., et al., "Subframe Switching in Data Communications," *Proc. Int. Telemetering Conf.*, Los Angeles, November 1978.
GALL 77	Gallager, R. G., "A Minimum Delay Routing Algorithm Using Distributed Computation," *IEEE Trans. Commun.*, January 1977.
GERL 78A	Gerla, M., and G. de Stasio, "Integration of Packet and Circuit Transport Protocols in the TRAN Data Network," *Comput. Network Protocol Symp.*, Liège, February 1978.
GERL 78B	Gerla, M., and D. Mason, "Distributed Routing in Hybrid Packet and Circuit Data Networks," *Proc. of COMPCON '78*, Washington, D.C., September 1978.
GERL 79	Gerla, M., "Routing and Flow Control in Virtual Circuit Networks," *Proc. INFO II, 2nd Int. Conf. Inf. Sci. Syst.*, Patras, Greece, July 1979.
GERL 80	Gerla, M., and L. Kleinrock, "Flow Control: A Comparative Survey," *IEEE Trans. Commun.*, May 1980.

GIES 78   Giessler, A., et al., "Free Buffer Allocation—An Investigation by Simulation," *Comput. Networks,* Vol. 2, 1978.

GITM 78   Gitman, I., and H. Frank, "Economic Analysis of Voice and Data Networks: A Case Study," *Proc. IEEE,* November 1978.

HEAR 70   Heart, F., et al., "The Interface Message Processor for the ARPA Computer Network," *SJCC Proc.,* 1970

ITOH 73   Itoh, J., et al., "An Analysis of Traffic Handling Capacity of Packet Switched and Circuit Switched Networks," *Proc. 3rd Data Commun. Symp.,* St. Petersburg, Fla., November 1973.

JACO 78   Jacobs, I., "General Purpose Packet Satellite Networks," *Proc. IEEE,* November 1978.

JENN 76   Jenny, C., and K. Kummerle, "Distributed Processing within an Integrated Circuit/Packet-Switching Node," *IEEE Trans. Commun.,* October 1976.

KAHN 77   Kahn, R., "The Organization of Computer Resources into a Packet Radio Network," *IEEE Trans. Commun.,* January 1977.

KERM 79   Kermani, P., and L. Kleinrock, "A Trade-off Study of Switching Systems," *Proc. ICC 79.*

KEYE 78   Keyes, N., and M. Gerla, "Report on Experience in Developing a Hybrid Packet and Circuit Switched Network," *Proc. ICC '78,* Toronto, June 1978.

KLEI 76   Klein, D., and S. Frankel, "A Hybrid Circuit and Packet Switching System," *Proc. NTC '76,* Dallas, November 1976.

KLEI 78   Kleinrock, L., and M. Gerla, "On the Measured Performance of Packet Satellite Access Schemes," *Proc. Int. Conf. Comput. Commun.,* Kyoto, October 1978.

KOPF 77   Kopf, J., "Tymnet as a Multiplexed Packet Network," *NCC Proc.,* 1977.

KRON 75   Kroneberg, D., "A Packet/Message Switch for the SITA Network," *ICC '75 Conf. Proc.,* San Francisco, June 1975.

KUMM 76   Kummerle, K., and H. Rudin, "Packet and Circuit Switching: a Comparison and Cost Performance," *Proc. NTC '76,* Dallas, November 1976.

MANN 78   Manning, E., "On Datagram Service in Packet Switched Networks," *Comput. Networks,* Vol. 2, 1978.

MCAU 78   McAuliffe, D. J., "An Integrated Approach to Communications Switching," *Proc. ICC,* Toronto, June 1978.

MIYA 75   Miyahara, H., et al., "A Comparative Evaluation of Switching Methods in Computer Communications Networks," *Proc. ICC '75,* San Francisco, June 1975.

NAYL 76   Naylor, W., and L. Kleinrock, "On the Effect of Periodic Routing Updates in Packet-Switched Networks," *NTC '76 Proc.,* Dallas, November 1976.

NEWP 77   Newport, C. B., and P. Kaul, "Communications Processors for Telenet's Third Generation Packet Switching Network," *Proc. EASCON Conf.,* 1977.

OPDE 76   Opderbeck, H., "The Performance of a Terminal Emulation Interface to a Packet-Switched Data Network," *Proc. ICCC '76,* Toronto, August 1976.

OPDE 78   Opderbeck, H., et al., "Software Architecture for a Microprocessor Based Packet Network," *Proc. Berkeley Workshop Distributed Process.,* August 1978.

ORNS 72   Ornstein, S., et al., "The Terminal IMP for the ARPA Computer Network,"

SJCC Proc., 1972.

PORT 76   Port, E., et al., "A Network Architecture for the Integration of Circuit and Packet Switching," *Proc. ICCC '76,* Toronto, August 1976.

POST 80   Postel, J. B., "Internet Protocol Approaches," *IEEE Trans. Commun.*, Vol. Com. 28, No. 4, April 1980.

POUZ 73   Pouzin, L., "Presentation and Major Design Aspects of the Cyclades Computer Network," *Proc. 3rd Data Commun. Symp.*, St. Petersburg, Fla., November 1973.

POUZ 74   Pouzin, L., "Virtual Circuits vs. Datagrams: Technical and Political Problems," *AFIPS-NCC*, June 1976.

POUZ 76   Pouzin, L., "Flow Control in Data Networks: Methods and Tools," *Proc. ICCC Conf.*, Toronto, August 1976.

RAUB 76   Raubold, E., and J. Haenle, "A Method of Deadlock-Free Resource Allocation and Flow Control in Packet Networks," *ICCC '76 Conf. Proc.*, Toronto, August 1976.

RIND 76   Rinde, J., "Tymnet I: an Alternative to Packet Technology," *ICCC '76 Proc.*, Toronto, August 1976.

RIND 79   Rinde, J., and A. Caisse, "Passive Flow Control Techniques for Distributed Networks," *Proc. Int. Symp. Comput. Networks*, Versailles, France, February 1979.

ROBE 70   Roberts, L. G., and B. D. Wessler, "Computer Network Development to Achieve Resource Sharing," *AFIPS Conf. Proc.*, Vol. 36, SJCC, 1970, pp. 543–599.

ROBE 75   Roberts, L. G., "Telenet: Principles and Practice," *Proc. Eur. Comput. Conf. Commun. Networks*, London, 1975.

ROBE 77   Roberts, L. G., "Packet Network Design: the Third Generation," *IFIP Conf. Proc.*, 1977.

ROBE 78   Robert, L. G., "The Evolution of Packet Switching," *Proc. IEEE*, November 1978.

ROSS 78   Ross, M. J., "System Engineering of Integrated Voice and Data Switches," *Proc. ICC*, Toronto, June 1978.

RYBC 77   Rybczynski, A. M., and D. F. Weir, "DATAPAC X.25 Service Characteristics," *Proc. 5th Data Commun. Symp.*, Snowbird, Utah, September 1977.

SAND 76   Sanders, R., and V. Cerf, "Compatibility or Chaos in Communications," *Datamation*, March 1976.

SEVC 78   Sevcik, P. J., "Why the Datagram Is Needed—and How It Will Operate," *Data Commun. J.*, March 1978.

SIMO 79   Simon, J. M., and A. Danet, "Contrôle des ressources et principes du routage dans le réseaux TRANSPAC," *Proc. Int. Symp. Comput. Networks,* Versailles, France, February 1979.

THUR 77   Thurber, K., and G. Masson, "Recent Advances in Microprocessor Technology and Their Impact on Interconnection Design in Computer Systems," *Proc. ICC '77.*

TRAN 79   TRAN Internal Report, "Small Switch Design Specifications," June 1979.

VAND 76   Vander Mey, J., "The Architecture of a Transparent Intelligent Network," *Proc. NTC '76*, Dallas, November 1976.

17

Integrating
Data, Voice,
and Image

R. ANDREW PICKENS
Aeronautical Radio, Inc.

KATHRYN W. HANSON
State of North Carolina

17.1 INTRODUCTION

During the last years of the 1970s, intense interest developed in integrated telecommunications services. Such services would be provided by common telecommunications facilities, on a subscriber-to-subscriber-basis, supporting a mixture of communication formats for voice, data, video, text, graphics, and facsimile. At present, different formats usually require different access and transmission arrangements. In some cases wholly different networks are required. Where commonality does exist, the compromises necessary to handle one kind of traffic in facilities designed for another often result in awkward use, limits on available service, and suboptimal performance in terms of quality and cost.

The potential applications of integrated services networks are imaginative extrapolations of advanced technology to future service possibilities. Those applications with broadest potential—in "offices of the future" and in homes, combining entertainment, communications, remote computing, and telemetering functions— presently exist only in limited or experimental forms. Services to the home could include low-speed telemetry for remote meter reading and control of energy consumption, video library and news services, two-way video transmission for education and telemedicine, and still-picture transmission for teleshopping, in addition to the presently pervasive unidirectional audio, video and telephony services.

Integration in offices of the future will include support for communicating word

© 1981, R.A.P. All rights reserved.

processing, data processing, telecommunications, facsimile and electronic mail, financial services, audio mail, voice and video conferencing, voice-actuated typewriters, and all-electronic file storage and retrieval of voice, data, and image forms. Numerous other possibilities have been detailed in the literature [MART 77, LICK 78, TOMS 78]; Tab. 17.1 lists some examples. As unlikely as some projections may

Table 17.1.   *Sampling of Integrated Network Applications.*

GENERAL COMMUNICATION
  • Electronic mail, messages
  • Teleconferencing
  • Speech
  • Encrypted speech
  • Still pictures
  • Moving pictures
ELECTRONIC OFFICE AND WORK ASSISTANCE
  • Remote work via telecommunication terminals
  • Computer-enhanced output quality
  • Computer-assisted task management and coordination
  • Remote meter reading
MANAGEMENT
  • Farm management services
  • Data collection
  • Computer-assisted problem solving and decision making
  • Modeling
COMMERCE
  • Electronic markets and auctions
  • Computerized commerce
  • Employment services
  • Electronic fund transfer; banking services
  • Remote shopping
PROFESSIONAL
  • Monitoring patients and population groups
  • Remote medical consultation and diagnosis
  • Medical records
  • Medical, legal, and other knowledge data bases
GOVERNMENT
  • Military command, control, and communications
  • Logistics
  • National Crime Information Center
  • Social Security
PROTECTION
  • Home and business security—fire and burglar alarms
EDUCATION, INFORMATION, AND ENTERTAINMENT
  • Computer-assisted education
  • Customized news selection
  • On-request television programs
  • Video games
  • Remote instruction and interactive training
  • Teletex services

Source: After [LICK 78], © 1978 IEEE.

seem now, by the turn of the century they will probably seem primitive. Certainly, many possibilities are completely unforeseen.

These concepts, providing a range of service in varying communication formats via a common network, have become generally known as the Integrated Services Digital Network (ISDN). Explicit in the appellation is the assumption that digital technology will be employed; indeed, the arguments supporting this eventuality are overwhelming and are reviewed in this chapter. Implicitly, the ISDN will evolve in some form from the existing telephone networks, at least on an international basis. The latter, however, is not necessarily foreordained in all situations; and, it will be some time before all-digital transmission facilities are available to those concerned either with large-scale public networks or with networks intended for more limited private requirements. For these reasons, a somewhat broader perspective has been adopted in this chapter. A more generalized concept of "integrated service networks" affords the opportunity to explore ideas and techniques useful to a broad range of interests in integrated services, as well as the primary stream of ISDN development itself.

This chapter identifies trends that are shaping integrated services networks. It examines the technical issues that affect integration options, covers network building blocks for integrated switching and transmission, and highlights some of the many integration techniques in use and under development.

17.2   TRENDS AND MOTIVATIONS

Transmission of different types of communications traffic on a common circuit is not new. The great majority of circuits carrying digital data are established via the telephone networks, which are designed for analog voice transmission. The telephone networks, in turn, grew out of transmission techniques originally developed for telegraph operation, basically a digital form of communication.

Improving technology and increasing demand are making possible not only new services but also substantial improvements in quality, flexibility, and cost of currently available kinds of services. It is important to realize that technological possibility alone is not enough to bring a new telecommunications service into being—demand (or at least potential demand) must be sufficient to warrant the substantial investment costs required, and the regulatory environment must be favorable. In this section, both technical and nontechnical trends that influence integrated services are presented briefly. These trends, including the already mentioned expanding applications, are diagrammed in Fig. 17.1.

17.2.1   Technology and Costs

Cost reduction is probably the most powerful motivation for change and improvement; technology provides the means for cost reduction. The raw costs of communications have been decreasing at a rate of about 11% per year [BRAN 79] and

TRENDS LEADING TOWARDS INTEGRATION

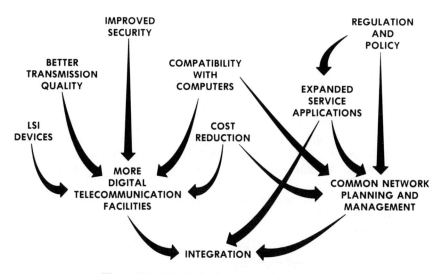

Figure 17.1. Trends leading toward integration.

processing costs have been dropping at about 25% per year [MILE 79]. The decline of both costs is providing the major impetus to the burgeoning application of telepro-cessing and distributed processing systems. Since the decline is in real terms, there is a strong incentive to substitute telecommunications/teleprocessing applications for traditional services whose costs are rapidly rising, such as those that are labor intensive or involve the significant expenditure of energy. One straightforward exam-ple is electronic mail; other examples are applications that substitute for increasingly expensive travel, such as teleconferencing, work stations in the home, or teleshopping.

The *relative* trend of communications versus processing costs also is having a profound impact. Processing costs are decreasing at a rate about double that for communications per se. The classical distinction between the communications func-tions of transmission (transportation of signals over some distance) and switching (establishing the desired end-to-end connectivity of a communications path) has become blurred as digital processing techniques invade each function to effect greater efficiencies. Computers are being assimilated rapidly as part of the communications process, and computers are increasing in number as the users of communications increase. Both of these developments further support the movement toward incorpo-rating digital technology in telecommunications.

The principal reason for the decline in processing costs, and for the involvement of computers, is the advance of large-scale integrated circuit (LSI) technology. The impact of LSI has been most visible in areas involving digital processing—in particu-lar, computers and specialized computer-like functions. More recently, the attention of LSI producers has also turned to the analog and quasi-analog processing needs of telecommunications; they are making available low-cost implementations of such functions as analog-to-digital and digital-to-analog converters, amplifiers, filters, modems, and subscriber line interface circuits. These devices are necessary both for the realization of fully integrated digital services (e.g., analog-to-digital conversion of voice) and for the hybrid techniques required in the transitional stages of integration (e.g., modems).

17.2.1.1 *Digital Communication*

Implicit in the long-term future of integrated services networks is all-digital communication. Digital technology is rapidly supplanting older analog technology in key areas of telecommunications networks for many economic and technical reasons. These are discussed in detail in Chaps. 5, 6, 7, and 18, which should be reviewed. In general, economic advantages center on three factors:

1. Lower overall systems costs, due to integration of functions and processing
2. Lower maintenance cost, due to greater reliability and robustness of digital technology
3. Lower allocated costs, because of the greater flexibility and efficiency of digital multiplexing, concentration, and switching functions.

Any traffic can be transmitted in either digital or analog form. Information that is intrinsically digital, such as computer input–output, obviously is better matched by digital transmission. Information that interfaces with human beings, however, is usually in analog form (e.g., voice and images); it must be converted to digital form for digital transmission and reconverted after reception for presentation to the user (see Chap. 18). However, a technical advantage of digital transmission is that its quality, as measured by signal-to-noise ratio, error rate, and distortion, is normally superior to analog transmission even for analog information. Another technical advantage is that information in digital form can also be protected with a greater degree of security than can analog signals.

The advantages can be sufficient to offset the costs of the processing necessary for analog/digital conversion; and conversion costs are decreasing. Previously all-analog networks, such as the public telephone system, are becoming hybrid networks. Rapid conversion to digital transmission is proceeding in the high-volume trunking and switching area, where major economic advantages exist. Transmission facilities of increasingly wider bandwidths offer possibilities of economies of scale and facility sharing that were previously infeasible. Conversion is being extended to intermediate network levels, and can be seen in large digital central offices and wideband optical fiber interoffice trunks.

It is in local distribution, where communication services are carried to the end user, that motivation for digital service has not been very strong. In the United States, the total investment in telephone system plant is too large to be scrapped quickly, so it is unlikely that pervasive and public all-digital transmission will be available soon. The analog local loop plant provides plain old telephone service (POTS) quite well. It has been mostly adequate for data communications needs to date.

In countries with less investment in local distribution, all-digital facilities on a large scale are feasible; some have been implemented in Japan, Canada [DEWI 79], West Germany [GERK 79], France [KEEN 80], and the United Kingdom [ORBE 79]. Digital facilities and digital techniques are making new network architectures possible. These architectures simultaneously offer solutions and raise problems with the concept of integration, as discussed in Sec. 17.4.

17.2.1.2   *Increased Bandwidth Utilization*

The use of idle channel capacity for different types of traffic is economically advantageous in some cases. A simple example is the insertion of data under voice (DUV) in multiplexed microwave links. The lowest 564 kHz of the approximately 8000-kHz bandwidth is unsuitable for high-quality analog voice-grade transmission. However, the low-frequency range can carry accurate transmission of a digital data stream at rates up to about 2 Mbps. DUV is not a service offering but a clever transmission technique [DOLL 78] used by the AT&T Dataphone Digital Service (DDS) on part of its transmission facilities.

Other approaches to shared use of transmission facilities also take advantage of the bandwidth, or channel time, that is unused for the primary traffic. Subcarriers for data transmission in an FM radio broadcasting channel provide an example of increasing a channel's capacity for carrying information without increasing its overall bandwidth. Insertion of data in the flyback interval of television transmission is an example of channel sharing in time. Some approaches take advantage of bandwidth available during gaps in interactive terminal transmissions or voice conversations. Other examples, described in Sec. 17.5.3, demonstrate the gains in utilization of existing transmission facilities that can be obtained by combining traffic types.

17.2.1.3   *Economies of Scale*

Terrestrial microwave radio, communications satellite, coaxial cable, optical fiber, and other wide-bandwidth media offer economies of scale when their large bandwidth can be well utilized. In some cases, capacity requirements of any single traffic type are insufficient and traffic must be combined to justify use of an economical wideband medium. The combination is achieved by multiplexing, concentration, or switching techniques. Excess bandwidth can be made available at the same, or even lower, marginal cost when traffic is combined. The excess can mean better service and can allow reduction of processing overhead and system complexity.

Economy of scale is evident in a comparison of paired cables, where 10 circuits have a relative cost of over $200 per circuit mile, with optical fiber transmission, where investment cost per circuit may well be under $2 per mile when 10,000 or more circuits are installed (see Fig. 7.2). The potential bandwidth of optical-fiber transmission is so high that the cost of the transmission medium itself will be trivial; the primary cost components will be installation (trenching, rights-of-way, etc.) and access (termination, multiplexing, etc.).

Table 17.2 displays excerpts of a study that compared the cost of an integrated optical fiber system with separate wire-pair telephone lines and coaxial-cable televi-

Table 17.2. *Cost Comparison of Separate and Integrated Systems.*

Subscriber Density Per km²	Model	Number of CATV Channels	Telephony on Pairs	Dollars per subscriber		
				CATV on Coax	Telephony Plus CATV	Optical Fiber System
10 (Rural)	Aerial Grid	21	800	725	1525	845-1838
	Buried Grid	21	1075	1063	2138	1139-2140
300 (Suburban)	Aerial	21	225	203	428	398- 859
	Buried	21	650	689	1339	818-1363
5,000 (Urban)		21	225	185	410	421- 764

Source: [CHAN 79], © 1979 IEEE.

sion. Low-high estimates are shown for optical fiber. Integration of telephone and television transmission facilities on optical fiber offers potential economy for rural and surburban areas.

17.2.1.4 Common Network Planning and Management

Integration of traffic implies integration of traditionally separate telecommunications and computer communications network planning and management. Managers are recognizing that telephone, data processing, and office operations are related functions that must be considered together to lower costs and improve communications [DMW 79]. Upgraded services and equipment from traditional suppliers, together with new offerings and equipment from new vendors, are allowing communication network designers to plan their own private networks for voice, facsimile, and video, as well as for data. Such systems are being developed as a result of expanding communication capacity and interoperability needs.

With integration, the technological distinctions between telecommunications and computer communications are blurring. Some users are finding it desirable to abandon the classical separation of communication interests of the data processing, telephone, Telex, and mail departments. Clearly, the growing importance of the creation, storage, retrieval, and movement of information will have a profound impact on organizational structures in the future.

17.2.2 Some Regulatory and Policy Issues

Technology is the major aspect of integration considered in this chapter, but technology alone will not determine the shape of future integrated networks. Regulations and policies will have a significant impact as potential uses of data and computer communications grow. Countries establishing programs which incorporate traffic integration are laying groundwork that can have a major impact for future developments on a global level.

Carriers, vendors of telecommunications and data processing equipment, offerers of time-sharing and on-line data-base services, and the entire international/ multinational user community must now take into account regulations motivated by political, economic, and social considerations. Many governments, particularly those in Western Europe, have enacted or are planning to enact regulations intended to control transborder data flow [BARN 78, HEBD 79, PIPE 79, ROBI 79]. Generally, such regulations are aimed at the primary concerns of protection of data of a personal nature and information that could adversely affect a country's economy, security, sovereignty [BACH 79, PANT 78], and protection of national teleprocessing industries. Mechanisms of control include discriminatory tariffs, taxation, required divulgence of encryption keys, registration, licensing, and disclosure of messages.

In a broader sense, and perhaps with even greater impact on the development of integrated services networks, are the increasingly rigorous demands for a "New World Information Order." International agreements for exercising control over information of a more general nature, such as news reports and television coverage, are being sought by numerous governments which feel that the (usually external) mass media tend to emphasize the more sensational, negative aspects of the national scene at the expense of a "balanced picture."

Clearly, the accessibility and transparency of telecommunications can be limited by more than strictly technical considerations; in fact, technological advances are provoking demands for standards, regulations, and policies. At the international level, the CCITT has assigned the questions of Integrated Services Digital Networks to a newly-created study group (SG XVIII).

Some countries have devised their own national information policies.[1] Most such policies include plans for developing improved national telecommunications infrastructures, in which integrated services digital networks play a key role. The plans cover a wide range of approaches to integration. It is not clear yet which will be dominant; each approach is reasonable for some circumstances and each is contributing to the shape of future integration options.

Among the most advanced and comprehensive plans is the French Télématique Program, which traces its origins to a governmental decision in the late 1960s to support research and development activities in digital transmission and switching technology. The Télématique Program was made the top national priority of France in 1975. The stated intention of the program is "to provide the public with access to a wide range of new and complementary methods of communication which facilitate dialogue and create a more democratic, equitable society. Mass computerization will take hold, becoming as indispensable to society as electricity" [KEEN 80]. It is also recognized that the economic benefits are potentially staggering, measured in terms of

---

[1]*Information policy* is defined by [PIPE 79] as an information management technique combining computer and telecommunications technologies with administrative infrastructures.

dramatically lower costs of telecommunications and data processing costs in the long term, and both the immediate support and long-term market position of a key high-technology industry.

The Télématique Program incorporates telephone, television, facsimile, computer terminals, and other media into a harmonious network which permits data, still image, video, audio, and other forms of information to be transferred speedily using advanced digital transmission and switching techniques. The overall network implementation concept is based on satellites, optical fibers, time-division multiplexing (TDM), circuit switching, packet switching, and pulse-code-modulation (PCM) transmission. A primary feature of the program is an emphasis on a large market and a corresponding low cost of products and services. Low-cost terminals are particularly notable. It is foreseen that alphanumeric keyboard-display terminals can be produced for less than $100; and medium-speed (Group II) facsimile units, for less than $500. The Télématique products and services are described in Sec. 17.6.1.

Similarly oriented programs are under way elsewhere, although with somewhat less ambitious priorities. In West Germany, a cooperative effort between the Deutsche Buendespost (the national telecommunication service organization) and industry is developing integrated services based on applications of viewdata, teletext, electronic directory, electronic mail, advanced telephone, and telefax technologies, with an increasing emphasis on digital techniques [WHIT 80].

The British Post Office and industry in the United Kingdom are developing the "System X" digital transmission and switching network, and were the first to implement viewdata and teletext services [TANT 79, BRIG 79]. Canadian provinces, particularly Saskatchewan and Alberta, are well along on major installations bringing integrated services to individual homes by broadband optical fiber and video cables. The Federal Department of Communications is developing an advanced, high-resolution graphics videotex system [BOWN 79].

The Japanese HI-OVIS system, providing full two-way video, audio, telephone, and data services to individual homes via optical fiber cables (see Chap. 7), was undertaken both for national economic and sociological reasons. The latter is best explained by a paraphrase of the Japanese spokesman at the system's dedication:

> *Our principal natural resource in Japan is our people. We cannot increase them in numbers because of population constraints—the country just isn't big enough. . . . Therefore, our recourse is to increase productivity by enhancing the quality of life. We're going to do this by cultural and educational enrichment by means of a two-way, multimedia communication system encompassing the entire island of Japan. [ELIO 77]*

In the United States, integrated services is a very complex issue because of a particular combination of institutions, driving forces, and contraints (see, e.g., [WALK 73]). A base of advanced technology, a tradition of private enterprise, and a large market are the elements responsible for most technological progress in the United States. In telecommunications, however, some important inhibitions exist. For one, the sheer size of the market means that a very large investment exists in plant based on earlier technological advances; the rapid and universal provision of new services based on substantially different technology would require new investment of a magnitude perhaps impossible for any single private entity to make, especially if the older investment had to be abandoned. On the other hand, where the focus can be smaller and more specific, potentially successful undertakings are possible in the private sector. For example, there are the independent telephone companies such as Continental and United, specialized common carriers such as MCI and Satellite Business Systems, value-added carriers such as Telenet and Graphnet, data-base services such as Lockheed and The Source, advanced CATV networks such as Warner QUBE, and the many firms offering teleprocessing services.

Even within the single sphere of government, there are numerous elements influencing U.S. telecommunications policy. Many state and local Public Utility Commissions zealously guard their prerogatives for regulation. At the federal government level, the executive, judiciary and legislative branches play major roles. The National Telecommunications and Information Agency (NTIA) is an amalgamation of several previous organizations, and has the executive-branch charter to recommend policy. Results have been tentative but positive [PERR 80]. The NTIA has pursued its projects under the general policies of promoting competition, supporting deregulation whenever feasibile, and relying on the beneficial forces of the marketplace.

Although the United States almost uniquely depends on private corporations for its telecommunications products and services, tight regulation has been exercised by the Federal Communications Commission (FCC) under the articles of the Communications Act of 1934. In addition to creating the FCC, the Act institutionalized the privately-held telephone system and telegraph monopolies, and radio broadcasting oligopolies. During the past several years, there has been much public debate questioning the applicability of the provisions of the Act in the light of today's technological and economic possibilities. Efforts continue in Congress to rewrite the Communications Act. The FCC itself took a giant stride toward less restrictive controls through its preliminary findings on Docket 20828 (so-called Computer Inquiry II) issued in May 1980. Determining that it is hopeless to attempt definitions of what constitutes data processing services (not regulated) as opposed to telecommunications services (regulated), the effect of the FCC decision is to restrict its regulation to basic transmission/switching networks and plain old telephone service. Enhanced services and all terminals, including standard telephone sets, would be deregulated by January 1983.

Yet another arena that is profoundly affecting the U.S. telecommunications industry is found in the judicial system. Certainly the most dramatic case is the anti-trust suit being pressed by the Department of Justice against American Telephone and Telegraph (the Bell System). The final ruling in *U.S. vs. AT&T* required, among other things, divestiture of the regional Bell operating companies responsible for local distribution services and deregulation of customer premises equipment. Of much lower public visibility, but also of major importance to the direction of integrated telecommunication services, are the myriad litigations in the various courts having to do with challenges to FCC rulings, local *vs.* federal purviews, scope of existing legislation and other related matters.

Although numerous petitions for modifications, court challenges, and legislative initiatives are yet to come, the regulatory environment appears now to be conducive to the rapid development of many advanced services. A common trend is to favor competition, letting the marketplace decide the technical and economical merits. In such an atmosphere, there will be failures but the successes will lead to the integration of services in networks and provide new levels of utility and economy.

17.3 TECHNICAL ISSUES OF INTEGRATION

Implicit in the preceding discussions of motivations and trends are numerous complex issues concerning integrated services. In this section and others that follow, concentration is on the technical issues facing the designer. One key set of considerations concerns the types of traffic to be integrated—voice, data, text, the various forms of images—and the terminals to be provided for each. Another set has to do with the communication facilities, in particular with the digitization devices used. In some cases, available facilities may dictate the mix and method of integration; in other cases, the necessary traffic may require the acquisition of new facilities. Finally, the scale and scope of an integrated network will have a significant bearing on its architecture.

17.3.1 Impact of Traffic Characteristics

Each type of traffic has different characteristics. The traffic might be sporadic or continuous, and might have different bandwidth, delivery time, and error control requirements. The requirements can limit the extent of line sharing that is possible and affect the selection of transmission facilities, switching approaches, protocols, and other options for network design.

Table 17.3 illustrates the wide variance in transmission requirements for several forms of data and image traffic. Traffic such as voice, which requires real-time transmission, does not allow the trade-off between transmission time and bandwidth shown for other traffic. The rates used for illustration in Table 17.3 represent:

- 1.2 kbps—speed of a typical full-duplex, dial-up connection
- 4.8 kbps—speed of a typical dedicated connection
- 56 kbps—DDS speed available in some cities
- 256 kbps—potential subscriber data rate.

For comparison, typical rates of digital speech are:

- 2.4 kbps—voice coded at a low digitization rate
- 16 kbps—voice after delta modulation coding

Table 17.3. *Transmission Requirements.*

Content	Typical Number of Bits	Approximate Transmission Time (sec)			
		At 1.2 kbps	*At 4.8 kbps*	*At 56 kbps*	*At 256 kbps*
Page of videotex	6×10^3	5	1	0.1	0.02
Page or full CRT screen of black-and-white text, uncompressed	2×10^4	16	4	0.4	0.08
One frame of Picturephone	2×10^5	175	44	4	0.8
Black and white facsimile, compressed	4×10^5	300 (5 min)	80	8	1.5
One frame of color TV, compressed	5×10^5	400 (7 min)	100	9	2
One frame of color TV, DPCM coded	1.5×10^6	1200 (20 min)	300 (5 min)	30	6
Three-color, high-quality facsimile, heavily compressed	5×10^6	4000 (1 hr)	1000 (15 min)	100	20
20-cm floppy disk, double density	5×10^6	4000 (1 hr)	1000	100	20
Reel of computer tape, 6250 bpi	1×10^9	(10 days)	(2 days)	(5 hr)	(1 hr)

Source: After [MAND 79], © 1979 IEEE.

- 64 kbps—current telephone pulse-code modulation standard (including signaling).

17.3.1.1 Voice Traffic

Voice traffic requires a steady rate of output and a relatively low end-to-end delay. Interruptions in the normal flow of speech output can make content unintelligible. Delays of a half-second or more make two-way conversation difficult or, at the least, require the speakers to modify their conversational pattern. Network design must allow for smooth output or, in other words, essentially zero delivery time variance, and for relatively small delay. The speech continuity requirement is met most easily by dedicating the necessary portion of facilities for each conversation. Traditional dedicated full-duplex communication facilities are poorly utilized for conversations because usually only one of a pair of people is speaking at a given instant. Also, a speaker pauses frequently, and even during speech some signal transmission is redundant.

Speech patterns are important in their effect on the extent of line sharing that can be achieved. Most approaches to integrating voice with other traffic depend particularly on the on–off nature of voice statistics as characterized by the speech activity (talkspurt) and silence (pause) distributions. In general, a channel is required for one direction of a voice conversation only 25% of the time. However, actual voice detector circuits find activity levels of 35 to 40% because of the addition of crosstalk, Gaussian and impulse noise, and other disturbances [LYGH 74]. In effect, then, a voice half-circuit (half of a full-duplex channel) is unused 60 to 65% of the time and could be used for other traffic.

Markov models have been developed to predict speech patterns more precisely. The sophisticated models describe not only talkspurt and pause, but also include additional states of speech—double talk, mutual silence, alternation silence, pause in isolation, solitary talkspurt, interruption, speech after interruption, and speech before interruption. Analytical formulations for such models are not very tractable; simulation is necessary for useful quantitative results. A comprehensive six-state model, shown in Fig. 17.2, was developed by [BRAD 69]. This model matches empirical speech data [BRAD 68].

Bandwidth is a major determinant of voice quality. The dependence between voice digitization rate and quality is detailed in Chap. 18. Traditionally, voice has been carried in the public telephone network by analog channels with bandwidth of 3 to 4 kHz. Currently, digitized voice of the same (toll) quality requires at least six times as much capacity. Compensating advantages are lower facility cost, efficient signal

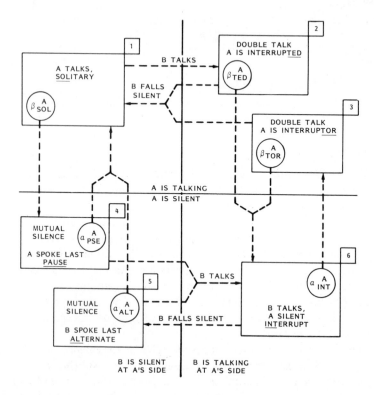

Figure 17.2. Model for speech pattern. (From [BRAD 69], Copyright 1969, American Telephone and Telegraph Company, reprinted by permission).

regeneration, and encryptability of digitized voice. When digitized voice is necessary for integration, bandwidth must be increased or quality standards lowered.

Voice delay constraints mean that transmission distance and the number of transmission hops or links taken through the network can be very significant. Propagation velocity through a network comprising conventional terrestrial transmission equipment (radio, cable, loading circuits, etc.) is roughly three-fourths the speed of light; consequently, long-distance telephone calls can experience transmission delays on the order of 10 msec. One satellite hop adds about 270 msec of signal propagation delay. Most talkers can adjust to the delay of one or two hops, but longer delays are troublesome. Where the network includes a mixture of analog and digital switching and transmission facilities, analog/digital conversions are required, which also add to delay. Other techniques, such as packet switching, can add significant delay.

Another measure of transmission delay is also important. With speech, it is necessary to maintain "temporal coherence" between the speaker and the listener; i.e., it is necessary to maintain a reasonably accurate time relationship between individual segments of the speech (low variance in delay). This requirement imposes constraints on channel-sharing techniques based on forms of time-division multiplexing or concentration (such as packet switching).

A third form of network delay, *setup delay,* must be considered. In the circuit-switched telephone system, setup delay is the time required to establish a connection with the central office, dial the number, wait for switches to establish a circuit to the called subscriber, and wait for the called subscriber to answer. In some instances it is necessary also to wait for manual operator switching. Generally, telephone users have been trained to expect and accept rather long call setup delays, and are happy with the considerably shorter time made possible more recently by automatic switchboards and the newer generation of computer-controlled circuit switches. Call setup, however, can still be delayed as long as 10 to 20 sec in the telephone system.

17.3.1.2 Other Forms of Audio Traffic

Even for speech transmission, some intended applications may require a fidelity higher than can be provided by "toll quality" telephone channels (see Chap. 18). The primary parameters of interest are bandwidth, signal-to-noise ratio (SNR), dynamic range, and distortion. For example, program quality audio channels intended for radio broadcast can have specifications two to five times more stringent than a telephone circuit. The results of the Project Prelude experiments indicate preference for similar quality in teleconferencing applications [RUSH 78A,B].

Of course, channels intended to carry complex audio material, such as music, must possess full high-fidelity characteristics. Typical performance objectives are 20 to 20,000 Hz bandwidth, 80 dB dynamic range, and less than 0.5% distortion. Recent trends in digital audio technology suggest 16-bit encoding at a sampling rate of 48 kHz. Since stereo reproduction requires two channels, stereo transmission would just fit a T1 circuit (1.544 Mbps).

17.3.1.3 Data Traffic

Data traffic is defined as messages in digital form. Data traffic is generated by computers and their peripherals and terminals, and also by specialized terminals such as those used by Telex and digital facsimile. A rapidly growing type of data traffic originates from sensors that monitor events (e.g., exceeding a temperature threshold, detecting an intrusion) or measure and transmit information (e.g., telemetering actual temperature and position).

Data message lengths increase, typically with an increase in tolerable delivery time variance and delay, through a range of applications as depicted in Fig. 17.3. Trade-offs between delay and transmission rate were noted in Tab. 17.3. Bulk/batch data traffic is characterized by very long message lengths of 100,000 bits or more. For a reasonable transmission time, this type of traffic requires wider bandwidths than those for interactive data, and its peak-to-average traffic ratio is lower. Unless facilities are dedicated for the duration of each message, network overhead can be very high.

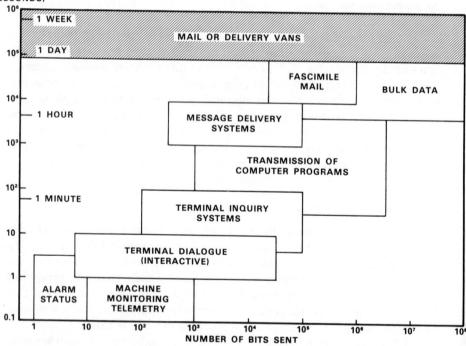

Figure 17.3. Desirable delivery times and typical quantities of data for common uses of data transmission. Terminal dialogue systems are the most common. (After [MART 1976], reprinted by permission).

An increasingly important type of data traffic is categorized as *interactive.* Interactive traffic must have a low end-to-end delay, like voice, but a small variance in the delivery time is acceptable. Unless facilities are dedicated for consecutive interactions, setup delay must also be short to maintain low end-to-end delay. The burstiness of transmissions and the short message lengths mean that such dedication wastes bandwidth. Bandwidth requirements are small enough for a number of terminals to share a 3-kHz channel. Interactive data also can be inserted in gaps left by other traffic, as in the insertion of data in voice gaps on a satellite downlink and other examples detailed subsequently as integration options.

Several studies of interactive data traffic indicate that average terminal-to-computer traffic activity is in the range of 1 to 5% of holding time, while computer-to-terminal traffic varies from 13 to 35% [JACK 69, FUCH 70, DAVI 73]. *Holding time* is the total time of user terminal transmission, computer terminal transmission, and pauses by either in the midst of a transmission. The duty cycle of a typical interactive data user consists of a "think" time of 10 sec followed by an average message size of 1000 bits [HARR 80].

17.3.1.4   Video Traffic

Television has a voracious appetite for bandwidth. Conventional broadcast television (TV) requires a minimum bandwidth of 4.5 MHz in North America, and up to 6 MHz elsewhere, depending on the standards used. Some special-purpose, high-resolution video monitors require a bandwidth in excess of 20 MHz.

Digital transmission of video traffic demands commensurately high data rates. Currently, full-motion color television is digitized and transmitted at rates of 90 or 45 Mbps, which can be accommodated in the more recent wideband digital transmission systems. Compression techniques are being developed to reduce bandwidth requirements, but a savings of more than a factor of 4 is unlikely in the near future (see Chap. 18).

The outstanding characteristic of video traffic, then, is its demand for bandwidth. A single digital television channel at 45 Mbps could support 1344 telephone-grade circuits (using delta modulation), or about 30,000 synchronous data terminals operating at 1200 bps. Consequently, transmission of a full video channel is much more expensive than other single communication channels considered here.

In many applications of video, a continuous full-motion television-like presentation is not needed. For example, a single frame of graphics information may be held and viewed for a considerable length of time. Even with "real" pictures, such as of participants in a teleconference, slow-motion displays and lower resolution of the image may be adequate. Both techniques characterize Picturephone service. Equipment allowing such techniques to be used is becoming more readily available, affording substantial reductions in transmission bandwidth and increased possibilities for sharing channel bandwidth with other types of traffic.

As with other communications, video communication requires time and space coherence in the interface with human beings. With full-motion, high-resolution video, extremely low variance in delivery delay is necessary, and the transmission is characterized by a continuous need for channel capacity. With slow-scan and frame-on-demand techniques, these requirements can be relaxed with appropriate protocols and buffering in the receiving terminal. Transmission delay is seldom important, but may need to be matched with other channels in some instances (such as sound synchronization).

17.3.2 Impact of Digitization Techniques

The integration of services in a common network necessarily implies the use of analog-to-digital (A/D) and digital-to-analog (D/A) conversions. Audio and video are intrinsically analog, while data traffic is inherently digital in nature. It is necessary to convert traffic from one form if the transmission network responds to the other form. The most common example is D/A conversion for transmission over the analog telephone network, and A/D reconversion on reception. Intervening conversions are becoming rather common as portions of the analog network are replaced with digital transmission equipment.[2]

There are many different digitization techniques, each with a different set of characteristics. A particular technique may be chosen to fit a given combination of signal type, environment, and transmission constraints. In general, those techniques requiring higher bit rates have a higher quality of reproduction and are less sensitive to transmission errors. On the other hand, techniques are available to achieve a quality level satisfactory for certain purposes at a bit rate an order of magnitude lower than conventional techniques. The potential savings in bandwidth make such techniques attractive in integrated services network design.

Chapter 18 treats in detail the subject of digitization techniques and the many trade-offs. In this section, the more significant network-level consequences of using digitizers (codecs) are examined.

17.3.2.1 Code Conversion and Tandeming

A digitization technique good for one network application might not be best for another. For example, a steady-rate analog/digital (A/D) coder avoids the need for complex interfaces in the circuit-switched telephone network, but a variable-rate coder with high peak-to-average bit rate is better suited to packet-switched networks [COVI 77]. Code conversions become important when systems that use more than one code are interconnected. Even within a particular system, different codes might be used for

---

2. More and more frequently, a D/A converter (modem) is seen separated by a few feet of wire from an A/D converter (a voice channel codec in a digital PBS. Integrated services digital networks eliminate the need for such conversions when both input and required output forms are digital.

Note: The word "codec" is derived from the combination of "coder–decoder." Codec is coming into general usage, like the word modem, to mean a device that performs both functions.

transmission and storage. Issues of code compatibility and conversion have been more carrier-oriented than user-oriented. Today, problems are rarely seen in the commercial environment despite the many devices, techniques, and digitization rates because most users establish digital services within small, closed user groups. As such services become more common, however, interoperability will be desirable and will require conversions between nonstandard devices. The military has great interest in code conversion because of the many different types of equipment which need to be interoperable over common transmission facilities.

Digitization techniques can be broadly categorized as wideband or narrowband. *Wideband* techniques encode a signal in a straightforward manner; an example is pulse-code modulation (PCM). *Narrowband* techniques take advantage of particular characteristics of the input signal in order to achieve lower data rates. As a general rule, wideband techniques can be satisfactorily converted for interoperability; less interest exists for converting between narrowband techniques; and conversions

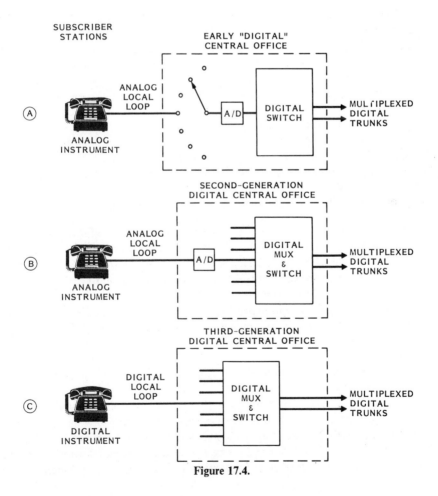

Figure 17.4.

between wideband and narrowband techniques are difficult or, for some particular combinations, effectively impossible because of intrinsic properties of the techniques that lead to unacceptable distortion.

All-digital conversion implementations are preferred because they convert from one code to another without demodulating the input bit stream and returning to the analog domain. The greatest quality loss comes usually from the first encoding of an analog signal. But additional quality loss from successive recodings, including A/D conversions, is significant enough to limit the number of tandem codings that are practical to the range of two to four [FLAN 79]. One bad but not unrealistic illustration of multiple A/D conversions in the current predominantly analog environment is shown in Fig. 17.4. The occurrence of tandem conversion can be minimized by good routing design. The effect of tandeming can be minimized by using higher, more robust digitization rates.

17.3.2.2 Location of Digitizers

A key network design issue is the location of digitizers for those types of traffic requiring digitization. Digitizer location strategy has a major impact on network architecture, and is particularly important in hybrid and transitional integrated services networks. The strategy also has considerable influence on costs. In the telephone system, for example, a voice codec could be placed at the backbone trunk exchange, the central office exchange (as in Fig. 17.4), in the local PABX, or in the subscriber's handset itself.

The first application of digital transmission in the telephone network was the 24-channel T1 carrier over wire pairs for interoffice trunking. The logical location for the A/D and D/A conversion processes was within the T1 channel bank; in fact, the final PCM digitization process (see Chap. 18) took place at the aggregate channel level, rather than for each individual input line. This technique still predominates today, in central office and PBX switches, and has two important ramifications:

1. The existing analog outside plant can be used without modification. *Outside plant* comprises that part of the telephone system from the central office to the individual subscriber, and includes the local loops, various circuit extension equipment, and the subscriber sets. It is estimated that 40 to 45% of the total telephone system investment is in outside plant.
2. The fact that the digitization process is at the backbone switch level means that the individual line input–output at the channel banks is analog; the capability of digital input–output does *not* exist.

A major reason for digitization at the higher-level originally was the high cost of codecs; the application of individual codecs to each line could not be justified economically. In the late 1970s, however, a number of manufacturers introduced LSI circuits, implementing delta-modulation as well as μ-law and A-law standard pulse-code modulation (PCM) codecs at low cost. In short order, electronic private branch exchanges and DS-1 (T1) channel banks became available, some allowing the choice of individual channel cards offering conventional analog telephone line interfaces or direct access to the 56- to 64-kbps equivalent digital channel rate. Some equipment includes a further choice of 24 PCM voice channels (64 kbps), 48 continuously variable slope delta modulation (CVSD) voice channels (32 kbps), and direct digital interfaces, singly or in mixed combinations. Such equipment will play a key role in the movement toward integrated services digital networks.

If the codec is moved from the channel bank input to the individual subscriber sets, full digital transmission through all portions of the network is possible. The advantages are several:

1. A medium-speed direct digital interface with the network is available at each subscriber's location, thus taking a major step toward providing integrated digital services.
2. The lower vulnerability of digital signals to noise and distortion is realized.
3. Privacy and security can be achieved with high quality and low cost (since analog security devices are both expensive and generally unsatisfactory in performance).

There are, however, at least equally compelling reasons why this will not come into being overnight. One problem is power supply to the telephone handset for ringing. Another is the cost of the subscriber handset alone, which represents an average investment of perhaps $25. With large-scale production of LSI codecs, a "bare bones" digital telephone set could possibly be produced for $40. It is estimated that 450 million sets exist in the world today, representing an investment of over $10 billion. To replace all sets would require an additional investment of nearly $20 billion—truly a staggering sum.

Private and specialized networks are much smaller in scope and have far fewer subscribers. In these cases, the advantages of digitization at the source may be economically justifiable. [GITM 78] considers in-depth economic analysis of communication networks applicable to the needs of the Department of Defense.

Another major impediment to location of digitizers at the subscriber point is the limited capability of the local subscriber loop, which is described in Sec. 17.4.2.2.

17.4 IMPLEMENTATION OF FULLY INTEGRATED NETWORKS

The principal orientation of this chapter is toward large-scale, common-user integrated networks that allow universal access and connectivity for any kind of telecommunications traffic—much like the ubiquitous telephone networks that presently offer communication between essentially any two subscribers. There is little doubt that this rather idealized view will be effectively realized in the future. However, at the present it is impossible to predict just what forms of fully integrated networks and services will evolve because of the many factors that are shaping their development. Some of these factors were discussed in Sec. 17.2. It is possible to examine the basic building blocks of telecommunications networks from a technical point of view and to reach some general conclusions about relative advantages and drawbacks of techniques that are potentially applicable to implementation of fully integrated networks.

Telecommunications networks have been divided classically into two functional areas: switching and transmission. In broad terms, switching is the network control mechanism for concentrating and routing traffic over appropriate circuits. Transmission is the network transport mechanism, carrying information over specific circuits from one point to another. Distinctions between switching and transmission have become blurred with the introduction of computers as part of the communications process, with the advent of new transmission possibilities (such as satellites), and with the evolution of new concentration and sharing techniques (such as adaptive TDM). The CCITT has recognized the eventualities of these trends by adopting the term Integrated Digital Network (IDN), implying the integration of switching and transmission systems using digital technology. Nevertheless, the design strategies available to the network architect continue separate emphasis on switching and transmission concepts.

In this section, these concepts are examined with respect to the technical issues of integration that were discussed in Sec. 17.3. References are provided to other chapters and to external material with pertinent detailed background information.

17.4.1 General Approaches to Integrated Network Switching

Switching techniques applicable to large-scale telecommunications networks generally follow the classifications of circuit switching and store-and-forward switching. The latter classification contains the two important and distinct subdivisions of message switching and packet switching. More recently, there has been intense development activity in hybrid switching techniques which combine elements of circuit and packet switching. The following is an overview of switching techniques as they relate to integrated networks.

17.4.1.1 Circuit Switching

Circuit switching has come to mean that category of switching techniques which establishes direct connection between two or more communication circuits. Normally, the connection is temporary, existing as long as the "call" requires. Circuit switching is the basis of both the telephone and telegraph (Telex, TWX) networks [JOEL 77, JOEL 79].

Basically, a circuit switch consists of a switching matrix, a control unit, and service circuitry needed to monitor and control the various signaling functions. The switching matrix interconnects the input and output lines, which define the level in the hierarchy of the overall network.[3] For example, the input side of a local exchange switch would be represented by individual subscribers, and the output side by the trunk circuits to other exchanges in a city or to toll exchanges for long-distance calls.

---

[3]The use of "input" and "output" is not meant to imply the direction of signal flow, but rather the distinction between hierachical levels in the network. Normally, circuits are switched on a full-duplex basis.

Circuit-Switching Architectures

There are three general kinds of switching matrices: spaces division, time division, and frequency division. Frequency-division switching is very rarely used; by far the most common switching technique in telephone systems is space division, wherein the input and output lines are joined by a direct electrical connection. Most space-division switching matrices are electromechanical; the crosspoint connections are established by metallic contact points in various kinds of relays and electrically activated switches. Within the last decade, there has been a major shift to solid-state devices (e.g., transistors, diodes, thyristors) as crosspoints; these devices consume less power, induce less noise in the communication paths, and interface more easily with modern digital common control circuitry.

One of the developments responsible for the digital revolution in telecommunications networks is the appearance of time-division switching.[4] This switching can be thought of as back-to-back time-division multiplexing. Circuit-to-circuit connections are defined by the relative assignment of time slots. Each input and output channel is sequentially sampled by a processor. If the information to be switched is in digital form, the sample time of "time slot" allocated to each channel can be so timed as to accommodate one binary word. A word appearing in a channel is then associated with a particular time slot, and the switching process involves moving this word into the slot associated with the desired output channel. Advantages of time-division switching include nearly instantaneous setup and clear-down of circuits, and essentially noiseless switching.

Another major advantage of time-division switching is a result of the multiplexing nature of its operation. Instead of having many low-bandwidth output lines, the output side of the switch can be taken directly as one or a few high-rate digital bit streams suitable for direct transmission on a wideband digital trunk. Thus time-division switching can inherently provide the concentration and multiplexing functions without the additional equipment required for space-division switching. Such capability is a principal reason for the merging of the traditionally separate switching and transmission areas.

Yet another advantage of time-division switching derives from the fact that a route through the switch is established by assignment of a time slot coordinating the input and output sides. Within technological limits, the size of the time-slot pool can be made arbitrarily large and can equal the number of lines. Consequently, a time-division matrix can be made to be nonblocking ("blocking" is said to occur when a switch cannot accept a request for service). Further, even a significant reduction in number of time slots still provides a large number of alternate routes through the matrix, with the result that service has almost no blocking.

In contrast, a single space-division matrix has only one path for a given input–output route, and complexity and cost increase very rapidly with the number of lines served. Alternate routes are provided for by architectures using combinations of smaller space-division matrices in tandem.

The capacity of a time-division matrix is currently limited to about 1000 time

---

[4]Another development is the application of computers to the common control functions required of a switch—so-called Stored Program Control (SPC) switches.

slots, due primarily to circuitry limitations. Therefore, large digital switches accommodating a large number of lines are designed with a combination of space and time switching. Earlier designs were space–time–space matrices, but the present-day trend is toward time–space–time matrices. Many considerations enter into the development of a "best" architecture for a given application. Skaperda's work [SKAP 79] contains an excellent survey of the concepts involved, together with considerations important to integrated services in the context of existing constraints.

Transparency of Circuit-Switched Networks

A communication path established through a circuit-switched network exists as essentially a dedicated circuit for the duration of a call, and fundamentally is limited only by the bandwidth and other transmission characteristics of the intervening equipment. Implicitly, the circuit is "solid"—whatever goes in comes out, although with delay, noise, and possible distortion. Complete transparency may not be possible, however, due to certain signals that may be reserved for network control functions and thus be forbidden to the user [MART 76]. Examples are frequencies corresponding to control tones in analog transmission, and certain bit patterns in digital transmission.

Circuit-Switching Delay and Line Utilization

Delay considerations, at the same time, constitute both a major advantage and a major disadvantage of current circuit-switched networks. Once a call is established, the delay through the network is effectively determined by the transmission delay of the communication links. Further, message delivery time variance is essentially zero—a necessity for voice and video transmission, and highly desirable for interactive data transmission.

The major problem with circuit switching is the time required to set up and clear down a call. Transmission cannot begin until the complete circuit is established; and the terminal equipment, the transmission facilities, and the switch paths cannot be applied to other uses until the circuit is completely broken down. Setup and clear-down delays are a result of the older in-band signaling technology and the speed limitations of older electromechanical switches. *In-band signaling* refers to the technique of transmitting dial pulses or Touchtone frequencies within the bandwidth of the communication circuit itself. Because interoperability with many different types of switches of various vintages is necessary in the telephone network, the speed of signaling is limited in most cases.

In present-day telephone systems, call setup time is normally in the range 5 to 25 sec and clear down is of the order of 1 sec. This is generally acceptable for telephone conversations, narrative message transmissions, and bulk data transfers because initial delay is either tolerated or unimportant, and the overhead is a relatively small portion of a call duration measured in minutes or more. However, for traffic types such as interactive and query/response that are characterized by short duration, both the initial delivery delay and the poor circuit utilization can be unacceptable.

Another factor affecting line utilization is bandwidth. Today's circuit-switched networks provide a bandwidth equivalent to a single voice-grade circuit; these circuits are commonly operated for data at rates of 110 to 1200 bps and rarely exceed 4800 bps. The "lost" number of bits that could have been transmitted had the setup/clear-down time been very small does not represent a large proportion of an overall "transaction" for most traffic types. However, if a larger bandwidth is switched with these delays, the line utilization is quite poor. For example, consider the transmission of a typical facsimile page, involving a total of about 10^5 bits, on a 56-kbps circuit-switched line. The transmission itself requires approximately 2 sec. While the transmission delay *per se* is not particularly problematical with facsimile, a call setup/clear-down time of 10 sec would mean that a total of 12 sec is needed for the transaction—a utilization factor of only $2/12 = 17\%$, or an equivalent throughput of only 9.3 kbps on the 56-kbps circuit.

Enhanced Circuit Switching

There are many arguments for the use of circuit switching in integrated services digital networks, not the least of which is that the ubiquitous telephone network is based on circuit switching. Consequently, development activities are under way to alleviate some of the problems. A major improvement in circuit setup time is foreseen, with a possibility of achieving setup in 140 msec [GITM 78, HARR 80]. Such a low delay would satisfy even the strict end-to-end delay requirements of about 250 msec for interactive data applications. Other developments in circuit switching architecture are focusing also on the substantially different characteristics of data calls as compared with voice traffic [GIES 84].

Special techniques are being considered to enhance the utilization of circuit switching; included is the incorporation of digital speech interpolation (DSI) outlined in Sec. 17.5.4.

17.4.1.2 Message Switching

Classical store-and-forward switching, often referred to as message switching, is a technique for increasing the utilization of communications circuits in networks for telegraph traffic. In the earliest networks, telegraph messages were manually relayed from point to point along a route that eventually would get the message to its destination. The store-and-forward switching technique is so named because messages are stored at each relay point (network node) and then forwarded (transmitted) on the next link of its route as that circuit becomes available.

The availability of automatic send–receive (ASR) teletypewriter terminals and associated paper tape devices (transmitter-distributors and reperforators) did much to speed up the network process. Storage of messages in each relay center was in the form of punched paper tapes, that could be "replayed" without manual rekeying. More recently, tremendous increases in network capacity, speed, and efficiency have been made possible by the use of computers and their associated rapid-access bulk storage media.

Quite elaborate procedures have evolved for message-switching network operation. Many are based on the idea of network accountability. A message is treated as an entity throughout the network, which requires acceptance of a message by its intended recipient(s) and which assumes responsibility for guaranteeing against misdelivery. For example, quite unlike a packet-switching network, it is a major transgression in a message-switching network to lose, much less deliberately discard, a message. To aid in discharging the responsibilities, accountability is broken down to each link on which a message is transmitted. An audit trail is built that can be used to identify and recover lost messages, guard against duplicates, and establish alternate routes around failed links or nodes.

The application of computers to automate these procedures is resulting in message-switching networks of high capacity and efficiency. The computers are also making practical such "value-added" functions as transmission speed and code conversion, automatic broadcast, and long-term storage and retrieval. Message-switching networks, however, are normally designed to deal with messages containing narrative text or relatively small amounts of data—say, in the range of a few characters to perhaps 10,000 characters. They are also usually designed to maximize efficiency at the expense of delay, and delivery variance can be substantial. Consequently, classical message-switching networks are ideally suited for Telex, recorded message, and electronic mail services, but are unsuitable for interactive data, voice, and most imagery traffic, and may become overloaded with large bulk transmissions.

17.4.1.3 Packet Switching

Packet switching is basically a form of data store-and-forward switching. A major distinction between packet switching and message switching, however, is that packet switching normally operates with higher-speed links between nodes and tends to minimize delay at the expense of efficiency. In packet switching, a message is broken into limited-size packets which are transmitted separately through the network and then reconstituted. Although there are exceptions, packet switching usually does not provide the forms of network accountability found in message switching; a result is that the mass storage required in a message switch is not needed, nor is the considerable processing power required to manage that storage. The fundamentals of packet switching are given in Chap. 16.

Packet switching can readily handle the burstiness of speech but not so readily maintain continuous, steady voice output and small total delivery delay. Each message is subject to delays from the packetization process itself; backbone subnetwork nodal processing and queuing; standard line-level protocol procedures, such as automatic retransmission; reassembly with possible resequencing when different routes have been used; and for voice, buffer smoothing and voice synthesis [FRAN 78]. These delays lead to increased delivery-time variance. Essentially zero delivery time variance is necessary for most voice and video transmission, so traditional packet switching is unacceptable for such traffic. The problems with straightforward implementation of packet-switching voice on ARPANET, for example, involve the error control mechanism and packet length formulas [GOLD 77]. In general, the number of voice channels on a link and the number of tandem links in an end-to-end connection have a significant effect on the comparison of circuit- with packet-switched voice [COVI 79].

Packet switching bulk data also presents complications. Where long messages or blocks of messages must be packetized, overhead is significantly increased because each packet must include identifiers. Nevertheless, interest in packet switching for integrated networks remains high because it offers the potential for better facility utilization than can be achieved with the dedication of facilities under circuit switching. Packet switching allows advantage to be taken of speech silences over multiple links without separate silence detection at each link, as would be required for TASI (see Sec. 17.5.4) and digital speech interpolation schemes. The TASI advantage in a packetized speech multiplexer, and its tradeoff with delay, is investigated in [WEIN 79]. Another study [ROSN 76] indicates that packet switching is preferable to circuit switching when one or the other has to be selected for data with 50% long and 50% short messages; voice was not included. That study and others [KUMM 78, MIYA 78] have found packet switching to be most cost effective for short messages, and circuit switching (or message switching) best for long messages.

Packet switching is also preferred over circuit switching in the case study that is the basis of [FRAN 78], [FRAN 79], and [GITM 78]. A single voice link model was used because it was tractable; no numerical evaluations were made of the tandem link model, nor were extensions made to a network model with its more complex topography and routing alternatives [NAC 77]. Different packet sizes and transport protocols were designed for voice to meet its more stringent delay requirements. The voice packet size, typically about 50 bits, needed for good intelligibility is usually much smaller than the best size, typically about 1000 bits, for data packets. When voice packets are lost or discarded because of excessive delay and packet size is 250 msec, intelligibility is only 10%; a packet size of 19 msec results in 80% intelligibility with marginal degradation when speech loss is as high as 50% [NAC 77].

Two protocol options were proposed for the voice packets in a conversation: fixed path (via pointers and not reservation) and independent path. *Fixed path protocol* (FPP) has an initial signaling message that sets up the logical path pointers at the switches for the entire conversation. This is similar to circuit switching except that no facilities are dedicated. Short headers are adequate to indicate the conversation to which a packet belongs. Little processing in the intermediate switches is needed for the packets, but the switches have the operational burden of handling path maintenance for the conversations. No resequencing of voice packets is needed at the destination.

Path independent protocol (PIP) has no path setup, so processing for each packet at each switch is higher than for FPP, and PIP header size must be larger. To keep the same small packet length (header plus contents), the packet content must be smaller than for FPP. With the increased overhead, the potential for better facility utilization is reduced. However, PIP is less vulnerable to failures in the network. It is the protocol that has been used most commonly for packet switching data. Voice packets from several speakers with the same destination switch can be companded to reduce overhead under either protocol.

The fixed path protocol, also used in [BIAL 80] for voice traffic, is similar to the *packetized virtual circuit* (PVC) proposed in [FORG 77]. Under PVC, all packets belonging to a common connection follow the same route when packet overhead as small as 32 bits is required. Voice and data are handled uniformly, but each is assumed to be in a separate queue for each link. Voice packets are given priority. In one design variation [MOWA 79], PVC is used for voice and bulk data, while pure packet switching is used for interactive data. The time-division packet switch in another variation [ARTH 79] multiplexes data and voice packets in a manner similar to PVC, but it blocks (refuses to accept) voice packets instead of allowing them to be delayed and thus has lower storage requirements.

As these approaches show, most proposals for packet switching integrated voice and data traffic incorporate modifications that emulate circuit switching, at least for voice, without requiring the same facility dedication. Packet switching for voice and image traffic is still in the experimental stage.

17.4.1.4 Hybrid Switching

It is possible, and often desirable, to combine characteristics of the basic switching techniques in an integrated network. For example, the Telex networks normally operate as a circuit-switched network, establishing direct connections between teletypewriters. Many Telex operating companies have added the store-and-forward feature of message switching in order to provide delayed delivery if a destination's terminal is busy or temporarily inoperative. Similar ideas are being developed for delayed delivery of voice messages in telephone networks. Packet-switched networks are adding message-switching functions to handle electronic mail, as in Telenet's Telemail service.

For fully integrated networks, some fundamentally different hybrid switching architectures are being investigated. Among the most important are hybrid switching schemes which combine packet switching and circuit switching to take advantage of the most suitable features of each for different traffic types. One suggested traffic division [FRAN 79] is to circuit switch bulk data and to packet switch voice and interactive data. Cost is saved by integrating use of facilities. Having a switching option also means that a user can choose the least expensive switching, which might not be the one best suited to his or her traffic, or choose the switching that best meets security requirements [GITM 77]. A network architecture for a system allowing user selection is given in [PORT 76].

Although no complete models have been created for determining the design parameters of a hybrid network, some guidance is available. One treatment [KUMM 78] considers the number of tandem nodes, path length, intermittent and continuous messages, the length of message blocks, the intervals between consecutive blocks, the duration of dialogue, the cost ratio of the circuit-switching network to the packet-switching network, and the packet-switching operation of either permanent virtual circuits or switched virtual circuits. Results of experiments based on a range of scenarios including separate networks and hybrid designs are described in [DYSA 81]. In [MIYA 78], message, packet, and circuit switching are compared based on transmission time delay and throughput characteristics for varying traffic volumes and message lengths. An example of the results is illustrated in Fig. 17.5. It shows the effect of message length on message transmission delay where line utilization is held

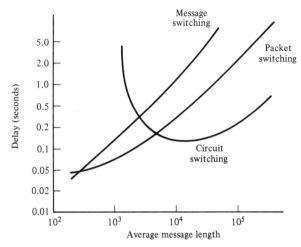

Figure 17.5. Delay vs. message length at 50% line utilization. (After [MIYA 1978] © 1978 IEEE.)

fixed. Additional important factors are network control methodology, delivery-time variance, error control, reliability, and digitization for analog sources (e.g., voice).

The detailed modeling in [GITM 78] and [GITM 79] is based on one particular environment (Department of Defense) with very high traffic volumes. Voice quality is assumed acceptable even at low digitization rates. (The significant effect of digitization rate on voice quality is described in Chap. 18.) For the most part, the cost of digitization is not considered. Hybrid switching is modeled without consideration of interpolation schemes for voice, which is assumed to be circuit-switched. Emphasis is on the impact of the voice digitization rate and on backbone network installation, operation, and maintenance costs for user-owned switching and transmission facilities. Many network designers may be more interested in their access costs and in usage costs of common-carrier facilities.

Given that common access is desired, the implementation of hybrid network schemes range from independent packet-switched and circuit-switched networks, with the packet-switching network accessed through the circuit-switching network, to full integration with access, transmission facilities, control, and switching functions shared between packet switching and circuit switching. Three basic options are depicted in Fig. 17.6.

The performance of integrated switches is still being evaluated, particularly in the cases with movable transmission-time-frame boundaries. The slotted envelope network (SENET) approach [COVI 75], which reserves some portions of all time frames for circuit switching calls and for packet switching data, includes a movable-boundary feature to allow use by data of residual circuit-switching capacity. Recent similar approaches have used a fixed frame of 10 msec on a 1.544-Mbps T1 carrier, as shown in Fig. 17.7. Intuitively, a movable-boundary scheme should give better service than a fixed-boundary scheme, or it should allow a reduced capacity to handle traffic adequately.

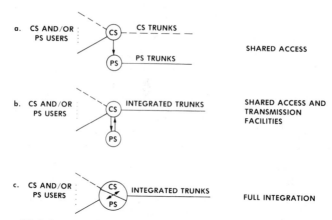

Figure 17.6. Integrated circuit and packet switching [JENN 1976], © 1976 IEEE.

Analyses of the capacity reduction limits have been based on earlier results that indicated significant savings of channel requirements of an integrated system over separate packet-switching and circuit-switching systems. An error in the results has been found—data packet delays are larger than predicted if the frame portion reserved for data is smaller than the data traffic load [WEIN 79]. Long queues of data result when the voice traffic load exceeds its statistical average. This means that the communication requirements for data are not met. Some flow control mechanisms can reduce delays; buffer limitation is the most successful of these.

With proper design, both fixed- and movable-boundary hybrid switching networks can give good service in addition to improved line utilization. One proposed technique [MIYA 79] gains greater utilization in an essentially fixed-boundary case by allowing frame-length extensions for a packet that is too long to fit entirely in the frame. The extension is limited to allow the resynchronization necessary for circuit switching traffic. Design issues involve much more than capacity determination based on a model of communication requirements. Provision must be made for allocation management and system control, including CCIS (common channel interoffice signaling [THUR 79]) for circuit-switching traffic. Many options, such as a centralized approach, a multiprocessor system, or distributed processing, are available [ROSS 77, PORT 76].

Another variant on hybrid techniques is referred to as "burst switching" [HASE83]. Burst switching may be generally viewed as packet switching using packets of highly-variable length and having a simplified structure that adds routing bytes to pieces of an individual bit stream, which are interleaved in the multiplexed bit streams of DS1 or higher levels. Special circuitry detects periods of "silence" in the higher-level bits streams, and inserts other "active" pieces of data or voice in a manner similar to TASI/DSI. The principal difference of "burst switching" as compared with other techniques is that the switching decisions necessary for the insertion of pieces of an individual subscriber's data stream are made at the higher levels of the multiplexing/

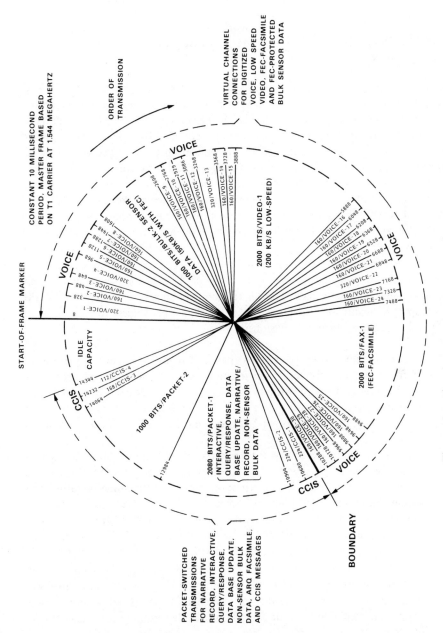

Figure 17.7. Time frame with movable boundary [ROSS 1977], © 1977 IEEE.

297

switching hierarchy, based on information obtained at lower levels in the overall architecture. Channel utilization efficiencies in excess of 99% have been claimed.

A detailed overview and analysis of hybrid switching techniques can be found in [ROSS 82].

17.4.2 Transmission Alternatives for Integrated Networks

The second major network component applicable to large-scale integrated networks, in addition to switching, is *transmission.* Transmission is the provision of circuits or links between the switching nodes and subscriber terminals. There are two fundamental media forms for transporting information between two points. One is guided media such as wire lines, coaxial cable, and optical fiber cable. The guided media require a physical link between the points. The second form comprises the various radio media, taken here broadly to encompass all possibilities of "wireless" transmission through the atmosphere of "free space." This includes microwave, satellite, and even light waves. The possibilities for these transmission media to support wide bandwidths and other characteristics necessary for integrated services are discussed in detail in Chaps. 5, 6, and 7.

Since network nodes and terminals are normally viewed as discrete points, the transmission components provide a spanning of distances between and among network nodes and terminals. Hence, transmission forces consideration of the topography of a network. For a universal network, it is convenient to think in terms of the following topographical divisions:

1.   The *backbone network* spans global, national, regional, and intercity distances of, say, 10 km and greater. In the telephone system, the backbone network is usually referred to as the long-haul or long-lines component. It is typified by wideband microwave radio, satellite, and cable transmission. Switching at the nodes reroutes traffic to other backbone circuits or to a local distribution network.

2.   The *local distribution network* transports traffic within individual cities or smaller regions. Typically, transmission distances range from 1 to 10 km. In the telephone system, the local distribution network interconnects subscribers within the locality, and connects subscribers to the backbone network for long-distance calls. In both kinds of connection, a call is often transmitted through several switches in the local distribution network. The "local loops" serving subscriber premises are contained within the local distribution network.

3.   *Subscriber-level distribution* is required if subscriber premises require further routing and distribution of traffic. A common example of a subscriber-level distribution network is the private branch exchange (PBX) and associated wiring and telephone sets found in offices. Another example is the telecommunications network that provides connection between an organization's proces-

sors and its computer terminals. Normally, subscriber-level distribution is intra-premises, but greater distances, up to 10 km, could be spanned to provide internal communications for the multiple premises of a large organization; this is called campus distribution. To date, most transmission at this level is accomplished by wirelines.

Just as in the telephone system, different architectures are appropriate for different levels of integrated services networks. The differing transmission requirements must be considered with respect to the new technical issues presented by integration of traffic. These are discussed in the next sections. Although the orientation is toward large-scale, universal networks, private networks quite different in scope and scale require similar considerations.

17.4.2.1   Backbone Network

In the backbone portion of a network, the concentration of traffic volume and resulting economy of scale justify wideband digital transmission facilities. Long-haul transmission facilities—microwave radio, satellite, and cable—today are carrying all kinds of telecommunications traffic, including voice, data, television, facsimile, and telemetry. A high degree of integration presently exists in such long-haul facilities. Further, the addition of new all-digital media and the conversion of older analog circuits to digital ones are proceeding rapidly at this level. It is estimated that 40% of the long-haul facilities of the telephone network in the United States are now digital.

Thus, on an individual circuit basis, the present state of the art is generally suitable for the backbone portion of integrated services digital networks. The primary issue is that there may not be enough backbone to support the bulk capacity that would be required if every subscriber is to be provided with dedicated video bandwidth on demand. Certainly, with current technology, the radio media alone could not provide so much bandwidth; the available spectrum and space are insufficient. From today's vantage point, guided lightwave transmission via optical fiber cables appears most promising for meeting needs. It is probable that a multimedia approach, combined with more efficient utilization of facilities, will provide the necessary capacity.

17.4.2.2   Local Distribution

The access portion of a network is usually quite different in character from the higher-level backbone portion. In general, distances spanned are shorter (up to a few tens of kilometers) and the degree of traffic concentration and circuit utilization are lower. As a result, the architecture of access subnetworks is usually constrained by factors quite different from those in the backbone subnetwork.

The access subnetwork is intended to serve users at the local level. In an extreme case, such as the public telephone network, the objective is to provide access essentially to anyone, anywhere. An integrated services network then would greatly increase the complexity by further adding the requirements of providing service to any terminal wishing to communicate using any type of traffic.

This section contains an examination of the candidate access subnetwork architectures currently considered to be the most likely to be used in integrated services networks.

Telephone System

The public circuit-switched telephone system is an immediate and obvious possibility for a local distribution network. It satisfies the desire for ubiquity and essentially universal connectivity and, perhaps above all, it already exists. An estimated 45% of the total investment in telephone system plant is in the local distribution network, defined as all parts of the system from the local central office exchange downward to the subscriber level.[5] In the United States alone, this represents an investment of billions of dollars. It would be difficult indeed to ignore such an investment, or to duplicate it. Exacerbating the economic picture is the unrealistically long term of depreciation (often 25 years or longer) usually required of local telephone operating companies.[6] In the long-range view of integrated digital services, the telephone system has serious technical limitations as will be discussed.

One representative view of an integrated services digital network based on the telephone system is shown in Fig. 17.8: it is a model of the "System X" being developed by the British Post Office. Interface with the backbone network is effected by digital circuit switches (exchanges) and digital transmission following the hierarchy currently established for European telephone systems. It can be assumed that the exchanges are equipped with enhanced circuit switches that take advantage of the fast switching, common-channel signaling, and DSI techniques outlined previously. The transitional stages have been accommodated by allowing for internetworking with existing analog subnetworks and also for connection with conventional analog telephone handsets and local loops for POTS (plain old telephone service).

The view in Fig. 17.8 is that access will be via existing individual digital local lines from digital terminals, and that "primary multiplexers" will allow a division of the available loop capacity into voice and nonvoice paths. The capacity of existing two-wire local loops is the first problem. Recent investigations indicate that the substantial majority of existing local loops are limited to transmission rates lower than 100 kbps, even after substantial reworking to remove loading coils, and so on (see Chap. 7). It has been suggested that a standard of 80 kbps be adopted, which would be allocated as shown in Tab. 17.4. More recently, standardization activities

---

[5]The terminology "local distribution" has long been used in this sense in the communications industry. Similar terminology—"local area networks" or even "local networks"—has recently developed in circles concerned primarily with computer communications. The latter usage implies a much more restricted area of service, usually confined to a user's premises. At the risk of confusion, but in deference to common usage, both terminologies are used in this chapter.

[6]Generally, local telephone operating companies have been regulated under accounting rules which require depreciation schedules that have been appropriate when technological change was not so rapid. Since a company may be "stuck" with an investment over a long period of time, there is no great incentive for technological risk taking. Compare this with computers, which are usually depreciated over a 5-year interval.

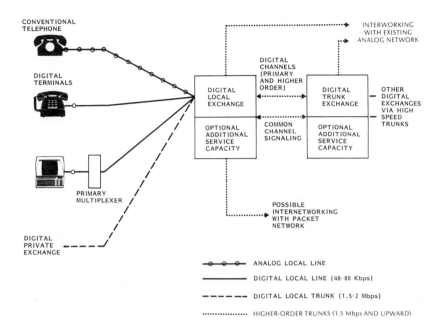

Figure 17.8. A view of an integrated services digital network based on the telephone system. (After [ORBE 1979], © 1979 IEEE.)

with the CCITT suggest a rate of 144 kbps (see Sec. 17.7.1). Implicit in both suggestions is at least one direct 64 kbps digital circuit, which would be a major improvement as compared with current limits of 2.4 to 9.6 kbps. However, some types of traffic which are of considerable interest to the individual subscriber—such as video and high-fidelity audio—cannot be accommodated at that rate. Consequently, minor modification of the existing telephone plant, as attractive as it will be for a large number of new voice and data services, cannot be regarded as satisfactory for a fully integrated services network.

The approach of Fig. 17.8 does provide for higher-speed lines, at 1.544 or 2.048 Mbps, for service to digital private exchanges. Since most existing local loops cannot support these rates, however, it must be presumed that such lines will have to be provided by an expensive overbuild program involving new installation, or by extensive modification with repeaters for selected cables having appropriate characteristics.

Fig. 17.9 highlights the need to introduce evolutionary, rather than revolutionary, technology in the telephone system. The basic rate retained for voice is 64 kbps, reflecting the desire to maintain compatibility with the substantial investment in existing PCM equipment. The option of 56 kbps voice plus 8 kbps data is achieved by robbing the least significant bit of each PCM octet; however, compatibility would be retained.

Although "digital" exchanges are rapidly being installed in the various tele-

302 Chap. 17   Integrating Data, Voice, and Image

Table 17.4.   *One Proposed Plan for Distribution of Data Rates on a Digital Local Loop.*

	Customer Terminal Functions			Exchange Terminal Functions
User Channels	Bit-Rate	Customer Network Signaling	Alignment If Required	
Voice at 64 kbps OR Nonvoice at 64 kbps OR Combined voice/ nonvoice at 56 to 58 kbps	64 kbps			Switching at 64 kbps
		2 kbps		Switching at 64 kbps
Data at 8 kbps	8 kbps			Reiteration followed by switching at 64 kbps
		2 kbps		
Telemetry	2 kbps			Termination with other telemetry channels on local muldex
		Nil		
			2 kbps	
Cumulative transmission requirements	74 kbps	78 kbps	80 kbps	

Source: [ORBE 79], © 1979 IEEE.

phone networks, the great majority of these switches accept *analog,* rather than digital, local loops. The reason is that, until very recently, the cost of the A/D and D/A converters precluded their use on an individual line (not to mention individual handset) basis. In most of the switches that provide a PCM output, the A/D conversions are performed on a mass digroup (24 channels), similar to the original T1 carrier system equipment (see Chap. 18). A result is that exchanges so equipped will not be suitable for direct digital services.

A possible path of evolution of the telephone network toward integrated digital transmission and switching of the various levels is shown in Fig. 17.9. In the earlier phases [levels (a) through (c)] digital technology is introduced at the higher levels of the network and progresses downward to the lower levels. This trend is likely to continue; digital local offices should appear before digital local loop transmission, rather than the reverse as depicted in levels (d) and (e).

Cable TV Systems

Another, frequently overlooked possibility for distribution of integrated services resides in cable TV (CATV) systems[7] (see Chap. 7). In many ways, CATV is the complement of the telephone system—the latter is limited in bandwidth, which

[7]The idea, however, is by no means new. See, for example, [SMIT 72].

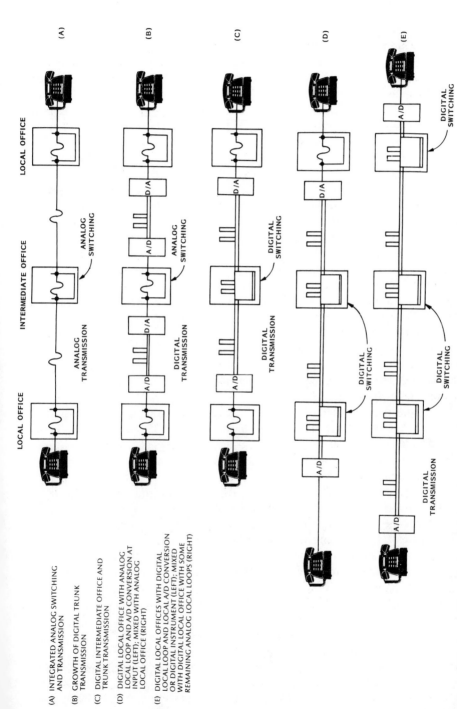

(A) INTEGRATED ANALOG SWITCHING AND TRANSMISSION

(B) GROWTH OF DIGITAL TRUNK TRANSMISSION

(C) DIGITAL INTERMEDIATE OFFICE AND TRUNK TRANSMISSION

(D) DIGITAL LOCAL OFFICE WITH ANALOG LOCAL LOOP AND A/D CONVERSION AT INPUT (LEFT); MIXED WITH ANALOG LOCAL OFFICE (RIGHT)

(E) DIGITAL LOCAL OFFICES WITH DIGITAL LOCAL LOOP AND LOCAL A/D CONVERSION OR DIGITAL INSTRUMENT (LEFT); MIXED WITH DIGITAL LOCAL OFFICE WITH SOME REMAINING ANALOG LOCAL LOOPS (RIGHT)

Figure 17.9. A possible evolution of the telephone network toward integrated transmission and switching. (After [Joel 1979, © 1979 IEEE].)

303

CATV has in abundance; but the telephone system has nearly complete penetration to all potential service points, whereas CATV at present does not.

The major attraction of a CATV network is its relatively enormous bandwidth. As indicated in Sec. 17.3.1.4, television-type traffic requires far more bandwidth than any other form of individually channeled communication. Since CATV is designed for full-bandwidth video, no compromises are needed for that type of traffic. Furthermore, a single analog television channel is allocated a bandwidth of 6 MHz, easily capable of supporting a DS-2 carrier (6.3 Mbps), the equivalent of 96 channels at a rate of 64 kbps each for voice and/or data. Modern coaxial cable CATV networks carry at least 20, and new designs carry up to 100, video channels. The eventual application of optical fiber techniques can further extend that capacity.

A CATV system is intended ideally to be a true local distribution network serving all possible subscriber locations within a given area. The requirement of ubiquity must be addressed on several geographic levels. In areas where a CATV network exists or is planned, all subscribers could be connected, but not all may choose to be (and probably will not, particularly as long as the service is solely entertainment television). Within a given region, or even a large metropolitan area, not all local areas may have CATV networks. Individual political subdivisions in the United States are exercising jurisdictional prerogatives which determine the character of CATV services, their supplier, and when (sometimes even whether) they will be in place. On the other hand, market forces may determine the degree of inclusion of potential subscribers in towns and rural areas of low population density, because of the allocated expense of connecting individual subscribers as compared with reasonable revenue. The latter consideration is receiving the attention of many governmental and private organizations.

In spite of these issues, CATV networks are proliferating rapidly. By 1984, it is estimated that, of all potential subscriber locations, about 35% are connected in the United States, over 60% in northwestern Europe, and nearly 70% in Canada. It can be expected that demand will increase and more construction will follow, as the range of services continues to grow.

The nature of a CATV network differs somewhat from the telephone system. A CATV network was originally intended to be a wired broadcast system; therefore, there is at some point a single hub or "head end" from which information flows. The actual network arrangements vary widely, but most are dendritic—structured like a tree. Some carry all information from the head end to each individual subscriber line, while others use simple circuit-switching devices to connect individual subscriber lines to selected channels. In almost all cases, however, there is a hub that essentially corresponds, geographically and topologically, with the local exchange office of the telephone system. In the larger CATV networks, these hubs are connected in a star configuration to the head end. These hubs could be interconnected with switches and interhub trunks to form a network that looks very much like the telephone system. A typical CATV system is ilustrated in Fig. 17.10. The normal "downstream" direction of transmission is from head end to subscriber.

A second distinction of CATV systems, although they were originally intended for broadcasting, concerns the possibilities of full-duplex communication. One-way

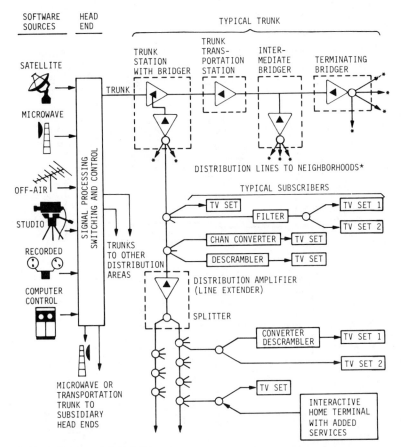

Figure 17.10. A typical modern coaxial cable CATV system block diagram. (Courtesy GTE Lenkurt [GTE 79].)

transmission obviously satisfies the original objectives of CATV. In some older systems using subscriber switching, requests for a particular channel are made by telephone. In 1972 the FCC required that all subsequently installed CATV networks have the "capability" of two-way communications, although not necessarily at full downstream bandwidth. The actual implementation was not required, but the networks must have been so designed and installed that the "upstream" capability could be implemented by minor addition of equipment. The majority of existing networks have at least this minimum capability. Most of the recently installed networks have the possibility of substantial upstream bandwidth, with many approaching the downstream bandwidth.

By the early 1980s, two-way information services via CATV networks had begun to proliferate rapidly in the United States. The Warner QUBE system, originally established in Columbus, Ohio (see Chap. 7), added consumer access to banking services and the Compuserve system. Dow Jones Information Services, following tests in the Dallas, Texas, area, reached agreements with CATV operators in New Jersey, Florida, California, Colorado, and Missouri to offer information call-up from, and transactions with, several sources, including the *Wall Street Journal,*

305

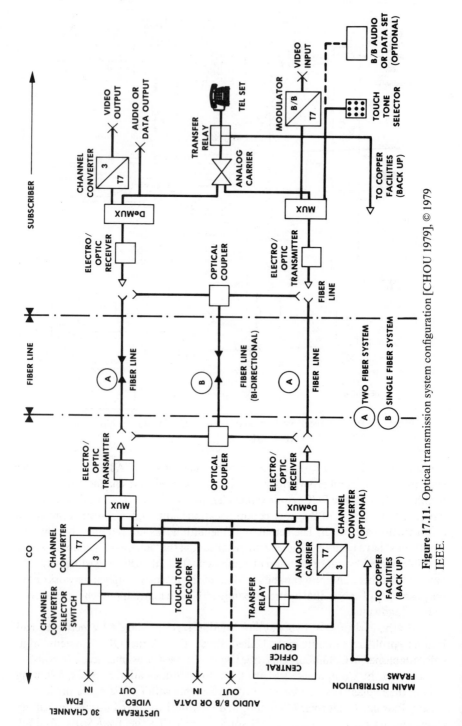

Figure 17.11. Optical transmission system configuration [CHOU 1979], © 1979 IEEE.

306

Baron's, the Dow Jones News Service, and local newspapers, banks, and stores [NARR 81].

One view of an advanced consumer-oriented integrated services network based on CATV principles is shown in Fig. 17.11. Although this system serves as an example of future possibilities, it is already in existence, serving 40 individual subscribers in Yorkville, Ontario. The system is particularly interesting in that optical fiber cable is used for the transmission medium, while analog transmission techniques are employed (because of the present high cost of very wideband digital/analog converters).

Any of the 30 analog video channels is accessed by the subscriber's entering a selection on the Touchtone pad. The signal is carried by a data channel with transmission at 0.3 to 3 kHz. Telephone service is provided by analog modulation on a 76-kHz carrier to the subscriber, and on a 32-kHz carrier from the subscriber. Video to the subscriber is at 5.25 to 11.25 MHz, the T7 CATV subchannel. It is converted to channel 3 for the television set. When video from the subscriber is included by unidirectional two-fiber lines, it is on the T8 subchannel (11.25 to 17.25 MHz). A 58-kHz pilot carrier is applied to the central office transfer module. Backup facilities of copper wire are used for telephony if the subscriber's power fails or if the optical fiber system fails. Field trials of similar systems for rural and urban distribution on optical fiber are planned in Canada [CHAN 79].

Another example of a fully integrated network is the HI-OVIS system in Japan, detailed in Chap. 7. The HI-OVIS system provides for full two-way television in addition to voice, high-fidelity stereophonic audio, and data. A key feature is the home terminal, which comprises a TV receiver, keyboard, terminal controller, TV camera, and microphone.

One obstacle in the path of providing integrated services via CATV network in the United States involves the current FCC regulations in force. Telephone service per se is prohibited. In fact, provision of private-line data service apparently requires at present that the CATV operator be certified as a specialized common carrier.[8] Certain jurisdictions in Canada, however, have solved the problem in individual cases by effecting a combination of telephone and television interests.

Local Distribution by Radio

The broadcast nature of radio makes it an attractive alternative for communications distribution over areas equivalent to those served by telephone and CATV systems (see Chap. 5). In the AM and FM radio entertainment bands, of course, communication is in one direction only. In other bands allocated for other services, two-way communication is established. One widely known (though rather raucous) example is the citizen's band (CB) radio service. Local area coverage for mobile users

---

[8]Conversely, telephone companies are generally prohibited from supplying CATV services. However, regulation of telecommunications is in foment. In the United States, the movement is toward a minimum of regulation. However, it is not yet clear what the impact on integrated services will be, as the various approaches combine elements of areas where domains are being redefined (e.g., "plain old telephone service," "enhanced services," and "broadcast services").

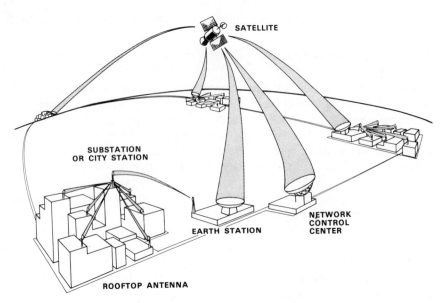

Figure 17.12. Microwave and satellite links for multiple traffic types as was proposed for XTEN.

of the telephone system is provided by two-way radio in most major metropolitan areas; capacity will expand rapidly as a result of the new cellular radio technology.

The viability of radio as a distribution medium for fixed users has been made possible by recent developments in time-division multiple access (TDMA) digital transmission and microwave radio technologies. One example of the potential use of radio is illustrated in Fig. 17.12, which depicts the concept of the Xerox XTEN network that was planned for the continental United States. The backbone network connectivity could have been provided via satellite communication with earth stations located in the major areas to be served. Local distribution from the earth stations to subscribers was to have been accomplished via one or more microwave radio substations which communicate with subscriber stations via rooftop antennas. More details are provided in Chap. 5.

The XTEN subscriber links were to support a basic data rate of 256 kbps to as high as 1.5 Mbps. The design objectives indicated that the microwave link would have been less costly than T-carrier local loops in the telephone system. Radio link costs may not compete with wire lines in 4-kHz telephone local loops for some time to come where the telephone plant is already in place. XTEN was to provide for conventional telephone system access to its substations or earth stations.

XTEN plans were to use TDMA techniques on the subscriber links to increase utilization and to lower individually allocated costs. However, it is reasonable to expect that some subscribers could have made full use of their available bandwidth for reasonably extended periods of time—for example, by teleconferencing and utilization of an internal intra-premises network controlled by a computer branch exchange. In such cases, circuit switching or even dedicated links could be employed effectively.

Another radio technique suitable for local access networks is the Packet Radio technology being developed by the Defense Advanced Research Projects Agency

308

(DARPA). Packet Radio can be further expanded to regional area coverage, and can provide service to mobile users. A completely independent local distribution computer communication network using Packet Radio to interconnect a number of Ethernet local networks is described in [SHOC 79]. Packet Radio is discussed in detail in Chap. 12.

Future possibilities for radio local distribution lie in special service areas, such as the Community Antenna Radio Service (CARS) band at 12.7 to 12.95 GHz, intended for transmission of entertainment television and radio by channels, and the newly created Digital Termination Service at 10.55 to 10.68 GHz for internodal and node-to-terminal services. DTS has been modeled by the FCC to very closely resemble the local distribution of digital electronic message services as envisioned in the XTEN proposal. Applications are being received for two classes of service, providing 2.5 or 5.0 mHz channel bandwidths in each major metropolitan area. Such bandwidths are capable of serving only a relatively small set of users; hopefully, DTS with larger bandwidths will be opened up in higher frequency bands in the near future.

Outlook for Local Distribution of Integrated Services

To date, most attention in networking has focused on the long-haul (global) and subscriber-level (sublocal) areas. The gray area in between, which is defined here as the local distribution portion, has been largely ignored. Most likely, this is true because the technological, economic, and policy problems associated with the "last mile" in a truly universal integrated services network have been so intractable. A few of the issues affecting local distribution have been mentioned; many others of importance are beyond the scope of this chapter (see, e.g., [HATF 81]). These issues will have to be dealt with if benefits of integrated services are to be realized.

In the technological realm, the principal possibilities and their associated bottlenecks have been discussed:

- The telephone network is ubiquitous, but has severe bandwidth limitations and will be slow to change. The telephone network is in place and cannot be ignored; it is also well integrated with long-haul services and is supported by numerous kinds of subscriber-level subnetworks.
- CATV offers large bandwidth, but is not available everywhere and varies in the extent of two-way capabilities. CATV networks are growing rapidly and are also acquiring significant long-haul connections via satellite networking (although so far most network transmission is unidirectional).
- Radio techniques offer a rapid solution to many problems, but are unlikely in the foreseeable future to offer sufficient capacity for universal, individual access. Local distribution via radio is also the least mature option, with significant development work yet to be done. Most plans, however, are based on inherent integration with a corresponding long-haul backbone network.

For the next decade, while the present issues are being resolved and technological advances create new ones, integrated services distribution at the local level will be accomplished by hybrid techniques. The combination of direct radio link access and access via the telephone system to the backbone network is an illustration of a hybrid approach to local distribution. At least during the transitional period, while new services and modes of delivery are being established, hybrid distribution will be the general rule. This will be particularly true in those cases in which substantial data transmission or video bandwidth is required.

For consumer-oriented services to individual homes and small businesses, it has been argued that there is a significant discrepancy between the transmit and receive bandwidths needed by the user. For example, the *request* for information from a central data base, or for a video image (or even a television program), requires much less transmission capacity than does the delivery of that information. Rarely, so the argument goes, does the individual have the need to transmit as much information as he desires to receive. As long as that is true (as it generally will be in the near-term future) "integrated" service requests can be accommodated by lower-speed upstream channels in CATV networks, or via the telephone system to the source or point of origin of the desired data, and then delivered by another medium.

Examples of the latter—a hybrid system using the telephone for requests and a conventional broadcast television channel for delivery—are the nascent Teletext systems. These and other radio/television "piggyback" techniques for information delivery are outlined in Chap. 5. Another example of the current thinking concerning necessary upstream *vs.* downstream bandwidths can be found in the numerous field trials of Videotex systems; generally, the source-to-subscribers data rate is 1200 bps, while the subscriber-to-source rate is 75 bps.

17.4.2.3 Subscriber-Level Distribution

The focus in the preceding section has been on the distribution of communications capability over areas measured in terms of several kilometers, and perhaps tens of kilometers. Within such an area, a network termination is viewed as a single point. That single point, however, may represent a subscriber's premises or campus containing a large population of individual users of many different types of terminals for accessing integrated services. The issues of integration appear once again at this level, but the scale of the network has shifted significantly and different designs become appropriate. For instance, one would not seriously consider communication via satellite between two offices within a building. On a somewhat more subtle level, a designer normally would not consider radio techniques because of severe propagation and interference problems that would exist in most situations. Radio, however, is a very effective method of transmission in campus distribution, involving transmission between buildings.

The most useful transmission media for intrapremises communications are the guided media—wire lines, coaxial cable, and optical fibers. Many network architectures, existing and proposed, use these media. This section concentrates on two bases for such networks, which are representative of the possibilities. They illustrate two rather different points of view concerning the direction of integrated services networks—centralized control versus distributed bus architectures.

Private Branch Exchange

As many feel that the telephone system is the correct point of departure for an integrated services network on a global and local distribution basis, many also feel that an organization's internal telephone system is the logical foundation for internal distribution of integrated services. Such an internal network normally appears as a star network hubbed on the central element, a private branch exchange (PBX), as exemplified in Fig. 17.13.[9]

In this view, each terminal is wired to a discrete port of the PBX. "Wiring" would normally be accomplished with wire-pair cables, perhaps using existing copper wiring if it is adequate, or coaxial or optical fiber cables if their attributes are required. The central switching technique is circuit switching, just as in current PBXs. Peripheral service modules could be added to perform additional functions, such as message switching for Telex and electronic mail applications, and perhaps interfacing directed data calls to packet-switching networks.

The PBX approach is heavily oriented toward the telephone system. The primary purpose of a PBX is to provide internal service to the individual telephone sets located within the premises, and external services with the public telephone network via trunks connected to the local telephone company central office. Sometimes PBXs at different locations are also interconnected by various arrangements using dedicated lines to form a nationwide intracorporate private telephone network.

As the costs of computers continue to drop, it has become economically possible to incorporate very sophisticated functions in even small PBX systems. Modern PBXs offer features unimagined only a few years ago. The features demonstrate a high level of value added by a PBX, in addition to the normal switching, controlling, and concentration functions. The demand for such features, coupled with the low manufacturing costs made possible by use of computer and electronic switching techniques, has created a sizable so-called "interconnect market," aggressively pursued by many new independent suppliers as well as by the traditional telephone equipment manufacturers.

Because of their telephone orientation, however, most PBXs of current design are not well suited for integrated services applications. As in the local distribution level of the telephone networks, wideband video is out of the question. Data transmission is limited by the same factors as those discussed earlier for circuit switches. Call setup procedures and delay are constrained by telephone signaling methods. Although

---

[9]There is as yet no general agreement on terminology. To some, a private branch exchange (PBX) is any of a generic class of equipment intended to provide intrapremises communications functions and connected to external telephone systems. That is the sense used in this chapter. To others, however, the term "PBX" is reserved for the older operator-assisted, manual switchboard type of equipment. In that case, the next generation of exchange incorporating electrically controlled circuit switching matrices is known as a private automatic branch exchange (PABX); and the introduction of computers led to the electronic private automatic branch exchange (EPABX), and so on. Still others refer to a computer branch exchange (CBX), but there are differences of opinion as to whether a CBX is an EPABX providing only POTS, or a CBX is an EPABX providing enhanced functions useful for computer-oriented services. To further provide confusion, CBX is the trade name of a line of exchanges manufactured by the Rolm Corporation. These problems are avoided by using "PBX" generically, with adjectives where distinction is required.

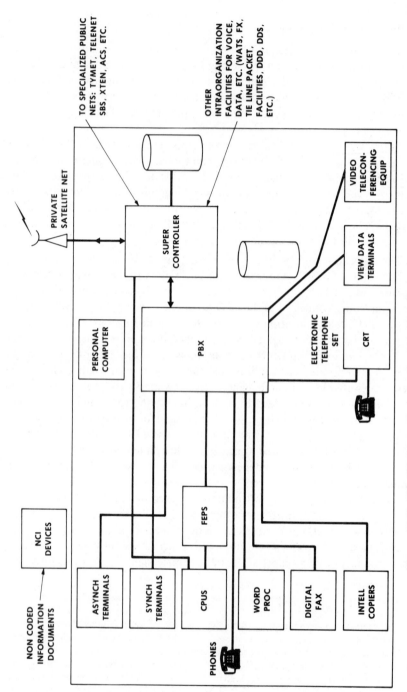

Figure 17.13. The PBX hub view of intrapremises distribution of integrated services [DMW 1979], with permission.

most "modern" PBXs are based on PCM time-division principles, ports must be accessed at the analog level, thus requiring the use of modems to interface with digital equipment. Generally, this limits the available data rate to 9600 bps. In fact, the internal architecture of many popular PBX designs imposes lower limits—ranging from 4800 bps in some cases to less than 1200 bps in others. Some PBXs provide for full medium-speed digital access at the subscriber's instrument, but digital transmission is accomplished by an additional, separate wire pair.

New PBXs have been announced that are capable of providing directly to the user the 56-kbps equivalent of a digital voice circuit.[10] In addition to advanced PBX functions, the InteCom Integrated Business Exchange (IBX) supports simultaneous voice and data calls over conventional two-wire pairs via ports operating at 128 kbps. A user's work station contains a standard μ-law codec, an RS-232 or RS-449 data port for synchronous or asynchronous data transmission at selectable rates from 110 bps to 56 kbps, and a means for multiplexing the voice and data channels. Data are transported without modems, and can be switched directly into public packet switching networks and advanced digital transmission systems at the T1 level. If access to a direct digital circuit is not available, such as a call via the public telephone network, the IBX will assign a modem from a shared pool of modems for that call. Plans for advanced PBXs having similar capabilities have been revealed by Rolm and Northern Telecom.

The Datapoint Corporation has announced the Information Switching Exchange (ISX), which performs similar functions. In addition to switching data and voice calls within the customer's premises and with external public networks, the ISX can also be interfaced with Datapoint's ARC high-speed local area coaxial cable network. Within a given ISX system (which can be distributed through remote units over a "campus"), data calls are accomplished directly without modems. The initial ISX system configuration can use existing analog telephone instruments, which require a separate pair of wires for the analog channels.

Many devices similar to these are expected to appear on the market in the near future. The range of possible services will widen. There is no basic limitation to the bandwidth or data rate that could be supported on the individual service lines of PBX-type equipment, nor is there any reason why bandwidth could not be assigned on an as-needed basis in response to different kinds of calls placed on any given line. Code and format conversions could be performed by auxiliary modules and implemented in hardware or software in the control unit, based on information available about characteristics of the calling services. Such features could be easily accommodated in a PBX based on time-division circuit switching with stored program control.

Distributed Bus Networks

An alternative to the centralized control of the PBX approach for integrated services is a system based on architectures and techniques being developed in the field

---

[10]Although a standard PCM voice channel is digitized at a 64-kbps rate, it is common practice to rob the least significant bit of some 8-bit words for signaling purposes. Thus most PCM voice channels support a transparent rate of 56 kbps (see Chap. 18).

Table 17.5. *Typical Local Area Network.*

Local network	Company	Trans-mission medium	Max No. of nodes	Network archi-tecture	Access scheme	Max length of interno-dal trans-mission medium	Max data rate	Applications	Comments
Attached Resource Computer (ARC)	Datapoint Corp.	Broad-band coax/non-coherent infrared energy	255	Bus	Proprie-tary	4 miles for coax, 1 mile for infrared	2.5 Mb/s	Office auto-mation, data processing	Each processor node can partici-pate in up to 6 ARCs.
Cluster/One Model A	Nestar Systems Inc.	Baseband multi-conductor cable	64	Arbitrary (bus, star, etc.)	CSMA/CD	1000 ft	250 kb/s	Office auto-mation, person-al computers, general-purpose	Free-form topology due to low data rates.
Distributed Operating Multi Access Interactive Network (DOMAIN)	Apollo Computer Corp.	Broad-band coax	Several hundred*	Ring	Token passing	3000 ft	12 Mb/s Mb/s	Engineering/ scientific, CAD/CAM, gen-eral-purpose	Virtual file accessing, can page across net-work in a vir-tual environment.
Ethernet	Xerox Corp.	Baseband coax	100	Bus	CSMA/CD	2.5 km	10 Mb/s	Office automation	Maximum separa-tion between sta-tions is 2.5 km.
HYPERchannel	Network Systems Corp.	Base-band coax	16	Bus	CSMA/CA	Unavailable	50 Mb/s	Scientific, large computer centers	Link adapters allow a node to be at-tached to 4 inde-pendent trunks. Trunk-to-trunk interfacing via microwave, fiber optics, and com-mon-carrier lines.
Localnet Systems 20 and 40	Sytek Inc.,	Broad-band coax	256/ channel	Bus	CSMA/CD	30 km	120 kb/s, 2 Mb/s	Distributed processing design auto-mation	Each channel has CSMA/CD access-ing. Up to 120 channels per cable.
Modway	Modcon Div. of Gould Inc.	Base-band or broad-band coax, fi-ber optics	250	Arbitrary (bus, star, etc.)	Token passing	15,000 ft	1.544 Mb/s	Data process-ing, process control	Compatible with microwave and satellite-communi-cations facilities for common-carrier transmissions.
Net/One	Unger-mann-Bass Inc.	Base-band coax	250	Bus	CSMA/CD	4000 ft	4 Mb/s	OEM systems, data process-ing, scientific, office automa-tion, process control	Intelligent network interface units can be programmed to interface to a wide variety of terminals.
Omnilink	Northern Telecom Inc.	Broad-band coax	9	Ring	Token passing	5000 ft	40 kb/s	Data process-ing, office automation	Each node can have independent and accessible files, peripherals, and processor.
Primenet	Prime Computer Inc.	Base-band coax	15	Ring	Token passing	750 ft	10 Mb/s	Data process-ing, large computer centers	CCITT X.25-com-patible for inter-facing to other networks over long distances.
Z-Net	Zilog Inc.	Base-band coax	255	Bus	CSMA/CD	2 km	800 kb/s	Office automa-tion, small business computers	Emulator package allows data trans-fer between Zilog equipment and other vendors' equipment.

*Theoretical limit is 2^{16}.

Source: [ALLA 81], reprinted with permission from *Electronic Design*, Vol. 29, No. 8; copyright Hayden Publishing Co., Inc., 1981.

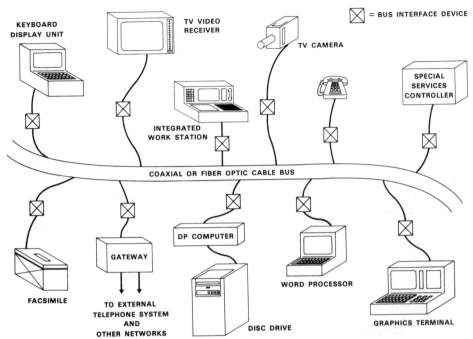

Figure 17.14. Concept of an integrated services bus network for local distribution. Several specific implementations are possible, as discussed in the text.

of "local area networks" [see Chap. 13; CLAR 78, SHOC 80][11]. Some typical local area networks, their transmission mediums, the distances they cover, their architectures, and other descriptive information are listed in Tab. 17.5. Of such architectures, a particularly attractive class for providing subscriber-level integrated services is based on a bus network, as illustrated in Fig. 17.14. The basic idea is that a guided transmission medium, such as coaxial or optical fiber cable, can support a large bandwidth that can be shared by many different users. A cable can be routed through an office building, for example, so that any terminal desiring communication service would simply tap into the network via a bus interface device (BID). The attractions of this concept are:

1. Adding a terminal does not require finding an additional port on PBX equipment.
2. Additional wiring from the PBX to a new terminal location is not necessary.
3. Bandwidth is not restricted to that of telephone channels.

   An integrated service bus netowrk can be implemented in several rather different combinations of technologies. The following discussion highlights some of the most important possibilities, for which more detailed treatment can be found in other chapters of this book.

[11]"Local area networks" or "local networks" should not be confused with the "local distribution networks" of Sec. 17.4.2.2. See footnote 5.

A.   Topography

Implicitly, a distributed bus network is not implemented in a star configuration. Possible topographies include ring,[12] tree-shaped, and open-ended structures, each with particular advantages and disadvantages (see Chaps. 10 and 11). Subnetworks can be coupled together; gateway devices can be used with high-level structures.

B.   Duplex Capability

An integrated service network must provide for full and half-duplex communication. From the viewpoint of a subscriber's terminal, this can be accomplished in five general ways:

1.   Two physically separate cables, one for each direction.
2.   FDM, whereby directionality is separated by two discrete portions of the available bandwidth.
3.   TDM, whereby the direction of transmission is alternated at a rapid rate (ping-pong).
4.   Contention—an ALOHA-like technique whereby each device "broadcasts" to a bus capable of bidirectional transmission.
5.   A unidirectional, closed-end ring structure, wherein all traffic eventually circulates to all terminals.

C.   Transmission Medium

Because of interference considerations and the bandwidths and distances foreseen (even in an intrapremises network), the use of coaxial or optical fiber cable is indicated (see Chap. 7). Coaxial-cable technology is relatively mature, and inexpensive components based on CATV applications can be used. Coaxial cable can be tapped with relative ease, and can support a large number of taps. Because of its highly frequency-sensitive attenuation characteristics, however, large baseband bandwidths (and corresponding high individual data rates) are difficult to implement at reasonable cost. Current technology suitable for intrapremises networks provides for data rates to about 10 Mbps. Larger bandwidths are more readily implemented with radio-frequency FDM channelization techniques analogous to the television channels of a CATV system. Thus a single coaxial cable can support a number of such channels which can be devoted to different applications. This approach has become known as *broadband cable*. Typical quantities are 30 channels, each of which carries about 5 MHz or Mbps.

The advantage of direct baseband transmission is that simpler interface devices are required at each tap. The bandwidth of "broadband cable" is achieved at the cost of the additional modems and frequency multiplexers required.

Optical fibers have a relatively flat attenuation characteristic that can support larger baseband bandwidths and data rates. FDM (wavelength multiplexing) and TDM techniques can be used, separately or together. However, tapping or insertion of junctions is very difficult and expensive with current techniques and components.

---

[12]Ring networks usually are structured such that the devices contained in the network intersect the transmission links, rather than tap into a continuous transmission medium. For present purposes, this distinction is ignored.

D.   Bus Network Architectures

A wide range of network architectures is possible, employing combinations of the preceding techniques with various multiple access techniques and network protocols (see Chaps. 1, 4, 5, 6, 7, 12, and 13). One of the range of possibilities can be thought of as a kind of packet broadcast "wired ALOHA" system, operating with baseband digital transmission, in which the entire bus bandwidth is potentially available to any user on a contention basis. Access can be effected as purely synchronous TDMA, or by any of the modified distributed control schemes. In this type of architecture, the bus interface device (BID) can be quite simple and of common design throughout the system. For transmission, the BID bids for the bandwidth necessary for its purpose by simple procedures; for reception, the BID examines each packet on the bus for its own address, accepting those that match and ignoring others. Ethernet and the data channel of Mitrenet are examples of this approach.

Such architectures work well in most computer-communication situations, but exhibit the problem of packet switching in general with integrated services, as discussed in Sec. 17.4.1.3. In particular, attention must be paid to the distributed control scheme. Quasi-random techniques, such as carrier-sense multiple access with or without collision detection, may provide adequate throughput on the average, but the delivery delay variance could be unacceptable for voice and video traffic. The same problem could exist for token-passing schemes without an extended fairness doctrine. (In token-passing schemes, a token message is circulated through the network and a user can transmit only when it has the token.)

A bus network opposite extreme is illustrated in Fig. 17.15. In this approach, based on an extension of current CATV technology, individual FDM channels are created and controlled by a centralized "head end" in a multiple-access, multidrop architecture. In effect, the network is similar to a "super PBX" system, but has significant physical and operational differences. Terminal devices have access to wholly different bandwidth and services in accordance with their needs, while the physical network retains the advantage of connection by simple taps. The bus interface device functions, however, are more complex, since they must incorporate modems (of different types) for digital service and the additional circuitry necessary for FDM operation.

Other architectures are possible, with different advantages and disadvantages in an integrated services environment. Mitrenet, a hybrid of the previously described configurations, is an interesting example. It is set up as a FDM network with discrete channels for video, audio, and data. The data channel, once separated by filtration, operates as a packet broadcasting system in a contention mode. There is no reason why other FDM channels could not be operated digitally with other protocols suited to special types of traffic.[13]

---

[13]An advanced TDM approach has been proposed to handle voice, data, and image traffic on a wideband local network [HANS 81]. Access for traffic with bursty characteristics is by a contention scheme; access for traffic with stream characteristics, e.g., video, is by contention to make a reservation in the queue for assured uninterrupted transmission.

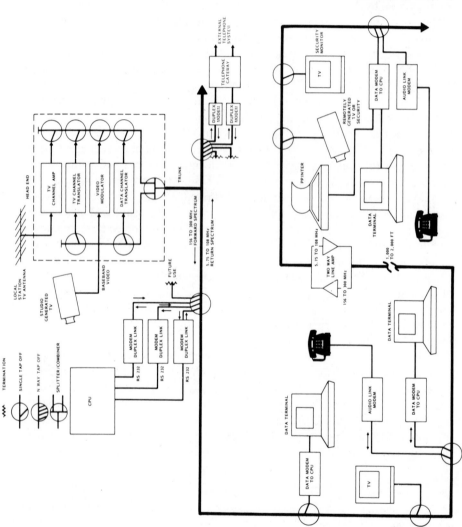

Figure 17.15 An example of an FDM channelized approach to bus distribution of integrated services based on CATV technology. (After [BROA 1980], with permission). The available frequency spectrum is divided for store and forward paths.

318

To illustrate another possibility, consider a distributed bus system patterned after a very wideband version of Ethernet. Normal interterminal and terminal-gateway calls could be handled by the usual packet broadcast/reception process, thus avoiding the need for centralized control for the majority of traffic. Requests for special services, such as those provided by advanced PBXs, could be recognized and serviced by a controller located anywhere on the bus. The controller would be just another device on the bus. It could be combined with a gateway function for interconnection with other networks, such as the public telephone and data networks, or private campus distribution and long-haul systems. Advantages of distributed control would be retained, while added functions most efficiently performed by common control would be available.[14]

Future Developments in Subscriber-Level Distribution

Intense development activity is under way in both PBX and bus networks to provide for future demands, including integrated services. Currently, the focus is on voice and lower-speed data in PBX systems, and medium-speed data in bus systems. It is likely that the near-term emphasis will remain in those areas. Interest in high-speed data, voice, and video applications to bus systems will command increasing attention as the demand develops and relative economies are realized. This may occur with concomitant development in optical fiber technology, such as inexpensive taps, and in integrated circuit technology, and allow the implementation of very high rate digital transmission with inexpensive bus interface device functions.

The PBX approach to integrated services has a head start and enjoys the advantage of a generally perceived "natural" extension of current network arrangements. Of great importance to all but the casual user, telephone-type networks will enjoy the advantage of responsive, essentially universal maintenance and support for some time to come. Independent manufactureres, in particular now Northern Telecom, Mitel, and Rolm, are aggressive in producing and marketing PBX-based networks. It has been predicted that IBM will enter the U.S. market with an upgraded version of the 3750 PBX, already sold elsewhere in the world [PBXC 80]. Other manufacturers with high stakes in the future of communications have a different view: Xerox, Datapoint, DEC, and DCC, among others, are placing their bets on bus network technology. From the products that issue from both camps, the user will be the beneficiary.

---

[14]Wang Laboratories' Wangnet does exactly this. Wangnet incorporates three bands. The "Utility Band" provides for seven conventional video channels. The "Wang Band" is intended for interconnection of Wang equipment via the equivalent of a 12 Mbps Ethernet. The "Interconnect Band" comprises three additional channels, each offering a different type of network service between a large number of Wang devices or equipment of other manufacturers. Included in these channels are point-to-point, multipoint, and switched subchannels [BROA 1981].

17.5 CURRENT INTEGRATION TECHNIQUES AND OPTIONS

Although full integration lies sometime in the future, networks today are handling, or are capable of handling, multiple traffic types. The levels of integration that can be achieved vary almost as widely as organizations' needs vary. Modification is necessary for some networks to handle additional traffic types; however, integration, motivated by the need to reduce costs or increase service for multiple separate applications, does not require conversion to a single network for all traffic. Many of the savings or improvements associated with integration can be achieved by sharing transmission facilities.

The technology already exists for widespread and versatile shared use of existing facilities. A range of approaches is shown in Tab. 17.6. Some of the examples that follow rely on innovative but straightforward use of existing facilities and networks. Included are approaches that use fixed allocation of frequencies for

Table 17.6. *Approaches to Shared Usage of Telecommunications Facilities.*

Approach	Network Media Examples	Extent of Integration	Traffic Applications
"Manual" switching	Telephone networks	Dial-up use of public telephone lines for voice conversations and computer systems access	Analog voice, data, facsimile
	Broadband services	Alternate use by subscriber selection	Data, voice, slow-scan video
Fixed allocations	FM radio	Shared one-way broadcast facilities but use limited by FCC regulations	Analog sound programs, data
	Telephone network local loops	Shared local loop with data above voice; not for loaded pairs or loops employing local carriers	Voice, data
	Voice networks	Shared transmission facilities with data inserted in a reserved trap in the middle of the voice bandwidth	Voice, data
	Television	Shared one-way broadcast facilities using the flyback interval of the TV signal	Data, teletext
Multiple accessing or dynamic switching of channels (space, frequency, or time division)	Satellite frequency plans	Sharing of satellite transponder bandwidth by a mixture of services (frequency-division multiple access)	Voice, data, full video
	Coaxial cable TV	Shared transmission facilities	Full video, data, voice
	PBX accessed networks	Shared network access and transmission facilities	Voice, data, slow-scan video
Integrated switching	Modified packet, circuit, or hybrid switched networks	Shared network transmission and switching facilities	Data, voice, slow-scan video

transmitting more than one type of traffic over the same media. Such approaches take advantage of any portions of the spectrum that would otherwise go unused, the concept used in data under voice on microwave transmission links. Another type of approach is based on fixed allocation of time intervals during transmission. In most of the fixed-allocation examples, applicability is restricted to a particular transmission media.

17.5.1 Line Sharing in a Telephone Network

The public telephone network is an obvious starting point when considering integration options. Indeed, the majority of the current activities focused on Integrated Services Digital Networks is based on this presumption. However, a network designed for a single traffic type can be difficult to retrofit for other traffic types. This is illustrated by the difficulty with which data have been accommodated in the telephone system (and, incidentally, by the difficulty with which voice is interfaced with a packet-switched network [GOLD 77, WEIN 83, GRUB 83]). Ten to fifteen years were required to develop technology for carrying data on a voice network with acceptable quality. Even in the late 1950s, the highest bit rate over a telephone channel was 75 bps.

Today, an immediately available integration option is use of the public telephone Direct Distance Dialing (DDD) network for voice conversations part of the time and for data transmission between, say, a terminal and processor at other times. Data can be transmitted at about 2400 bps with no special treatment and at 4800 bps in many cases; however, the user must provide modems (to *mo*dulate/*dem*odulate) signals between digital equipment and analog local loops to convert signals from digital to analog or back. Filters must be used to preclude any effect the data signals might have on network control signaling systems, and often special signals must be generated. An example is the signal to disable echo suppressors required for long-distance voice circuits.

Several problems can arise in using the DDD network for data:

1. Even with auto-dial and answer modems, call establishment delay can be as much as 30 sec, although tone-dialing and the Common Channel Inter-office Signaling (CCIS) are reducing this to less than 5 sec.
2. The transmission characteristics of the circuit-switched telephone network are highly variable and are subject to considerable noise due to the signal's transit through switches. Noise from this and other sources limits the data rates that can be achieved at reasonable bit error rates. Currently, the usual "safe" limits are 2400 bps for half-duplex operation, or 1200 bps for duplex. Higher rates are becoming increasingly possible, however, because of improvements in modems and circuit quality.
3. Transmission time through the network varies because of the different trunk interfaces and points of amplification as well as modem characteristics. The two-line turnarounds required to send a block and receive an acknowledgment can add as much as 0.4 sec delay.

4. Transmission is restricted to point-to-point circuits, except in private-line service, where multipoint circuits are possible.

Most of these problems can be obviated by the use of private leased lines, assuming, of course, that the cost of these full-time circuits can be justified by the traffic volume and performance requirements. Analog circuits can be specially conditioned for data transmission at 9600 bps; new modems are appearing that allow operation at 14.4 and 16 kbps. In many of the larger cities, wider bandwidths are available in the form of both analog and digital lines. Digital Data Service (DDS) is an example of the latter.

Designing for alternate use of lines in a private network can be complex. Networks designed for voice conversations may have their capacity strained by the addition of data, not only on the basis of volume but also on data "conversation" characteristics. The designer must ensure that the number and characteristics of the lines can handle the traffic.

Data transmissions are characterized by much longer holding times than telephone conversations. Separate calculations may be required to determine the necessary channel capacities for data and voice [MART 72]. Bulk data transmissions have very high channel utilizations compared with voice conversations, so they greatly affect the extent of concentration that can be achieved. When most lines are highly utilized, a line failure can have a major impact. Also, long strings of certain digital patterns cause regenerators to lose synchronization. Provision must be made to change such strings.

17.5.2 Cable Television Networks

Cable television (CATV) networks are proliferating and offer attractive but frequently overlooked possibilities for integration. Traditionally, CATV networks provide video and audio broadcast; other services can be provided with relative ease because of their very wide bandwidth. CATV networks are not restricted to alternate use for different traffic types, however; their wide bandwidth permits simultaneous sharing of facilities. Frisch [FRIS 77] tested a prototype system for random-access packet transmission on commercial CATV with a central minicomputer controller. Data were carried on a channel not used for television. With a signal level for data less than or equal to the video level, there was no interference. At a 20-dB or less difference, the bit error rate was better than 10^{-8}.

Normally, a CATV system carries at least 20 channels, each of which is assigned a bandwidth of 6 MHz. If only one channel were devoted to data transmission, a potential data rate in excess of 10 Mbps could be supported. Data transmission is also possible in unoccupied portions of the CATV spectrum. For example, data can be transmitted below the 54-MHz lower edge of Channel 2 if the cable system has not squeezed an extra TV channel between 48 and 54 MHz. The 72- to 76-MHz spectrum between Channels 4 and 5 is also available and can be used for data rates up to 6 Mbps. Applications of CATV-type systems, sometimes called "broadband networks," to data communications are discussed in [SWIT 72] and [MUSG 80].

Possibilities of integrated services are detailed in [DINE 80], where some current equipment is also mentioned.

When digital telephony or data signals are frequency-division multiplexed with analog video signals over the same coaxial cable system, the major problem is intermodulation noise and crosstalk of the signals caused by nonlinearity in the analog repeater amplifiers. Since digital signals are less sensitive to intermodulation noise, they are generally transmitted at much lower levels than the video signals. Commercial cable operators are likely to accept data channels only on a noninterfering basis. The effects of noise and interference are analyzed in [CHAN 76] to determine the level at which digital and video signals are compatible. The noise power expressions derived also can be used to determine the repeater spacing needed when CATV is used for digital signals only.

Interactive systems have been developed for home services. An interactive cable television system in The Woodlands, Texas, is used to summon fire departments in response to smoke and heat detectors, police in response to security alarms, and rescue squads in response to medical alert alarms [ELIO 78]. Other systems provide viewer participation entertainment and education. The uses of CATV distribution systems for two-way computer communication are detailed in Chap. 7. CATV systems for local distribution in integrated networks are described in Sec. 17.4.2.2.

17.5.3   Data Insertion Techniques

With the increasing demand for low-cost data transmission, a number of techniques have been developed to allow the insertion of data in existing channels carrying analog services. Some transmission media and source traffic types contain time or frequency gaps that can be used for digital traffic. Others can tolerate deliberately created gaps, a more restricted bandwidth, or lower signal-to-noise ratio. One example is a conventional CATV network, described previously. Several other examples are outlined below and in Chap. 5.

17.5.3.1   Data under Audio Broadcast (Infocast)

Standard FM radio broadcasts can carry additional information on a subcarrier without affecting the primary channel (see Chap. 5). This capacity has been exploited for some number of years as an "SCA" channel, normally used to pipe background music into stores and restaurants. Radio receiver–decoders can receive digital information broadcast in these channels and convert it to printed copy for the deaf in the Philadelphia area, for grain operators in midwestern states, and for produce shippers and wholesalers around Chicago. The DBC Infocast system for general electronic message service is entering trial operation in several U.S. cities. The Federal Communications Commission (FCC) restricts such FM radio use to information that is of broad interest and suitable for general broadcast on the main band [DAVI 78].

17.5.3.2   Data above Voice (Local Loop Wire lines)

Service on twisted-pair local loop wire lines can be expanded to include alarm monitoring, remote utility meter reading, electrical energy management and load shedding, opinion polls and surveys, digital data services, and interactive videotex for data retrieval on demand using the telephone network for transmission and a television set for display. Transmission facility sharing is achieved by using the highest frequencies for data and adding filters and modems at either end of each loop, as shown in Fig. 17.16. At least one system (Teltone DCS-2B) on the market superimposes data over voice through PBX networks. The system can support full-duplex asynchronous data rates to 9600 bps on a 26-gauge wire pair over distances to 5000 ft.

The Vidon multiple-service broadband telephone system in Calgary, Canada, uses data above voice on a single twisted pair or uses two twisted-pair lines with one pair for voice and one for data. Data service is at 1200 bps. Services offered at the residences are shown in Fig. 17.17 as a part of the system diagram.

17.5.3.3 Data in Voice

A 0.5-kHz band can be taken from the voice bandwidth and used for half-duplex digital transmission at a rate up to 200 bps. The data insertion, shown in Fig. 17.18 using the low channel of a CCITT-V21 modem, is said to have an imperceptible effect on voice quality [LORI 79]. Although such a digital channel can obviously be used for any sort of data transmission, one of the more interesting applications of this technique is for telewriting. Telewriting is incorporated in the French audiographic conference service, which uses the television set to display a slow-moving picture accompanied by an audio commentary.

A telewriting, or teleboard, system communicates a changing "blackboard" display, usually in combination with speech. (This is why the term "audiography" is also used for such systems.) The "blackboard," a graphic tablet, can be written on in a selected color or tone, pointed at, and erased by the sender. In the configuration shown in Fig. 17.19, the sender sees the same image on his television screen or other display terminal that the receiver sees. A light pen applied directly to the screen, or an interactive "mouse," might be used instead of the graphic tablet.

The tablet or light pen control contains a microprocessor that converts signal values to X and Y coordinates, detects working mode changes and pen lifts, and computes writing speed. The information is used to construct a data frame which is transmitted to the graphic (micro)processor on request. The graphic processor, diagrammed in Fig. 17.20, interpolates between frames to reconstruct the drawing in image memory. Therefore, frame request frequency can be based on writing speed.

Writing is coded for bandwidth transmission as low as 200 bps. The low coding

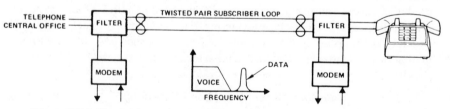

Figure 17.16. Data above voice on telephone local loops [CLAI 1979], © 1979 IEEE.

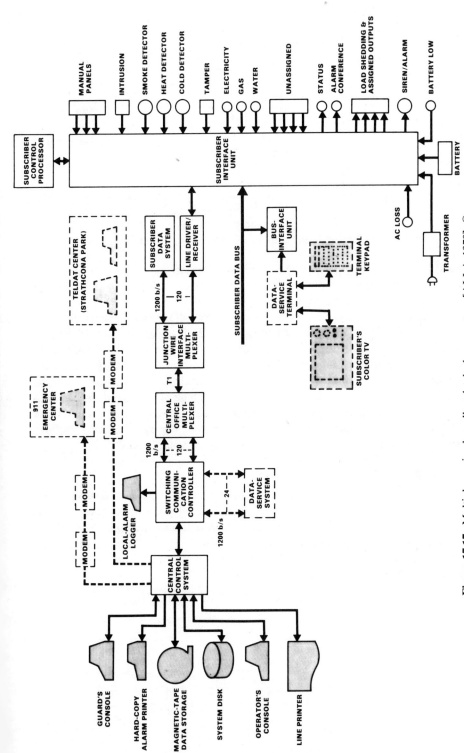

Figure 17.17. Multiple-service broadband telephone system [ALLA 1979], © 1979 IEEE.

325

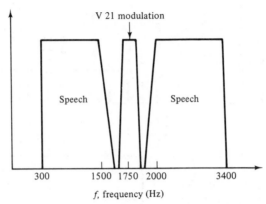

Figure 17.18. Telewriting data insertion [LORI 1979], © 1979 IEEE.

rate is achieved by approximating the writing as a succession of vectors and using variable-length Huffman coding (noiseless coding; see Chap. 18) to encode differences in direction between successive vectors.

Another technique, dubbed "data-with voice", allows simultaneous data and voice transmission on an analog circuit [MOSE 82]. Data-with-voice (DWV) provides four low-speed (8-16 bps) data channels suitable for applications such as remote monitoring, alarms, or low-rate telemetry. DWV uses spread-spectrum techniques (see Chap. 5) to spread the energy of the data channels quasi-randomly across the entire 4 KHz bandwidth of the voice circuit. With a high ratio of bandwidth to data rate, the effect is apparent to the voice user as a small increase in background noise level. Conversely, proper encoding and spreading of the transmission waveform protects the data channels from being jammed by the voice signals.

17.5.3.4 Data in Video (Teletext)

Teletext services include the (noncommercial) British Broadcasting Company's CEEFAX, the (commercial) Independent Broadcasting Authority's Oracle, and the French Antiope system. In the United States, several test systems are based on various modifications of these services and on interactive CATV [SPEC 79]; no standard has been established yet. Text and graphics information is displayed on the screen of a specially modified television receiver.

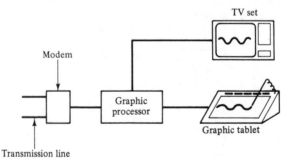

Figure 17.19. Telewriting system [LORI 1979], © 1979 IEEE.

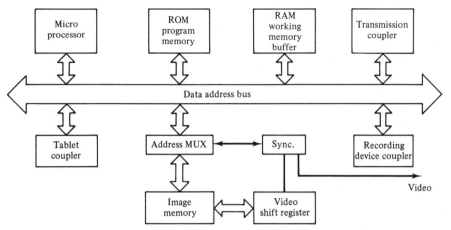

Figure 17.20. Graphic processor [LORI 1979], © 1979 IEEE.

Teletext data transmission works as follows. At the transmitter site, pages of characters are cyclically repeated as digitally encoded information and inserted in the vertical blanking intervals of a television signal. A page of data requested by a user is extracted at its next repeat. One blanking interval occurs with each transmitted field of picture lines. Two fields give a complete frame of a television picture where lines of successive fields alternate on the screen. No picture or synchronization signals are carried when the scanner is moving vertically to begin the next field, so two scan-line time slots are available each frame.

The number of bits that can be transmitted varies with the television standard. The North American television standard (NTSC, National Television System Commission) has 525 lines per frame and 30 frames per second. One version of a compatible Teletext scheme transmits two packets each frame, one per blanking interval, where a data packet comprises a 20-byte data block plus an 8-byte header. two bytes for clock run in, one for framing synchronization, three for source identification, one for packet continuity check, and one for packet format. The last five bytes of the header are Hamming code protected. The effective data rate is 9.6 kbps. The standard display page is 20 lines with 40 characters per line.

One European standard has 625 lines per frame, 25 frames per second, and an effective data rate of 12.8 kpbs for 32-byte data blocks plus 8-byte packet headers. The European display page is 24 lines of 40 characters each.

The French Antiope system carries between 16 and 34 pages per second [HUGH 79]. A functional diagram of the Antiope system is shown in Fig. 17.21. The data broadcasting network, DIDON, handles the multiplexing of the data (D) with the video (V) signal. A keypad at the receiver is used to indicate the page wanted for display. Details of the access and reception techniques are given in [NOIR 78].

17.5.4 Multiplexing and Compressing Voice Signals

Transmission facility sharing is an important aspect of network design for traffic integration. In fact, many approaches to integration involve sharing transmission

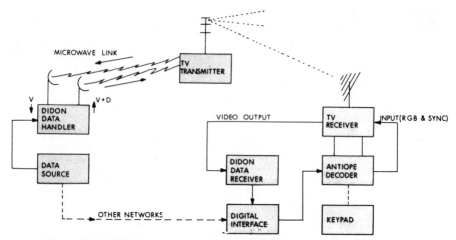

Figure 17.21. Teletext system functions [HUGH 1979], reprinted with permission from the October 1979 issue of Computer Design, copyright 1979, Computer Design Publishing.

facilities only. When traffic boundaries are fixed, as for the examples in the preceding section, the result is a fixed-allocation approach with limited integration advantages; backlogs of traffic of one type cannot be relieved even if channel capacity dedicated to another type of traffic is temporarily unused.

Multiplexing and dynamic allocation schemes are more flexible. Currently, the primary emphasis is focused on time-division multiplexing (TDM). Analog or digital signals can share a transmission facility by TDM or frequency-division multiplexing (FDM), but FDM has several disadvantages. Guard bands are needed to separate subchannels; these reduce the maximum achievable utilization. Filters for FDM are relatively expensive. Complexity of the modulation equipment and inflexibility of spectral reallocation make it difficult to vary transmission rates; the inflexibility restricts the transmission facility sharing to fixed (frequency) allocations.

An important part of multiplexing voice with other traffic is the compression and multiplexing of the voice conversations themselves. Time Assignment Speech Interpolation (TASI) was the earliest technique for compressing the conversations of a number of speakers onto a smaller number of channels. The trans-Atlantic telephone cables have been expensive enough, and in sufficient demand, to warrant the processing cost required to take advantage of silences in speech. A channel is dedicated to a talker until he or she is silent longer than a set time, then that talker's channel can be switched to another talker if necessary.

The matching of input source channels with fewer transmission channels is achieved in TASI by fast time-division switching of the source-to-cable connection. By proper design of large trunk groups (50 to 100 conversations), enough channels are available as needed for active speakers. However, initial segments of speech can be clipped if a channel is not immediately available. The TASI system for transmission in one direction is shown in Fig. 17.22.

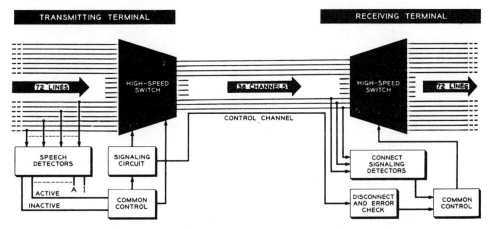

Figure 17.22. Major parts of a TASI system [ONEI 1959], copyright 1959, Bell Telephone Laboratories, Incorporated, reprinted by permission.

Since during most of a conversation, only one of the two parties is talking at any one time, and sometimes both are silent, TASI can more than double cable capacity over that of a normal full-duplex operation [ONEI 59, BULL 59]. More details are given in Sec. 17.3.1.1 about conversation and speech characteristics that allow efficient concentration of voice with other traffic types. Improved versions to TASI continue to be used in speech detection schemes [UN 78, DRAG 76]; silent periods during speech are detected, and coding or packet transmission rate can be reduced.

The speech predictive encoding communications (SPEC) technique, illustrated in Fig. 17.23, is one of the digital speech interpolation (DSI) successors to TASI. SPEC [SCIU 73] removes redundancies for active speech as well as for speech silences. The last value sent is held and used by the receiver until a new value is sent. Each signal sample is examined, through a zero-order predictor, to determine whether it differs from the preceding sample and must be sent. SPEC reduces perceived speech clipping since the most recent sample value is carried until the next transmission.

The original DSI approach [LYGH 74] eliminates clipping by temporarily reducing the number of bits used to specify amplitude. The reconstructed amplitude approximations are then not as accurate, but the effect is perceived as not so objectionable as segment clipping. The idea is that some degradation of all channels is a favorable trade-off against more severe degradation for fewer channels. DSI, including SPEC, is possible only when voice is digitized.

Nearly Instantaneous Companding (NIC) is another important compression technique that operates in a quite different manner [DUTT 76]. Rather than interpolating, NIC re-encodes a group of conventional PCM channels by use of an adaptive algorithm. One significant result is that performance is largely insensitive to input signal statistics, and, thus, can be used with voice-grade circuits operating with modems for data transmission. Compression of the equivalent per-channel bit rate in

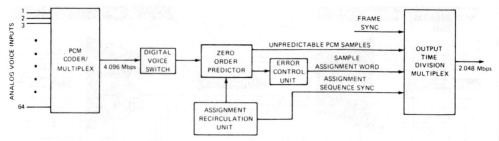

Figure 17.23a. SPEC Transmitter [SCIU 1973, © 1973 IEEE]

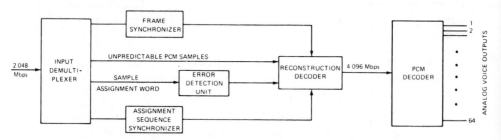

Figure 17.23b. SPEC receiver [SCUI 1973], © 1973 IEEE.

the aggregate output stream can exceed one bit per sample with negligible degradation in quality. One commercial implementation (Nippon Electric Corp.) derives 40 voice-grade channels, as compared with the usual 24, from a DS1 (1.544 Mbps) channel.

Another commercial device (Aydin Corp.) doubles the number of voice channels to 48, by the simple expedient of 32 kbps CVSD encoding. While satisfactory for voice, operation of modems on a CVSD-encoded channel is limited to data rates of 1.2 to 2.4 kbps.

17.5.5 Local Area Data Transport Service

Introduced by Southern Bell in July 1983, the Local Area Data Transport (LADT) service is the first commercial integrated voice and data service to be offered in the United States [EHL184]. The architecture of LADT, shown in Fig. 17.24, is reminiscent of the British System X plan (see Sec. 17.4.2.2 and Fig. 17.8), but there are some important distinctions.

At the local subscriber level, both dial-up and direct access are provided. Dial-up access provides an alternate-use voice and data service over existing analog local loops terminated at an existing local exchange (central office). Voice calls are routed through the local exchange to the conventional higher-order hierarchy of the switched telephone network. Data calls are supported at 1200 bps (synchronous) by the use of the popular 212A modem at the subscribers premises, and an equivalent

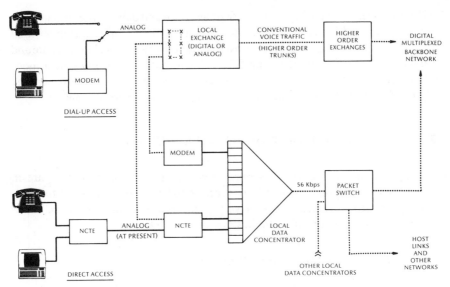

Figure 17.24. A representation of the local area data transport service (LADT). (After [EHLI 84].

212A interface at the local exchange. At this point, data calls are routed by the local exchange to a port in the local data concentrator.

Direct access supporting simultaneous voice and data is provided over analog local loops by Network Circuit Terminating Equipment (NCTE) located at both the customers premises and within the central office that contains both the local exchange switch and the local data concentrator. The NCTE supports full-duplex data transmission at 4.8 kbps by data-over-voice techniques (Sec. 17.5.3.2); voice is carried at the conventional analog baseband, while data is handled by special modems in the NCTE that remodulate on carriers placed above the voice spectrum in a fashion similar to frequency-division multiplexing. The central office NCTE routes the voice call to the conventional telephone network and the data call to the local data concentrator.

For both subscriber access methods, voice traffic is carried by the existing telephone network while data traffic is carried by separate paths via the local data concentrator and the packet switch(es). However, the high-order levels of the network, which are based on digital multiplexing and transmission, can carry both voice and data traffic.

A third access level is provided at packet switches for high-usage hosts at rates of 4.8 to 56 kbps. Full X.25 support exists at this level, including LAPB, multiple virtual circuits and X.121 addressing. It is envisioned that users of this level will be limited to information service providers (e.g., Videotex), gateways to other networks and possibly large-volume data subscribers.

The LADT service is important in serveral respects. As previously mentioned,

LADT represents the first U.S. public integrated voice and data service. It illustrates several concepts of integration alternatives discussed earlier in this chapter, and utilizes different solutions to the problems existing at the backbone, intermediate and local distribution levels. Future plans for LADT include support of asynchronous terminals (e.g., most personal computers) and integrated digital local loops operating at higher data rates. Such features will be necessary for widespread usage.

17.6 APPLICATIONS OF INTEGRATED SERVICES

Some applications of integrated services have already appeared. Others are in advanced stages of development and are expected to be in operation by the time this book is published. Several examples have been mentioned in earlier sections. In this section more examples are given to illustrate the possibilities.

17.6.1 The French Télématique Program

In 1975, France decided that its top national priority would be the modernization of its telecommunications facilities. Now known as the Télématique Program, the concept is based on transmission of all forms of information—oral, visual, and written—over a radically revamped telephone network. Gerard Thery, Director General of Telecommunications, notes: "The integrated services digital network must be able to meet all communications needs by use of a single line. The subscriber will only need to adapt his terminal equipment to his immediate purpose and the telephone network will be able to provide the requested service" [KEEN 80].

Six communications technologies are considered to be the primary elements of the Télématique network:

1. Digital transmission over all media
2. Optical-fiber transmission
3. Satellite communications
4. Digital SPC/TDM switching
5. New services, including data transmission
6. Application of computers and microprocessors to all network functions.

Great progress has been achieved in each field, in both the backbone and local distribution areas, with substantial gains in network capacity as well as quality. New services available include TRANSPAC, the national public packet-switched data service, which is the outgrowth of the earlier CNET[15] experimental network. Antiope, an enhanced teletext service, commenced trial service in 1980, while videotex service, Teletel, is to become generally available in 1981.

The unique, and perhaps most interesting, aspect of the Télématique program is

---

[15]Centre National d'Études des Telecommunications is the national telecommunications research organization.

the simultaneous concentration on development of terminal equipment complementing the planned services. These are outlined below.

Electronic Telephone Directory

The cost of directory services—publishing and delivering directories, and information operators—is rising rapidly. The French feel that in the long run it will be less expensive to give away CRT terminals, which can access a constantly updated directory data base. Integrated modems send data at 756 bps and receive at 1200 bps. Four manufacturers are in the final stages of design: it is expected that production will reach 800,000 in 1983, and that 30 million terminals will be in place by 1992. The projected cost of a stand-alone directory terminal is $75 to $100 each; one model with an integrated digital telephone set should cost only slightly more [CASW 80].

Equipped with a 20-cm diagonal monochrome CRT screen and an alphanumeric keyboard, the electronic directory terminal is actually a conventional mini-CRT interactive that can also be used for other services, such as Antiope, Teletex, and direct computer access. The result is a clever solution to the problem of equipping a sufficient number of subscribers to make new services worthwhile; in this case, an economic justification has been made for a mass giveaway to the general public.

Mass Fax

A consumer facsimile (Fax) terminal complements the Telefax service launched in 1978. Based on Group II machines (see Chap. 18), the mass fax unit can transmit and receive documents up to 21×20.7 cm in times ranging between 40 sec and 2 min, and can also be operated as a simple photocopier. With a target price of about $500, France has projected that 10 to 15 million units will be in homes and businesses by the early 1990s. When operated in conjunction with the mini-CRT terminal, hard copies can be made of material received via the videotex networks.

Telewriter

Another product associated with the early stages of the Télématique program is a telewriter that permits the real-time transmission of written or drawn material. The telewriter is based on a pressure-sensitive graphic tablet that is responsive to manuscript or sketches. Initial versions will transmit and receive in a restricted portion of the analog audio bandwidth, permitting simultaneous voice and telewriter transmission—an example of the "data in voice" technique of Sec. 17.5.3.3.

Video Telephone

Over 100 subscribers in four cities are involved in an experimental network which provides slow-scan video in conjunction with the conventional audio transmission.

The Télématique program is a bold and massive venture, and is clearly leading the way in one approach to integrated services networks. There are many doubters; nevertheless, the plan is on schedule and it appears that the price targets can be met. Can 50 million Frenchmen be wrong?

	Form of telecommunication	Flow of information	Network	Output on
Text	Communication typewriter	Dialog	Data-or-Telephone	Paper (P)
	Video text	Distribution	TV- OR CATV-	Screen (S)
	View data (Bildschirmtext)	Retrieval	Telephone-	S
Still picture	Facsimile	Subscrib. to Subscriber	Telephone- or data-	P
	Facsimile newspaper	Distribution	Telephone-or CATV-	P
	Video- still picture	Retrieval	CATV-	S
	Slow-scan TV	Retrieval	Telephone-	S
	Electronic mail	Subscrib. to Subscriber	Telephone- or data	P
Tele-metering	Remote control	Center to subscrib.	Telephone-, data-or CATV-	Remote control equipment
	Remote metering	Collection		

● Center   ○ Subscriber

Figure 17.25. New forms of telecommunications in existing networks in Germany. [KAIS 1979], © 1979 IEEE.

17.6.2 The German Network Services and Plans

In the Federal Republic of Germany, the Bundespost (administration for postal, telephone, and telegraph services) is implementing new services on its telephone network and on the Integrated Digital Network (IDN). IDN is the public switched data network that offers transmission rates from 50 bps to 48 kbps; connections are presently circuit switched, but a packet mode for data is planned. The variety of data rates should be helpful for the introduction of a variety of services.

Among the advanced services planned for early implementation by the Bundespost is Teletex, defined by the CCITT as the provision of communication between terminals used for the preparation, editing and printing of correspondence.[16] Information is transferred on a memory-to-memory basis. Teletex can be viewed as a form of electronic mail, or as an enhanced, higher-speed (2400 bps) version of Telex, the international telegraph service for alphanumeric text. Manipulation of information by word processing functions is implied.

The "Commission on the Future of Telecommunications" (KtK) has discussed new forms of telecommunication in the telephone, data, and CATV networks. These are shown in Fig. 17.25.

17.6.2.1 Hard-Copy Communication

Telefax service with Group II machines (see Chap. 18) was introduced in 1979 on the existing telephone network. Its typical transmission rate of three minutes per page is suitable for many purposes, and further standardization efforts will probably

---

[16]See CCITT Recommendations F. 200, S.60–62, S.70.

334

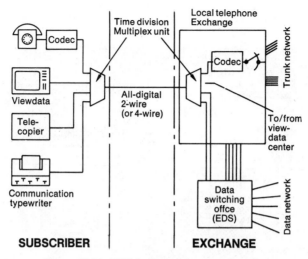

Figure 17.26. PBX facilitated integrated services.

result in more of the approximately 4000 facsimile sets in Germany [KAIS 79] being on a common service.

Higher transmission speeds of textual pages, and of course additional advantages based on the features of its associated (micro)processor, can be achieved with a communicating typewriter. In Germany, a standard transmission speed of 2400 bps has been selected, which allows transmission of an average page in ⅛ min. Other standards will be established before the service is promoted.

Combination of Telefax and communicating typewriters could provide a form of electronic mail. However, equipment that is expensive relative to the telephone handset would be needed, thus limiting most initial uses to interoffice communications.

17.6.2.2 Video Communication

The Bundespost's videotex service, Bildschirmtext, is very similar to the British Viewdata. It works over an unmodified telephone network or a CATV network to access data banks of text. An attachment is required to the television set to display the text pages and still-frame pictures, and a modem is needed to convert the signals sent through the telephone handset. A subscriber requests a particular page using a telephone handset or a keypad. The response page is returned over the telephone or cable network and displayed on a television set.

The videotex service can be provided together with telephone, Telefax, and other services, as shown in Fig. 17.26. The entire EXCHANGE side might be replaced eventually by an integrated services digital network.

17.6.2.3 The Japanese Information Network System

The Nippon Telegraph and Telephone Public Corporation is planning a nationwide integrated services digital network called the Information Network System (INS) [CCIT 82A]. INS will combine the public switched digital network, information processing centers, and customer premises equipment. Transmission between switching centers will utilize optical-fiber and coaxial cables, microwave, and

Figure 17.27. Configuration of teleconferencing via satellite transmission. [Courtesy of American Satellite Company.]

satellite links. At the local level, subscribers having light traffic requirements will be connected by wireless, while those having heavy traffic requirements will be provided with optical-fiber cables.

Services will be oriented to business, government, and individual home subscribers. Among the all-digital services planned are enhanced telephone, Centrex, low-cost facsimile, high-speed facsimile, circuit- and packet-switched data network, video transmission, video teleconferencing, still video, teleprocessing, Teletex, Videotex (the CAPTAIN system), telewriting, and various processing services such as speed, code, and mode conversion.

Construction of a pilot project in Musashino/Mitaka, a suburb of Tokyo, began in 1982, with services commencing in 1984. About 2,000 selected customers will be provided with telephone sets and various nonvoice terminals [KAPL 84, KUWA 84].

17.6.3   Teleconferencing

The purpose of teleconferencing is to allow two or more people to work together when they are geographically separated. Until very recently, teleconferencing has been restricted almost entirely to audio communication by "conference call" or meetings surrounding special equipment such as Speakerphones. The advent of special terminal equipment and availability of wideband communication channels, however, has led to enhanced teleconferencing techniques such as those shown in Fig.

17.27, including free-frame video. digitized voice, facsimile, and computer terminals. Thus teleconferencing is a specialized but obvious example of integrated services.

In 1978, business travel expenses in the United States totaled $21 billion. It has been estimated that 30% of this national annual expenditure could be saved by substituting teleconferencing. Thus a potential cost avoidance of $6.3 billion exists, against which teleconferencing equipment and transmission costs of $1.8 billion are

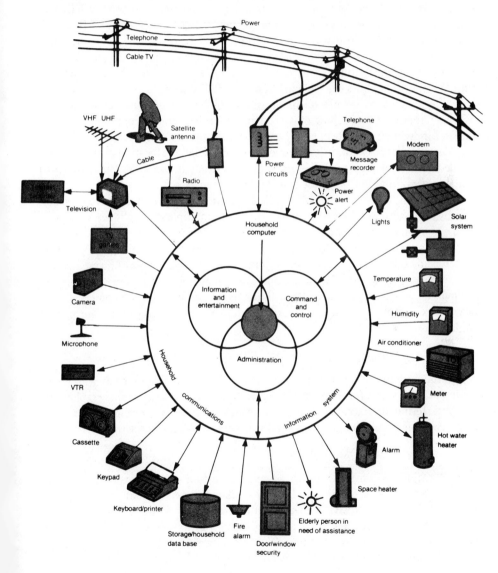

Figure 17.28. A "Total Household Communications/Information System." [CARN 1979], © 1979 IEEE.

estimated, giving a potential savings of $4.5 billion. At the same time, it is estimated that 4 to 5% of this country's petroleum requirements would be saved [SONN 80].

17.6.3.1   Audio Conferencing

At the simplest level of teleconferencing, any telephone subscriber can request that a conference call be set up by a telephone operator. Theoretically, up to 58 subscribers could be bridged; the time required by the operator to manually dial each conference, however, leads to a typical limit of five. Subscribers served by SPC central offices can establish a three-way call unassisted. Private firms such as Darome, Inc., offer "meet-me bridges," special equipment that can interconnect 20 or more lines; a participant wishing to join a conference dials a predetermined number at an agreed time. Similar capabilities are included in recent PBX designs.

Even with conventional telephone-grade voice circuits, it has been found that "subconferences," the grouping of participants at each location as opposed to isolating each individual with a telephone handset, makes for more effective teleconferencing. The presence of two or more people at each participating location provides a less sterile environment and facilitates interaction not only between the "subconferees" but also seems to stimulate a sense of meeting between the remote groups. Equipment to facilitate this procedure includes the Bell System's Speakerphone. More sophisticated station apparatus are appearing, some with multiple microphones and loudspeakers intended for permanent installation in conference rooms.

An advantage of audio conferencing is its low cost compared with other conferencing options; however, it does have disadvantages. Recognizing who is the speaker, establishing speaking order, and even following what is being said can be difficult. Some systems do have identification lights. Many audio conferences would be greatly enhanced if exchange of written or drawn material was possible during the conference.

17.6.3.2.   Audiography

Audiographic teleconferences combine some form of image display with voice conferencing. Typical forms are facsimile, electronic blackboards, graphic tablets, or computer terminals. Facsimile with slow transmission speed is often unacceptable for conferences: facsimile does not provide for spontaneous and interactive exchange.

17.6.3.3   Video Conferencing

A major experiment in advanced communication applications called Project Prelude was conducted in 1977 and 1978 by Satellite Business Systems in conjunction with NASA [RUSH 78A,B]. A major part of the experiment dealt with teleconferencing. Enhanced teleconferencing facilities were set up at several sites of the participating host companies (Montgomery Ward, Rockwell International, and Texaco). The following equipment was used:

- Computers providing data entry/retrieval and word-processing functions
- Large-screen color television projector

- Color video monitors (25-inch)
- Color television cameras
- Full-motion and freeze-frame video transmission devices
- High-speed (20 seconds per page) fascimile
- High-quality (100 Hz to 10 kHz) audio equipment
- Intelligent communicating alphanumeric data terminals.

Transmission between sites was accomplished via the United States/Canadian Communications.

Among the key conclusions relevant to teleconferencing were these [RUSH 78A,B]:

1. Teleconferencing as demonstrated is often an acceptable, and in many cases a preferable, substitute for face-to-face conferences.
2. Motivation to use teleconferencing flows from a need to increase responsiveness—saving time, not just money.
3. Business managers today have little understanding of new communication tools and techniques, but have the ability to perceive their uses rapidly, once they have an understanding of what is involved.
4. While freeze-frame video is acceptable for a high percentage of teleconferences, full-motion video is required for some sessions.

The last point is particularly important to the design of teleconferencing facilities, because by far the largest demand for bandwidth comes from full-motion video. Freeze-frame video, the display of slowly scanned television pictures, requires much less bandwidth and can be made compatible with transmission rates ranging from 56 kbps to 1.5 Mbps. During the Project Prelude experiments, the question was asked: "If only freeze-frame (video) were available, would the proportion of meetings susceptible to teleconferencing stay the same, or decrease to zero?" Over 33% of the evaluators responded "stay the same"; 60% said it would have some impact; and 7% responded "decrease to zero."

Other studies confirm suggestions that full-motion video adds marginal benefit to most teleconferencing situations as compared with freeze-frame video [STAM 80], although Project Prelude offers the general conclusion that visual contact of some sort is an essential ingredient. However, some companies, such as Westinghouse and Sperry Univac, who have had considerable experience with teleconferencing, feel that freeze-frame video is suitable only for workaday purposes; for meetings at middle- and upper-management levels, full-motion video is believed to be essential [PERH 81].

Video conferencing is unquestionably much more expensive than audio conferencing even when audio is augmented with some image exchange. Flipcharts and slides (which fit naturally in the freeze-frame video mode) were held by most respondents to be particularly important to successful teleconferencing. Following next in importance were pictures of the remote participants.

The future of teleconferencing appears to be very bright, as the major advantages are more generally realized by business, government, and other organizations. The impact on telecommunications will be large. It has been projected that the demand for satellite circuits to support two-way video teleconferencing will rise from near zero in 1980 to over 30,000 by 1990 [STAM 80]. An overview of products and services, and surveys of technique preferences by users, can be found in [SONN 80]. The advantages and disadvantages of the various approaches to teleconferencing are considered in [JOHA 79], while some users' experiences with early systems and future plans are reported in [PERH 81].

17.6.4 Home Communications

Although office communication functions might be integrated earlier or involve more forms of communication, home communication functions will certainly be increasingly integrated and the number of homes involved will grow, abetted by the explosive growth in numbers of personal computers [EDLI82]. Many education, information, and entertainment applications mentioned in Sec. 17.1 fit particularly well at home. The potential exists for allowing more people to work at home; the confines of offices are extended by communication networks. In effect, each home ultimately might be a teleconference center.

Potential exists for unwanted interference and control from outside the home, but potential also exists for many benefits. Energy savings, safety, and pleasure are among these. A total household communication system is shown in Figure 17.28. Some enterprising people already are using personal computers to put their own homes in a similar picture.

17.7 INTEGRATED SERVICES DIGITAL NETWORKS (ISDN)

World-wide activities in planning Integrated Services Digital Networks (ISDN) have intensified. As observed in the Introduction, ISDN activities are dominated by the

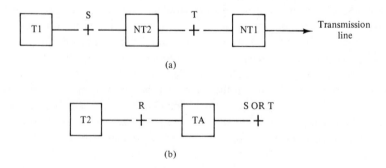

Figure 17.29

administrators of public telephone systems; consequently, the concept of ISDN has taken on a strong orientation to classical telephony.

Generally, ISDNs are viewed as evolving from Integrated Digital Networks (IDN), the name adopted by the world's telephone administrators[17] for the integration of digital transmission and switching in their telephone networks. It should be noted that "integrated' carries different meanings in the two acronymns—that which is integrated in an ISDN is a variety of services and their differing communication formats, while that which is integrated in an IDN is the technologies of the underlying transport system (see Secs. 17.3 and 17.4) [KOST 84].

There is as yet no generally agreed, specific definition of an ISDN. The CCITT offers[18], "an integrated digital network in which the same digital switches and digital paths are used to establish connections for digital services, for example, telephone, data, etc."—a rather vague definition clearly reflecting the telephone orientation of its protagonists. Another view [PICK 82A] attempts to establish the essential, user-oriented attributes of an ISDN:

- *Digital* (inherent in the name)
- *Wideband* (a minimum data rate of 56 kbps, in deference to near-term telephone network constraints)
- *Two-way* (eliminating some restrictive simplex technologies)
- *Ubiquitous* (at least relative to the intended subscriber/set)

To this should be added: *Transparency* (to any format required for any service). Even within this framework, many disparate opinions exist concerning the nature and scope of ISDN.

For example, will there be a single, worldwide ISDN much like the existing global telephone system, through which one can access any other subscriber (or service provider) without any constraint of location, service format, etc.? Or, will there be a large number of sub-subnetworks, with varying degrees of dedication, interconnectivity, service offerings, etc.? Will the providers of services be distinct from the providers of the communications facilities? Such issues and the driving forces behind them are an exceedingly complex mixture of technology, economics, and national policies and governance. Some of them have been discussed earlier in this chapter; some further illumination can be found in [ANDR 81, ANDR 84, BROW 84, DEHA 82, DORR 81, FRAN 84, ICC 81, IRME 82, MARS 82[19], PICK 82B and SPEC 82].

A recent survey [CCIT 82B] of the 14 nations' plans for ISDN reveals some

---

[17]"Administrators" is used here, somewhat loosely, to refer to the owners, operators or those who otherwise control the various public telephone systems throughout the world. In most nations, there exists a single telephone and telegraph administration that is an agency of the government. Notable exceptions are the United States, Canada, and (very recently) the United Kingdom, where a multiplicity of private organizations exist.

[18]CCITT Recommendation G.705

[19][MARS 82] is exceptional in that it contains both a detailed view of ISDN development in the U.S. and an extensive bibliography.

distinctly different positions regarding the timing of ISDN developments, tariffing issues, and degree of service integration. Some general conclusions are that:

- Prospective introduction of ISDN in two or three major cities in a nation will occur as early as 1984, and as late as 1990.
- Penetration to half of the country may be realized between 1995 and 2010; while almost all nations do not expect complete implementation before 2020.
- Most nations do not plan for integration of packet-switched and wide-band networks in the initial stage of ISDN.
- Pilot schemes are already under way, or planned for no later than 1984, in the majority of nations (some of these are described in Secs. 17.2.2 and 17.6.2).

17.7.1 ISDN Standards Activities

In recognition of rapid technological advances and the increasing importance of services other than conventional telephony, it has been proposed within the CCITT to revise the definition of ISDN to "a network evolved from the telephony IDN that provides end-to-end digital connections to suggest a wide range of services, including voice and non-voice services, to which users have access by a limited set of standard multi-purpose customer interfaces" [IRME 82]. Study Group XVIII has been concentrating on the aspect of access and interfaces, and has produced three draft recommendations [(DEHA 82, COLL 83]).

Draft Recommendation I.xxw deals broadly with the general principles of user-network interfaces. It states that these interfaces should be standardized and multipurpose, allowing connection of different types of (globally portable) terminals and other networks (public or private). Among the interface characteristics should be provisions for multi-drop connections and user selection of bit rate, switching node, coding method, compatibility negotiation with a called terminal, etc. These characteristics would be defined by a modular approach based on the ISO Open Systems Interconnection (OSI) Reference Model.

Draft Recommendation I.411 groups the interface functions and provides their reference points. The latter are the conceptual points that partition the functional groupings, and do not necessarily correspond to physical interfaces. The general user-network interface, shown in Fig. 17.29(a), can be interpreted with respect to the following definitions:

T1   Type 1 Terminal, an ISDN-compatible terminal supporting one or more ISDN services and complying with ISDN specifications

NT1   Network Termination 1, broadly implementing the Physical Layer of the OSI Reference Model. NT1 provides the physical and electrical termination of the transmission line to the network, and may include functions such as timing, power feeding, timing, multiplexing, and line maintenance (e.g., test loopbacks)

NT2   Network Termination 2, may include functions relating to the lowest three layers of the OSI Reference Model, including additional Physical Layer Functions not allocated to NT1. Enhanced functions relating to the Data Link and Network layers are contained in NT2, which would support Local Area Networks, PBX's, and terminal controllers.

Reference Point T would serve as the connection point for individual, dedicated terminal equipment designed for ISDN. To accommodate the notion of universal portability expressed in the proposed new definition, such terminals must also be capable of interconnection with Reference Point 5. This requires that the physical and electrical characteristics of S and T be the same.

Connection of a terminal not compatible with ISDN (but complying with other recommendations such as the X-series) is accomplished as in Fig. 17.29 (b). The physical interface is at Reference Point R. TA is a Terminal Adapter providing the functions necessary for ISDN interface at either points S or T of Fig. 17.29 (a). Note that, if TA is made an integral (perhaps modular) part of a T2, then that terminal becomes a T1.

Draft Recommendation I.412 User-Network Interface Channel Structure and Access Capabilities, specifies the various channel types and their data rates. These channels are summarized as follows:

B-Channel.   A completely transparent digital channel operating at 64 kbps. A B-channel can carry any ISDN service node, not necessarily limited to a single type or a given call. Types operating at a lower data rate (e.g., 32 kbps CVSD voice) would be up-converted to the standard 64 kbps.

D-channel.   A channel used to carry network signaling information, telemetry and packet-switched data. D-channel uses LAPD, a frame-oriented link access procedure similar to LAPB of X.25.

C-channel.   A hybrid channel that could carry analog or digital information, the latter similar to the D-channel. The C-channel would be used, for example, during the transition to full digital access to ISDN. The associated digital channel is specified to operate at 8 or 16 kbps.

The *Basic Channel Structure* of ISDN access comprises two B-channels and one D-channel; *viz.*, 2B+D, where the D-channel bit rate is 16 kbps. The interfaces are presumed to always have a 2B+D structure; however, one or both B-channels may not be supported by the network; i.e., user access capabilities may be 2B+D, B+D or D alone. Where two B-channels are supported, operation of each is independent of the other. The last situation is to be preferred, because full-duplex operation at 64 Kbps plus out-of-band signalling would be supported.

A *Primary Channel Structure* has been defined as mB+D, where D is 64 kbps. The quantity m would be 23 for those networks using the North American multiplex heirarchy (see Chap. 5) based on 1.544 Mbps channels; m=30 for those networks using the CEPT or Japanese standard rate of 2.044 Mbps. The possibilities of providing intermediate rates, and higher rates for wideband services such as video, are under further study.

17.7.2 ISDN Services: Videotex

The previously-mentioned ISDN survey reveals some significant disagreements among nations regarding services to be offered. The majority foresee the eventual integration of all conceivable services, although some place the integration of services requiring very wideband facilities, such as video applications and high speed/high volume data transfer, as a distant future happening. One nation adopted the rather unique position that very few services are to be integrated in ISDN *per se*; rather, such services as message switching and information retrieval would be provided by specialized computers attached to, and accessible through, the ISDN.[20]

The survey indicates a broad agreement on the following ISDN services:

Telephony
Circuit-switched data
Packet-switched data
Teletex (see Sec. 17.6.2.)
Videotex
Slow-scan TV
Leased circuits
Facsimile
Message switching
Telemetry
Electronic funds transfer
Information retrieval
Mailbox
Electronic mail
Alarms
Telecontrol
Enhanced network services
Text communication for the handicapped.

[20]It is interesting to note that the latter view, although expressed by a nation other than the U.S., implies a concept of separation of content and conduit—a major issue in the restructuring of U.S. telecommunications policy. The sociological and economic ramifications are being recognized on a broader scale.

Some of these services are already available in various forms through the existing analog telephone networks, by use of compatible modems and protocol interface devices, or by access to data networks (which largely depend on the analog local loops of the telephone networks). These have been discussed in prospect and by example in the earlier sections of this chapter.

17.7.2.1   Videotex Techniques

One wholly new service is Videotex, the generic name for a service provided to subscribers having a keyboard and display terminal by which alphanumeric text and graphics information may be exchanged. The basic service is interactive information retrieval from remote data bases; however, the specific service applications can be very broad, including games and entertainment, transactions of all types such as home banking, electronic mail, time-shared data processing, etc. [TYDE 82]. Thus, Videotex may be more broadly viewed as a format for the delivery of many of the specific services foreseen for ISDN.

The first commercial development of Videotex took place in the United Kingdom in the late 1970's. Originally called Viewdata, it is now known as Prestel. Subsequently, intensive development of alternative systems has occurred in France (Antiope), Canada (Telidon), Japan (Captain) and the United States (NAPLP). In their original forms, each system was substantially different [SPEC 79, CLAR 82].

Alphamosaic Systems

The original Viewdata/Prestel approach was intended to be a simple, thus potentially low cost, modular applique to a conventional home TV receiver. The applique comprised a keypad, a 300 bps modem for attachment to a telephone line and a buffer/character generator that could display 24 x 40 characters on the TV screen. In addition to an alphanumeric character set based on ASCII, the TV screens could display graphics by using alphamosaics—a technique that divides the space normally occupied by an alphanumeric symbol into a mosaic of cells, each of which can be "illuminated" or "not illuminated" in accordance with a predefined mapping of the cell pattern. With Prestel, the mosaic was made up of two horizontal and three vertical cells. Each defined mosaic, along with presentation control information such as color, graphics mode and other attributes, were coded along with the alphanumerics as an extended set of an eight-bit character code, of which a fixed number were assigned to the memory for each display line. Thus, each symbol could either display a symbol, or contain attribute information, but not both. This technique became known as "serial attributes," the simplicity of which limited the flexibility and resolution of screen displays.

The French Teletel system, subsequently merged with the Antiope teletext technique, associated an additional 8 data bits (total of 16) with each screen symbol position. By allowing 8 bits to define the symbol (character or mosaic) and an additional 8 bits for the attributes, the resultant "parallel attributes" scheme allowed much greater flexibility in the screen display in exchange for increased decoder complexity and more stringent demands on the transmission medium. An important advantage was the ability to extend the character set to include accent and diacritical marks as in French.

More recently, a new European Videotex standard has been defined by the Council of European Posts and Telephones (CEPT) that increases the transmission rate to 1200 bps and accommodates extension of both Prestel and Antiope [HUDS 83]. One of the most important of these extensions is the technique of "dynamically redefinable character sets" (DRCS), by which additional display flexibility (including use of non-Roman alphanumerics) can be achieved.

Alphageometric Systems

Alphageometric coding, widely known in the field of computer graphics, can create high-resolution graphics. The display screen can be treated as a bit map, displaying combinations of shapes such as arcs and rectangles. The descriptions and coordinates of these shapes are encoded and transmitted in Cartesian and/or conic form. For example, a circle is transmitted by the definition of its radius and the coordinates of its center. The application of alphageometrics to Videotex was first achieved in the Canadian Telidon system, and results in a very high-quality display. Of course, the decoder complexity is accordingly greater, but resolution can be a variable subject to tradeoff with cost.

In 1981, AT&T proposed a U.S. Videotex standard based on the application of Telidon alphageometric techniques to the principles of the ISO open-system interconnect (OSI) reference model's Presentation Level. The resultant Presentation Level Protocol (PLP) has received support from a number of broadcasters and manufacturers, and has been proposed by both the American National Standard Institute (ANSI) and the Canadian Standards Association (CSA) as a common North American standard (hence, NAPLP).

NAPLP provides an extended code sit by using, when necessary, more than one octet (8-bit character) to describe a graphics instruction [FLEM83A and 83B]. The extended code-set tables are known as *C-sets*, for control information; and *G-sets*, for text and graphics information. Six G-sets are currently defined:

- Primary Character Set, comprising essentially the ASC II character set.
- Supplemental Character Set, containing international text characters and symbols.
- Mosaics, containing block-type alpha symbols familiar to users of microcomputers.
- Picture Description Instruction Set, containing alpha-geometric primitives such as "line," "arc" and "polygon."
- Macro Set, in which more complex pixel mapping can be defined.
- Dynamically Redefinable Character Set, a blank table that can be filled with symbols; for example, combination of the above.

The power and flexibility of NAPLPS is such that several microcomputer graphics programs based on the protocol have recently appeared [LAX 83].

Picture Systems

In Japan, none of the preceding techniques has been found satisfactory for the generation of the 3000 Kanji idiographic characters used in its printed language. To provide for the necessary detail, the Japanese Videotex system uses literal picture coding and compression techniques similar to those described in Chap. 18 for facsimile. Called CAPTAIN (for Character and Pattern Telephone Access Information Network), the system also provides for a graphic capability comparable with Telidon and NAPLP.

In the quest for higher-quality Videotex displays, others have also experimented with photographic techniques. For example, a further extension of Prestel allows the presentation of still pictures as part of the screen display by using advanced forms of picture data compression techniques (see Ch. 18). The most useful appears to be transform coding, by which the initial image is presented at a speed equal to that of a normal Videotex screen; advantage is taken of continued display (and transmission) time to build up the picture detail by capturing additional transmitted information.

17.7.2.2   Market Implications

Videotex is seen by some [e.g., MARS 82, HIND 82, HARR 83] as the most important of the new services to be offered by ISDN. It has certainly most captured the imagination of people following development in the services area.

It is not yet clear, however, just what Videotex is. As mentioned in the preceding section, Videotex was originally conceived as a means of providing a user-friendly, interactive information retrieval service, to be universally and inexpensively available to anyone equipped with a telephone and a television set. Subsequent developments raise important questions about so simple a view [HIND 82A, 82B, TYDE 82, MILL 83, MCQU 84].

For example, a mass market depends on the existence of universal standards, and the availability and costs of associated terminal equipment and service access. The developments in ISDN *per se* only partially help in these regards. The technological trends of Videotex developments portend the existence of at least three potentially incompatible worldwide standards. At the same time, the complexity of the respective designs is increasing, which implies higher costs in the production and delivery of Videotex information, as well as in the user's terminal equipment.

This state of affairs is by no means solely due to technological tinkering—"It's possible, so let's do it." Many of those concerned with the market potential believe that the quality of early Videotex graphics was insufficient to present, for example, effective advertising or displays for "shop-at-home" service. Others have felt that such features as hierarchical menu selection and text formats were inadequate for utilization by businesses. More recently, it has been questioned whether a simple mass-oriented keyboard/television set terminal setup is the right focus, in view of burgeoning personal computer sales [DAVI 82].

A logical extension of the last thought is that perhaps Videotex should not be thought of as the only way which information is created, stored, retrieved, and presented. The many existing and sophisticated information banks, accessible directly or through networks such as the Source and Compuserve, will undoubtedly continue to exist for quite some time, possibly moving in a direction more closely matching the needs of specialized subsets of subscribers and incorporating some forms of graphics capabilities.

The questions now being raised, however, do require those seeking success in Videotex to rethink the concepts of Videotex along several dimensions. Technologically, it must be viewed in the broadest sense as a communication service and a database as well as a vehicle for presentation. As a market, several tiers or categories of subscribers, each with different characteristics, will evolve. Institutionally, the roles of the information creator, the information provider, and the information mover must be clarified [PICK 82B]. This most exciting example of ISDN service is a complex issue, indeed [PICK 84, POKR 84, TYDE 82].

REFERENCES

ALLA 79   Allan, R., "Digital Telephony Slowly Taking Over," *IEEE Spectrum,* October 1979, p. 56.

ALLA 81   Allan, R., Commun. ed., "Local Net Architecture, Protocol Issues Heating Up," *Electron. Des.,* Vol. 29, No. 8, p. 93.

ANDR 81   Andrews, F. T., Jr., "Meeting Report, ISDN '81," *IEEE Communications Magazine,* July 1981, pp. 41–43.

ANDR 84   Andrews, F. T., Jr., "The ISDN '83 Symposium," *Journal Telecomm. Networks,* Spring 1984.

ARTH 79   Arthurs, B., and W. Stuck, "A Theoretical Performance Analysis of an Integrated Voice-Data Virtual Circuit Packet Switch," *Int. Conf. Commun.,* June 1979, pp. 24.2.1–24.2.3.

BACH 79   Bach, G. G. F., "International Data Flow and Protection Regulations," *Telecommunications,* May 1979, pp. 89–92.

BARN 78   Barna, B., "A New Threat to Multinationals," *Computer Decisions,* August 1978, pp. 34–38.

BHUS 84   Bhusri, G. S., "Considerations for ISDN Planning and Implementation," *IEEE Comm. Magazine,* January 1984, pp. 18–32.

BIAL 80   Bially, T., B. Gold, and S. Seneff, "A Technique for Adaptive Voice Flow Control in Integrated Packet Networks," *IEEE Trans. Commun.,* Vol. COM-28, No. 3, 1980, pp. 325–333.

BOWN 79   Bown, H. G., et al., "Telidon: A New Approach to Videotex System Design," *IEEE Trans. Consumer Electron.,* Vol. CE-25, July 1979, pp. 256–268.

BRAD 68   Brady, P. T., "A Statistical Analysis of On–Off Patterns in 16 Conversations," *Bell Syst. Tech. J.,* Vol. 47, No. 1, 1968, pp. 73–91.

BRAD 69   Brady, P. T., "A Model for Generating On–Off Patterns in Two-Way Conversations," *Bell Syst. Tech. J.,* Vol. 48, No. 7, September 1969, pp. 2445–2472.

BRAN 79   Branscomb, L. M., "Computing and Communications—A Perspective of the Evolving Environment," *IBM Syst. J.,* Vol. 18, No. 2, 1979, pp. 189–201.

BRIG 79   Bright, R. D., "Prestel—The World's First Public Viewdata System," *IEEE Trans. Consumer Electron.,* Vol. CE-25, July 1979, pp. 251–255.

BROA 80   "Broadband Coax Cable Communications Comes On Strong," *Electron. Products Mag.,* February 1980, pp. 25–26.

BROW 84   Brown, Charles L., "The Future of World-Wide Integrated Communications Networks and Services," *Journal Telecomm. Networks,* Spring 1984.

BULL 59   Bullington, K., and J. M. Fraser, "Engineering Aspects of TASI," *AIEE Trans. Part I Commun. Electron.,* Vol. 78, 1959, pp. 256–260.

CARN 79   Carne, E. B., "The Wired Household," *IEEE Spectrum,* October 1979, pp. 61–66.

CASW 80   Caswell, S. A., "France Launches Mini-CRT Campaign," *Mini-Micro Syst.,* November 1980, pp. 125–127.

CCIT 82A   "Pilot Scheme of Information Network Systems," CCITT Ad Hoc Group for Question 21/III, Information Paper, Geneva, 9 June 1982.

CCIT 82B   "Summary of Replies to Trial Questionnaire on the ISDN Development Plan," CCITT Ad Hoc Group for Question 21/III, Temporary Document No. 501-E, Geneva, 9 June 1982.

CEPT 82   CEPT Special Group on ISDN (GSI), *1982 Report on Integrated Services Digital Network Studies,* September 1982, Stockholm.

CHAN 76   Chang, K. W., "Transmission of Analog Video and Data Signals over Analog-Repeatered Coaxial Lines," *IEEE Trans. Commun.,* Vol. COM-24, No. 9, 1976, pp. 1008–1017.

CHAN 79   Chang, K. W., "Fiber Optic Integrated Distribution and Its Implications," *Int. Conf. Commun.,* June 1979, pp.10.1.1–10.1.6.

CHOU 79   Chouinard, P. H., M. Larose, F. M. Banks, and J. R. Barry, "Description and Performance Review of Yorkville Integrated Services Fiber Optic Trial," *Int. Conf. Commun.,* June 1979, pp. 28.3.1–28.3.8.

CLAI 79   Claire, E. J., "A Multiple Service Broadband System for the Existing Telephone Local Loop," *Int. Conf. Commun.,* June 1979, pp. 2.2.1–2.2.4.

CLAR 78   Clark, D. D., K. T. Pogran, and D. P. Reed, "Introduction to Local Area Networks," *Proc. IEEE,* Vol. 66, No. 11, 1978, pp. 1497–1517.

CLAR 82   Clarke, K. E., "Videotex Display Technology," *The Radio and Electronic Engineer,* February 1982, pp. 59–66.

COLL 83   Collie, B., L. Kaiser and A. Rybczynski, "Looking at the ISDN Interfaces: Issues and Answers," *Data Communications,* June 1983, pp. 125–136.

COVI 75   Coviello, G. J., and P. A. Vena, "Integration of Circuit/Packet Switching by a SENET (Slotted Envelope NETwork) Concept," *Natl. Telecommun. Conf.,* December 1975, pp. 42(12)–42(17).

COVI 77   Coviello, G. J., O. L. Lake, and G. R. Redinbo, "System Design Implications of Packetized Voice," *Int. Conf. Commun.,* 1977, pp. 38.3(49)–38.3(53).

COVI 79   Coviello, G. J., "Comparative Discussion of Circuit- vs. Packet-Switched Voice," *IEEE Trans. Commun.,* Vol. COM-27, No. 8, 1979, pp. 1153–1159.

DAVI 73   Davies, D., and D. Barker, *Communications Network for Computers,* Wiley, New York, 1973.

DAVI 78   Davis, G. R., and R. Sarch, "Seeds of Network Change Planted during Past Year," *Data Commun.,* December 1978, pp. 37–43.

DAVI 82   Davis, D. B., "U. S. Businesses Targeted as Major Videotex Market," *Mini-Micro Systems,* Sept. 1982, pp. 145–51.

DEHA 82   de Haas, T., "International Standardization and the ISDN," *Journal of Telecommunication Networks,* Vol. 1, No. 4, Winter 1982), pp. 333–340.

DEWI 79   DeWitt, R. G., "Emergence of the Integrated Services Digital Network," *Comput. Des.,* June 1979, pp. 14–28.

DINE 80   Dineson, M. A., and J. J. Picazo, "Broadband Technology Magnifies Local Networking Capability," *Data Commun.,* February 1980, pp. 61–79.

DMW 79   DMW Group, "Computerized PBX Key to Future Corporate Communications Networks," *Telecommunications,* November 1979, pp. 27, 58.

DOLL 78   Doll, D. R., *Data Communications: Facilities, Networks, and Systems Design,* Wiley, New York, 1978.

DORR 81   Dorros, I., "ISDN," *IEEE Communications Magazine,* March 1981, pp. 16–19.

DRAG 76   Drago, P. G., A. M. Molinari, and F. C. Vagliani, "Digital Dynamic Speech Detectors," *Natl. Telecommun. Conf.,* December 1976.

DUTT 76   Duttweiler, D. L., and D. G. Messerschmitt, "Nearly Instantaneous Companding for Nonuniformly Quantized PCM," *IEEE Trans. Commun.,* Vol. 24, No. 8, 1976, pp. 864–878.

DYSA 81   Dysart, H. G., M. J. Krone, and J. E. Fielding, "Integrated Voice/Data Private Network Planning," *Int. Conf. Commun.,* June 1981, pp. 4.2.1–4.2.5.

EDLI 82   Edlin, J., "A Tale of Two Cultures," *PC Magazine,* September 1982, p. 18.

EHLI 84   Ehlinger, J. C., and M. Neil Ransome, "Local Area Data Transport Service," *Journal Telecomm. Networks,* Spring 1984.

ELEC 81   *Electrical Communication,* Vol. 56, No. 1, 1981 (an issue devoted to ISDN, containing 10 articles on various aspects of the subject.)

ELIO 77   Elion, H. A., "Fiber Optic Communications Needs of Developing Countries," *Proc. INTELCOM 77,* Vol. 2, Atlanta, October 1977, pp. 645–649.

ELIO 78   Elion, G. R., and H. A. Elion, *Fiber Optics in Communications Systems,* Marcel Dekker, New York, 1978.

FCC 83   Federal Communications Commission, *Notice of Inquiry, Integrated Services Digital Networks,* Docket 83–373, August 10, 1983.

FLAN 79   Flanagan, J. L., M. R. Schroeder, B. S. Atal, R. E. Crochiere, N. S. Jayant, and J. M. Tribolet, "Speech Coding," *IEEE Trans. Commun.,* Vol. COM-27, No. 4, 1979, pp. 710–737.

FLEM 83A   Fleming, J., and W. Frezza, "NAPLPS: A New Standard for Text and Graphics," *Byte,* February 1983, pp. 203–254.

FLEM 83B   Fleming, J., "NAPLPS: A New Standard for Text and Graphics," *Byte,* March 1983, pp. 152–185.

FORG 77   Forgie, J. W., and A. G. Nemeth, "An Efficient Packetized Voice/Data

Network Using Statistical Flow Control," *Int. Conf. Commun.*, June 1977, pp. 38.2(44)–38.2(48).

FRAN 78 Frank, H., I. Gitman, and B. Occhiogrosso, "Packet-Switched Voice and Data Networks Advantages and Costs," *Telecommunications,* December 1978, pp. 23–30.

FRAN 79 Frank, H., and I. Gitman, "Study Shows Packet Switching Best for Voice Traffic, Too," *Data Commun.,* March 1979, pp. 43–62.

FRAN 84 Frank, Carl F., "Legal and Policy Ramifications of the Emerging Integrated Services Digital Network," *Journal Telecomm. Networks,* Spring 1984.

FRIS 77 Frisch, I. T., "Experiments on Random Access Packet Data Transmission on Coaxial Cable Video Transmission Systems," *IEEE Trans. Commun.,* Vol. COM-25, No. 10, 1977, pp. 1199–1203.

FUCH 70 Fuchs, E., and P. Jackson, "Estimate of Distributions of Random Variable for Certain Computer Communication Traffic Models," *Commun. ACM,* December 1970.

GERK 79 Gerke, P., and P. Bocker, "DTN, An All-Digital Telephony Network for Voice, Data, Text, and Fax Communication," *Int. Conf. Commun.,* June 1979, pp. 29.5.1–29.5.6.

GIES 84 Giesken, Kenneth F., "ISDN Features Require New Capabilities in Digital Switching Systems," *Journal Telecomm. Networks,* Spring 1984.

GITM 77 Gitman, I., H. Frank, B. Occhiogrosso, and W. Hsieh, "Issues in Integrated Network Design," *Int. Conf. Commun.,* June 1977, pp. 38.1(36)–38.1(43).

GITM 78 Gitman, I., and H. Frank, "Economic Analysis of Integrated Voice and Data Networks: A Case Study," *Proc. IEEE,* Vol. 66, No. 11, 1978, pp. 1549–1570.

GITM 79 Gitman, I., B. Occhiogrosso, W. Hsieh, and H. Frank, "Sensitivity of Integrated Voice and Data Networks to Design Variables," *Proc. 6th Data Commun. Symp. (Asilomar),* November 1979, pp. 181–192.

GOLD 77 Gold, B., "Digital Speech Networks," *Proc. IEEE,* Vol. 65, No. 12, 1977, pp. 1636–1658.

GTE 79 GTE Lenkurt, "CATV Part 1," *Demodulator,* July–August 1979, pp. 2–19.

HANS 81 Hanson, K., W. Chou, and A. Nilsson, "Integration of Voice, Data and Image Traffic on a Wideband Local Network," *Proceedings, Computer Networking Symposium,* December 8, 1981, Gaithersburg, MD., pp. 3–11.

HARR 80 Harrington, E. A., "Voice/Data Integration Using Circuit Switched Networks," *IEEE Trans. Commun.,* Vol. COM-28, No. 6, 1980, pp. 781–793.

HARR 83 Harris, M. A., "Is the Waiting Over for Videotex?" *Electronics,* July 14, 1983, pp. 108–109.

HASE 83 Haselton, E. Fletcher, "A PCM Frame Switching Concept Leading to Burst Switching Network Architecture," *IEEE Communications Magazine,* September 1983, pp. 13–19.

HATF 81 Hatfield, D., "Long-Haul Services Overshadow the Crucial Local Distribution Issues," *Commun. News,* February 1981, pp. 56–57.

HEBD 79 Hebditch, D., "Will Data Flow be Stemmed?" *Telecommunications,* May 1979, pp. 75–82.

HIND 82A   Hindin, H. J., "Videotex Seeks Its Market," *Electronics,* July 14, 1982, pp. 119–122.

HIND 82B   Hindin, H. J., "Videotex Looks Brighter As Developments Mount," *Electronics,* August 25, 1982, pp. 89–100.

HOPK 82   Hopkins, G. T., and N. B. Meisner, "Choosing Between Broadband and Bareband Local Networks," Mini-Micro Systems, June 1982, pp. 265–274.

HUDS 83   Hudson, G., "Prestel: The Basis of an Evolving Videotex System," *Byte,* July 1983, pp. 61–78.

HUGH 79   Hughes, J. W., "Videotex and Teletext Systems," *Comput. Des.,* October 1979, pp. 10–16.

ICC 81   A number of papers dealing with ISDN architectural issues, Session 19, *Int. Conf. Commun.,* Denver, June 1981.

IRME 82   Irmer, T., "The International Approach to the ISDN," *Telecomm. Journal,* Vol. 49, VII/1982, pp. 411–415.

JACK 69   Jackson, P., and C. Stubbs, "A Study of Multiaccess Computer Communications," *Proc. AFIPS Spring Joint Comput. Conf.,* 1969.

JAVE 84   Javetski, J., "Datacomm IC's Make Micros More Resourceful," *Electronic Products,* January 11, 1984, pp. 69–73.

JENN 76   Jenny, C. J., and K. Kummerle, "Distributed Processing within an Integrated Circuit/Packet Switching Node," *IEEE Trans. Commun.,* Vol. COM-24, No. 10, 1979, pp. 1089–1100.

JOEL 77   Joel, A. E., Jr., "What Is Telecommunications Circuit Switching?" *Proc. IEEE.,* Vol. 65, No. 9, 1977, pp. 1237–1253.

JOEL 79   Joel, A. E., Jr., "Digital Switching—How It Has Developed," *IEEE Trans. Commun.,* Vol COM-27, No. 7, 1979, pp. 948–959.

JOHA 79   Johansen, J. V., and K. Spangler, *Electronic Meltings: Technical Alternatives and Social Choices,* Addison-Wesley, Reading, Mass., 1979, Chaps. 2, 6.

KAIS 79   Kaiser, W. A., "New Services and Their Introduction into Existing Networks," *IEEE Commun. Mag.,* July 1979, pp. 4–12.

KAPL 84   Kaplan, Gadi, "Japan's Information Network System," *IEEE Spectrum,* May 1984, pp. 50–52.

KARP 82   Karp, P., and I. D. Socher, "Designing Local Area Networks," *Mini-Micro Systems,* April 1982, pp. 219–232.

KEEN 80   Keene, J. M. D., ed., "French Telecommunications: Digital Technology and the Télématique Program," Special Supplement to *Electron. News,* November 10, 1980; and *Sci. Am.,* September 1980, pp. 26–43.

KOST 84   Kostas, D. J., "Transition to ISDN—An Overview," *IEEE Comm. Magazine,* January 1984 pp. 11–17.

KOTE 82   Kotelly, G., "Local Area Networks: Part 1—Technology; Part 2—Low and Midrange Products; Part 3—High Performance Products," *EDN,* February 17, 1982, pp. 109–150.

KUMM 78   Kummerle, K., and H. Rudin, "Packet and Circuit Switching: Cost Performance Boundaries," *Comput. Networks,* Vol. 2, 1978, pp. 3–17.

KUWA 84   Kuwabara, Moriji, "Japan Tests Its Model Communications System," *IEEE Spectrum,* May 1984, pp. 53–56.

LAX 83   Lax, L., and M. Olsen, "NAPLS Standard Graphics and the Microcomputer," *Byte,* July 1983, pp. 82–92.

LEVY 82   Levy, W. A., and H. F. Mehl, "Local Area Networks: Searching for the Right Approach," *Mini-Micro Systems,* February 1982, pp. 227–242.

LICK 78   Licklider, J. C. R., and Albert Vezza, "Applications of Information Networks," *Proc. IEEE,* Vol. 66, No. 11, 1978, pp. 1330–1346.

LORI 79   Lorig, B., and J.-P. Dagnelie, "Teleboard System," *Int. Conf. Commun.,* June 1979, pp. 56.4.1–56.4.3.

LYGH 74   Lyghounis, E., I. Poretti, and G. Monti, "Speech Interpolation in Digital Transmission Systems," *IEEE Trans. Commun.,* Vol. COM-22, No. 9, 1974, pp. 1179–1189.

MAND 79   Mandey, T., "Accessing the New Services," *IEEE Spectrum,* October 1979, pp. 46–50.

MARS 82   Marsh, D. J., "ISDN Evolution Possibilities in the U.S.," *Journal of Telecommunication Networks,* Vol. 1, No. 2, Summer 1982, pp. 107–125.

MART 72   Martin, J., *Systems Analysis for Data Transmission,* Prentice-Hall, Englewood Cliffs, N.J., 1972.

MART 76   Martin, J., *Telecommunications and the Computer,* 2nd ed., Prentice-Hall, Englewood Cliffs, N.J., 1976.

MART 77   Martin, J., *Future Developments in Telecommunications,* 2nd ed., Prentice-Hall, Englewood Cliffs, N.J., 1977.

MCQU 84   McQueen, John C., and F. Brown Whittington, "Videotex Field Trials: Implications for the Future," *Journal of Telecomm. Networks,* Spring 1984.

MIER 82   Mier, E., "Competitors Fear AT&T's New $1 Billion Scheme," *Data Communications,* December 1982 pp. 39–42.

MILE 79   Miles, D. B., "Telecom and Data Com—Merging," *Telecommunications,* July 1979, pp. 23–26.

MILL 83   Miller, D., "Videotex: Science Fiction or Reality?," *Byte,* July 1983, pp. 42–56.

MIYA 78   Miyahara, H., Y. Teshigawara, and T. Hasegawa, "Delay and Throughput Evaluation of Switching Methods in Computer Communication Networks," *IEEE Trans. Commun.,* Vol. COM-26, No. 3, 1978, pp. 337–344.

MIYA 79   Miyahara, H., and T. Hasegawa, "Performance Evaluation of Modified Multiplexing Technique with Two Types of Packet for Circuit and Packet Switched Traffic," *Int. Conf. Commun.,* June 1979, pp. 20.5.1–20.5.5.

MOSE 82   Moses, D., "Spread Spectrum: The Technology," *Telephone Engineering & Management,* June 1, 1982.

MOWA 79   Mowafi, O. A., and W. J. Kelly, "Integrated Voice/Data Packet Switching Techniques for Future Military Networks," *Comput. Networks Symp.,* December 1979, pp. 216–223.

MUSG 80   Musgrave, B., "Coaxing on Coax," *Datamation,* Special Issue, 1980, pp. 40–44.

NAC 77   Network Analysis Corporation, Eighth Semiannual Technical Report for the Project "Integrated DOD Voice and Data Networks and Ground Packet Radio Technology," March 1977, 4 vols.

NARR 81   Narrod, D., "Dow Jones Markets 2–Way Info Service," *Multichannel News,*

June 8, 1981, p. 7.

NOIR 78 Noirel, Y., "DIDON, The Experimental Data Packet Broadcasting System of the French Administration," *Int. Conf. Comput. Commun.,* September 1978, pp. 631–636.

ONEI 59 O'Neill, E. F., "TASI," *Bell Lab. Rec.,* Vol. 37, No. 3, 1959, pp. 83–87.

ORBE 79 Orbell, A. G., "Preparing for Evolution toward an Integrated Digital Services Network," *Int. Conf. Commun.,* June 1979, pp. 29.1.1–29.1.6.

OST 82 "Bibliography of Documents on the Integrated Services Digital Network (ISDN)," Office of Science and Technology (FCC), OST Bulletin No. 57, August 1982 (available from Copy Center, 1114 21st St., N.W., Washington, D.C. 20036.)

PANT 78 Pantages, A., "Canada's Economic Concerns," *Datamation,* November 1978, pp. 67–75.

PBXC 80 "PBX Competition Drives Development of More Advanced Features for Users," *Commun. News,* July 1980, pp. 48–50.

PERH 81 Perham, J., "Business' New Communications Tool," *Dun's Rev.,* February 1981, pp. 80–82.

PERR 80 Perry, T. S., "NTIA: A Small Agency Tackles Large Issues," *IEEE Spectrum,* December 1980, pp. 60–62.

PICK 82A Pickens, R. A., "Integrated Service Digital Networks: The Time Has Come," *Journal of Telecommunication Networks,* Vol. 1, No. 1, Spring 1982, pp. 82–83.

PICK 82B Pickens, R. A., "ISDN—An International Affair," *Journal of Telecommunication Networks,* Vol. 1, No. 2, Summer 1982, pp. 191–192.

PICK 84 Pickens, R. Andrew, and Donald J. Marsh, eds., Special Issue on Integrated Services Digital Networks, *Journal Telecomm. Networks,* Vol. 2, No. 4, Spring 1984.

PIPE 79 Pipe, G. R., "Trans-national Data Regulation," *Telecommunications,* May 1979, pp. 71–72.

POKR 84 Pokress, R., ed, Special Issue on Integrated Services Digital Ntwks., *IEEE Comm. Magazine,* January 1984.

PORT 76 Port, E., K. Kummerle, H. Rudin, C. Jenny, and P. Zafiropulo, "A Network Architecture for the Integration of Circuit and Packet Switching," *Int. Conf. Comput. Commun.,* 1976, pp. 505–514.

ROBI 79 Robinson, D., "Strategic Issues Related to Transborder Data Flow," *Telecommunications,* May 1979, pp. 85–86.

ROBI 81 Robin, G., and S. R. Treves, "An Introduction to Integrated Services Digital Networks," *Electrical Communications,* Vol. 56, No. 1, 1981, pp. 4–16.

ROSN 76 Rosner, R. D., and B. Springer, "Circuit and Packet Switching," *Comput. Networks,* Vol. 1, 1976, pp. 7–26.

ROSS 77 Ross, M. J., A. C. Tabbot, and J. A. Waite, "Design Approaches and Performance Criteria for Integrated Voice/Data Switching," *Proc. IEEE,* Vol. 65, No. 9, 1977, pp. 1283–1295.

ROSS 82 Ross, M., and D. Mowafi, "Performance Analysis of Hybrid Switching

Concepts to Integrated Voice/Data Communications," *IEEE Trans. Communications,* May 1982.

RUSH 78A   Rush, C. T., "Prelude: Communications of the 80's," Evaluation Report on Project Prelude, Satellite Business Systems, Inc., McLean, Va. 22101, May 30, 1978.

RUSH 78B   Rush, C. T., "Prelude: Communications of the 80's," Evaluation Report on Project Prelude, Experiment No. 26 in the CTS Program, Satellite Business Systems, Inc., McLean, Va. 22101, 1978.

SAST 84   Sastry, A.R.K., "Performance Objectives for ISDN's," *IEEE Comm. Magazine,* January 1984, pp. 49–55.

SCIU 73   Sciulli, J. A., and S. J. Campanella, "A Speech Predictive Encoding Communication System for Multichannel Telephony," *IEEE Trans. Commun.,* Vol. COM-21, No. 7, 1973, pp. 827–835.

SEAM 82   Seaman, J., "Local Networks: Making the Right Connection," *Computer Decisions,* June 1982, pp. 124–158.

SHOC 79   Shock, J. F., and L. Stewart, "Interconnecting Local Networks via the Packet Radio Network," *6th Data Commun. Symp. Proc., Asilomar, CA.,* November 1979, pp. 153–158.

SHOC 80   Shock, J. F., "An Annotated Bibliography on Local Computer Networks," Xerox Palo Alto Research Center, April 1980.

SKAP 79   Skaperda, N. J., "Some Architectural Alternatives in the Design of a Digital Switch," *IEEE Trans. Commun.,* Vol. COM-27, No. 7, 1979, pp. 961–972.

SKRZ 81   Skrzypczak, C. S., J. H. Weber, and W. E. Falconer, "Bell System Planning of ISDN (Integrated Services Digital Network," *Int. Conf. Commun.,* June 1981, pp. 19.6.1–19.6.6.

SMIT 72   Smith, R. L., *The Wired Nation,* Harper & Row, New York, 1972.

SMIT 81   Smith, E. A., W. A. G. Walsh, and M. J. Wilson, "Impact of Non-Voice Services on Network Evolution," *Electrical Communications*, Vol. 56, No. 1, 1981, pp. 17–30.

SONN 80   Sonneville, W., "Teleconferencing Enters Its Growth Stage," *Telecommunications,* June 1980, pp. 29–34.

SPEC 79   "Special Issue on Consumer Text Display Systems," IEEE *Trans. Consumer Electron.* Vol. CE-25, No. 3, July 1979.

STAM 80   Stamminger, R., "Teleconferencing in the 1980's," *Signal,* July 1980, pp. 41–43.

SWIT 72   Switzer, I., "The Cable Television System as a Computer-Communications Network," *Proc. Symp. Comput.-Commun. Networks Teletraffic,* April 1972, pp. 493–499.

TANT 79   Tanton, N. E., "UK Teletext — Evolution and Potential," *IEEE Trans. Consumer Electron.,* Vol. CE-25, July 1979, pp. 1246–1250.

THUR 79   Thurber, K. J., "Circuit Switching," *Computer,* June 1979, pp. 9–22.

TOMS 78   Toms, N., "An Integrated Network Using Fiber Optics (INFO) for the Distribution of Video, Data, and Telephony in Rural Areas," *IEEE Trans. Commun.,* Vol. COM-26, No. 7, 1978, pp. 1037–1045.

TYDE 82   Tydeman, J., H. Lipinski, et al., *Teletext and Videotex in the United States,*

McGraw-Hill, New York.

UN 78   Un, C. K., "A Low-Rate Digital Formant Vocoder," *IEEE Trans. Commun.*, Vol. COM-26, No. 3, pp. 344–355.

WALK 73   Walker, P. M., and S. L. Mathison, "Regulatory Policy and Future Data Transmission Services," in *Computer-Communication Networks,* Abramson and F. F. Kuo, eds., Prentice-Hall, Englewood Cliffs, N.J., 1973, Chap. 9.

WEIN 79   Weinstein, C. J., M. L. Malpass, and M. J. Fisher, "Data Traffic Performance of an Integrated, Circuit- and Packet-Switched Multiplex Structure," *Int. Conf. Commun.*, June 1979, pp 24.3.1–24.3.5.

WHIT 80   White, C. E., "German Telecommunications," *Telecommunications,* October 1980, pp. 35–50.

ZESK 81   Zeskind, D., "Videotex—Technology Advances Could Spur Data-Delivery Revolution," *EDN,* August 5, 1981, pp. 56–66.

18

Digitization Techniques

R. ANDREW PICKENS   **KATHRYN W. HANSON**
Aeronautical Radio, Inc.   *State of North Carolina*

18.1 INTRODUCTION

All types of communications traffic can benefit from digital transmission. In particular, a likely future scenario for integrated services is based on all-digital transmission techniques (see Chap. 17). Some traffic types, however, are intrinsically analog. Primary examples are those that involve human communication via the senses of sound and sight. It is also necessary to transmit other intrinsically analog information, such as temperature and pressure, for monitor/control purposes.

When transmission of analog information is to be by digital signals, conversion from analog to digital form (A/D encoding) must be made prior to transmission. If the communication is between human beings, the digital form must then be reconverted to analog form (D/A decoding). In cases involving human/machine or machine/machine communications, only one conversion may be necessary. For example, voice or other analog input to a computer requires only the A/D conversion. A voice-response computer requires only D/A conversion to produce signals intelligible to a human listener.

Strictly speaking, digitization is the process whereby a continuous (analog) signal is approximated by a finite number of digitally encoded steps. However, in common usage, the term "digitization" frequently includes both A/D and the interrelated D/A conversions. In fact, when certain rules are met, the conversion processes can be symmetrical and can lead to a reconstruction of the original signal. In other cases, such as some compression techniques for severe bandwidth conservation, only the information essential for a specific purpose is retained.

© 1980, 1981, 1983, R.A.P. All rights reserved

18.1.1   Why Digitize?

There are a number of compelling arguments for digital transmission. Other chapters in this book make the individual cases in detail. Summarized below are the key issues.

18.1.1.1   Transmission Fidelity

Digital techniques can greatly improve the fidelity of signals that are transmitted over practicable communication channels. Historically, the greatest amount of attention in the design and maintenance of the telephone network has been devoted to the many problems besetting transmissions—nonlinear distortion, phase and amplitude distortion, interference, noise, echo, and others. In analog transmission systems, amplifying and impedance-matching repeaters are required at frequent intervals along the transmission path. For wire-line systems the spacing ranges from 1/2 mile upward; for microwave radio systems, repeater spacing is measured in tens of miles. Noise, crosstalk, and other signal degradations imposed by the repeaters and added by the intervening transmission medium are cumulative, and generally cannot be "undone" by subsequent processing. Properly modulated digital signals are inherently more robust in the face of these deleterious effects. In addition, purely digital signals can be cleanly regenerated at each repeater so that any deterioration on each "hop" is not cumulative.

18.1.1.2   Economy

The following are some of the conditions under which digitization influences cost, mostly to advantage, as compared with analog technology:

- Where channels are underutilized, digitized traffic makes channel sharing easier.
- Where channels are overloaded, or available bandwidth is restricted, digitization allows compression coding techniques.
- Where traffic volume is high, digital transmission facilities cost less.
- Where digital transmission facilities are used, digital switches eliminate A/D conversions.
- Where value-added features are needed, digital manipulation is better (security) or essential (e.g., code, protocol conversion).
- Where computers are involved, digitization is mandatory.
- Where highest-quality signals are required, digitization can meet the need but requires higher bandwidth than analog signals.
- Where analog signals are transmitted, digitizers add to network cost, but efficiencies in transmission and switching can offset this cost.

The last two points are potentially negative and deserve additional comment. On a per-channel comparative basis, digitized traffic normally requires more bandwidth than the simplest possible analog transmission techniques—roughly an order of magnitude more. However, some of the higher-quality analog techniques (e.g., frequency modulation) also require more bandwidth and thus tend to narrow the gap between analog and digital bandwidth requirements. Trade-offs can be made in the power–bandwidth–information rate domains that favor digital transmission and hold promise in economy of another resource that is fundamentally limited—the electromagnetic spectrum.

The second potentially negative point relates to a key issue in network design—the trade-off between terminal costs and network costs. When the source is not digital, the need for digitizing equipment does add highly visible network cost, but savings resulting from digital transmission could be greater. With continuing advances in VLSI circuitry, processing costs (as in digitizers) are dropping more rapidly than conventional analog transmission costs. This will lead to even more favorable trade-offs. A major motivation for common carriers' conversion to digital transmission is the greatly reduced maintenance costs.

18.1.1.3 *Facility Sharing*

The most efficient means of sharing communication channels, time-division multiplexing (TDM), and methods of access to network facilities, time-division multiple access (TDMA), both require that traffic be digital in nature. These techniques are the basis of integrated services digital networks (see Chap. 17). Examples of their application to various communications media are given in Chaps. 5, 6, and 7.

The first high-speed digital transmission technique to be widely used in a communications network is the T1 carrier system, which can carry 24 telephone voice signals over a wire pair originally dedicated to a single analog voice circuit (see Sec. 18.2). The motivation for the T1 system was the need to increase the capacity of the underground conduits connecting telephone exchanges. In 1962 when the T1 system was introduced, many such facilities were saturated and traffic requirements were rapidly growing. This necessitated some form of efficient sharing of facilities. The cost of the T1 equipment was much lower than the cost of laying additional cable in urban environments.

The T1 analog-to-digital (A/D) conversion process itself is another example of facility sharing. In the original designs, still being produced in some instances, the A/D circuitry *follows* the interleaving of time-sliced samples of the 24 individual voice circuits; thus, the then-prevailing high cost of A/D conversion was spread over that number of circuits. Today, however, LSI circuits implement the sampling and A/D processes at low cost, allowing the conversion of individual circuits and thus obviating some major disadvantages of the shared conversion device (e.g., lack of data transparency).

18.1.1.4 *Value-Added Functions*

The rapid and continuing decline in VLSI costs is also having a major impact on services that involve specialized processing or storage of certain traffic. In most instances processing and storage can be implemented in digital form much more effectively than in analog form. Some services are possible only with digital techniques. Computer voice recognition, voice synthesis, and format and code conversion are examples. Voice response and store-and-forward voice and facsimile messages can be more efficient in digital form.

Another example of particular importance is the provision of security in communications. It has been estimated that at least 10 to 30% of the traffic in industrial, financial, and government networks should be protected [MCCA 73]. Analog voice privacy devices are costly, give a poor quality of reconstructed speech, and provide relatively low levels of security. Encryption and decryption of digital bit streams offers the highest security, can be accomplished without degradation, and today can be provided at relatively low cost.

18.1.1.5 *Interoperability and Compatibility*

Some types of traffic are intrinsically digital (e.g., computers), some types require digitization for their applications (e.g., computer voice entry), and other types benefit from digitization (e.g., code conversion, security). In the meantime, analog-oriented networks are rapidly moving toward digital transmission and switching at the higher levels. It is reasonable to expect that computers will be a part of all major communication systems of the future, as well as being users of those systems. Digitizing all traffic would be one step toward intranetwork compatibility and interoperability of different kinds of terminals. This is another of the major motivations for integated services.

18.1.2 Trade-offs

In spite of the many advantages of traffic digitization, all problems do not end with its use. New problems face the designer of digital transmissions systems. For example, on an analog circuit the matching of sources and sinks can be (and frequently is) relatively imprecise; the result may be a degraded but still useful and intelligible signal. As a general rule, digits either match or they do not; a significant difference in signaling levels, or essentially any difference in code, protocols, and format, will result in complete loss of information.

The network architect is also faced with the trade-offs among digitization rate, output quality, and cost. The *digitization rate* is the number of bits per unit time used to represent a signal. It determines the necessary transmission bandwidth. Typically, as digitization rate increases, bandwidth and corresponding transmission cost increase and quality improves while device cost decreases. Further, no one digitization technique is "best" in every sense for all types of traffic, nor is one technique necessarily best for a specific traffic type under all circumstances.

18.1.2.1 *Digitization Rate versus Quality*

Digitization rate has a significant effect on robustness and quality. As the digitization rate drops, less information can be conveyed about the source signal. If the signal has redundancies which can be eliminated, some important characteristics that contribute to quality can be maintained to a point while the digitization rate drops. Since most input–output is human oriented, perceptual criteria for quality are discussed with the techniques for digitizing each specific type of traffic. In general, the fewer the redundancies, the greater the impact of errors will be.

Different techniques at different digitization rates are necessary for consistent quality under different source environments and channel errors. Figure 18.1 shows an impression of the trade-off between quality and digitization rate for the two basic classes of digitization devices.[1]

18.1.2.2 Digitization Rate versus Equipment Cost

Maintaining a given level of quality while decreasing digitization rate requires increased processing and corresponding equipment complexity, both of which add to cost. The cost, power, weight, and space requirements, and any loss of quality have to be weighed against the cost savings in bandwidth. Figure 18.2 gives an indication of the balance across a range of digitization rates for an exemplary network. Determining costs of transmission and devices is not so simple, however, as the figure might make it appear. For example, large-scale production of a particular type of high data rate digitizer could result in a smaller unit cost lower than that of a low data rate digitizer, because of the relative production economies of scale. Further, criteria for network design are not all easily translated into dollars. A design that provides lowest total cost for today's services might impose severe restrictions on the kinds of future services (and hence future revenues) that could be implemented.

With the costs of digitizers dropping, most notably now at 16 to 32 kbps, the consideration of such criteria can be significant; the quality may not remain sufficiently high for a given environment when the digitization rate or technique is changed. It is also necessary to decide where to digitize, on how many lines to digitize traffic, and the cost for each. Line length and expense affect decisions. The crossover

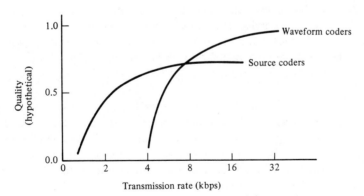

Figure 18.1. Example of digitization rate versus voice quality. (After [PLAN 79], © 1979 IEEE.)

[1]The word "codec" is derived from the combination of "*co*der–*dec*oder". Codec is coming into general usage, like the word modem, to mean a device that performs both functions.

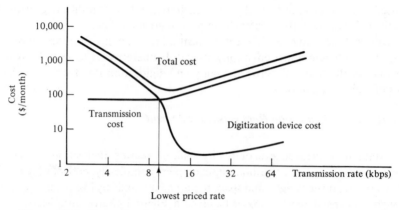

Figure 18.2. Example of digitization rate versus equipment cost. (After [OCCH 79] and [OCCH 80].)

point for the lowest rate will decrease with the continuing decrease in the device cost. For example, large-scale production of a particular type of high data rate digitizer could result in a smaller unit cost lower than that of a low data rate digitizer, because of the relative production economies of scale. Further, criteria for network design are not all easily translated into dollars. A design that provides lowest total cost for today's services might impose severe restrictions on the kinds of future services (and hence future revenues) that could be implemented.

18.1.3   General Digitization Techniques

The principles and techniques introduced in this section are generally applicable to all types of traffic. Techniques for specific traffic types are discussed in Secs. 18.4 and 18.5. For the system designer, selection of a technique depends primarily on what is available. Consequently, emphasis is placed on those techniques in current use and on those likely to be the most important in the future. Table 18.1 lists these techniques and some others that are encountered for specific applications. Since voice is by far the most commonly digitized type of traffic, the examples and descriptions are so oriented.

In Tab. 18.1 the "domain" of the technique refers to the basic approach taken for processing; one can operate directly on the frequency spectrum or, equivalently, in the time domain. In the capsule descriptions, the word "pitch" implies the fine structure of the voice spectrum, including voiced/unvoiced determination and pitch extraction. These terms are explained along with the characteristics of voice in Sec. 18.4.

Some general ranges of transmission rates are shown in Tab. 18.1 for medium- to high-quality *voice* waveform coding (shown separately in [FLAN 79]) and for synthetic quality vocoding [CUCC 77, OCCH 78, FLAN 79]. Redundant signal types generally include voice, still image, and television. However, video transmission

Table 18.1.   *Digitization Techniques.*

Acronym and Domain	Meaning (Capsule Description)	Coding type and Typical Rate for Voice (kbps)	Realm of Applicable Traffic
(L) PCM; time	Linear pulse-code modulation (linearly quantized amplitude steps)	Waveform; 54–64	General
Log PCM; time	Logarithmic PCM (logarithmically quantized)	Waveform; 48–64	Voice
APCM; time	Adaptive PCM (adaptively quantized)	Waveform; 32–64	Signals with redundancies
DPCM; time	Differential PCM (differences transmitted instead of step levels)	Waveform; 32–48	Signals with redundancies
ADPCM; time	Adaptive DPCM (adaptively quantized differences)	Waveform; 16–32	Signals with redundancies
DM; time	Delta modulation (DPCM typically with 1-bit quantizer—step one up or one down)	Waveform; 24–48	Signals with redundancies
ADM; time	Adaptive DM (DM with adaptive step size)	Waveform; 24–40	Signals with redundancies
ATC; frequency	Adaptive transform coding (block quantized)	Waveform; 7.2–16	Signals with redundancies
CVSD; time	Continuously variable slope DM (syllabically companded ADM)	Waveform; 16–32	Voice
SBC; frequency	Sub-band coding (fixed division of bandwidth)	Hybrid; 9.6	Voice
APC; time	Adaptive predictive coding (predicted envelope and pitch with ADPCM for error)	Hybrid; 6–16	Voice
VEV; frequency	Voice-excited vocoding (PCM for low and CV for high frequencies)	Hybrid; 7.2–9.6	Voice
LPC; time	Linear predictive coding (predicted amplitude plus pitch)	Source; 2.4	Voice
CV; frequency	Channel vocoding (sampled envelope at specific frequencies plus pitch)	Source; 2.4–4.8	Voice
FT; frequency	Formant [tracking] vocoding (tracked formants plus pitch)	Source; 0.6–2.4	Voice

requires much higher rates than those shown for voice. For example, full-motion television requires from 12 to 92.6 Mbps; while slow-motion video, such as the Picturephone, requires 1.5 to 6.3 Mbps.

Digitization techniques can be generally categorized as (1) waveform coding or (2) source coding. Waveform coding techniques operate on discrete divisions of time and amplitude. The intent is to code a signal so that the original waveform can be reconstructed at the receiver with good fidelity. Waveform coding is applicable to any signal that varies over time within a set range of frequencies, which may be forced by filtering. These bandwidth-limited time functions are exemplified by an image signal's intensity waveform, a sequence of data bits' channel waveform, or a voice's resonance in an acoustic waveform. The techniques vary in complexity based on how an analog signal is replaced by discrete values.

Source coding techniques are designed to preserve only the perceptually significant properties of the waveform. They transmit selected characteristics of the source signal which are extracted by analysis. Synthesis is required at the receiver. A source coder is tailored to a specific type of analog signal, most often voice or even a particular kind of voice. Because source coding is so intimately related to the type of traffic, discussion of this category is deferred to Sec. 18.4. Generally, source coding techniques remove signal redundancy to reduce bandwidth requirements, but in doing so they sacrifice some signal quality and gain sensitivity to channel errors.

Currently, waveform coding predominates the digital transmission environment. Source coding has more potential for reducing the digitization rate and so is a subject of great interest. Hybrid techniques compromise between quality and bandwidth requirements by using combinations of waveform and source coding techniques.

18.2 PULSE-CODE MODULATION

Pulse-code modulation (PCM) is the foundation of today's digitization and digital transmission technologies, and is the basis for comparison of other digitization techniques. PCM is the first waveform reconstruction technique that was put to practical use. It was developed in 1937 by Alec H. Reeves but was not commercially installed until 1962, in the Western Electric T1 carrier system, after the use of semiconductors made production of the equipment economically feasible. Since that time, PCM-modulated speech signals have been used to establish the whole hierarchy of the telephone network. Details can be found in numerous references, such as [GREG 77], [GTE 75], [FREE 75], and [REFE 77].

PCM can respond to very abrupt changes in signal amplitude, and thus offers high fidelity and transparency. Its broad applicability is attained at the price of wide bandwidth. Understanding PCM depends on understanding the basic processes of sampling, quantizing, and coding/decoding. These processes also form the foundation built upon by other techniques.

18.2.1 Sampling and Quantizing

The cornerstone of digitization of analog signals was laid in 1928, when Nyquist theorized that a bandwidth-limited signal can be completely characterized by sampling its amplitude at a uniform rate equal to, or greater than, twice the highest frequency component of the signal [NYQU 28]. Several proofs of this important theorem have been developed; one [OLIV 48] is based on the fact that a continuous function can be completely described by coefficients of the sine and cosine terms of a

Fourier series. In digitization technology, the term "Nyquist rate" has come to mean a sampling rate of twice the highest frequency component of interest.

In typical telephone systems, it can be assumed that the maximum frequency present in a voice signal is 4kHz. This can be assured by passing the signal through a filter that attenuates all frequencies above 4kHz, with no apparent degradation in signal quality because of the limited frequency response of other elements of the telephone system such as microphones, receivers, and intervening equipment. The telephone voice signal, then, could be sampled at a rate of 2 x 4 kHz = 8 kHz, leading to a time interval between samples of $1/8$ kHz = 125 μsec.

Sampling is illustrated in Fig. 18.3. A time segment of an analog waveform is represented in Fig. 18.3a, overlayed by instants of time corresponding to a given sampling rate. The resultant samples, illustrated in Fig. 18.3b, can be thought of as very small time slices of the analog waveform at the instant of sampling.[2] Such an amplitude-varying pulse train is a form of Pulse Amplitude Modulation (PAM).

The PAM samples are still a quasi-analog waveform because the amplitudes of the pulses are varying in a continuum. At this point it would be possible to reconstruct completely the original waveform merely by passing the PAM samples through a low-pass (integrating) filter with a cutoff frequency of 4 kHz. In fact, this is the basis of reconstruction on reception.

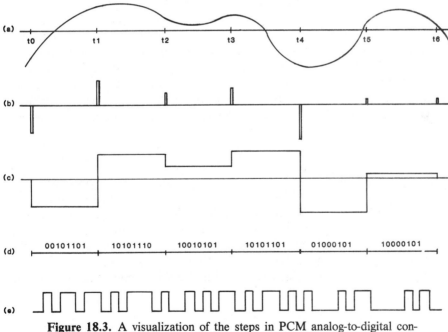

Figure 18.3. A visualization of the steps in PCM analog-to-digital conversion.

[2]In theory, sampling should be accomplished with an impulse function (i.e., zero pulse width) at precise sampling intervals.

To help visualize the sampling process, suppose that the width of each pulse were stretched to just equal the sampling interval. The resultant waveform would appear as in Fig. 18.3c. Examination of this "sample-and-hold" waveform will reveal that it has an appearance similar to the original waveform delayed by one sampling interval. One could further visualize that the sample-and-hold waveform would resemble the original waveform even more closely if the transitions between amplitude levels were slowed down, having a more rounded appearance. This is exactly what would happen if the sample-and-hold waveform were passed through a low-pass filter, which again would result in reconstruction of a delayed replica of the original waveform.

The next step in the A/D conversion process is quantization, wherein each amplitude level is represented by a number in digital form. In telephony, it has been determined that 256 discrete amplitude levels provides an adequate description of a voice signal. An 8-bit binary-encoded word gives the necessary $2^8 = 256$ levels, thus, an 8-bit word can be substituted for the amplitude of each sample obtained previously. One possible representation is shown in Fig. 8.3d. If each word were so encoded as to occupy one sampling interval, the result would be a PCM bit stream as illustrated in Fig. 8.3e.

In the example, the original analog waveform is limited to a maximum frequency component of less than 4 kHz, leading to a Nyquist sampling rate of 8 kHz. The PCM bit stream contains 8 bits per sample; therefore, the data rate of the digitized PCM waveform is 64 kbps (a universally standard rate).

Since the amplitude information of the original signal is encoded in the bit structure of the PCM data stream, the only meaning of amplitude in the latter has to do with the binary decision process. The PCM signal can be transmitted, processed, stored and manipulated just as with any digital data stream. Particularly as regards digital transmission, there is no need to preserve carefully a continuum of amplitudes as is the case with analog transmission—a major advantage of digital transmission.

18.2.2 Reconstructed Signal Quality

Although PCM digitization could result in a reconstruction of the original signal with an arbitrarily small error, the use of a practical number of bits to represent the amplitude of each sample results in certain errors. These errors, called *quantization distortion* or *quantization noise,* are a consequence of the quantization process.[3] The simplest quantization scheme is to divide the total range of expected amplitudes (the dynamic range) into equal quantum steps. Thus if a dynamic range of ± 1 volt were desired for the input analog waveform of the previous example, each 8-bit digital

---

[3]Strictly speaking, *distortion* and *noise* are different parameters, and their subjective effects can be quite different. The distortion effects of many digitization techniques, however, tend to be noise-like qualitatively although not necessarily quantitatively. The desire to reduce undesirable signal energy of components to a measure of "noise" is a holdover from common practice in analog telephony (see [MARS 78]).

word would represent a step of $1/128 = 0.00781$ V. The actual amplitude would be encoded as the value of the nearest step. This mapping of a continuous signal into discrete approximations is the essential mechanism of analog/digital signal conversions [GERS 77].

The sampling rate, and the number and size of steps, determine quantization distortion or noise, as can be seen in Fig. 18.4. The error is the difference between the source and quantized waveforms and can be viewed as amplitude error, phase (time) error, or both. Quantization noise, or the mean-square distortion D, is the statistical expectation of the square of the error:

$$D = \int_{-\infty}^{\infty} [Q(x) - x]^2\, p\,(x)\, dx$$

For a signal value x, $Q(x)$ is the correspondingly assigned quantized value and $p(x)$ is the probability of the signal value x occurring.

Overall quantization distortion is subdivided into specific components; for example, granular noise, idle noise, and overload distortion. *Granular noise* is related to the step size; the fewer the levels of quantization, the greater the granular noise. *Idle noise* results from the fluctuations that occur when an attempt is made to approximate a zero-signal condition in the presence of noise. *Overload distortion* (a form of clipping) appears when the dynamic range of the quantizer is exceeded. Generally, all digitization techniques suffer from these types of noise and distortion problems, although the cause and effect may be quite different.

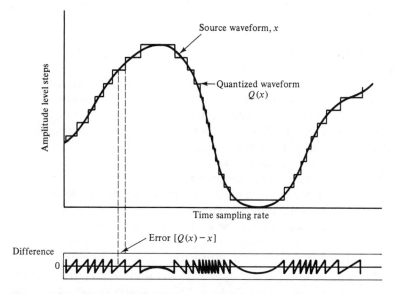

Figure 18.4. Time, amplitude level, and error between a source and quantized waveform. (After [BLAC 53], copyright 1953 Bell Telephone Laboratories, reprinted by permission.)

The perceived effects of quantization distortion varies depending on the type of traffic as well as on the particular quantization method. Since the signal is usually intended as input to human beings, subjective quality is most important. Speech digitization techniques are usually subjected to evaluation by a statistically valid sample of human beings who rate the intelligibility of the reproduced speech. Standard tests, such as those in the IEEE Recommended Practice for Speech Quality Measurements (No. 297–69; see Sec. 18.4), have been developed for such evaluations. Video and image digitization techniques are similarly evaluated, usually in terms of scoring as "just perceptible degradation," "significant degradation," and so on.

Quantizing accuracy of PCM can be related objectively to the signal-to-noise ratio (SNR). The false noise caused by a receiver's incorrect interpretation of pulse values can be eliminated by the selection of signal power (mean square amplitude). When false noise is thus eliminated, SNR is considered to be the ratio of the signal-to-quantization noise alone. The long-term SNR is often defined in the form

$$\text{SNR} = 10 \log^{10} \frac{\sigma^2}{D}$$

where D is the quantization noise and σ^2 is the variance of the samples [GERS 77].

Other possible objective measures besides long-term SNR include: segmental SNR, compensated SNR, average gain, gain fluctuation, maximum SNR, frequency weighted SNRs, and in the frequency domain, log likelihood ratio, Bharucha index, and spectral signal-to-noise distortion ratios [SCAG 79]. Objective measures, however, have not been found to correlate very well with the more subjective tests (see Sec. 18.4.7).

18.2.3   PCM Encoding

In the prior construction of PCM digitization, the number of quantization levels together with the sampling rate needed for the desired quality determines the data rate, or the number of bits per second required to encode and transmit a PCM signal. Since the sampling rate has been chosen to satisfy the Nyquist criterion and the quantization steps have (presumably) been chosen to be equal in amplitude, the encoding is referred to as linear PCM.

Viewing encoding from another perspective, nontrivial questions arise concerning the tradeoff possibilities of encoding. For a given data rate, is it better to transmit more samples having lesser resolution (fewer quantization levels), or fewer samples having higher resolution? Could some more complex encoding algorithms be employed to reduce the sampling rate—quantization level product, and, hence, required data rate, or to improve reconstructed signal quality at a given data rate? The answers to these questions are not simple; they also depend to a major extent on the kind of source waveform being digitized and the characteristics of the receiver. Generally, some interesting tradeoffs are possible, particularly in those cases where human perception is involved, as in speech and imagery. The possibilities lead to variations on the basic PCM digitization technique, discussed in this section; and also other forms of digitization and compression examined subsequently.

18.2.3.1   Variable-Rate Coding

A variable-rate PCM coder can take advantage of gaps or redundancies in a source signal to reduce the total number of bits transmitted. Silence detection (the complement of activity detection) in voice signals illustrates the simplest approach, which is deciding with each sample whether speech is occurring and must be transmitted [DHAD 79, MCAU 77, SCHA 76]. Activity detection already has been mentioned as an integral part of Time Assigned Speech Interpolation (TASI; see Chap. 17). Block processing [DUBN 79, COX 79] is an alternative where blocks of fixed length are transmitted. Through the use of buffers, a varying number of bits can be used for each sample in the block. Bits can be allocated to maximize SNR. Another approach, used by variable-frame-rate devices [HESS 78], involves transmitting code only when the change in the signal since the last transmission becomes significant. This is the principle used in Speech Predictive Encoding Communication (SPEC; see Chap. 17). Variable-rate coding can involve the transmission of a variable number of bits per sample, as in the Huffman coding described next.

18.2.3.2   Noiseless Coding

"Noiseless" coding, also called entropy coding, can reduce the PCM bit rate without changing the number of quantization levels [ONEA 71]. Instead of N bits in each code group for each of the 2^N amplitude levels, a variable-length coding such as Huffman coding [DORG 72, HUFF 62] is used. Each code group must not appear as the first part of any other code group. Otherwise, an additional indication would be needed at the end of a code group. One of the many allowable binary code group combinations is 10, 000, 011, 110, 111, 0101, 00100, 00101, . . . With a properly constructed code, a bit stream such as 11001101011000100 can be read only one way: 100 011 0101 10 00 100. Buffering is required to produce a steady output bit stream. Buffer overflow and underflow problems, as well as the possibility of increased error propagation, are the price paid for the bit reduction [JELI 72].

Levels corresponding to amplitudes that occur most often are optimally coded by groups containing the smallest number of bits. The word "optimally" is used in the sense of yielding the lowest average code group length. The required average length theoretically approaches the average information per code group, the so-called minimum redundancy, when code group length is allowed to approach infinity. In this limit the coding would indeed be noiseless. However, for any given transmission bit rate, quantization noise has a lower bound beyond which no further removal of signal redundancy is warranted to free capacity for specifying the signal [ONEA 67].

18.2.3.3   Companding

Linear PCM has uniform quantization; it uses evenly spaced levels—a good design when all signal voltages are equally likely. Uniform quantization is almost optimal when noiseless coding is used [WOOD 69, GISH 68]. The mean-square distortion of linear PCM grows approximately as the square of the step size, S: $D \approx S^2/12$. This distortion is essentially independent of the spectrum of the input signal. Linear PCM provides a high level of performance but it also results in a high output bit rate which is expensive to transmit. Other coding methods, and techniques such as companding and adapting, represent efforts to resolve the disparity between economy and efficiency.

For signal types with amplitudes known to be nonuniformly distributed, concentrating the quantization levels where signal values are concentrated improves quantizing accuracy for a given number of quantization levels and bits transmitted. The amplitude resolution is high only in the ranges where it will have the greatest effect. In other ranges the source signal is, in effect, compressed for coding. On receipt, the signal is expanded back to its original form. The compress/expand phrase is itself compressed into the word compand. Log PCM, a PCM digitization technique with compression, is the standard in the telephone network (see Sec. 18.4).

The advantage of companding is illustrated in Fig. 18.5. While the strong signal is represented well by linear coding, the weak signal is poorly approximated. Reconstruction of the weak signal would be accompanied by a high level of granular noise. Compare the results when a compandor is used with the same number of levels but with unequal step sizes (here, following a logarithmic law). The strong signal is still approximated well but, more important, the low-level signal's representation is greatly improved.

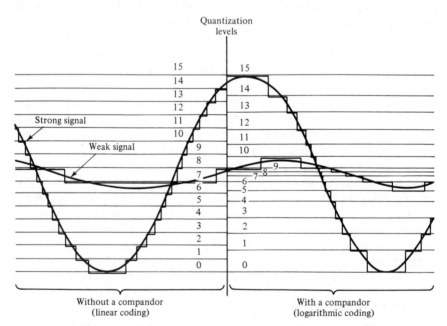

Figure 18.5 Comparison of linear and companded PCM encoding. (After [MART 77], with permission from Prentice-Hall, Inc.)

18.2.3.4   Adapting

Quantization levels need not necessarily be fixed as either linear or nonlinear (companded). A quantizer with memory can adapt step size to its determination of signal variance [JAYA 73]; or switch between two or more quantizers with different fixed step sizes [SCHL 72, COHE 74, DIET 74]; or use a syllabic, noninstantaneous technique where step size is considered for change only after a constant time interval, say 5 to 10 ms for voice, instead of at every step [WILK 71]. Syllabic adaptation is best known for use in delta modulation techniques, which are described shortly. The objective of adaptive quantization is to reduce error without increasing bandwidth requirements. Coders using such quantization methods are referred to as adaptive PCM (APCM) coders.

Adaptive quantization schemes use either forward or backward estimation [NOLL 75A]. Forward estimation relies on samples of the source signal. The samples are buffered and used to determine estimates, which are transmitted to the receiver together with quantized samples. Nearly instantaneous companding (NIC) [DUTT 76] is an application of forward estimation. Samples are encoded and buffered in a block. The largest sample in a block is determined and the samples are uniformly rescaled and reencoded for transmission. That is, the compression is tailored for each block. The scaling factor is transmitted with each block of samples.

Forward estimation increases transmission requirements. The increase can be avoided by basing adaptation on a history of quantized samples rather than on the source signal itself. The receiver duplicates the transmitter adapting circuitry to infer the quantizing parameter changes. This backward estimation is easier to implement but is more affected by transmission errors. Forward estimation becomes more attractive when the input is in digital form already, as it is for code conversion between two types of coders [MESS 76]. Instantaneous adaptive quantizers use backward estimation. Examples of forward and backward estimation are diagrammed in Fig. 18.6.

18.3   OTHER PCM WAVEFORM CODING TECHNIQUES

Although "straight" PCM is currently the most prevalent encoding technique, the majority of recent research and development work has been focused on other techniques because of their promise of reduced bandwidth requirements. Many are based on the direct quantization and encoding of the input waveform. These techniques include variations of PCM with or without compressed quantization (i.e., nonlinear or linear), blocking, special encoding, prediction, and adaptation. Most are tailored to exploit the characteristics of a particular type of traffic.

18.3.1   Differential Pulse-Code Modulation

A major variation of PCM is differential pulse-code modulation (DPCM). Like PCM, basic DPCM can be modified by compression, adaptation, and so on. SNR can

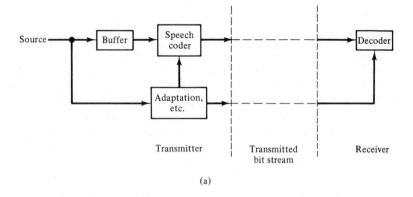

(a)

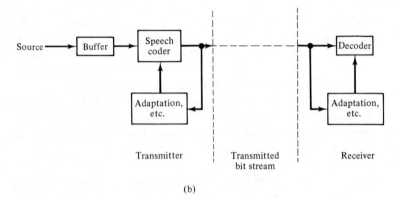

(b)

Figure 18.6 (a) Forward estimation. (b) Backward estimation. (After [MESS 76], © 1976 IEEE.)

be improved by reducing the dynamic range of the source signal. The difference between a current amplitude sample and the predicted value for that sample, estimated from past samples, is transmitted instead of the level of the sample.

Any continuous, bandlimited analog signal is predictable, or redundant, in the sense that the difference between successive samples is usually much less than the full range of the signal itself—provided the sampling rate is fast enough. This is particularly true of speech. Redundancy is reduced by subtracting from the signal that part which can be predicted from its past. More precisely, if the correlation between adjacent samples is greater than 0.5, the difference between adjacent samples has smaller variance than the sample values themselves. This yields smaller error variance and increased SNR; or, for a given SNR, fewer quantization levels are needed, so the required transmission bandwidth is less. As always, a price must be paid. Memory is required to make predictions. The signal is encoded more intelligently than by PCM. Transmitting differences instead of coded amplitude values is the principle of the predictive technique, differential PCM.

The simplest variation of DPCM uses a first-order predictor; it establishes a predicted value based only on the immediately preceding sample. The predicted value is $y'(i) = wy(i-1)$, where w is a fixed weight calculated using long-term statistics of a representative signal sample. A more general (linear) M-order predictor, one that requires M times the memory, uses fixed predictor coefficients $a(i)$ in

$$y'(i) = \sum_{i=1}^{M} a(i)y(i-1)$$

Proper use of feedback around the quantizer, as shown in Fig. 18.7, ensures that quantization errors are not accumulated. The predictor in the feedback loop removes much of the signal redundancy prior to digitization. The value of M significantly influences device complexity. Fortunately, most of the improvement available by prediction is obtained even for $M = 2$. Values of M greater than 4 are probably not worthwhile [GOOD 75].

18.3.2   Adaptive DPCM

Adaptive DPCM (ADPCM) is an important digitization technique for the future, as it is expected that 32 kbps ADPCM will be widely used in the public telephone systems to reduce voice bandwidth requirements by a factor of 2:1. ADPCM incorporates an adaptive quantizer for coding the differences in the signal from one sample to the next. It is an adaptive scheme which is "multibit" as opposed to single-bit adaptive delta modulation. An analysis of quantization noise for ADPCM is given in [GOLD 77]. Performance measurements of an ADPCM/TASI system are reported in [TOWN 81]. As with PCM, step size might be changed to follow changes in signal power.

Updating the prediction weights themselves, say every 10 to 30 ms for voice, to reflect changing signal statistics removes more redundancy in the error signal and allows a lower digitization rate to be used. Coders with such adaptive predictors in addition to adaptive quantizers are described in Sec. 18.4.5.2.

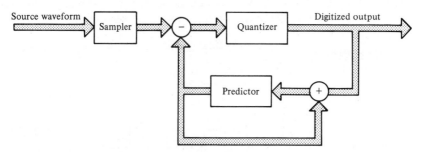

Figure 18.7. Differential pulse-code modulation system. (After [BAYL 73], © 1973 IEEE.)

18.3.3   Delta Modulation

Delta modulation is a special and important case of DPCM that uses a two-level quantizer and, almost always, a first-order predictor. For signals that do not change abruptly, such as voice, it takes advantage of the fact that only a small change normally occurs between one sample and the next. Based on the predicted signal value, a single-bit code is sent to indicate the sign of the error (whether the prediction was high or low) and thus the direction of the step, down or up. Coder structure is inherently simpler than for PCM because of the 1-bit words and because no sample-and-hold operation is required [GHOS 78]. With 1-bit coding, a much higher sampling rate than the Nyquist rate is required. Faster-than-Nyquist sampling has an associated noise enhancement problem, but the circuit implementation simplicity of DM is attractive, especially with LSI implementations further lowering its cost. The absence of standards has been a barrier to greater acceptance in the commercial market; the military, however, have well-developed standards. A simplified diagram of DM is in Fig. 18.8. More detailed diagrams for delta codecs are in [DHAD 80].

The dynamic range of DM is limited by fixed step sizes. It is very susceptible to slope overload and granular noise problems. With DM, slope overload occurs when the signal changes too fast for the quantizer steps to keep up. Low level or slowly varying signals are severely distorted (granular and idle noise) if companding is not used. These situations are illustrated in Fig. 18.9. It has been empirically determined that overload distortion is more objectionable than granular noise [JAYA 71]. For this reason, delta modulation quality is improved dramatically by oversampling, that is, quantizing at a rate significantly higher than the Nyquist rate.

In the range of practical interest, the SNR of DM with oversampling and filtering is proportional to the cube of the sampling frequency [FLAN 79]. Increasing the sampling rate can also reduce overload.

18.3.4   Delta Modulation Variants

The problems with "pure" DM can be minimized by adaptive DM (ADM)—making step size vary with the slope of the input signal based either on error signal characteristics fed back from the coder (feedback control, using backward estimation), or on a control signal derived from the input signal and transmitted separately to the receiver

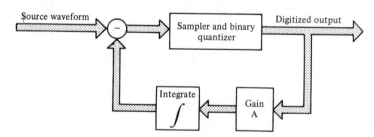

Figure 18.8. Delta modulation system. (After [BAYL 73], © 1973 IEEE.)

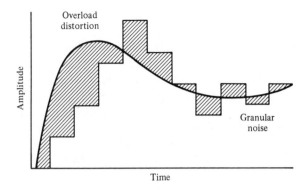

Figure 18.9. Illustration of quantizing errors with delta modulation.

(forward control, using forward estimation) [SCHI 74]. The change might be made in a predetermined manner known to the receiver, for example, a series of three or four 1's or of three or four 0's (coincidence condition) could logically indicate an increase in step size. Alternatively, the change might be encoded in the bit stream and transmitted to the receiver as in forward estimation.

Continuously variable slope delta modulation (CVSD) is a popular special case of ADM that changes step size based on average signal power. Step size increases are precipitated by the coincidence condition, typically a series of three or four 1's or three or four 0's. Continued absence of coincidence, particularly consecutive alternating bits, leads to step size decreases through reducing multiplicative factors. (Note that only an analog step size adaptation technique produces truly continuously variable-slope delta modulation.) Thus step size is not changed instantaneously at every sampling time; rather the companding is so-called "syllabic." This slow adaptation decreases granular noise but increases slope overload distortion. When transmission channel error rate is low (say, less than 10^{-2}) a faster adaptation can be used to produce a better voice quality; if the error rate is expected to be higher, a slower adaptation can be employed to ameliorate somewhat the effect of the high error rate.

18.4 DIGITIZATION OF VOICE TRAFFIC

A single approach to digitization, one best for all traffic and environments, would be ideal; however, different communication systems have different traffic characteristics and application objectives. Pulse-code modulation, the subject of Sec. 18.2, is generally applicable as a digitizing technique for arbitrary analog waveforms, and has quite properly become the current standard in the telephone networks. In its modern implementations with full 8-bit quantization, PCM has also proved to be very capable of handling nonvoice waveforms, such as data modems and facsimile, that also are frequently present. Of all digitization techniques, however, PCM requires the largest bandwidth (data rate). Consequently, there are substantial motivations to seek other techniques usable perhaps in more restricted applications, where only speech is of interest.

One class of generally applicable digitization techniques includes the variants of PCM and delta modulation discussed in Sec. 18.3. These achieve savings in bandwidth by the effective use of predictors or estimators to remove redundancy from the input waveform. If the prediction algorithm is optimized for speech, waveforms from other sources may be poorly reproduced by the system. For example, one study has been made of how DPCM designed for voice performs poorly for data signals [ONEA 72]. This section discusses the tailoring of such techniques for voice digitization, and describes "source coding" techniques intended only for voice digitization.

18.4.1   Current Status and Future Trends

Because the great majority of communications traffic is voice, most past work in digitization techniques has been directed to voice digitization. In 1929, Homer Dudley at Bell Laboratories developed the coder/vocoder compression device for speech analysis and artificial synthesis. Alec Reeves proposed the concept of PCM in 1937. A PCM device was patented in 1938, but hardware technology was too rudimentary for its practical implementation. Subsequent development of the transistor, integrated circuits, the digital switch, and digital transmission motivated rapid advances in the 1960s and 1970s. The impact of PCM voice technology has been so profound that the digital hierarchy of the entire commercial telephone system is based on the basic 64-kbps PCM data rate. PCM codecs on a single VLSI chip are now available from several integrated-circuit manufacturers.

In spite of the ubiquity of PCM, new demands are stimulating continued research and development in voice digitization. Such demands include security, accommodation of increasing traffic, greater bandwidth efficiency, integrated services, and special applications. The quest is not only for techniques offering PCM-quality voice at a lower bandwidth, but also for techniques affording large reductions in bandwidth with a quality that is acceptable for special situations. There is considerable research and development activity directed toward both ends, particularly for voice at very low data rates; a considerable portion of this work is defense oriented.

18.4.2   Characteristics of Voice

Almost all voice coder techniques operate on the fact that human speech is characterized by a high degree of redundancy and predictability. The method by which a particular technique takes advantage of these characteristics differs by type. Waveform techniques look for correlated statistics in the time or frequency domains of the electrical waveform to achieve processing gains. Source coding techniques are generally based on modeling the human speech-producing and -hearing mechanisms.

Voice has frequently occurring low amplitudes with a high probability of amplitudes near zero (silences). Also, very high amplitudes occur in speech with sufficient probability to require a wide dynamic range in coding. Increases in intensity are often abrupt, but decreases are generally slower. These facts have been important, for example, in the design of compandors and adaptive waveform coders.

The most significant physical characteristic of voice with respect to efficient digitization is the redundancy and predictability of the voice analog waveform signal. The two main sources of redundancy in the speech waveform are the quasi-periodicity caused by vocal cord vibration and the highly structured form of the short-term spectral envelope.

Another form of "redundancy" represented in longer-term speech patterns results from frequent pauses by a speaker and the half-duplex nature of conversations. It been capitalized on by the Time Assigned Speech Interpolation (TASI) and newer Digital Speech Interpolation (DSI) techniques of multiple voice channel concentration for transmission (see Chap. 17). The factors of redundancy and predictability are also used in some digitization techniques and are significant in voice privacy applications.

The development of source coding techniques, which involve analysis of input speech for transmission and synthesis at reception, has required much more extensive knowledge of the nature of speech. Much of the work in this area has contributed heavily to more recent applications, such as voice recognition, voice data entry, and voice-response devices.

One of the most important lines of research has been the development of a model of the production of speech based on three mechanisms which convert the steady air flow from the lungs into speech [SCHR 66, FLAN 72, RABI 78]. These mechanisms are outlined in Tab. 18.2.

Another major contribution to voice source coding has resulted from studies of the spectrum of speech. The short-term power spectrum of speech, as illustrated in Fig. 18.10c, is a composite of the quasi-periodic excitation function (spectral fine structure), determined by the pitch, and the short-term spectral envelope function, determined by the shape of the vocal tract. *Formants* are the peak positions of the spectral envelope. Their positions, which change with changes in the shape of the vocal tract, convey what is being said. Pitch and average amplitude convey voice inflection or intonation. Below 3 kHz there are typically three formants for each voice segment of speech.

The key parameters useful for electrical analysis and synthesis of speech are thus:

- Voiced/unvoiced (whether the vocal cords vibrate)
- Pitch (vocal cord vibration rate)
- Gain (sound volume or intensity of sound excitation)
- Filter parameters (instantaneous shape of vocal tract)

18.4.3 Log PCM Companding

The preceding information on voice waveform statistics clarifies the reasons why coding with compression and decoding with expansion improve voice PCM quality. A general objective in quantization coding is to achieve equiprobability for each of

Table 18.2. *Model of Human Speech Reproduction.*

Mechanism	Excitation Function	Examples	Name of Sound[a]
Vocal cords opening and closing chop airflow into short pulses	Quasi-periodic pulses	/ae/,/a/,/i/,/u/ (vowels including diphthongs)	Voiced
Vocal tract constrictions create turbulence[b]	Continuous noise	/f/,/h/,/s/	Fricatives, unvoiced
Vocal tract occlusion is followed by release of the excess pressure that builds up	Single pulse	/b/,/d/,/p/,t/	Plosives or stop, un-voiced

[a]Voiced fricatives, such as /v/ and /z/, have both voiced and unvoiced excitation simultaneously and are modeled by a mixture of the two excitation functions. Nasal sounds, such as /m/ and /n/, are not readily simulated by the traditional model.

[b]The vocal tract is formed by the throat, mouth, and nasal cavities. The throat consists of the pharynx and upper part of the esophagus, the larynx, and the trachea or windpipe.

the quantum steps. It has been determined that a logarithmic compression curve fits well the statistics of voice. Two such curves are in general use. By the North American standards, the mu-law companding curve can be plotted from the formula

$$Y = \begin{cases} \dfrac{\log (1 + \mu x)}{\log (1 + \mu)} & 0 \leq x \leq 1 \\[2ex] \dfrac{-\log (1 - \mu x)}{\log (1 + \mu)} & -1 \leq x \leq 0 \end{cases}$$

where $\mu = 255$. The CCITT standard generally used elsewhere in the world is

$$Y = \begin{cases} \operatorname{sgn}(x) \dfrac{1 + \ln(A| x|)}{1 + A} & \dfrac{1}{A} \leq | x | \leq 1 \\[2ex] \operatorname{sgn}(x) \dfrac{A| x|}{1 + \ln A} & 0 \leq | x | \leq \dfrac{1}{A} \end{cases}$$

A is usually assigned a value of 87.6. A-law companding is somewhat easier to implement but provides slightly poorer performance—24-dB improvement in signal-to-noise ratio as compared with 33 dB for the μ-law—because of the lower slope of the compression characteristics near the origin (noise level).

In practice the curve is approximated by piecewise-linear segments as illustrated in Fig. 18.11 for the $\mu = 255$ law. The approximation is called a 15-segment curve because the first two segments connected at the origin are collinear. The encoder input step size doubles from one segment to the next. There are several variations of the actual coding pattern. Even within the North American standard slight variations exist.

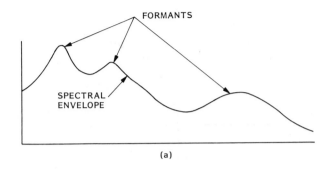

(a)

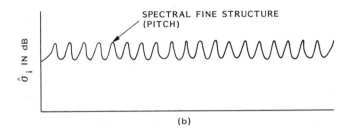

(b)

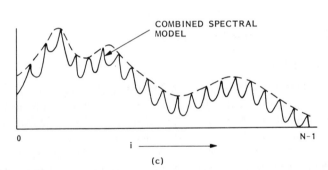

(c)

Figure 18.10. Components of the speech spectrum model. (After [FLAN 79], © 1979 IEEE.)

In the so-called DS-2 channel bank, 8-bit coding for each sample is used in the following fashion [GTE 75]:

Let: "SABCWXYZ" represent the 8-bit word for each sample
Then: s gives the sign of the sample, 1 for positive, 0 for negative
        abc gives the segment number, from 000 for 0 through 111 for 7
        wxyz gives the level number within the segment, from 000 for 0 through 1111 for 15

Thus each segment is divided into $2^4 = 16$ quantum steps.

Companding following other forms is usually applied to other waveform coding techniques. Also, companding is frequently useful in source coding methods. ADM and Continuously Variable Slope Delta modulation (CVSD) are two impor-

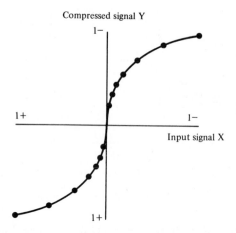

Figure 18.11. $\mu 255$ compressor characteristic.

tant waveform coding techniques for voice. Both are standard in the U.S. and other defense departments, and they offer great hope for future bandwidth savings. For example, CVSD at 32 kbps has quite good quality; at 16 kbps quality is good but somewhat degraded.

18.4.4 Delta Modulation Variants for Voice

18.4.4.1   Adaptive DM

The advantages of adaptive DM (ADM) for voice traffic are simple hardware, less strict filtering requirement, lower quality degradation on a noisy channel than PCM or ADPCM, and excellent speech quality at a lower digitization rate than PCM [UN 80]. Performance differences of ADM implementations arise primarily from the adaptation scheme followed for the single-bit quantizer. Alternatives to the syllabic companding of CVSD include instantaneous companding for example with exponential adaptation in step size at every sampling time, and hybrid companding with both syllabic and instantaneous companding.

18.4.4.2   Continuously Variable Slope DM

The companding in continuously variable slope DM (CVSD) applied to voice is optimized for voice characteristics. Step magnitude is changed by predetermined multiplicative factors. The factors applied for increases are usually larger than for decreases since speech can have abrupt increases in intensity levels but generally decays at a slower rate. Information transfer is efficient because the companding information is superimposed on the data bits. However, this means errors in transmission will affect companding as well as the data itself. A channel error can induce mistracking between the companding logics of the coder and decoder, causing severe quality degradation. Still, with its slower adaptation, CVSD is more error resistant than ADM.

18.4.5   Other Waveform Coding and Hybrid Techniques for Voice

Most of the general digitization techniques described in Sec. 18.3 are suitable for voice. Companding and amplitude adaptive techniques are best suited to exploit the nonstationary statistical properties of voice in waveform coding methods. Predictive coding exploits the strong frequency dependence of the short-term spectral envelope for voiced sounds. To achieve bit rates below about 16 kbps, the inherent redundancies in voice must be exploited to a great extent. This is accomplished primarily through source coding techniques, in particular, vocoding. Digitization rates as low as 10 kbps are achievable through waveform coding but distortion is substantial.

Despite their bandwidth requirements, waveform coding techniques predominate because they are less complex and have broader applicability. Hybrid techniques offer a means of achieving bit rates and complexity between those of waveform reconstruction and vocoding. In these, a waveform technique typically is used for low frequencies, which are the most critical and contain characteristics most difficult to analyze. A vocoding technique is used for higher frequencies. Another hybrid technique with a different approach is sub-band coding, which offers good quality at moderate cost and complexity [TRIB 78]. Sub-band coding, in turn, has been combined with other codings for improved performance [MALA 81].

18.4.5.1   Sub-Band Coding

Sub-band coding (SBC) takes direct advantage of the known frequency characteristics of speech. The speech spectrum is divided into sub-bands through a bank of bandpass filters. A four-filter example is shown in Fig. 18.12. A five-band example is described in [CROC 78]. The bands need not be contiguous as shown, but excessive spectral gaps can cause reverberant quality in the signal.

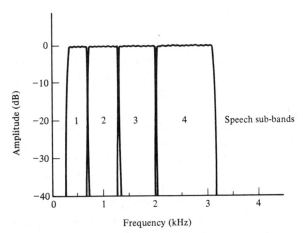

Figure 18.12. Sub-band partitioning of speech. (After [CROC 76], © 1976 IEEE.)

The signal within each band is sampled at the Nyquist rate for the band. The samples are APCM encoded at different bit rates for each band, with greater preference (a higher rate) used for the lower frequencies.

Quantization noise is not only reduced for the lower frequencies, it is segregated within each band so that errors occurring in one frequency range are precluded from extending into another range. The lower frequencies are important to pitch and formant structure, and contribute more to overall intelligibility of quantized speech than do higher frequencies, where unvoiced sounds and fricatives occur.

18.4.5.2   Adaptive Predictive Coding

Adaptive predictive coding (APC) [ATAL 70] is an enhancement of DPCM for speech. In a sense it is a hybrid of vocoding and waveform techniques. Pitch is predicted in exploiting the quasi-periodicity of voice signals (using a gain and delay circuit). Redundancies in the short-term spectral structure are removed (using a fourth- to eighth-order predictor with coefficients updated every 5 to 30 msec). The residual part of the signal not represented by the pitch and spectral structure is digitized by DPCM.

18.4.6   Source Coding: Vocoders

Source coding techniques are necessary for digitization of speech at bit rates below about 5 kbps. Today, such techniques are generally, if somewhat loosely, lumped under the term "vocoder," a contraction of "voice coder." Interestingly, the history of vocoders is as long as that of PCM speech digitization. Work on vocoders began in the 1930s at the Bell Laboratories with the channel vocoder, which demonstrated that waveform fidelity is not required by the human ear for intelligible synthesized speech. Because analysis/synthesis algorithms needed processing power that could be realized only in circuitry of considerable complexity and cost, vocoders until recently were used only in the most specialized situations.

With the advent of VLSI circuitry, the cost of vocoders should drop dramatically when sufficient demand exists. Key application areas are in the government and armed forces, where a level of voice communication security is required that can be provided only by digital encryption. This is combined with a requirement that communication channels be no more than standard voice bandwidth. Therefore, source coding is necessary.

The goals of vocoding are (1) to transmit speech meeting specific perceptual criteria (2) over the smallest possible bandwidth (3) with a device as small and inexpensive as possible (4) that is relatively insensitive to input speech characteristics and transmission errors. As a generalization, these goals could apply as well to waveform coding; the big difference, of course, revolves around the transmission bandwidth required by a vocoder. The "price" of the bandwidth reduction is measured in terms of the quality of the reproduced speech and robustness, as well as in dollars. Performance is often talker-dependent and, by definition, the speech output quality is synthetic. The degree of this effect is related to the precision of extraction and excitement of pitch.

The word "robustness" is meant to imply the degree of tolerance of a device (or system) to a less than ideal environment. The environment of a voice digitizer includes the communication channel interconnecting the transmitter/coder and the receiver/ decoder. The channel is subject to distortion and errors. The very fact that a vocoder achieves lower bandwidth by removal of redundancies makes it less tolerant of errors in transmission. Another environmental factor is background noise or extraneous sounds that may be mixed with the talker's voice. These are intrusions which a vocoder is not designed to accept; they lead to distortion by "confusing" the pitch algorithm. A related factor is talker dependency. Vocoders are characterized by careful adjustment of a large number of parameters. These parameters are all too often chosen from a limited sample of voices and the result is a poor fit whenever voice characteristics differ significantly from the sample [GOLD 79].

Vocoding can be defined as the creation of an electrical analog for voice. Most vocoders analyze the input waveform, or its short-term spectra, and compute the principal parameters for describing a simplified model of the voice at a particular instant. Included are the resonant structure of the vocal tract, that is, the formant structure; an estimate of pitch, or fundamental frequency; and the voiced and unvoiced excitation. Vocoders track envelopes primarily as a spectral rather than a temporal operation. A replica, although not exact, of the original speech is synthesized on the basis of the parameters. Vocoder techniques differ in the form of the parametric description, in how they extract speech features, and in how they reconstruct speech using these features. The different parametric descriptions of the voice signal that are used include:

- Channel vocoding—sampled envelope at specific frequencies plus pitch [GOLD 67, FLAN 72, BIAL 70, KING 80].
- Formant vocoding—formant frequencies plus pitch [UN 78].
- Cepstrum[4] vocoding—orthogonal function with logarithm of power spectrum expanded into a cosine series [SCHR 66, FLAN 72]. Also includes "homomorphic" vocoding [GOLD 79].
- Correlation vocoding—sampled short-term auto- or cross-correlation function [SCHR 66, FLAN 72].
- Linear prediction coefficient vocoding (LPC)—spectral envelope described by linear prediction coefficients [ATAL 71, MAKH 75, SAMB 77].

All vocoding techniques attempt to approximate the short-term power spectrum of speech but disregard most of the phase information in the waveform because the human ear is very sensitive to pitch but relatively insensitive to phase. Phase distortions that correspond to delay distortion exceeding 50 msec modify the short-

---

[4]"Cepstrum" is a term that refers to the spectrum of the log-amplitude spectrum. It is itself a transformation of the word "spectrum."

term amplitude spectrum and are audible as a reverberant quality of the voice signal [SCHR 66]. Reasonably natural sounding speech can result, but speaker recognition is not necessarily preserved.

Three of the more promising vocoding techniques for the future are channel, homomorphic (cepstrum), and linear predictive vocoding.

18.4.6.1   Channel Vocoding

(Spectrum) channel vocoding (CV) was the earliest analysis/synthesis technique. However, new applications continue to be found [GOLD 81]. A channel vocoder uses bandpass filters to divide the voice signal into frequency subchannels as sub-band coding does. But the short-term amplitude spectrum in each subchannel is measured after rectification, usually by a square-law circuit, and integration or low-pass filtering. This yields samples, spaced along the frequency axis, of the spectral envelope which is so important for perception. Simultaneously, separate circuitry is used to determine the spectral fine structure—voiced and unvoiced excitations and, when voiced, the pitch frequency.

Each of the parameters is encoded, often using PCM or DPCM for selected features which have significant redundancy or correlation, then multiplexed together and transmitted to a receiver where the composite bit stream is decoded and used to synthesize voice. A channel vocoder analyzer and synthesizer are illustrated in Fig. 18.13. Resulting voice quality is determined by the number of subchannels (from 8 to 100, where 16 is common) and their associated bandwidths, by the size of guard bands or degree of overlap between subchannels, by the voiced/unvoiced detection and pitch extraction circuits, by characteristics of the rectifiers and low-pass filters, and by the encoding techniques.

Although present technology is reducing its cost, channel vocoding remains relatively expensive and has inferior quality compared with other techniques. It does, however, work well for multiple-rate algorithms. Quality problems occur with discrimination of voiced and unvoiced sounds; preservation of the pitch inflection pattern over time; avoiding octave errors in pitch extraction; use of a pulse source that does not reflect details and changes in the source voice signal; imposition of granularity by the number, bandwidth, and spacing of the analyzing filters; and adequate coverage of the amplitude spectrum [FLAN 72]. Transmission of the spectral envelope samples requires much less bandwidth for a given quality than does transmission of signal samples, but further reductions are possible. Three techniques often mentioned for reducing redundancy in channel vocoders are pattern matching, peak picking (formant vocoding), and transformations. Attention to details in digital implementations and use of innovative methods to track pitch are improving channel vocoders also.

In pattern matching, frequency versus amplitude spectral information is approximately represented by a limited number of patterns. For each time sample, the best match is selected and a code is transmitted specifying the pattern or, for further bit reduction, the pattern address. Filter circuits smooth the transition from one

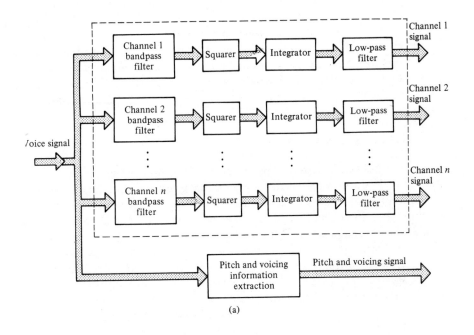

(a)

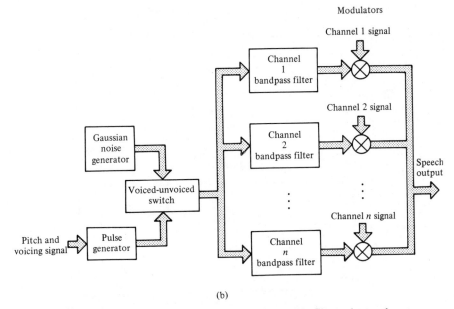

(b)

Figure 18.13. (a) Channel vocoder analyzer. (b) Channel vocoder synthesizer. (After [BAYL 73], © 1973 IEEE.)

pattern to the next. Pitch and voicing information must be transmitted together with the pattern for voice synthesis.

In peak picking, only a few (three to five) of the channel signals instead of the entire bank are transmitted at each instant. This eliminates transmission of redundant information since neighboring channels in the vocoder are strongly correlated relative to the spectral information (i.e., energy) but not on a sample-by-sample basis. The transmitted channels represent the local maxima of the short-term spectrum, the formants.

18.4.6.2 Cepstrum Vocoding

Speech is a combination of pitch from a voice source and shaping by the vocal tract into the form represented in Fig. 18.10. Cepstrum vocoding is based on separation of the source and tract effects. In the power spectrum, the vocal tract produces a low-frequency ripple and the vocal source produces a high-frequency ripple, which are emphasized by taking the logarithm. The logarithmic spectrum thus has a sharp peak corresponding to the high-frequency source ripples and a broader peak corresponding to the low-frequency format structure [NOLL 67]. Squaring the second spectrum makes the source periodicity peak more pronounced. The function, which is the square of the Fourier transform of the logarithm power spectrum, is called the *cepstrum*. A cepstrum is illustrated in Fig. 18.14b for a voiced speech interval like the one in Fig. 18.14a (and Fig. 18.10). The strong peaks correspond to the pitch period; it is the reciprocal of the period of the time signal.

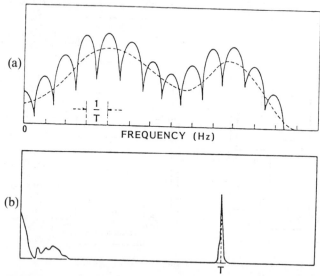

Figure 18.14. (a) Logarithm power spectrum of a voiced speech segment showing spectral periodicity resulting from pitch periodicity. (b) Cepstrum with sharp peak corresponding to spectral periodicity. (From [NOLL 67], by permission.)

A series of short-term cepstra are transmitted to a receiver, where they are examined to determine the maximum peaks and frequency of peaks. These can be used to determine whether the segment is unvoiced, or voiced with a particular pitch period.

Despite its increased precision and its relative insensitivity to phase and amplitude factors, cepstrum vocoding is characterized by degraded voice naturalness and speaker recognition. However, improved CCD (charge-coupled device) technology may yield compact, high-resolution Fourier transform devices and encourage further development of this method.

18.4.6.3 Linear Predictive Coding

Linear predictive coding (LPC) is a relatively recent technique [ATAL 71]. Like correlation vocoding, it uses the time waveform instead of the frequency spectrum to obtain the short-term amplitude spectrum, but LPC avoids the problems of correlation coding techniques by the way in which it uses autocorrelation information for synthesis. It is emerging as a preferred technique for digitization at low bit rates.

LPC is a source coder similar to an APC waveform reconstruction coder in that M-order predictor coefficients are updated for each short segment of speech. The vocal tract shape at periodic intervals is modeled as if it has M consecutive cylindrical segments, each of equal length. A transversal filter with M tapped delay lines in a feedback loop replaces the filter bank in a channel vocoder to represent the vocal tract. The filter is designed to be so accurate that transmission of an error signal like APC's is unnecessary. The residual signal after a sufficient number of prediction stages consists largely of vocal tract excitation information and is adequately represented by the parameters of voicing, pitch, and gain. LPC can use pitch excited, voice excited, or residual excited source excitation [MAKH 76]. The order M, which determines accuracy, is chosen as a function of waveform sampling rate and digitization; however, in practical implementations, use of more than eight coefficients gives very little improvement.

The predictor coefficients are functionally analogous to the subchannel signal components of a channel vocoder. The coefficients can be preferentially encoded as shown in Tab. 18.3, with more bits used for the relatively more important earlier taps. They set the gross spectral shape while later taps define details.

Use of higher bit transmission rates than 3.4 kbps can allow more frequent parameter updating, more taps, more precise quantization, and error correction for key bits. These improve performance but usually not in proportion to the increase in bits. The 600-bps digitizer uses pattern matching with $128 = 2^7$ patterns. It scored 72% intelligibility in a diagnostic rhyme test [KANG 76].

The prediction error is

$$e(n) = \sum_{i=0}^{M} a(i)s(n-i) = s(n) + \sum_{i=1}^{M} a(i)s(n-i) = s(n) - s'(n).$$

Table 18.3. *Typical LPC Parameter Coding Table.*

	2400 bps LPC	600 bps LPC
Frame rate	44.444 Hz	40 Hz
Vocal tract filter parameters		
First 4 taps	20 (5 each)	
Next 2 taps	8 (4 each)	Pattern matching
Last 4 taps	12 (3 each)	
Subtotal 10 taps	40 bits per frame	7 bits per frame
Excitation Parameters		
Voiced/unvoiced decision	1 bit per frame	1 bit per frame
Amplitude	6 bits per frame	4 bits per frame
Pitch frequency	6 bits per frame	5 bits per double frame
Subtotal	13 bits per frame	15 bits per double frame
Synchronization	1 bit per frame	1 bit per double frame
Total bits	54 bits per frame	30 bits per double frame

Source: [COUL 77], by permission.

$s(n)$ is the amplitude of the nth sample and $s'(n)$ is its predicted value. The predictor coefficients, $a(i)$, where $a(0) = 1$, provide a measure of each cylindrical segment's cross-sectional area and volume. In the z-transform domain,

$$E(z) = S(z)A(z) \quad \text{where } A(z) = 1 - F(z) = 1 + \sum_{i=1}^{M} a(i)z^{-1}$$

$A(z)$ is the inverse filter model whose parameters can be determined directly from the time waveform by applying a least-squares criterion to $e(n) = s(n) - s'(n)$. A linear criterion is chosen to obtain tractable equations. It also results in excellent speech analysis. Solution of the equations [MARK 76] varies with the index limits over which minimization occurs. The covariance method minimizes error over the interval $[M, N-1]$, where N is the number of sequential speech samples used in calculating the covariance matrix elements. The autocorrelation method minimizes error over an effective interval of $[0, N+M-1]$. The advantages and disadvantages of each method are discussed in [MAKH 75].

Minimizing the error signal of LPC is equivalent to estimating the voice signal more accurately at the formants than between them on the spectral envelope. Such concentration gives LPC an advantage over channel and cepstrum vocoding techniques that make no such distinction in sampling. Voiced/unvoiced determination and pitch extraction remain common problems. LPC can be refined by variable-rate transmission. Then only parameters that have changed significantly between time frames are transmitted.

18.4.7 Technique Comparisons

Each technique has a different device cost and complexity, requires different bandwidth, results in different quantizing error, and gives different quality of output under ideal and error-prone transmission environments. Some advantages and disadvantages of the voice techniques are mentioned as a part of each technique description. For the more general techniques applied to voice:

- PCM offers high quality at relatively low cost but requires bandwidth greater than the analog source.
- DM is highly intelligible although somewhat noisy at lower bit rates; low-cost LSI devices are available, but oversampling is necessary and required bandwidth is still high.

Comparison of the waveform techniques is important because they are being used to achieve good voice quality over telephone lines. Vocoding techniques are important where both digitized signals and low transmission rates are required. The waveform techniques yield poor-quality signals at the lower transmission rates.

18.4.7.1   Complexity and Cost

Voice digitization techniques can be compared on several bases. One comparative listing of complexity factors and ranges of digitization rates for medium- to high-quality voice, as taken from Tab. 18.1, is shown in Tab. 18.4. The trend is clear—digitization rates are lowered by increasingly complex equipment. It can also be

Table 18.4.   *Techniques Compared by Complexity and Digitization Rate.*

Technique	Complexity[a]	Digitization Rate (kbps)	Digitization Technique
Log PCM	2–5	48–64	
ADM	1	24–40	
CVSD	1	16–32	Waveform
ADPCM	2–3	16–32	reconstruction
SBC	10–100	9.6–24	and
APC	50	6–20	hybrids
ATC	50	7.2–16	↑
VEV	50	7.2–9.6	--------------------
LPC	100	2.4–9.6	↓
CV	100	2.4–4.8	Vocoding
FT	500	0.6–2.4	

[a]The complexity is calculated by a very approximate, relative count of logic gates.
Source: After [FLAN 79], © 1979 IEEE.

inferred that the lower the digitization rate, the higher the cost, since cost is closely related to complexity. Of course, cost is also determined by the volume of production and the scale of circuit integration, so it can be expected that the more popular techniques will have lower costs.

With vocoding at very low digitization rates, communication system cost and complexity can also be adversely affected by constraints associated with the pitch extraction problem mentioned previously. The quality of the microphone must be high, to minimize gross distortion of the voice waveform and to supply a high signal-to-noise ratio. For similar reasons, the speaker and the vocoder itself should be separated only by a short distance, high-quality transmission line. Conventional telephone handset carbon microphones and telephone lines are deficient in both respects.

18.4.7.2   Subjective Judgment

Use of SNR and distortion measurements for objective comparison of quality generally are inapplicable to most voice digitization (and particularly to vocoding) techniques. Some of the problems with objective evaluation of quality are addressed in [MAKH 76]. Subjective judgment of voice quality can be affected by the diction, intensity, and intonation of the speaker; the quality of the input and output transducers (microphones or loudspeakers); relative loudness of the reproduced voice; room size and acoustical qualities; foreknowledge of what is being said (which is an unavoidable problem when making the relative comparisons that seem more reasonable to obtain than absolute judgments); the content of the speech; and the listener [GOLD 67]. Waveform coders with their relatively high fidelity are not so bothered by background noise and individual speaker voice qualities. Work is continuing on objective evaluation of vocoders [VISW 78] and correlation of objective and subjective measures for speech quality from both waveform coders and vocoders [BARN 78]. An extensive overview is contained in [MARS 78].

The IEEE Recommended Practice for Speech Quality Measurements (Standard 297-69) describes three methods: the Isopreference Method, the Relative Preference Method, and the Category-Judgment Method. Each of the methods has some shortcomings and some relative advantages, so a single method was not recommended. These methods are briefly outlined below. Details of their use, evaluation, and references can be found in the standard.

In the *Isopreference Method,* the signal being evaluated is compared with a reference signal with various levels of degradation. The isopreference level is the SNR of the reference signal at the degradation level where the listeners are equally divided in their preferences between the evaluated and reference signals.

In the *Relative Preference Method,* the signal being evaluated is compared on a pairwise basis with a set of reference signals exhibiting different types of speech distortion. All combinations are compared in a random order. The results are analyzed to place the evaluated signal on a preference scale in relation to the reference signals.

In the *Category-Judgment Method,* the signal being evaluated is categorized, for example, as Unsatisfactory, Poor, Fair, Good, or Excellent. Presentation of one or more reference signals allows an experimenter to define the quality categories. An example of an extensive set of comparative tests using this method is reported in [DAUM 78].

To a listener, the most significant characteristic of speech is voice quality. The listener judges quality by whether he or she can determine:

- What is said (intelligibility, the barest requirement)
- Who said it (speaker recognition)
- How the talker felt (emotional state)
- Sex, age, and educational background of the talker

PCM provides good quality and is the standard against which other techniques are compared. Generally, reducing bandwidth much below that required for PCM sacrifices quality and "naturalness," which can only be measured subjectively. Naturalness, as opposed to having a mechanical "robot" accent, can be important. The substitution of electrically generated pulses or noise for part of the reconstructed signal is the source of the mechanical sound. Recognition of the speaker, his or her emotional state, and other individual qualities can be lost. The quality characteristics are difficult to quantify.

18.4.7.3   Quality Categorization

Four categories of voice quality have been defined [FLAN 79]. The current range of digitization rates for the four categories is shown in Fig. 18.15. Progress is still being made. Waveform coding techniques are usually designed for communications quality or better. Vocoding techniques generally give synthetic quality. Hybrid techniques usually achieve communications quality.

Toll quality matches the quality of voice typically achieved over telephone toll lines: 0.2 to 3.2 kHz frequency range, 30 dB or greater SNR, 2 to 3% harmonic distortion. Commentary quality is usually adequate for radio broadcasting. The SNR and harmonic distortion are the same as for toll quality but the frequency range is wider, 0 to 7 kHz or more. High-quality sound (e.g., music) for frequencies from 0 to

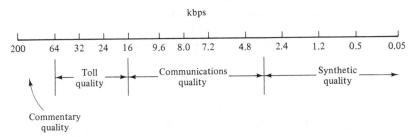

Figure 18.15. Digitization rates for quality categories. (After [FLAN 79], © 1979 IEEE.)

15 kHz requires a PCM sampling rate at 35 kHz and 13 bits per sample coding. The digitization rate is 450 kbps [CUCC 77]. Communications quality requires high intelligibility but allows detectable distortion and lessened speaker recognition. Synthetic quality lacks naturalness and its acceptability varies among individual speakers and listeners.

Each technique is affected differently by transmission errors. Quality degrades, and susceptibility to errors increases, with decreasing voice digitization rate and increasing removal of signal redundancies. The techniques with feedback, including all DPCM derivatives, propagate errors. But where differences are transmitted instead of signal values, the possible magnitude of errors is reduced. This can more than compensate, perceptually, for error propagation [JAYA 74]. Random errors and clustered errors have different impacts. Most studies have been made with randomly occurring errors. The analytic study of correlated errors in [WOLF 66] is an exception. This area will require much more work in view of future network possibilities (e.g., packetized voice) and because of the nature of errors in such networks (e.g., dropping an entire packet).

Digitized voice is much more tolerant of channel errors than are data. A BER of at least 10^{-5} is desirable for character text transmission; perhaps 10^{-8} or better is desirable for high-speed computer communication. In contrast, noticeable degradation of PCM voice occurs in the area of 10^{-4}, while severe degradation may be judged at 10^{-2} or even lower. Interestingly, delta modulation schemes, in spite of their lower bandwidth, are somewhat more tolerant than PCM to channel errors, remaining intelligible as low as BER $= 10^{-1}$, because the effective propagation of the error is less significant [UN 80]. As expected, vocoders are less robust, and may become hopelessly degraded at 5×10^{-2} [GOLD 79].

A comparison of $\mu255$ PCM with versions of three adaptive codec techniques—adaptively companded PCM, ADPCM, and ADM—are reported in [DAUM 78]. The tests were made in a simulated telephone network environment at various bit rates and bit error rates. The following conclusions can be drawn from the detailed results reported:

1. Compared with "straight PCM," the adaptive techniques have a bit-rate advantage of 12 to 24 kbps for equivalent subjective quality in a single encoding/decoding setup. In an extreme case, one version of ADPCM at 32 kbps had essentially the same rating as PCM at 64 kbps.
2. At extremes of bit-error rate (10^{-1} and 10^{-5}) the various techniques are tightly bunched in quality ratings. However, PCM is clearly inferior to the adaptive techniques in the important intermediate range, at equivalent bit rates. At an error rate around 10^{-3}, ADM is an order of magnitude more tolerant than PCM for the same quality rating.

Channel error effects are more marked with vocoding not only because of reduced redundancy at lower rates but also because of the sensitivity of simple pitch extraction and voicing detection circuits. The lower portion of the voice spectrum, which contributes little to intelligibility but might contain the fundamental frequency, is often missing in telephone signals. Vocoders must recreate the fundamental frequency from the available portion of the spectrum. Because it operates at lower data rates, vocoding requires accurate estimation of speech parameters for adequate voice synthesis; estimates are not reliable on a noisy or acoustically distorted signal or from a microphone in a standard handset. A noise-canceling microphone that requires the speaker's mouth to be very close helps eliminate some problems. All surrounding background noises are then blocked out. Only in unique circumstances where background noise has a known specific waveform, such as for rotating helicopter blades, can filters be designed to cancel the noise.

18.4.7.4   Error Control

Error control for real-time speech cannot be handled satisfactorily by error detection with automatic retransmission request (ARQ) as for data because of the excessive delay. Where channel error effects would become intolerable, say for a low voice digitization rate with much of the redundancy in speech eliminated, forward error correction (FEC) for bit protection is one option. FEC use is restricted primarily to crucial parameters, which might even be sent on a separate channel, to minimize overhead; but FEC requires redundancy to be built into the transmitted code so that error correction can be performed at the receiver. Redundancy in the code uses channel capacity just as redundancy in the signal does.

Effects of ideal error protection for the most significant bit and for the two most significant bits in waveform reconstruction techniques are described in [NOLL 75B]. The effect of sign and most significant magnitude (SIG MAG) bit protection on 3- and 4-bit APCM coder performance is described in [CROC 78], and shown for the 4-bit coder in Fig. 18.16.

18.4.7.5   Code Conversions

An additional source of errors for digitized voice traffic is conversion between code representations when more than one digitization technique is applied along the links between two users. The military has great interest in conversion because of their many different types of equipment which need to be interoperable.

The code conversion problem is a difficult one. Code conversion can be attempted by two basic methods: (1) by interfacing in the analog domain via an A/D → D/A → A/D sequence, or (2) by direct transformation via digital algorithmic or computational processes. In general, the latter is to be preferred but is more complex to develop and implement. Conversion via the analog domain is the more obvious approach, but results can be less than satisfactory.

Approaches have been proposed for a number of pairs of digitization techniques, but conversion is not possible between all the pairs. As a general rule, wideband techniques can be satisfactorily converted for interoperability; conversion between narrowband techniques is unsatisfactory; and conversions between wide-

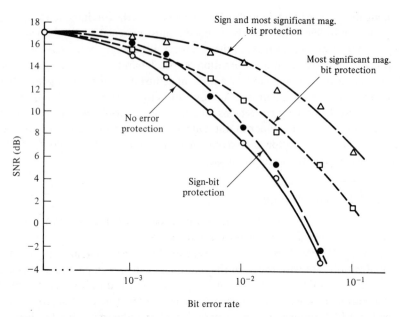

Figure 18.16. Effects of error protection on a coder. (After [CROC 78], copyright 1978, American Telephone and Telegraph Company, reprinted by permission.)

band and narrowband techniques are difficult or, for some particular combinations, effectively impossible because of intrinsic properties of the techniques that lead to unacceptable distortion.

Discussions of waveform code conversions are given in [OSBO 72], [OHNO 76], [GOOD 71], [LOCI 76], [LOCI 77], [GHOS 78], and [DUBN 78]; wideband/ narrowband conversions are covered in [CROC 77], [RABI 77], [GOOD 79], [SAMB 78], [GOLD 78], and [PECA 78]. Table 18.5 summarizes the results of some special conversion examples that are of particular interest. Acceptable conversions work in both directions. The marginal quality of conversions in both directions between LPC and SBC (five bands) is a combination of the mechanical buzziness of LPC and the reverberant effect of SBC [GOOD 79]. The conversion in either direction between LPC and CVSD is not acceptable because a CVSD codec has difficulty tracking a "peaky" waveform such as that of LPC, and coefficient determination by an LPC analyzer is highly inaccurate where CVSD has added quantization noise to the input voice [CROC 77, RABI 77, GOOD 79].

18.4.7.6 Tandeming

Many networks cannot support the higher digital transmission rates on an end-to-end basis; others may use differing digitization techniques. Frequently, reconversion of digitized signals to the analog domain is required to transmit a particular link or node. Successive A/D → D/A → A/D → D/A conversions, or "tandeming," result in significant loss of quality with some digitization techniques and unacceptable quality with others (in particular, vocoders). In general, the greater the digitization rate, the greater the number of tandem operations that can be tolerated. PCM is best in this regard, and delta modulation variants can be quite good.

In the previously mentioned tests reported in [DAUM 78], it was found that the quality 64-kbps PCM with tandem encodings (two to eight) is superior to that of adaptive techniques *operating at lower bit rates.* For example, eight tandem encodings of 64-kbps PCM could still be rated as "good," while eight tandem encodings of 32-kbps ADPCM rated as "poor."[5]

18.4.8   A Lower Bound on Speech Compression

One way to visualize a practical lower bound, and goal, for speech bandwidth compression is to consider the human input–output process. Information can be spoken and comprehended at a rate as high as 150 words/min. Assuming an average of six characters per word, this is the equivalent of 900 characters/min or 15 characters/sec. If ASCII encoding of characters were used at 7 bits/character, we would have a data rate of about 100 bits/sec. In most languages, statistical coding (such as Huffman coding) could reduce the bit rate to perhaps 70 bits/sec.

The objective of speech recognition systems is to convert speech input to a data stream representing words (see Sec. 18.6.3). A Speech Synthesizer system performs the conjugate function; it produces speech from an output data stream (see Sec. 18.6.4). It could be arranged for the Speech Recognizer output data stream to be coded in a fashion as outlined above, and for the Speech Synthesizer to accept the same code as its input. Then the Recognizer could be viewed as the transmitter and the Synthesizer as the receiver in a voice communication link operating at 70 bits/sec.

There would be two "costs" to be paid for such extreme compression. The first is the considerable cost of the processing power required by the Recognizer and the Synthesizer to operate with a substantial vocabulary in real time. The second price paid would be the completely synthetic quality of the reproduced speech—the information content would be contained wholly in the word meaning, since the subtleties of the speaker's voice would be lost. It should be possible, however, to encode inflections and other speech values with a few additional bits, perhaps taking advantage of speaker (as contrasted with speech) recognition techniques (see Sec. 18.6.2).

18.5   IMAGE PROCESSING AND DIGITIZATION

Images fundamentally differ from voice by the fact that images are at least two-dimensional, while voice is one-dimensional (with time). Consequently, even a still

---

[5]One author, however, has heard comparisons of a particular implementation of 32 kbps CVSD with 64 kbps PCM. The quality of each was equivalent in the range of 8 to 10 tandems.

Table 18.5. *Conversion Examples.*

Technique	Conversion	Technique
μ-law-log PCM	Acceptable	A-law log PCM
LPCM, log PCM	Acceptable	DM, ADM, ADPCM
PCM (64 kbps)	Acceptable	CVSD (32 or 16 kbps)
SBC (16 kbps)	Marginal	LPC (2.4 kbps)
CVSD (16 kbps)	Not acceptable	LPC (9.6–2.4 kbps)

image such as a photograph cannot be directly related to a simple serial amplitude-versus-time waveform as can a voice signal. The transmission of an image requires a representation of its spatial relationships in addition to a representation of its patterns of lightness and darkness.

The most common process for representing spatial relationships is based on an elemental coordinate system for the image. Consider a photograph on which has been ruled a large number of horizontal and vertical lines, where there are M rows and N columns. The result is a grid, or mosaic, pattern containing $M \times N$ cells called *pixels* (a shortened version of "picture elements"). The relative average value of brightness or darkness of each pixel can be mapped into the amplitude domain, as can color in the case of a colored image.

Clearly, the accuracy (resolution) with which an image is represented is a function of the number of pixels and the dynamic range of the amplitude function. Careful examination of many photographs reproduced in books will reveal that the image is made up of a series of dots arranged on diagonal rows and columns. Since the image is printed on a white background, the "amplitude" of a dot, represented by its area, determines the degree of blackness for that particular element. A range of resolutions can be achieved by this technique. Compare a photograph in this book with a photograph in a newspaper, typically printed with about 50 lines per inch.

18.5.1 Television Video Transmission

Television transmission is based on the sequential scanning of an image. The number of horizontal lines is 525 in the U.S. NTSC (National Television Standards Committee) system, or 625 lines in many foreign systems. Conceptually, a scanning "spot" starts at the upper left corner of an image and travels horizontally to scan the topmost row of pixels. Upon reaching the right edge of the image, the spot "flies back" rapidly to the left edge, is moved downward by the proper distance, and then proceeds to scan the second line; and so on, until the spot reaches the bottom right-hand position, whereupon it quickly returns to the starting position. (To be quite correct, the first picture field of NTSC television scans odd-numbered lines $\{1,3,5,\ldots\}$ and the second field scans even-numbered lines $\{2,4,6,\ldots\}$. The two fields are interleaved to make up a complete 525-line frame.)

The amplitude of the spot as it moves along its scan line is modulated by changes in the brightness of the image. The resultant signal is a monochromatic analog representation of the sequential lines of the picture, interrupted by the horizontal flyback and vertical retrace intervals. Synchronization pulses are added to these intervals to ensure that the receiver is properly tracking the transmitter provided for the correct spatial reconstruction of the image.

Vertical resolution of the image is fixed by the number of scan lines used, while horizontal resolution is determined by the bandwidth of the scanning–transmission–reproduction chain. The necessary baseband bandwidth can be roughly estimated as follows (ignoring retrace and blanking invervals):

1. Assume NTSC television with 525 lines vertical resolution. For equivalent horizontal resolution judged by the sharpness of an edge (i.e., sudden transition from black to white), determine the rise time of the video signal from one extreme value to the other. For this, the approximate relation of Eq. (7.7) can be used:

$$\text{bandwidth (MHz)} \approx 0.4 / \text{rise time } (\mu \sec)$$

2. With NTSC television, 30 complete frames of 525 lines are transmitted per second. Each line then requires $1/(3)\,(525) \times 63.5$ μsec.

3. The aspect ratio of a television picture is four units horizontal and three units vertical. Therefore, horizontal resolution comparable to vertical resolution would require the equivalent of $(525) \times (4/3) = 700$ lines of horizontal resolution. The required rise time is then $(63.5\ \mu\sec)/(700) = 90$ nsec. Using the approximation above, the required bandwidth would be about 4.4 MHz.

In fact, high-quality NTSC television transmission does require a bandwidth of about 4.5 MHz.

18.5.1.1 Color Television

So far, we have considered only monochromatic (black and white) imaging. Color television imaging is based on the principle of additive perception of color by the human eye. A particular shade of color can be produced by an appropriately weighted mixture of the three additive primary colors: red, blue, and green. In color television, the scene to be transmitted is viewed by three monochromatic imaging devices, each through a red, green, or blue filter. Reproduction of the image is accomplished by exciting red, green, and blue phosphors in the display screen by the correspondingly filtered monochromatic signals. If nothing more were done, color television would require three times the bandwidth of black-and-white television.

Advantage can be taken of psycho-optic phenomena to reduce the bandwidth required for image transmission. This is analogous to what is done in some methods of voice coding. In television, the feat of squeezing color transmission into the same bandwidth originally established for monochrome transmission is accomplished by application of two key contrivances, both dependent on the human perception of images and the subjective evaluation of adequate reproduction in the presence of compromises.

The first contrivance takes advantage of the fact that a color television picture is made up of two principal signals: the "Y" luminance signal, which corresponds to the normal monochrome picture; and the "I/Q" chrominance signal,[6] in which the color information is expressed as relative signal phases corresponding to the primary colors (red, green, and blue components). The "Y" signal is amplitude modulated on the carrier as is normally done for monochrome transmissions. Therefore, a monochrome receiver responds to a color transmission as though it were in black and white. The lower bandwidth "I/Q" chrominance signal is phase-modulated on a subcarrier and then interleaved in the higher-frequency (and lower energy) portion of the transmitted spectrum. There is no noticeable degradation of picture quality in a properly tuned receiver. An improperly tuned receiver will display a "wormy" picture due to interference between the high-frequency luminance and the chrominance signals.

The second contrivance permits the bandwidth of the chrominance signals to be much less than the luminance signal, thus minimizing potential interference effects. It has been shown that the eye can be fooled into accepting a smeared color boundary as "sharp" as long as the luminance component itself is sharp. Thus the eye accepts the degraded color information superimposed on the basic black-and-white picture as being acceptably equivalent in resolution for most television scenes. Some critical television viewers, however, do notice the degradation in some high-resolution images (e.g., cartoons) in which the demarcation between picture elements is marked. For this reason, color video display units using alphanumerics or graphics must have full color bandwidth.

18.5.2 Digitization of Television-Type Images

Broadcast television signals are analog and occupy an ideal baseband bandwidth of about 5 MHz. Sampling at the Nyquist rate would require a minimum sample rate of 10 MHz. The eye requires 50 or more discrete amplitude (gray scale) levels for acceptable image quality [PRAT 78]. Thus a minimum of 6 bits per sample is required for good quality. If straightforward PCM encoding is used, a bit rate of at least 60 Mbps would be necessary for digital transmission of monochrome television. An equivalent estimate can be made as follows, based on the rough analysis presented earlier in this section. Assume that equivalent vertical and horizontal resolution is desired and that the vertical/horizontal aspect ratio is 3:4. The number of pixels per frame is $(525) \times (4/3) \times (525) = 3.7 \times 10^5$. At 30 frames per second, this is approximately 11×10^6 pixels per second. Coding each pixel brightness level with 6 bits results in a rate of 66 Mbps.

If each of the three primary color images were equivalently coded, a rate of about 200 Mbps would be required for color television transmission. Higher-quality requirements, such as for networks, master tape digital recording, and the higher-resolution European standards, would necessitate even higher data rates.

[6]In-phase and Quadrature (I/Q) describe a two-dimensional phase space representing the color spectrum.

Fortunately, techniques are available to reduce this rather appalling requirement for bandwidth. One approach is to work with the previously described composite color video signal, in which chroma information is interleaved.

18.5.2.1   Pulse-Code Modulation (PCM) Encoding

The numerical example developed previously is the basic form of PCM coding. In practice, for color television the composite video baseband including the I/Q-modulated chrominance subcarriers is digitized. The sampling rate is fixed at an exact integral multiple of the chrominance subcarrier frequency of 3.579545 MHz. This maintains the proper phase relationships necessary for demodulation. Usually the multiple is 3, giving a sampling rate of about 10.74 MHz, which also satisfies the Nyquist criterion. Encoding at 8 bits/sample leads to a bit rate of 85.92 Mbps. Transmission of PCM-encoded television is accomplished on two DS3 carriers, providing a data rate of 89.47 Mbps. The extra bits are often used for separately modulated sound channel and additional synchronization and control information.

Just as in the case for digital transmission of speech, "straight" PCM is the foundation for transmission of images. Its data rate of nearly 90 Mbps requires prodigious transmission capacity and motivates considerable work toward the reduction of necessary bandwidth. The primary classes of techniques that have been proposed and investigated [PRAT 78, CAMA 79] are described briefly in the following section. Some techniques are directly analogous to those used in speech processing; others are more peculiar to the characteristics of images.

18.5.2.2   Digital Point Processing

Digital point processing techniques are based on the point-by-point nature of the scanning process. Thus these techniques can be regarded as one-dimensional processing, which is relatively simpler to implement than the two-dimensional processing described in the preceding section.

PCM with Companding

Strictly speaking, PCM encoding itself is a point processing technique. Bandwidth reduction could be effected simply by reducing the number of quantization levels, but degradation of image quality would result. Like the ear, the eye does not perceive changes in intensity linearly across the brightness scale.

Companding can be used in encoding television signals to reduce the number of quantization levels required, similar to the μ- and A-law companding used in speech processing and described in Sec. 18.4. Reductions of about 2:1 with subjectively equivalent visual results have been reported.

Pseudo-Noise Quantization

With smaller quantization steps, one of the most objectionable effects to the eye is the sudden jumping of brightness steps in an image area that should display a smooth gradation of levels. The addition of a low-level noise-like dithering signal

[SCHU 64] to the scanned image signal prior to quantization reduces the apparent "steppiness" of the image. The eye tends to average a field of small differences in brightness. The averaging effect is even more pronounced with successive images via television because the eye integrates the random granularity of the images. The same effect exists with motion pictures—the graininess of the image is much less apparent when the film is in motion as compared with the projection of a single frame.

Gray Scale Manipulation

Other schemes based on related psycho-optic phenomena have been proposed [BISI 66]. The Improved Gray Scale system relates a 3-bit code word for a given pixel to that of a previous pixel so as to induce a rapid fluctuation of displayed pixel levels; the averaging tendency of the eye gives the impression of less contouring than would be apparent with fewer bits per sample, but at the cost of a grainier picture. The coarse–fine system transmits either the three most significant (coarse) or the three least significant (fine) bits of a linearly quantized signal, depending on the degree of change in level. The decision can also be based on an adaptive algorithm involving the values of past samples. These techniques provide a compression factor approaching 2:1.

18.5.2.3 Statistical (Source) Coding Techniques

Images, like speech, contain a large amount of redundancy. An examination of the nearest photograph at hand will probably reveal relatively large areas of the same intensity or color. This suggests that some form of statistical coding, such as Huffman coding, could result in substantial savings in data rate. Those pixels having a high frequency of occurrence would be assigned short code words. The longer code words would be left for pixels occurring at low frequency. Although this is theoretically correct, there are serious practical implementation problems. Analysis of an image to determine its statistics requires a great deal of memory and computing power. Although this might be worthwhile under some circumstances for a single still image, the requirements for television would be overwhelming. If a deterministic assignment of pixel values in a code lookup table were made, an image with a poor match of statistics could even result in an increased bit rate.

A variant of statistical coding is based on the fact that most adjacent pixels are highly correlated. For natural monochrome images, it has been established that the most likely difference between pixels coded with 6 bits is about 2 to 3 bits. A codec can be constructed so that the code word for a given pixel is selected on the basis of a deterministic (or algorithmic) conditional probability based on the preceding pixel.

Encoders/decoders for either form of statistical coding involve a substantial amount of processing, but this disadvantage will be diminished with further advances in LSI circuitry. Statistical encoding can achieve compression ratios of 2:1 or better with little loss in image quality.

18.5.2.4 Frame-Oriented Coding

There is a very large amount of redundancy between contiguous frames in cases where the motion between frames is small. This is most often the case with television pictures and can be exploited in a number of ways. The simplest, although not truly a processing technique, is merely to reduce the rate at which frames are transmitted. The majority of commercially available video compression equipment is based on this idea. The most popular implementation is the so-called "frame grabber" or "freeze-frame" technique. "Slow-scan" TV is similar, differing primarily in the mode of buffering and presentation. The displayed result can be slowly scanned and changed as new data are received, or a new frame can be displayed as quickly as its recognition is completed.

If, for example, only one of 30 complete frames of PCM-encoded television is transmitted per second, the necessary bandwidth is reduced by 1/30, to 3 Mbps, where conventional PCM encoding is used. Some form of memory must be provided in the receiver to refresh the displayed image until receipt of the next frame is complete. Of course, the major drawback is an objectionable jumping of images in motion; in extreme cases, a visual jumble can result.

A more sophisticated form of processing is frame-replenishment coding. Comparisons are made between pixels of the current and the preceding frame and only differences are transmitted, accompanied by data necessary to locate a changed pixel properly (say, its address in X-Y coordinates).

Frame-oriented systems have the disadvantage of requiring substantial high-speed buffering in both transmitter and receiver equipments. They are quite costly at current levels of technology. Nevertheless, transmission savings can be substantial. Quality under a frame-replenishment system has been rated as excellent except during periods of extreme motion. The bandwidth reduction ratio is 6 to 8:1. The technique has been experimentally applied to Picturephone transmission.

18.5.2.5   Predictive Coding

Predictive coding techniques analogous to those used for speech coding have been successfully applied to television transmission, and the descriptions given in Secs. 18.3 and 18.4 also apply here. As with the equivalent speech coders, image prediction coding is based on establishing the amplitude value of a given pixel on some form of history of the immediately preceding pixel values.

Delta Modulation (DM)

In the simplest form of predictive coding, a single bit representing a fixed plus or minus amplitude value is transmitted for each pixel. Thus the transmitted bit is interpreted as a sign: plus or minus. The receiver simply adds or subtracts a fixed value to the value of the previous pixel to determine the value for the current pixel, and integrates the result for a reconstruction of the scanning waveform. Achievement of acceptable results with delta modulation requires oversampling (sampling at a rate greater than the Nyquist rate). In effect this increases the number of pixels per image, thus reducing somewhat the bit-rate advantage of delta modulation. Nevertheless, a bit-rate reduction of 2 to 3:1 can be achieved with acceptable image quality. The complexity of a delta-modulation codec is low.

Simple delta modulation for images has the same flaws as for speech—slope overload distortion and granularity. Again, variations of the scheme are advantageous. Various schemes modify the step size by basing it on previous sample history. It should be pointed out that application of such modifications to delta modulation results in a convergence of the technique toward DPCM and adaptive predictive coding, discussed below.

Differential Pulse Code Modulation (DPCM)

The problems inherent in simple delta modulation can be overcome to a major extent by increasing the number of quantization levels used to convey the difference signal information. Such a technique is embodied in the important Differential Pulse-Code Modulation (DPCM) concept. Its operation is described in Sec. 18.3. As applied for the coding of images, it is especially important that the quantizer is contained within the feedback loop to provide an uncorrelated coding error. In the human vision process, uncorrelated errors are much more tolerable than correlated errors. Usual implementations of DPCM coders quantize the difference signal to 3 or 4 bits, resulting in a 2:1 bandwidth reduction over conventional PCM using 6 to 8 bits. DPCM-encoded image quality has been rated as virtually indistinguishable when compared with PCM in most cases, including image motion.

Adaptive Predictive Coding (APC)

Advantage can be taken of the correlation between successive pixels by using information from the preceding pixels to form a prediction of the current pixel value. This technique can be applied to both delta modulation and DPCM coders. With adaptive delta-modulation coding, a single plus or minus bit is transmitted as before, but the actual amplitude difference added (or subtracted) in the decoder is made to be a function of the signs of the previous (typically, three) pixel values. This results in a variable slope of each pixel value and effectively reduces slope overload effects at points where brightness levels are changing rapidly and reduces granularity in areas where the level is changing slowly [WINK 65].

Some work has been directed toward a combination of DPCM and delta-modulation coding [FREI 71]. The idea is to use adaptive delta modulation during most picture areas in which pixel-to-pixel changes are small, then switch to DPCM in areas of frequent changes. Results with such a coder, at a bit rate of 2 bits per pixel, have been judged as equivalent to 3-bit DPCM. One disadvantage of this technique is codec complexity, but this could be overcome with VLSI circuitry. Another disadvantage is that the coding rate is variable, depending on frequency of image change, thus requiring a data buffer in both coder and decoder units.

Differential Frame Coding

Differential frame coding attempts to take advantage of the high degree of frame-to-frame redundancy by constructing a difference signal between pixels at the same location but in successive frames. Good performance has been achieved at 3-bits per pixel; the disadvantage of a large-capacity, high-speed buffer, however, does not appear to be warranted in view of equivalent results obtained by simpler implementation.

Linear Predictive Coding (LPC)

Linear predictive image coding uses *values* of previous pixels (again, typically three) to form a statistically weighted prediction of the current pixel value. Several algorithms have been proposed for determining the weights to be applied to previous samples [PRAT 78]. Theoretically, mean-square errors in the reconstructed image waveform are equivalent to 4-bit DPCM, using a second-order LPC coder at a rate of 1 bit per pixel.

Interpolative Coding

A simple example of interpolative coding with NTSC television is to delete every other field. (Recall that one frame comprises two fields; the first containing even-numbered lines, and the second containing odd-numbered lines.) This results in a 2:1 bandwidth reduction. In the receiver, the missing interlaced lines of the missing field are interpolated by an algorithm based on the transmitted field. Clearly, vertical resolution will correspondingly suffer, but a more acceptable, continuous-appearing image is presented.

Another form of interpolative coding is based on the idea of establishing a fixed error bound around the waveform resulting from the scanning operation. The coder attempts to fit a straight line of maximal length, containing points at the sample times within the error boundaries, such that the difference between the actual sample value and the line at the same instant in time does not exceed the error bounds. In a zero-order coder, the lines would be horizontal; the transmitted information is the amplitude of the line and its length. Higher-order coders can fit larger lines with given error boundaries because they allow a variable line slope; in these cases, information transmitted would consist of the line slope and its length.

An interpolative coder of zero order is also one form of run-length encoding. In the case of 1 bit of amplitude quantization, the technique effectively degenerates into two-level run-length encoding, an important data compression technique used in facsimile transmission.

18.5.2.6   Spatial Image Processing

The image coding techniques described in the preceding sections are characterized by their one-dimensionality; that is, they process one point (pixel) of an image in synchronism with the scanning or framing process. The adaptive and linear prediction techniques, while taking advantage of the high degree of correlation of a pixel value with its neighbors, do so only in a linear fashion, following the time sequentiality of the line scanning. Spatial processing techniques are not so constrained, and thus can take advantage of the two-dimensional correlation of a pixel with all its neighbors. Consequently, spatial processing can be expected to afford greater bandwidth reduction by virtue of the implicitly higher degree of redundancy avoidance.

By far the most important spatial processing techniques are those that are based on two-dimensional transforms of images [HABI 74B, CAMA 79]. The basic idea is to apply transforms having the property of orthogonality to blocks, or two-dimensional pieces, of the picture in such a way that components of low statistical or psychovisual significance can be discarded. Only the more significant components are transmitted, resulting in a "coding gain" or contraction of required transmission bandwidth.

Intraframe (Two-Dimensional) Transformation

Consider two samples of a picture and let X^1 and X^2 represent their values. If these samples are contained in a sufficiently small block, there will be on average a high degree of correlation between the samples, as illustrated in Fig. 18.17. A new coordinate system $Y^1 Y^2$ can be established to obtain two new variables, one having a larger variance than the other (although, since the transformation is linear, the sum of the variances remains the same). The Y^1 variable clearly contains more information than the Y^2 variable, which can be suppressed or discarded. Such a transformation is known as the *method of principal components*, or *Karhunen–Loeve transformation*, and results in variates with a maximum compaction of information in a given number of components.

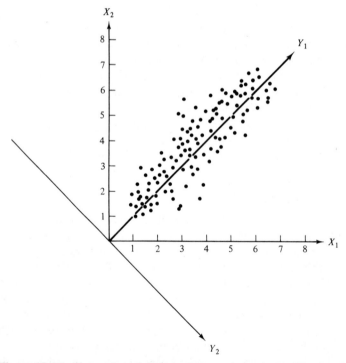

Figure 18.17. Illustration of the coordinate transformation describing two pixels X^1 and X^2 in a sub-picture block. The most likely values are contained within the shaded area. The new coordinate system is represented by Y^1 and Y^2.

The transformation process can be viewed as vector operations on data represented by two-dimensional matrices. With true Karhunen-Loeve transformation, the operators must be individually determined to match the covariance of the image (the precise statistics of a given scene). This results in major computational complexity in both the encoder and decoder—N^4 additions/multiplications for an $N \times N$ image.

Other transforms based on particular predefined operators possessing orthogonality can be implemented by $2N^2 \log N^2$ computer operations. Perhaps the most familiar is the Fourier transform, which uses complex exponentials as operators that rearrange the space/amplitude information of the original image into frequency-domain components of the image. In rough analogy with the principal components method, Fourier transformation concentrates the information in the low-frequency components of the frequency domain, which can be quantized to a large number of levels while maintaining a relatively low bit rate. The higher-frequency components, containing less information, can be more coarsely quantized with little subjective degradation of the reconstructed image.

Other transforms have received more attention because of performance advantages and lower complexity in implementation. In the linear transformation category, for example, the cosine transform (using real cosines as operators) and slant transform (using sawtooth waveforms) have produced lower mean-square-error results than the Fourier transform. Of particular interest are the Hadamard (operators $+1$ and -1) and Haar (operators $+1$, 0, and -1) transforms, which lead naturally to digital realizations, and which require only multiplication by ones and zeros rather than by variable factors. The latter feature results in a fivefold reduction in required computational power, although at the price of lower compression ratios.

Even with transforms of less computational complexity, block sizes are generally held to 32×32 pixels and smaller. Two-dimensional transform coding of good quality can be transmitted at rates of 3 to 1 bit/pixel, while useful results can be obtained with rates as low as 0.5 bit/pixel.

Interframe (Three-Dimensional) Transformation

The previously discussed high degree of correlation between frames of television images suggests the extension of transformation techniques to three dimensions. Excellent results have been obtained by applying Hadamard, Fourier, and cosine transform coding over cubes of $16 \times 16 \times 16$ pixels, at coding rates as low as 0.25 bit/pixel [ROES 75].

Transform Coding of Color Images

Clearly, transform coding can be applied individually to the signals representing the separated red, green, and blue images—the so-called *tristimulus components*—of a color picture. A further compression can be achieved by treating each of the red/green/blue coincident frames as correlated data in a kind of three-dimensional (interframe) coding implementation. Fairly good quality results have been obtained at a rate of 1.2 bits/pixel.

Another alternative is to work directly with the NTSC Y, I, and Q signal components, which are nearly uncorrelated as a Karhunen–Loeve coordinate system. There is a built-in advantage in this approach—the Y, or luminance, signal possesses full bandwidth (about 4.5 MHz in NTSC television), while the I and Q signals have bandwidths of about 1.5 and 0.5 MHz, respectively. Thus it is not necessary to achieve extreme compression ratios on three simultaneous images, as with red/green/blue coding.

Hybrid Transform/Predictive Coding

Various schemes have been proposed which combine the quite different transform and predictive coding techniques in implementations simpler than full-transform coding but retaining many of the operational attributes. One technique [HABI 74A] performs one-dimensional transform coding horizontally, while DPCM coding is performed between columnar pixels. Another [ROES 75] combines the normal two-dimensional transform coding of each frame with DPCM interframe coding. Good results have been demonstrated at rates of 1 bit/pixel, while a rate as low as 0.5 bit/pixel may provide reconstruction adequate for some purposes.

18.5.2.7   Comparison of Image Coding Techniques

As has been noted in the brief description of each coding technique, the bit rate reduction as compared with PCM ranges from marginal to substantial. Figure 18.18 illustrates the coding rate provided by some of the techniques of primary interest. The reconstructed image qualities could be rated from acceptable to good. As might be expected, the subjective quality of the reconstructed images, as a function of bit rate, differs for each technique. The degradation perceived in use of one technique might be quite acceptable for one particular application or type of scene, whereas it might be

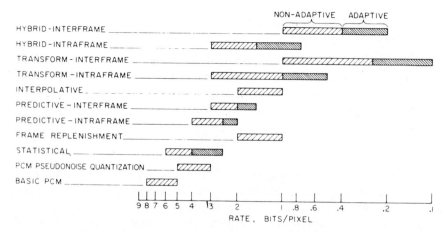

Figure 18.18. Coding rate of image coding systems. (From [PRAT 78], with permission from John Wiley & Sons, Inc.)

unacceptable for another. The reader is particularly directed to [PRAT 78], which reproduces many comparative examples of the results obtained with the various coding schemes, and under varying bit-rate conditions.

The coding techniques also differ with respect to image deterioration in the presence of errors. Because of the large degree of redundancy in an image, particularly in television pictures, relatively large errors are tolerable. For example, with PCM, error rates as low as 10^{-3} are usually not objectionable, while 10^{-2} provides a usable picture. On channels carrying compressed bit rates, however, deterioration with increasing error rate is more rapid, because the effect of an error tends to be more global. With DPCM or LPC coding, for example, error rates may need to be kept one or two orders of magnitude lower, for equivalent results.

18.5.2.8   Status and Future Outlook

For standard television, current interest is greatest in two techniques: DPCM and interframe coding. DPCM can provide high-quality transmission of commercial television within the standard DS-3 rate of 45 Mbps, and acceptable quality at half that rate. In the laboratories, variants of the interframe coding technique are being demonstrated at transmission rates as low as 12 Mbps. The usefulness of these rates can be appreciated by considering the current technology of analog television transmission by satellite. Network-quality transmission by FM modulation occupies an entire satellite transponder having a 36-MHz bandwidth. Using current modems, the same transponder can provide a digital channel at a rate of 60 Mbps; near-term future modems will operate at 90 Mbps. Thus the same communication channel can carry a single high-quality, full-motion digital television signal, and potentially several such signals.

A typical DPCM unit currently available is the Nippon Electric HO-DPCM digital television terminal. Picture quality is rated as very good at 32 Mbps, and excellent (broadcast quality) at 45 Mbps, both with scenes in full motion. The Nippon Electric NETEC terminal uses interframe coding to achieve nearly equivalent results at 22 Mbps; it is, however, considerably more expensive and bulky ($60 \times 74 \times 152$ cm). Newer, smaller models are expected (1983), which will provide full motion and full color at 16 Mbps. Another version of the NETEC equipment provides for transmission as low as 3 Mbps (two T1 channels) with acceptable quality for pictures with limited motion, and can tolerate error rates as high as 10^{-4} with optional error correction capability.

For special applications such as surveillance and teleconferencing, slow-motion "frame grabbers" are currently most popular (for analog as well as digital transmission) because of the relative ease of achieving major reductions in bandwidth. The Nippon Electric Model DFP-751 digital color video system allows transmission at a rate of 2.4 kbps to 1.544 Mbps, with respective transmission times of 300 sec/field to 0.5 sec/field. This unit can be used over channels ranging from conventional telephone lines to T1 lines. Using a 56-kbps private channel, such as is available from American Satellite's SDX service, new pictures are presented at a rate of about four per minute, which is useful for many video teleconferencing applications.

The particular requirements of a substantial number of defense-oriented applications, such as reconnaissance, have stimulated considerable research and development effort that is concentrated on spatial image processing techniques. Results of this work could be of great importance in commercial applications. One advanced development is the British work on picture-quality videotex service using transform coding (see Chap. 17). With this technique, not only is a large compression factor available, but also the major objection to "freeze-frame"—the long wait for a picture—is overcome. Transform coding allows the rapid presentation of a low-resolution still picture; as time progresses and more data are received, the resolution continues to improve.

Another realm of image processing is in the very early stages of development. The techniques reviewed in this section are all based on the electrical processing of electrically derived images. Processing in the optical domain, perhaps by holographic techniques, may very well hold the key for future improvements in the imaging process itself as well as gains in coding rates.

18.5.3 Facsimile Transmission

The coding techniques just described can, of course, be applied with varying degrees of success to any form of image. However, special image forms of general importance lend themselves to more advantageous coding compression which can be much simpler to implement.

Facsimile is the name that has been given to the process of scanning, electrical transmission, and remote reproduction of a still image. Such an image could have many shades of gray or even color. In this case the digitization and compression processes would be similar to those for a single frame of television transmission, discussed previously. For present purposes, the discussion of facsimile transmission is restricted to only two amplitude levels (or shades of gray): black and white. This definition covers the great majority of subjects of facsimile—letters, drawings, graphs, outlines, maps—in fact, any subject that has been or could be reproduced by typeset or line drawings. The scanning of such an image results in a natural binary sequence, wherein a 0 represents, say, white; and 1, black. Resolution is determined as in the scanning of a conventional image.

Facsimile reproduction is normally desired as hard copy. This can be accomplished by synchronizing the receiver to the transmitter so that the receiver's reproduction element is positioned in the same space/time coordinates as was the transmitter's scanning element.

Table 18.6 displays the nominal characteristics of facsimile equipment as delineated by the CCITT. The most familiar machines are contained in group I, which require 6 min for transmission of a 210 mm × 297 mm page with a resolution of 3.85 lines/mm. This requires the transmission of $(3.85)(210) \times (3.85)(297) \approx 900,000$ pixels in 360 sec, a data rate of about 2500 bps at 1 bit/pixel. A group IV machine in the high-resolution mode (7.7 lines/mm) could generate nearly 4,000,000 pixels, which would require 7 min to transmit at 9.6 kbps. However, if a data compression algorithm were used to reduce the number of bits transmitted by a ratio of 7:1,

Table 18.6. *Nominal Characteristics of Facsimile Equipment by CCITT Recommendations.*

CCITT Category	Nominal Scan Lines per Page[a]	Scan Frequency Lines per Minute	Resolution		Nominal Transmission Speed	Compression	Communication Interface	Application
			Vertical (lines per mm)	Horizontal (lines per mm)				
Group I	1114/762	180/240	~3.85/2.6	~4	6/4 min/page	No	Analog (modem built in)	Dial-up telephone circuit
Group II	1145	360	~3.85	~4	3 min/page	No	Analog (modem built in)	Dial-up or dedicated telephone circuit
Group III (proposed)	1145/2290	(Variable)	3.85/7.7	7.7	1 min/page	Yes	Analog (external modem)	Dial-up or dedicated telephone circuit
Group IV (proposed)	1145/2290	(Variable)	3.85/7.7	3.85/5.8/7.7	Unspecified; current devices to 56 kbps	Yes	Digital	Digital circuit

[a]A page is defined as 215 mm × 297 mm.

transmission could be accomplished in 1 min. With the same resolution and compression, a group IV machine could effect transmission in 10 sec at 56 kbps.

18.5.3.1   Run-Length Coding

Run-length coding is the basis for the most popular facsimile coding compression methods. In its simplest form, run-length coding can be implemented by measuring the length of a scan line (or, equivalently, the time or the number of pixels scanned) during which no changes in amplitude level occurs. A letter, for example, results in relatively long average runs along a scan line in the white regions between letters. Between typewritten lines, an entire scan line may be only white. The data transmitted could literally represent the lengths between transitions. Alternatively, the addresses of pixels containing a state transition could be transmitted. Depending of course on the character of the document scanned, a compression ratio approaching 4:1 can be achieved with such a simple one-dimensional coding, as compared with the straightforward coding of 1 bit/pixel for two-level quantization.

As with normal images as considered in previous sections, subjects for facsimile transmission also display high correlation between neighboring pixels, and further compression is possible by two-dimensional coding schemes. An example is the *zigzag scanning method*. The next pixel to be examined after the first pixel is immediately below the first rather than the adjacent pixel as in a linear horizontal scan. The scan then returns to the first row to examine the pixel immediately to the right of the first, then the pixel immediately below, and so on. It will be intuitively apparent by examining this page of text that such a scanning method will result in longer runs between transitions, and will lead to more efficient run-length coding. Other variations are possible and in use. These include *mode run-length coding* and the *rearranging picture elements method* [UENO 78].

As in processing of speech and multilevel images, predictive techniques are successfully applied to facsimile coding. Two-dimensional prediction is analogous to that used for television images, although, of course, the prediction is constrained to only two states. The *classified pixel pattern method* (CLAP) combines a form of mode classification with similar predictive coding [PREU 75].

18.5.3.2   Preprocessing

At first thought, the process of determining whether the value of a pixel is black or white would appear quite simple. There are problems, however, with the establishment of a fixed-amplitude threshold, above which is white and below which is black. Some of these problems relate to stability in the facsimile equipment itself. Others relate to the item being scanned; for example, a nonwhite background, variation in the reflectance of the image (the precise statistics of a given scene), thickness of paper, nonuniformities in character widths, and so on. The use of adaptive thresholds, although somewhat more expensive in implementation, results in practical compression ratios significantly greater than would be achieved otherwise [TING 78].

18.5.3.3 Performance Comparisons

The average compression ratios for 8-1/2 × 11 documents using the facsimile coding methods mentioned above are displayed in Table 18.7. The actual compression achieved is dependent on the nature of the scanned image. Consequently, the transmission time per page will vary when compression is used.

18.5.4 Symbol Recognition

Pattern recognition techniques have been successfully applied to machine reading of printed text material, as in optical character recognition (OCR) equipment (see Sec. 18.6.5). There is an important distinction between OCR and facsimile operation. An OCR machine scans a page of text, usually typed or printed in a special type font, and converts the text to a stream of encoded characters very much like the input to, or output from, a teletypewriter or printer terminal. In fact, OCR is one way to digitize textual material for transmission, processing, or storage. If a page contains, say, 1400 characters including spaces, carriage returns, line feeds, and so on, that page is represented in ASCII code by 8 bits/character × 1400 = 11,200 bits of information.

In contrast, we have seen in Sec. 18.5.3 that facsimile is a true *imaging* technique, which requires two orders of magnitude more bits to represent a page of information. For its greater data requirement, facsimile can (theoretically) reproduce any figures, lines, symbols, and so on, on a page; OCR is limited to representing only those symbols (usually alphanumeric characters) for which it has been programmed. Further, the printed output of OCR transmission may look quite unlike the original because of differences in the OCR reader input and the printer output type fonts. Nevertheless, OCR is an extremely useful and efficient method of text input in cases where the desired information is contained wholly within the characters, as opposed to the literal appearance of an imaged page.

One interesting compression technique, *combined symbol matching* (CSM), melds character recognition and conventional facsimile encoding [CAPI 80]. As the

Table 18.7. *Average Compression Ratios for Facsimile Coding Methods for an 8½ × 11 Inch Document.*

Coding Method	Compression Ratio	
	Without Preprocessing	With Preprocessing
Zigzag scan	4.8	8.0
Mode run length	5.3	8.8
Rearranging picture elements	5.9	9.8
Two-dimensional prediction	5.4	9.0
CLAP	7.4	12.3
Relative address	7.0	11.7

Source: After [UENO 78], © 1979 IEEE.

image roster is scanned, the local area around each block pixel is examined for possible feature matches with a library of stored symbols. If a match is found, the ID number and position of the symbol is transmitted, which requires fewer bits than even a compressed pixel-by-pixel representation of the symbol. When local matches are not found, the residual pixels are conventionally coded and transmitted. Compression ratios of about 49:1 in the facsimile mode and 257:1 in the symbol matching mode are reported.

18.6 APPLICATIONS FOR DIGITIZED TRAFFIC

Answers to the question of why to digitize data, voice, and image traffic have been indicated earlier in this chapter. Transmission fidelity, economy, facility sharing, value-added functions, speed, interoperability, and compatibility are improved or realized with digitized traffic in various specific cases. Further motivations exist in recognition of the trend to integrated services digital networks (see Chap. 17).

On an individual basis, the numerous applications for digital voice and image input, storage, and response fall in many domains. Commercial applications include handling directory assistance calls, telephone number changes, and other inquiry, announcement, and instruction services in telecommunications and at airports for example. Industrial use includes voice and image data entry, process and production line control, surveillance, and speaker recognition for security. Socially, telecommunication applications can open new employment opportunities to some of the handicapped and improve education and work for many people [ENDR 79, WAGR 82]. Audio mailboxes, filing systems, and typewriters can become integral parts of offices of the future. The potential for expanded applications grows as digitization and processing techniques are improved.

On a generalized basis, perhaps the best reason for digitization of traffic is the powerful processing available from digital circuitry and computers. The processing functions in some of the simpler examples mentioned above are self-evident, involving data storage, retrieval, and manipulation. This section examines some sophisticated processing techniques for which digitization affords major advantages.

18.6.1 Communication Privacy and Security

The need for communication privacy and security in industrial, financial, and civil government as well as military applications is long standing. Legislation dealing with issues of privacy has focused public attention on the need for protection of information during transmission and storage. Communications can be intercepted at various points in the transmission process. One study [ORCE 78] estimates the cost of interception at key points in the switched telephone network, as summarized in Tab. 18.8. An especially vulnerable point is the microwave transmission system, where interception is relatively easy and risk of detection is very low.

Secure communication systems are designed to meet, or compromise among, several criteria. Typical desired attributes [after BRUN 75] are:

Table 18.8.   *Interception in a Switched Network.*

	Local Loop	Cable Trunk	Microwave Trunk	Satellite
Cost to intercept (thousands of dollars)	1–10	50–250	10–100	100–1000
Risk of detection	High	High	Low	Low

Source: [ORCE 78], © 1978 IEEE.

1. Direct connection to existing system and use of existing channels
2. Minimum residual intelligibility of the encrypted signal
3. A level of complexity such that unauthorized deciphering requires a long time and complex equipment
4. No impairment of the decrypted and recovered signal
5. High tolerance for transmission errors (ideally, no more affected than the original signal would be)
6. Simple operation
7. Insignificant addition of delay
8. Economical, small, light, and sturdy, with low power consumption

18.6.1.1   Analog Security Devices

Numerous privacy devices have been developed for protection of voice signals during transmission over analog channels such as telephone and radio circuits [MCCA 73, BAKE 74, BRUN 75, KIRC 79]. The simpler, less expensive techniques (e.g., sideband inversion, noise masking, band splitting) are generally unsatisfactory because the residual intelligibility is still significant and methods for unauthorized recovery of information require very simple equipment and little time. As an example, word intelligibility after masking with a pseudonoise signal is reduced to only 73% in some tests [BRUN 75]. Some inexpensive scrambling devices actually degrade security by calling attention to messages containing sensitive information, not adequately protecting them, and providing a false sense of security. The high degree of redundancy of speech is the primary reason why analog-oriented voice privacy devices are not completely effective.

The more elaborate devices operate on analog voice waveforms by dividing the signal in the amplitude–frequency or amplitude–time domains, then "scrambling" or rearranging the "pieces" in accordance with a program presumably known only to the sender and the receiver. The program in more recent devices is represented by a digital bit pattern, which is synchronized between the transmitter and receiver during initiation of the conversation, and may be periodically resynchronized during the conversation. These devices offer a considerably higher level of security but remain susceptible to a determined and sophisticated attack because each "piece" of information still contains significant intelligence that can be operated upon. Typical dimensions of the "pieces" are several hundred hertz in frequency and several tens of milliseconds in time. Smaller dimensions would provide greater security, but the following problems would be exacerbated:

1. Recovered voice quality (intelligibility of the descrambled signal), already barely satisfactory in many instances, would be additionally degraded.
2. Tolerance of transmission circuit impairment would decrease.
3. Cost, already high due to a large number of complex analog processing circuits, would increase further.

18.6.1.2 Digital Security Techniques

No analog security measure is as effective as even some simple digital encryption techniques. Generally, a digital enciphering/deciphering process introduces no inherent degradation of the recovered signal; with synchronized transmitter/receiver devices (and, of course, assuming no channel errors) the deciphered signal is an exact replica of the original signal. Further, most digital encryption techniques operate in such a manner that there is no residual intelligibility in the encrypted waveform either before or after a D/A process.

The most secure digital encryption techniques operate on a bit stream by combinations of transposition and modulo-2 addition of a key bit stream, the pattern of which is determined by the selected crypt key. Various devices are now available using the Data Encryption Standard (DES) and other proprietary algorithms which provide a high level of security. Costs are dropping with increased production volume and use of LSI. Explanations and applications of these schemes on a network basis, including refinements dealing with public key systems and sender verification, have been developed in considerable detail [DAVI 79, HELL 78, RIVE 78, DIFF 76].

A less expensive technique, which is satisfactory for most commercial applications, is the digital bit masking mentioned earlier. The key stream is a pseudo-voice signal generated by a selectable algorithm known to both the transmitter and receiver. The features of a well-designed generator are listed in [BAKE 74].

For more casual privacy, encryption can be accomplished by the less expensive scrambling techniques in which bits are not changed but are rearranged within time blocks. Advantage can be taken of known signal characteristics in setting block length. For example, with PCM-encoded speech, a block length of at least one pitch period is necessary. DPCM and DM speech of 25 kbps require a block length of approximately 64 samples [SAMB 76]. Use of short blocks means a code could be readily deciphered by trying all the possible rearrangements. The longer the blocks, the longer unauthorized deciphering would take. Block enciphering and scrambling techniques do require synchronization information to be transmitted, which can take about 20% of channel capacity [PETR 78].

Perceptual evaluation of the effectiveness of scrambling within a block of given length indicates that scrambling a digitized signal is more efficient than scrambling an analog signal (PAM), where the ranking of efficiency includes several digitization techniques [KAK 77]:

$$PAM < ADM < APCM < ADPCM$$

the efficiency of frequency inversions is

$$ADM < PAM < APCM < ADPCM$$

Over high-quality transmission channels, the digital encryption/decryption process is transparent to the digital bit stream. Where the information to be secured originates in analog form (e.g., voice) the received signal quality is determined by the digitization technique employed. If, for example, digital encryption is applied to speech over conventional analog voice-grade circuits, it is necessary to use modems operating in the range 1200 to 9600 bps and appropriate coders such as LPC or APC in addition to the encryption devices. The quality of resultant recovered voice will not be equal to that obtained with straightforward (and unsecured) analog transmission, but the degradation is due to the required digitization process rather than digital encryption per se. Of course, if high-quality digital transmission were used at whatever speed, there would be no degradation as a result of encryption.

The encryption devices do require initial synchronization and maintenance of synchronization during the period of communication. Generally, this imposes two additional constraints on the transmission channel: error rate and bit-count integrity. Because of the nature of most encryption processes, a single bit error tends to propagate. The effect is highly dependent on the particular methods of encryption and digitization used (see references cited previously). In general, satisfactory results will be obtained at error rates two orders of magnitude lower than would be required for unencrypted transmission. Bit-count integrity means that the transmission channel must deliver to the receiver equipment a synchronous bit stream precisely as received from the transmitting/encrypting equipment, without missed or added bits and with bit-by-bit contiguity. With packet-switching networks, for example, this requirement may necessitate special deframing/reframing equipment.

Digital encryption can be applied to any digital signal, whether it is intrinsically digital in form, such as computer data, or is a digitalized analog signal, such as voice or video.

18.6.2   Speaker Recognition and Verification

Distinction is made between speaker recognition or identification, and speaker verification. Recognition involves identifying the unknown speaker from a potentially large population. Speaker verification seeks to verify that a speaker is who he or she claims to be based on information known about the identity claimed and on information taken from the speaker making the claim.

Spectrograms or voice prints can be accurately used for speaker identification in laboratory environments. Outside the laboratory, many factors remain unknown: what constitutes a match between voices, the distribution of voice-distinguishing characteristics across large populations, changes in the voice of an adult over time, and the effectiveness of mimicry or attempts to disguise the voice [ATAL 76]. Identification is made more difficult by a poor-quality communication system, an uncooperative speaker, or different environments for the references and test samples. Computerized systems are being developed to identify voice prints objectively using probabilities based on large speaker populations [BEEK 77]. A comparison of speaker recognition methods is given in [FURU 81B].

Speaker verification is applicable in industry to controlling access to restricted areas, for example. In commerce it can be used to control access to money or information. The military of course finds many applications and is also interested in being able to determine the emotional state of the speaker, particularly whether the individual is under stress. A review of automatic speaker verification approaches, evaluations, and implementations, and detailed large-scale systems, is given in [ROSE 76]. Some newer techniques are described in [FURU 81A].

18.6.3   Speech Recognition (Voice Data Entry)

Speech recognition has a completely different set of objectives than those for speaker recognition. The matching of characteristics or patterns is directed toward identifying what is said rather than who said it.

Voice data entry is the application of automatic speech recognition. It has been a long-sought goal for many environments, particularly those where the hands are otherwise occupied, as where the data gatherer is handling items about which input data are needed or where he or she must be moving; where immediately needed data are obtained by someone not able to enter them into a computer by traditional means; or where feedback to the originator for immediate verification of accuracy is important. Extension of data entry to include processor commands by voice would result in an extremely "user-friendly" terminal that, coupled with a tolerant high-level language, would be exceeded in ease of use only by the eventual "thought data entry." Voice data entry is useful in computer-aided design and manufacturing [SIMM 79]. Acceptance, however, is limited by marginal cost justification, orientation toward a restricted number of application areas, the newness of the approach, and the size and number of system marketers.

Speech recognition is difficult to accomplish electrically. In person-to-person interactions, the speaker receives information from listener appearance when talking face to face and, to some extent, when in a video conference; the listener gets many contextual clues for understanding even when the speaker makes mistakes; and the listener can ask for a repeat or rephrasing of information. In voice entry to a computer, these aids to understanding are not available, although feedback from the computer can let the speaker know if he or she was correctly understood and give the person a chance to make corrections.

One basic form of speech recognition system is shown in Fig. 18.19. The most important problem is distinguishing precisely where each word begins and ends. Once the word boundaries are known, the problem of matching the current pronunciation with expected characteristic patterns remains. The accuracy of the system is typically inversely proportional to the size of its vocabulary.

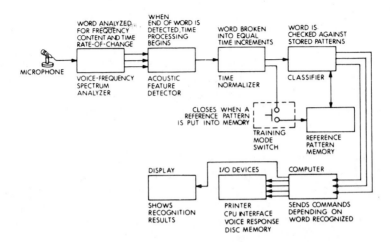

Figure 18.19. Basic speech recognition system. (After [SIMM 79], reprinted with permission from the June 1979 issue of *Computer Design,* copyright 1979 Computer Design Publishing.)

Early speech recognition systems were based on analog processing techniques; now, however, the power of LSI digital circuitry and advances in processing algorithms make digital processing more attractive. As examination of Figs. 18.19 and 18.20 might imply, the necessary analysis in a digital system is closely related to the general category of source-encoding speech digitizers described previously. In fact, most waveform encoding techniques would make subsequent processing more difficult, because the bit rate is higher and the resulting bit stream is not easily related to discrete voice sample. The latter is illustrated by the DPCM and CVSD techniques, wherein the value of a given "point" is influenced by past samples.

Speech recognition can be made less complex in many applications by requiring pauses between words to isolate them, and by limiting the size of the vocabulary to be recognized. Current isolated-word systems have vocabularies ranging from 10 to

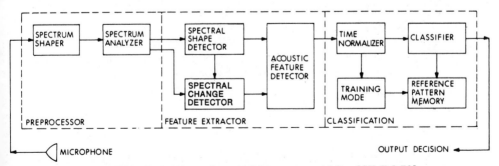

Figure 18.20. Isolated word recognition system. (After [SIMM 79], reprinted with permission from the June 1979 issue of *Computer Design,* copyright 1979 Computer Design Publishing.)

1000 words per speaker, provide response times of the order of 10^{-2} to 10^{-1} sec, and can achieve an accuracy greater than 99% [KAPL 80]. For further simplification, such systems are often trained to particular speakers. The problems of speaker-independent speech recognition are addressed in [GUPT 78]. Speaker adaptive systems are more restricted in who can use them (speakers for whom a reference pattern has been stored), but they are more flexible in that they can handle different pronunciations and even different languages or special sounds, such as those that might be made by someone with a speech impediment. An isolated word recognition system is shown in Fig. 18.20.

Between continuous word and isolated word stream systems are "connected speech" systems, which allow a limited number of words to be spoken together. The words might be three digits, for example, or a limited set of phrases [JOHN 78]. The connected systems have smaller vocabularies, cost more, and are less adaptable than isolated word systems to high-background-noise environments. One comparison of speech recognizers [SIMM 79] gives a 1:6 connected-to-isolated vocabulary ratio and a 6:1 cost ratio of machines handling connected words. Nevertheless, effective usage of speech recognition systems is increasing. A categorization of system types is shown in Tab. 18.9. Additional information can be found in [KAPL 80], [REDD 80], [KATO 80] and [SEAM 82]. Another survey [DODD 81] also reports the results of controlled tests of several speech recognizers costing between $2400 and $65,000.[7] In general, the most expensive machines recognized connected speech and produced the fewest errors; one machine achieved a word substitution rate of 0.2%. The least expensive machines were not capable of connected-speech recognition, and exhibited a substitution rate in the range of 2% to 8%.

In the early 1980's, following the explosive growth of personal computers, several improved isolated word and connected speech systems have appeared in the price range of $1,000 to $5,000. These systems are still characterized by limited vocabularies and allowed "connections"; thus, they are most applicable to do such chores as alternate input devices for operating system commands, menu selections, and spreadsheet entries. Progress is rapid; nevertheless, widespread installation of electronic dictation machines is unlikely in the 1980's.

18.6.4 Voice Storage and Response: Speech Synthesis

Computer voice-response applications that have been implemented include a system for computer-aided voice wiring of communication equipment, directory assistance at Bell Laboratories locations, stock price quotation, telephone data set testing, flight information, and feedback in speaker verification [RABI 76].

18.6.4.1 Storage

Voice storage, or the storage of voice characteristics, is an intrinsic part of voice-response systems. Storage in older systems is in analog form. Digital forms are

[7] A $500 device intended as a home-computer peripheral was also tested.

Table 18.9. *Speech Recognition System Types.*

	Mode of Speech	Vocabulary Size	Task-Specific Information	Language	Speaker	Environment
Word recognition—isolated (WR)	Isolated words	10–300	Limited use	—	Cooperative	—
Connected speech recognition—restricted (CSR)	Connected speech	30–500	Limited use	Restricted command language	Cooperative	Quiet room
Speech understanding—restricted (SU)	Connected speech	100–2000	Full use	English-like	Not uncooperative	—
Dictation machine—restricted (DM)	Connected speech	1000–10000	Limited use	English-like	Cooperative	Quiet room
Unrestricted speech understanding (USU)	Connected speech	Unlimited	Full use	English	Not uncooperative	—
Unrestricted connected speech recognition (UCSR)	Connected speech	Unlimited	None	English	Not uncooperative	Quiet room

Source: [REDD 76], © 1976 IEEE.

replacing analog because they can be smaller and cheaper, and they are more flexible. They can be compressed, edited, and manipulated for more natural sounding speech with a wider vocabulary.

Digitized sounds can be stored in uncompressed or compressed forms. Although they are still an imperfect reproduction of the original, quality improvement over analog techniques is possible with digital technology, as in digitally mastered stereo recording. The mastering is accomplished by use of PCM digital tape recording equipment typically operating at a rate of 800 kbps per channel (50,000 samples per second of 16 bits per sample). Although the final disk product is (to date) analog, the quality of the sound, in terms of frequency response, clarity, wide dynamic range, and high signal-to-noise ratio, is clearly superior to the older analog mastering techniques.

In most applications, however, storage of digital speech does not require extreme fidelity; the requirement generally is to reduce the number of bits and bit rate at the expense of moderate fidelity. Compression and low-rate digitization techniques such as those discussed earlier in this chapter are used. They include companding and adaptive quantization. Because storage in bits is directly related to digitization rate, the lowest storage requirements for direct speech storage are realized when vocoding techniques are applied. Since storage readout can be buffered and real time is not important, further storage reduction can be achieved with compression techniques similar to digital speech interpolation.

A centralized voice storage system (VSS) was introduced by the Bell System in 1979 as an extension of its custom calling services. It allows communication over the telephone network between people separated in time, as well as space, by call answering with an intercepting announcement and with features for manipulation of the file of accumulated messages; and by advance calling with stored-and-forwarded voice messages. Messages are stored in digital form [CORN 79] after bit serial adaptive delta modulation at 32 kbps. Delivery attempts begin at the specified time requested and delivery status checks are available to the sender [NACO 79].

18.6.4.2 *Response*

Speech response using an analog form of stored speech is a comparatively old technology. Stored speech from human voice recordings, analog or digital, is an approach restricted to smaller vocabularies than can be achieved by a speech synthesis approach. Human voice recordings can range from phrases, to words, to subword units. A response might be a discrete recording or a generated combination of recordings. The system providing the response might give only one message to a single output line at any given time, or it might give the same message to many lines, as in announcements of time, or it might be able to give different messages to different lines simultaneously. Some of the early voice storage/response systems are described in [CHAP 71]. Much more flexible devices are described in [SHER 79]. Electronic teaching games [BODL 78], talking calculators, and talking typewriters on the market are some of the consumer applications of the technology. The major device types are characterized in Tab. 18.10.

The two approaches to synthesis are to use formant data or printed text. Use of formant data saves storage space because it allows more natural sounding messages to be constructed from isolated words. The formant synthesis parameters for words are altered in timing and pitch to obtain a smoothly varying set of parameters for a message. Timing information can be taken from word duration as measured in spoken context, calculated by language rules, or specified in tables for limited context messages. Pitch information can also be obtained from either context or rules, or an archetypal contour can be shortened or lengthened based on timing rules. Details of these implementations are in [FLAN 70].

Synthesizing speech from text requires even less storage and is more flexible because words are generated from phonemes, an "alphabet" of speech sounds. One phonemic synthesizer system is shown in Fig. 18.21. The character strings are analyzed for the phonemes and attempts are made to recognize what syllables to stress or lengthen and when to change volume and pitch for emphasis. The analysis results in frequency-domain parameters for the phonemes and transitions between them. Most current applications involve relatively simple use of one of the two approaches. In the future, these are likely to combine into more comprehensive applications.

Phonemic synthesizers, based on Texas Instruments, Votrax, and similar integrated circuits, are now on the market at prices ranging upward from $200. These devices are finding use in the burgeoning personal computer market and in stand-alone applications in which speech quality is not particularly important. More elaborate devices, exemplified by the Vynet systems, provide PC plug-in boards

Table 18.10.   *Characteristics of Different Forms of Voice Response.*

	Form of Voice Response			
	Synthesized from Printed Text	*Compressed Using Formant Analysis*	*Waveform Digitized Using Log PCM*	*Analog*
Source	Alphabetic text characters	Synthetic vocabulary	Voice signal	Voice signal
Creation mechanism	Algorithmic production	Selection from word library	Digitized recording	Recording
Flexibility	Any sounds in language	Any sounds in vocabulary	Any voice-like sounds (redundant signals)	Any sounds
Quality	Low (synthetic)	Medium (synthetic)	High (toll)	High (toll)
Storage or transfer rate	75 bps	1000 bps	50,000 bps	Equivalent to 9600 bits or less
Duration of speech per 10^6 bits of storage	4 hr	17 min	20 sec	Not applicable

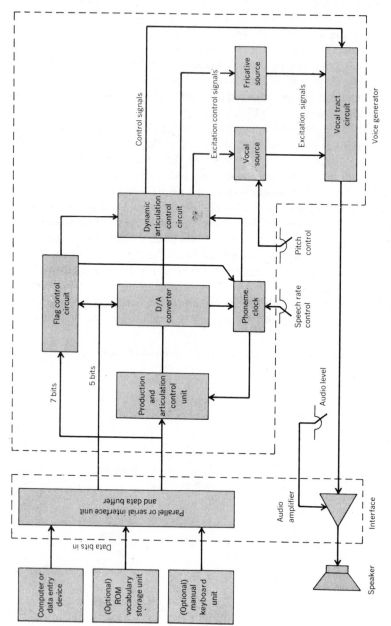

Figure 18.21. A text-to-speech system. [SHER 1979, © 1979 IEEE]

supporting high-quality speech by ADPCM digitization; the encoded data are contained in files residing in the computer's memory or disks drives.

18.6.5 Image Processing

Much progress has been made and is continuing in image processing. Image processing applications are analogous in many respects to speech processing applications described previously. Much of the work is not yet relevant to computer communications in general, and treatment of the techniques involved is beyond the scope of this chapter (see [LERN 80]). Some applications, however, should be mentioned.

Pattern recognition, a form of image recognition by a machine, is an application area of broad interest ranging from military usage to automated manufacturing and testing. Most approaches to pattern recognition depend on a digitized scanning process much like television or facsimile. Data representing the "image" are then operated on by various algorithms. Often the objective is a best match of predefined (or "learned") attributes, which can be expressed in terms of amplitude, time, or space. A simple example is the bar code used for product identification at supermarket checkout counters. *Byte* magazine, among others, is working on a similar idea for printing software for mass distribution.

A somewhat more sophisticated correlation technique is used in optical character recognition (OCR) equipment. OCR machines are in general use as text input devices for such applications as message communications and word-processing computers. Section 18.5.4 outlines an interesting comparison scheme that combines OCR-type symbol recognition with conventional facsimile encoding.

In the future, it can be expected that a considerable fraction of the demand for communications bandwidth will come from graphics. Examples of application areas are computer-aided design/manufacturing in manufacturing industries, charts and pictorial representations in the service and information industries, and videotex services for individuals as well as businesses. There will be strong motivations to conserve bandwidth or, alternatively, to squeeze more information through existing channels of limited bandwidth. It is likely that techniques will develop along three lines:

1.   *Alphamosaics,* which can be viewed as an extended character set displayed, for example, on a dot matrix cathode-ray tube terminal or printer. The additional "characters" are elemental shapes that can be chosen and aligned to produce graphics. This technique is used in the Prestel and Antiope videotex systems. Picture quality can be improved by extensions that allow dynamic redefinition of the character set.

2.   *Symbol matching and coding,* similar to current OCR techniques for alphanumerics but extended to allow the dissection, transmission, and reconstruction of graphic images using predetermined slopes and symbols. The Canadian Telidon videotex system has developed an extended symbol set for such purposes [SPEC 79]. Sometimes called alphageometrics, coded geometric symbols (e.g., rectangle, circle, arc) commonly referred to as "primitives" are

called up and located by transmitted information. Higher-quality graphics requiring less communication bandwidth is possible, at the cost of more processing power in each terminal.

3. *Vector representation of image elements,* such as lines and curves, as vectors. Encoded and transmitted data by each element of a decomposed image would contain information regarding its type, location, extent, and so on. Such techniques are already well developed in computer graphics applications.

ACKNOWLEDGMENTS

Portions of this work were supported under National Science Foundation Grant ENG-77-24110. Ben Occhiogrosso provided a number of useful references and suggestions when work on this chapter began. The draft was reviewed by Donald J. Marsh, J. Neil Birch, and Maurice J. Raffensperger, who made numerous helpful comments.

REFERENCES

ATAL 70   Atal, B. S., and M. R. Schroeder, "Adaptive Predictive Coding of Speech Signals," *Bell Syst. Tech. J.,* Vol. 49, October 1970, pp. 1973–1986.

ATAL 71   Atal, B. S., and S. L. Hanauer, "Speech Analysis and Synthesis by Linear Prediction of the Speech Wave," *J. Acoust. Soc. Am.,* Vol. 50, No. 2, Part 2, 1971, pp. 637–655.

ATAL 76   Atal, B. S., "Automatic Recognition of Speakers from their Voices," *Proc. IEEE,* Vol. 64, No. 4, 1976, pp. 460–474.

BAKE 74   Baker, H. C., "Voice and Data Scramblers," *Bus. Commun. Rev.,* September–October 1974, pp. 31–37.

BARN 78   Barnwell, T. P., III, and A. M. Bush, "Statistical Correlation between Objective and Subjective Measures for Speech Quality," *IEEE Conf. Acoust. Speech Signal Process.,* April 1978, pp. 595–598.

BAYL 73   Bayless, J. W., S. J. Campanella, and A. J. Goldberg, "Voice Signals: Bit-by-Bit," *IEEE Spectrum,* October 1973, pp. 28–34.

BEEK 77   Beek, B., E. P. Neuberg, and D. C. Hodge, "An Assessment of the Technology of Automatic Speech Recognition for Military Applications," *IEEE Trans. Acoust. Speech Signal Process.,* Vol. ASSP-25, No. 4, August 1977, pp. 310–322.

BIAL 70   Bially, T., and W. M. Anderson, "A Digital Channel Vocoder," *IEEE Trans. Commun. Technol.,* Vol. COM-18, No. 4, August 1970, pp. 435–442.

BISI 66   Bisignani, W. T., F. P. Richards, and J. W. Whelan, "Improved Gray Scale and Coarse-Fine PCM; Two New Digital Bandwidth Reduction Techniques," *Proc. IEEE,* Vol. 54, No. 3, 1966, pp. 376–390.

BLAC 53   Black, H. S., *Modulation Theory,* D. Van Nostrand Company, New York, 1953.

BLAC 77   Black, D., F. Meyer, and K. Thorsen, "An Adaptive Interface: The D-3 Channel Bank," *Telesis,* February 1977, pp. 10–15.

BODL 78   Bodley, N., "Here's a Breakthrough—A Low-Cost Speech Synthesizer on a Chip," *Electron. Des.,* July 19, 1978, p. 32.

BRUN 75   Brunner, E., "Review of One- and Two-Dimensional Speech Scrambling Processes and Their Application in the GRETACODER 101," GRETAG, Ltd., February 1975.

CAMA 79   Camana, P., "Video-Bandwidth Comparison: A Study in Tradeoffs," *IEEE Spectrum,* June 1979, pp. 24–29.

CAPI 80   Capitant, P. J., and R. H. Wallis, "The Application of Optical Character Recognition Techniques to Bandwidth Compression of Facsimile Data," *Natl. Comput. Conf.,* May 1980, pp. 415–421.

CHAP 71   Chapman, W. D., "Techniques for Computer Voice Response," *IEEE Int. Conv. Rec.,* 1971, Paper 2F.2, pp. 98–99.

COHE 74   Cohen, F. A., "Optimum Quantization of Speech for Constant Word Length Coding," *Int. Conf. Commun.,* June 1974, pp. 13D(1)–13D(5).

CORN 79   Cornell, R. G., and L. D. Whitehead, "A Centralized Approach to New Network Services," *Int. Conf. Commun.,* June 1979, pp. 3.3.1–3.3.7.

COUL 77   Coulter, D. C., "Low Bit Rate Speech Transmission," *Princeton Conf.,* March 24, 1977.

COX 79   Cox, R. V., and R. E. Crochiere, "Variable Rate Coding for TASI and Packet Transmission Systems," *Int. Conf. Commun.,* June 1979, pp. 25.6.1–25.6.4.

CROC 76   Chrochiere, R. E., S. A. Webber, and J. L. Flanagan, "Digital Coding of Speech in Sub-bands," *IEEE Int. Conf. Acoust. Speech Signal Process.,* April 1976, pp. 233–236.

CROC 77   Crochiere, R. E., D. J. Goodman, L. R. Rabiner, and M. R. Sambur, "Tandem Connections of Wideband and Narrowband Speech Communications Systems: Part I. Narrowband-to-Wideband Link," *Bell Syst. Tech. J.,* Vol. 56, No. 9, November 1977, pp. 1701–1722.

CROC 78   Crochiere, R. E., "An Analysis of 16 kb/s Sub-band Coder Performance: Dynamic Range, Tandem Connections and Channel Errors," *Bell Syst. Tech. J.,* Vol. 57, No. 8, October 1978, pp. 2927–2952.

CUCC 77   Cuccia, C.L., "New PCM Techniques Stress Spectrum and $ Conservation, Part II," *MSN,* February 1977, pp. 37–39.

DAUM 78   Daumer, W. R., and J. R. Cavanaugh, "A Subjective Comparison of Selected Digital Codecs for Speed," *Bell Syst. Tech. J.,* Vol. 57, No. 9, November 1978, pp. 3119–3165.

DAVI 79   Davies, D. W., "Data Security in Networks," Tutorial presented at *6th Data Commun. Symp.,* November 1979, to be published by IEEE Computer Society in 1980.

DHAD 79   Dhadesugoor, V. R., C. Ziegler, and D. L. Schilling, "Digital Silence Detection in Delta Modulation Packet Voice Networks," *Int. Conf. Commun.,* June 1979, pp. 24.7.1–24.7.5.

DHAD 80   Dhadesugoor, V. R., C. Ziegler, and D. L. Schilling, "Delta Modulators in

Packet Voice Networks," *IEEE Trans. Commun.*, Vol. COM-28, No. 1, 1980, pp. 33–51.

DIET 74   Dietrich, M., "Coding of Speech Signals Using a Switch Quantizer," *Zurich Semin. Digital Commun.*, March 1974, pp. A4.1–A4.4.

DIFF 76   Diffie, W., and M. Hellman, "New Directions in Cryptography," *IEEE Trans. Inf. Theory*, Vol. IT-22, No. 6, November 1976, pp. 644–654.

DODD 81   Doddington, G. R., and T. B. Schalk, "Speech Recognition: Turning Theory to Practice," *IEEE Spectrum*, September 1981, Vol. 18, No. 9, pp. 26–32.

DORG 72   Dorgelo, A. J. G., and H. van der Veer, "Variable Length Coding Increasing Traffic Capacity in PCM Transmission Systems," *Zurich Semin.*, 1972, pp. C6(1)–C6(6).

DUBN 78   Dubnowski, J. J., "A Microprocessor Log PCM/ADPCM Code Converter," *IEEE Trans. Commun.*, Vol. COM-26, No. 5, 1978, pp. 660–664.

DUBN 79   Dubnowski, J. J., and R. E. Crochiere, "Variable Rate Coding of Speech," *Bell Syst. Tech. J.*, Vol. 58, No. 3, 1979, pp. 577–600.

DUTT 76   Duttweiler, D. L., and D. G. Messerschmitt, "Nearly Instantaneous Companding for Non-uniformly Quantized PCM," *IEEE Trans. Commun.*, Vol. COM-24, No. 8, 1976, pp. 864–873.

ENDR 79   Endres, W. K., "Speech Synthesis and Recognition, Powerful Tools for Inquiry Services," *Int. Conf. Commun.*, June 1979, pp. 39.3.1–39.3.6.

FLAN 70   Flanagan, J. L., C. H. Coker, L. R. Rabiner, R. W. Shafer, and N. Umeda, "Synthetic Voices for Computers," *IEEE Spectrum*, Vol. 7, 1970, pp. 22–45.

FLAN 72   Flanagan, J. L., *Speech Analysis Synthesis and Perception*, Springer-Verlag, New York, 1972.

FLAN 79   Flanagan, J. L., M. R. Schroeder, B. S. Atal, R. E. Crochiere, N.S. Jayant, and J. M. Tribolet, "Speech Coding," *IEEE Trans. Commun.*, Vol. COM-27, No. 4, 1979, pp. 710–737.

FREE 75   Freeman, R. L., *Telecommunications Transmission Handbook*, J. Wiley, New York, 1975.

FREI 71   Frei, A. H., H. R. Schindler, and P. Vettiger, "An Adaptive Dual-Mode Coder/Decoder for Televison Signals," *IEEE Trans. Commun. Technol.*, Vol. COM-19, December 1971, pp. 933–944.

FURU 81A   Furui, S. "Cepstral Analysis Technique for Automatic Speaker Verification," *IEEE Trans. Acous. Speech Signal Process.* April 1981, Vol. ASSP-20, No. 2, pp. 254–272.

FURU 81B   Furui, S. "Comparison of Speaker Recognition Methods Using Statistical Features and Dynamic Features," *IEEE Trans. Acous., Speech, Signal Process.* April 1981, Vol. ASSP-29, No. 3, pp. 342–350.

GERS 77   Gersho, A., "Quantization," *IEEE Commun. Soc. Mag.*, September 1977, pp. 16–29.

GHOS 78   Ghosh, S., "Code Conversion Techniques for Digital Processing," *Comput. Des.*, August 1978, pp. 103–111.

GISH 68   Gish, H., and J. N. Pierce, "Asymtotically Efficient Quantizing," *IEEE Trans. Inf. Theory*, Vol. IT-14, September 1968, pp. 676–683.

GOLD 67   Gold, B., and C. M. Rader, "The Channel Vocoder," *IEEE Trans. Audio Electroacoust.*, Vol. AUD–15, No. 4, 1967, pp. 148–161.

GOLD 77   Goldstein, L. H., and B. Lin, "Quantization Noise in ADPCM Systems," *IEEE Trans. Commun.,* Vol. COM-25, No. 2, 1977, pp. 227–238.

GOLD 78   Goldberg, A. J., "2400/16,000 BPS Multirate Voice Processor," *IEEE Conf. Acoust. Speech Signal Process.,* April 1978, pp. 299–302.

GOLD 79   Gold, B., J. I. Raffel, and T. Bailey, "A Study of Future Directions for Low Rate Speech Processor Research, Development and Implementation," Lincoln Laboratories, MIT, August 17, 1979.

GOLD 81   Gold, B., P. E. Blankenship, and R. J. McAulay, "New Applications of Channel Vocoders", *IEEE Trans. Acoust. Speech, Signal Process.,* February 1981, Vol. ASSP-29, No. 1, pp. 13–23.

GOOD 71   Goodman, D. J., and J. L. Flanagan, "Direct Digital Conversion Between Linear and Adaptive Delta Modulation Formats," *Int. Conf. Commun.,* June 1971, pp. 1(33)–1(36).

GOOD 75   Goodman, D. J., "Adaptive Digitization Methods," *NCC Semin. Summ.,* 1975, pp. 4–5.

GOOD 79   Goodman, D. J., C. Scagliola, R. E. Crochiere, L. R. Rabiner, and J. Goodman, "Objective and Subjective Performance of Tandem Connections of Waveform Coders with an LPC Vocoder," *Bell Syst. Tech. J.,* Vol. 58, No. 3, 1979, pp. 601–629.

GREG 77   Gregg, W. D., *Analog and Digital Communications: Concepts, Systems, Applications and Services,* John Wiley & Sons, New York, 1977.

GTE 75   GTE Lenkurt, Inc., "PCM—Concepts, Developments and Potential," *Telecommunications,* 1975, pp. 36–46.

GUPT 78   Gupta, V. N., J. K. Bryan, and J. N. Gowdy, "A Speaker-Independent Speech-Recognition System Based on Linear Prediction," *IEEE Trans. Acoust. Speech Signal Process.,* Vol. ASSP-26, No. 1, 1978, pp. 27–33.

HABI 74A   Habibi, A., "Hybrid Coding of Pictorial Data," *IEEE Trans. Comput.,* Vol. COM-22, May 1971, pp. 614–624.

HABI 74B   Habibi, A., and B. S. Robinson, "A Survey of Digital Picture Coding," *Computer,* May 1974, pp. 22–34.

HELL 78   Hellman, M. E., "An Overview of Public Key Cryptography," *IEEE Commun. Soc. Mag.,* November 1978, pp. 24–32.

HESS 78   Hess, W. J., and J. Heiler, "Towards a Variable Frame Rate Speech Transmission System with Frame Selection by Time-Domain Segmentation—A Status Report," *IEEE Conf. Acoust. Speech Signal Process.,* April 1978, pp. 334–337.

HUFF 62   Huffman, D. A., "A Method for the Construction of Minimum Redundancy Codes," *Proc. IRE,* Vol. 40, No. 9, 1952, pp. 1098–1101.

JAYA 71   Jayant, N. S., and A. E. Rosenberg, "The Preference of Slope Overload to Granularity in the Delta Modulation of Speech," *Bell Syst. Tech. J.,* Vol. 50, December 1971, pp. 3117–3125.

JAYA 73   Jayant, N. S., "Adaptive Quantization with a One-Word Memory," *Bell Syst. Tech. J.,* Vol. 52, September 1973, pp. 1119–1144.

JAYA 74   Jayant, N. S., "Digital Coding of Speech Waveforms: PCM, DPCM, and DM Quantizers," *Proc. IEEE,* Vol. 62, May 1974, pp. 611–632.

JELI 72   Jelinek, R., and K. S. Schneider, "On Variable-Length-to-Block Coding,"

IEEE Trans. Inf. Theory, Vol. IT-18, No. 6, 1972, pp. 765–774.

JOHN 78   Johnson, D. H., and C. J. Weinstein, "A Phase Recognizer Using Syllabic-Based Acoustic Measurements," *IEEE Trans. Acoust. Speech Signal Process.,* Vol. ASSP-26, No. 5, 1978, pp. 409–418.

KAK 77   Kak, S. C., and N. S. Jayant, "On Speech Encryption Using Waveform Scrambling," *Bell Syst. Tech. J.,* Vol. 56, No. 5, 1977, pp. 781–808.

KANG 76   Kang, G. S., and D. C. Coulter, "600 BPS Voice Digitizer," *IEEE Conf. Acoust. Speech Signal Process.,* April 1976, pp. 91–94.

KAPL 80   Kaplan, G. "Words into Action: I," *IEEE Spectrum,* June 1980, pp. 22–26.

KATO 80   Kato, Y., "Words into Action: III," *IEEE Spectrum,* June 1980, p. 29.

KING 80   Kingsbury, N. G., and W. A. Amos, "A Robust Channel Vocoder," *Int. Conf. Acoust. Speech Signal Process.,* April 1980, pp. 19–22.

KIRC 79   Kirchofer, K. H., "Are Analog Voice Security Systems Obsolete?", *Int. Conf. Commun.,* June 1979, pp. 4.5.1–4.5.5.

LERN 80   Lerner, E. J., "Computers That See," *IEEE Spectrum,* Vol. 17, No. 10, 1980, pp. 28–33.

LOCI 76   LoCicero, J. L., and D. L. Schilling, "An All Digital Technique for ADM to PCM Conversion," *Natl. Telecommun. Conf.,* 1976, pp. 29.3(1)–29.3(6).

LOCI 77   LoCicero, J. L., "Non-parametric PCM to ADM Conversion," *Natl. Telecommun. Conf.,* 1977, pp. 29:2(1)–29:2(6).

MAKH 75   Makhoul, J., "Linear Prediction: A Tutorial Review," *Proc. IEEE,* Vol. 63, No. 4, 1975, pp. 561–580.

MAKH 76   Makhoul, J., R. Viswanathan, and W. Russell, "A Framework for the Objective Evaluation of Vocoder Speech Quality," *Int. Conf. Acoust. Speech Signal Process.,* April 1976, pp. 103–106.

MALA 81   Malah, D., R. E. Crochiere, and R. V. Cox, "Performance of Transform and Subband Coding Systems Combined with Harmonic Scaling of Speech," *IEEE Trans. Acoust. Speech Signal Process.,* Vol. ASSP-29, No. 2, 1981, pp. 273–283.

MARK 76   Markel, J. D., and A. H. Gray, Jr., *Linear Prediction of Speech,* Springer-Verlag, New York, 1976.

MARS 78   Marsh, D. J., "Subjective Effects in Digital Speech Communications," M.S.E.E. Thesis, University of Bridgeport, December 1978.

MART 77   Martin, J., *Future Developments in Telecommunications,* 2nd ed., Prentice-Hall, Englewood Cliffs, N.J., 1977.

MCAU 77   McAulay, F. J., "A Robust Silence Detector for Increasing Network Channel Capacity," *Int. Conf. Commun.,* June 1977, pp. 38.4(54)–38.4(56).

MCCA 73   McCalmont, A. M., "Communications Security for Voice—Techniques, Systems, and Operations," *Telecommunications,* April 1973, pp. 35–42.

MESS 76   Messerschmitt, D. G., "Speech Encoding for Digital Transmission," *EASCON 1976,* pp. 88(A)–88(G).

NACO 79   Nacon, R. J., and D. P. Worrall, "New Custom Calling Services," *Int. Conf. Commun.,* June 1979, pp. 3.2.1–3.2.5.

NOLL 67   Noll, A. M., "Cepstrum Pitch Determination," *J. Acoust. Soc. Am.,* Vol. 41, No. 2, 1967, pp. 293–309.

NOLL 75A	Noll, P., "A Comparative Study of Various Quantization Schemes for Speech Encoding," *Bell Syst. Tech. J.,* Vol. 54, No. 9, 1975, pp. 1597–1614.
NOLL 75B	Noll, P., "Effects of Channel Errors on the Signal-to-Noise Performance of Speech Encoding Systems," *Bell Syst. Tech. J.,* Vol. 54, No. 9, 1975, pp. 1615–1636.
NYQU 28	Nyquist, H., "Certain Topics in Telegraph Transmission Theory," *AIEE Trans.,* April 1928, pp. 617–644.
OCCH 78	Occhiogrosso, B., "Digitized Voice Comes of Age: Part 1. Trade-Offs," *Data Commun.,* March 1978, pp. 45–51.
OCCH 79	Occhiogrosso, B., Private communication.
OCCH 80	Occhiogrosso, B., Private communication, 1980.
OHNO 76	Ohno, T., H. Kuwahara, M. Miyata, and K. Imai, "Voiceband Analog-PCM Conversion System Using Delta Modulation," *Int. Conf. Commun.,* 1976, pp. 31 (22)–31 (26).
OLIV 48	Oliver, B. M., J. R. Pierce, and C. E. Shannon, "The Philosophy of PCM," *Proc. IRE,* Vol. 36, November 1948, pp. 1324–1331.
ONEA 67	O'Neal, J. B., Jr., "A Bound on Signal-to-Quantizing Ratios for Digital Coding Systems," *Proc. IEEE,* Vol. 55, March 1967, pp. 287–292.
ONEA 71	O'Neal, J. B., Jr., "Entropy Coding in Speech and Television Differential PCM Systems," *IEEE Trans. Inf. Theory,* Vol. IT-17, November 1971, pp. 758–761.
ONEA 72	O'Neal, J. B., Jr., and R. W. Stroh, "Differential PCM for Speech and Data Signals," *IEEE Trans. Commun.,* Vol. COM-20, October 1972, pp. 900–912.
ORCE 78	Orcayre, M. J., and R. M. Heller, "An Approach to Secure Voice Communication Based on the Data Encryption Standard," *IEEE Commun. Soc. Mag.,* November 1978, pp. 41–50.
OSBO 72	Osborne, P. W., H. Kaneko, and M. R. Aaron, "Synthesis for Code Converters for Segment Companded PCM Codes," *Proc. IERE Joint Conf. Digital Process. Signals Commun.,* Vol. 23, April 1972, pp. 305–316.
PECA 78	Pecar, J. A., S. J. Schretter, D. A. Garloin, and R. C. Crutchfield, "Multiple Rate Processing in Secure Voice Network Applications," *Int. Conf. Commun.,* 1978, pp. 23.2.1–23.2.5.
PETR 78	Petrovic, P. M., "Adaptive Delta Modulator for Mobile Radio Communications," *Int. Conf. Commun.,* 1978, pp. 4.4.1–4.4.5.
PRAT 78	Pratt, W. K., *Digital Image Processing,* Wiley, New York, 1978.
PREU 75	Preuss, D., "Comparison of Two-Dimensional Facsimile Coding Schemes," *Int. Conf. Commun.,* June 1975, pp. 7.8–7.11.
RABI 76	Rabiner, L. R., and R. W. Schafer, "Digital Techniques for Computer Voice Response: Implementations and Applications," *Proc. IEEE,* Vol. 64, No. 4, 1976, pp. 416–432.
RABI 77	Rabiner, L. R., M. R. Sambur, R. E. Crochiere, and D. J. Goodman, "Tandem Connections of Wideband and Narrowband Speech Communications Systems Part 2—Wideband-to-Narrowband Link," *Bell Syst. Tech. J.,* Vol. 56, No. 9, November 1977, pp. 1723–1741.
RABI 78	Rabiner, L. R., and R. W. Schaefer, *Digital Processing of Speech Signals,* Prentice-Hall, Englewood Cliffs, N.J., 1978.

REDD 76   Reddy, D. R., "Speech Recognition by Machine: A Review," *Proc. IEEE,* Vol. 64, No. 4, 1976, pp. 501–531.

REDD 80   Reddy, D. R., "Words into Action: II," *IEEE Spectrum,* June 1980, pp. 26–28.

REFE 77   *Reference Data for Radio Engineers,* Howard W. Sams, Indianapolis, 1977.

RIVE 78   Rivest, R. L., A. Shamir, and L. Adelman, "A Method of Obtaining Digital Signatures and Public Key Cryptosystems," *Commun. ACM,* Vol. 21, No. 2, 1978, pp. 120–126.

ROES 75   Roese, J. A., et al., "Interframe Transform Coding and Predictive Coding Methods," *Int. Conf. Commun.,* June 1975.

ROSE 76   Rosenberg, A. E., "Automatic Speaker Verification: A Review," *Proc. IEEE,* Vol. 64, No. 4, 1976, pp. 475–487.

SAMB 76   Sambur, M. R., and N. S. Jayant, "Speech Encryption by Manipulation of LPC Parameters," *Bell Syst. Tech. J.,* Vol. 55, No. 9, November 1976, pp. 1373–1388.

SAMB 77   Sambur, M. R., "Recent Advances in LPC Speech Vocoding," *Int. Conf. Commun.,* 1977, pp. 13.3(297)–13.3(300).

SAMB 78   Sambur, M. R., "High Quality 9.6 KBPS Algorithm That Satisfies the Embedded Bit Concept," *Int. Conf. Commun.,* 1978, pp. 12A.2.1–12A.2.4.

SCAG 79   Scagliola, C., "Evaluation of Adaptive Speech Coders under Noisy Channel Conditions," *Bell Syst. Tech. J.,* Vol. 58, No. 6, Part 2, July–August 1979, pp. 1369–1394.

SCHA 76   Schafer, R. W., K. Jackson, J. J. Dubnowski, and L. R. Rabiner, "Detecting the Presence of Speech Using ADPCM Coding," *IEEE Trans. Commun.,* Vol. COM-24, No. 5, 1976, pp. 563–567.

SCHI 74   Schindler, H. R., "Linear, Nonlinear, and Adaptive Delta Modulation," *IEEE Trans. Commun.,* Vol. COM-22, No. 1, November 1974, pp. 1807–1823.

SCHL 72   Schlink, W., "A Redundancy Reducing PCM System for Speech Signals," *Zurich Semin. Integrated Syst. Speech Video Data Commun.,* March 1972, pp. F41(1) to F41(4).

SCHR 66   Schroeder, M. R., "Vocoders: Analysis and Synthesis of Speech (A Review of 30 Years of Applied Speech Research)," *Proc. IEEE,* Vol. 54, No. 5, 1966, pp. 720–734.

SCHU 64   Schuchman, L., "Dither Signals and Their Effect on Quantization Noise," *IEEE Trans. Commun.,* Vol. COM-12, 1964, pp. 162–165.

SEAM 82   Seaman, J., "Voice: New Ways with an Old Medium," *Computer Decisions,* March 1982, pp. 62–70.

SHER 79   Sherwood, B. A., "The Computer Speaks," *IEEE Spectrum,* August 1979, pp. 18–25.

SIMM 79   Simmons, E. J., Jr., "Speech Recognition Technology," *Comput. Des.,* June 1979, pp. 95–101.

SPEC 79   Special Issue Consumer Text Display Systems (Teletext and Viewdata), *IEEE Trans. Consumer Electron.,* Vol. CE-25, No. 3, July 1979.

TING 78   Ting, D., and B. Prasada, "Pre-processing Techniques for Digital Facsimile," *Int. Conf. Commun.,* 1978, pp. 48.5.1–48.5.6.

TOWN 81   Townes, S., K. V. Kou, J. P. Agrawal, J. G. O'Neal, Jr., and D. N. Mobdjina, "Performances of an ADPCM/TASI System for PCM Speech Compression," *IEEE Trans. Acoust. Speech Signal Process,* Vol. ASSP-29, No. 2, 1981, pp. 302–310.

TRIB 78   Tribolet, J. M., P. Noll, B. J. McDermott, and R. E. Crochiere, "A Study of Complexity and Quality of Speech Waveform Coders," *IEEE Conf. Acoust. Speech Signal Process.,* April 1978, pp. 586–590.

UENO 78   Ueno, Y., F. Ono, T. Semasa, S. Tomita, and R. Ohnishi, "Comparison of Facsimile Data Compression Methods," *Int. Conf. Commun.,* 1978, pp. 48.4.1–48.4.6.

UN 78   Un, C.K., "A Low-Rate Digital Formant Vocoder," *IEEE Trans. Commun.,* Vol. COM-26, No. 3, pp. 344–355.

UN 80   Un, C. K., and H. S. Lee, "A Study of the Comparative Performance of Adaptive Delta Modulation Systems," *IEEE Trans. Commun.,* Vol. COM-28, No. 1, 1980, pp. 96–101.

VISW 78   Viswanathan, R., W. Russell, and J. Makhoul, "Objective Speech Quality Evaluation of Narrowband LPC Vocoders," *IEEE Conf. Acoust. Speech Signal Process.,* April 1978, pp. 591–594.

WAGR 82   Wagreich, B. J., "Electronic Mail for the Hearing Impaired and Its Potential for Other Disabilities," *IEEE Trans. Comm.,* Vol. COM-30, No. 1, January 1982, pp. 58–65.

WILK 71   Wilkinson, R. M., "An Adaptive Pulse Code Modulator for Speech," *Int. Conf. Commun.,* June 1971, pp. 1(11)–1(15).

WINK 65   Winkler, M. R., "Pictorial Transmission with HIDM," *IEEE Int. Conv. Rec.,* Part I, 1965, pp. 285–291.

WOLF 66   Wolf, J. "Effects of Channel Errors on Delta Modulation," *IEEE Trans. Commun. Technol.,* Vol. COM-14, No. 1, February 1966, pp. 2–7.

WOOD 69   Wood, R. C., "On Optimum Quantization," *IEEE Trans. Inf. Theory,* Vol. IT-15, March 1969, pp. 248–252.

Additional References for Facsimile

ARPS 74A   Arps, R. B., "Bibliography on Digital Graphic Image Compression and Quality," *IEEE Trans. Inf. Theory,* Vol. IT-20, January 1974, pp. 120–122.

ARPS 74B   Arps, R. B., "System for Compression of Digital Data," US Patent 3,813,485, 1974.

ARPS 75   Arps, R. B., "An Introduction and Digital Facsimile Compression Review," *Int. Conf. Commun.,* 1975 pp. 7.1–7.3

GRAP 77   Graphic Sciences, Inc., et al., CCITT Study Group XIV, Contribution No. 3, March 1977.

HUAN 75   Huang, T. S., "Easily Implementable Suboptimum Runlength Codes," *Int. Conf. Commun.,* June 1975, pp. 7.8–7.11.

KOBA 74   Kobayashi, H., and L. R. Bahl, "Image Data Compression by Predictive Coding," *IBM J. Res. Dev.,* 1975, pp. 164–179.

KOKU 75   Kokusai Denshin Denwa Ltd., "Proposals for Redundancy Reduction Technique of Digital Facsimile Signals," CCITT Study Group XIV, Temp. Doc.

No. 18, April 1975.

LIAO 77   Liao, H. H. J., "Upperbound, Lowerbound and Run Length Substitution Coding," *Natl. Telecommun. Conf.,* 1977, pp. 49.3.1–49.3.6.

MAHA 72   Maharir, P. S., and B. Prasada, "Two Dimensional Picture Processing," *Picture Bandwidth Compression,* T. S. Huang and O. J. Tretiak, eds., Gordon and Breech, New York, 1972, pp. 487–513.

MEYR 74   Meyr, H., H. G. Rodolsky, F. Schaerer, and T. S. Huang, "Optimum Run Length Codes," *IEEE Trans. Commun. Technol.,* Vol. COM-22, 1974, pp. 826–835.

MORR 75   Morrin, T. H., "Recursive Contour Coding of Nested Objects in Black/White Images," *Int. Conf. Commun.,* June 1975, pp. 7.17–7.21.

NETR 76   Netravali, N., et al., "Ordinary Techniques for Coding of Two-Tone Facsimile Picture," *Bell Syst. Tech. J.,* Vol. 55, No. 10, 1976, p. 1539.

OHNI 76A   Ohnishi, R., et al., "Data Compression for Binary Sources," *Natl. Conf. IECE Jpn.,* March 1976, p. 1032.

OHNI 76B   Ohnishi, R., et al., "Nonredundant Encoding by Classified Pel Patterns," Paper of Tech. Group Image Eng., *IECE Jpn.,* IE 76-1, April 1976.

OHNI 76C   Ohnishi, R., et al., "Nonredundant Encoding by Classified Pel Patterns, Part II," Paper of Tech. Group Commun. Syst., *IECE Jpn.,* CS 76-49, July 1979.

OHNI 77   Ohnishi, R., J. Uneo, and F. Ono, "Optimization of Facsimile Data Compression," *Natl. Telecommun. Conf.,* 1977, pp. 49.1.1–49.1.6.

TERA 76   Teramura, H., Y. Wakahara, and Y. Yamazaki, "Digital Facsimile Equipment, 'Quick-Fax' Using a New Redundancy Reduction Technique," *Natl. Telecommun. Conf.,* 1976, p. 06.2–1.

USUB 75   Usubuchi, et al., "Data Compression of Facsimile Signals by Cascade Division Coding," *Int. Conf. Commun.,* June 1975, pp. 7.22–7.25.

WEBE 75   Weber, D. R., "An Adaptive Run Length Encoding Algorithm," *Int. Conf. Commun.,* June 1975, pp. 7.4–7.7.

YAMA 76   Yamazaki, Y., et al., "Digital Facsimile Equipment 'Quick-FAX' Using a New Redundancy Reduction Technique," *Nat. Telecommun. Conf.,* 1976.

Additional Sources of Information

DAVI 76   Davisson, L. D., and R. M. Gray, eds., *Data Compression,* Benchmark Papers in Electrical Engineering and Computer Science 14, Dowden, Hutchinson & Ross, Stroudsburg, Pa., 1976.
(Collection of papers first published elsewhere on noiseless source coding, distortion rate theory, quantization, block data compression, and nonblock data compression.)

DIXO 79   Dixon, N.R., and T.B. Martin, eds., *Automatic Speech and Speaker Recognition,* IEEE Press, New York, 1979.
(Collection of papers first published elsewhere on reviews of speech recognition, discrete utterance recognition, word spotting, continuous speech: automatic speech recognition and speech understanding systems, reviews of speaker recognition, and speaker recognition systems.)

FLAN 73   Flanagan, J. L., and L. R. Rabiner, eds., *Speech Synthesis,* Benchmark Papers in Acoustics 3, Dowden, Hutchinson & Ross, Stroudsburg, Pa., 1973. (Collection of papers first published elsewhere on history and fundamentals of speech synthesis, simulation and modeling of the vocal system, terminal analog synthesis of speech, predictive coding of speech, speech synthesis by rule, and computer voice response).

HAWL 77   Hawley, M. E., ed., *Speech Intelligibility and Speaker Recognition,* Benchmark Papers in Acoustics 11, Dowden, Hutchinson & Ross, Stroudsburg, Pa., 1977. (Collection of papers, most first published elsewhere, on origins, factors affecting speech intelligibility, statistics of speech and prediction of speech intelligibility, methods of measuring speech intelligibility, applications to: architectural acoustics, audiology, communications engineering, research on speech and hearing, and speech synthesis and analysis, and speech quality and speaker recognition.)

JAYA 76   Jayant, N. S., ed., *Waveform Quantization and Coding,* IEEE Press, New York, 1976. (Collection of papers first published elsewhere on basic principles, theoretical work, speech waveforms, picture signals, data signals, code conversions, and effects of transmission errors.)

SCHA 79   Schafer, R. W., and J. D. Markel, eds., *Speech Analysis*, IEEE Press, New York, 1979. (Collection of papers first published elsewhere on properties of the speech signal, speech analysis methods, estimation of excitation parameters and vocal tract parameters, and analysis/synthesis systems.)

19

Principles of Distributed
Data-Base Design

WESLEY W. CHU
Computer Science Department
University of California
Los Angeles, California

19.1 INTRODUCTION

With the advent of computer network technology, reliable, efficient, and economical transfer of data among computers and terminals becomes feasible. Such advances provide us with a technological foundation for implementing distributed computing and distributed data bases on a computer network. The motivation for connecting a group of geographically separate data bases into a network of data bases or a distributed data base is that these separate data bases need to process common information files. Examples of such systems are transaction-oriented systems (such as credit checking, electronic funds transfer) and medical, business, and library management information systems. The advantages of linking together all the remote data bases include not only sharing of data bases, but also real-time retrieval, update, and distribution of large quantities of information. Such information-handling capability over a geographically separated data-base system not only provides more economical service, but also provides real-time information handling which was previously unachievable. For example, a user can instantaneously find out the current inventory level of a part from several geographically separate warehouses. Such a system also allows simultaneous file transactions against a common data base by users remotely located from each other. Because multiple copies of data bases may be contained in a distributed data-base system, the system may still be operational even when a certain site is down, which provides fault tolerance capability.

In organizing a distributed data base, we first must allocate the individual data files to the computers (sites) in the network. This allocation is based on file usage rates, response-time requirements for different files at different sites, communication and storage costs, and reliability requirements. The data base at each site forms a local data base and is maintained by itself. It also consists of a local directory that lists all the files in that computer. To list all sharable files in the distributed data-base system for all the sites, a directory system is needed. When a user presents a transaction or a query to the system that involves files not stored at his or her local site, the system first examines the directory to obtain information on the physical, logical, security, and operational characteristics of the set of files relevant to the query. Based on information such as resource availability, access capabilities, and work-load profile of the system, the system assigns resources and performs data translation if necessary to process the transaction. When a transaction or query involves several sites, the system, based on the directory information, also needs to determine the optimal sequence of operations and sites for processing the transaction or query.

In organizing and planning a distributed data-base system, there arise many problems in need of solution, such as file allocation policy, directory design and distribution, avoidance of deadlock, integrity and consistency in updating multiple copies of data bases, optimal query processing policy, reliability and recovery, and privacy and security issues. In this chapter we present results on the above-mentioned areas except security and privacy which are covered elsewhere.

19.2   FILE ALLOCATION

It is apparent that when a given information file is required in common by several computers, it may be stored in at least one of them and accessed by the others when needed. The overall operating cost related to the files is considered to consist of transmission and storage costs. The problem is the following: given a number of computers that process common information files, how to allocate the files so that the allocation yields minimum overall operating costs subject to the following constraints:

1. The expected time to access each file is less than a given bound.
2. The amount of storage needed at each computer does not exceed the available storage capacity.
3. The availability of each file is above a certain level.

19.2.1   File Allocation Model

The file allocation problem can be formulated as an integer (0 or 1) programming model. Let X_{ij} indicate that the jth file is stored in the ith computer:

$$X_{ij} = \begin{cases} 1 & j\text{th file stored in the }i\text{th computer} \\ 0 & \text{otherwise} \end{cases}$$

where $i = 1, 2, \ldots, n; j = 1, 2, \ldots, m; n =$ total number of computers in the distributed system; $m =$ total number of distinct files in the distributed system.

The availability of the jth file, A_j, is that portion of time when the system is in operation so that the jth file is available to users. It should be noted that the availability is independent of any queueing delay that may be experienced by the file. For example, $A_j = 0.9985$ means that within a 10,000-hr period, the jth file is available (operating) for 9985 hr and unavailable (system down) for 15 hr. Clearly, the availability of the file is dependent on the reliability of the computers, the reliability of the communication channels, their average repair times, the network-routing algorithm, and the number of redundant copies of the file stored in the interconnected computer network. Thus, given the required availability of a file and the reliability of the system (computer and communication channels), a given availability constraint can be satisfied by selecting the required number of redundant copies of the file.[1] For example, if the computers within the network are allowed to communicate only with their immediate neighboring computers, and all equipment in the system is assumed to have exponential failure distributions, and if all computers within the system have identical availability[2] a_p, and all channels have identical availability, a_c, then the availability of the jth file given that r_j redundant copies are stored in the system is

$$A_j = a_p \left[1 - (1 - a_c a_p)^{r_j} \right] \tag{19.1}$$

For example, if $a_p = 0.98$ and $a_c = 0.99$, then $A_j = 0.951$ for $r_j = 1$ and $A_j = 0.979$ for $r_j = 2$. Equation (19.1) states that the availability of the jth file is equal to the product of the availability of the requesting computer, a_p, and the availability of the r_j copies of the jth file, $1 - (1 - a_c a_p) r_j$.

Then, storing r_j redundant copies of the jth file in the information system, we have

$$\Sigma_i \quad X_{ij} = r_j \qquad \text{for } 1 \leq j \leq m \tag{19.2}$$

To assure that the storage capacity of each computer is not exceeded, we have

$$\Sigma_j \quad X_{ij}L_j \leq b_i \qquad \text{for } 1 \leq i \leq n \tag{19.3}$$

where L_j = length of the jth file

b_i = available memory size of the ith computer

The expected time for the ith computer to retrieve and perform a transaction on the jth file from the kth computer (from initiation of request until start of reception) is denoted as a_{ijk}. The maximum allowable retrieval time of the jth file to the ith computer is T_{ij}. We require that a_{ijk} be less than T_{ij}, that is,

$$(1 - X_{ij})X_{kj}a_{ijk} \leq T_{ij} \qquad \text{for } i \neq k, \quad 1 \leq j \leq m \tag{19.4}$$

When $r_j = 1$ for all j, then from Eq. (19.2) we know that $X_{ij}X_{kj} = 0$ for $i \neq k$. Thus Eq. (19.4) reduces to

---

[1]The number of redundant copies of a file needed to be stored within a distributed data-base system should also be based on other constraints, such as response-time requirements, cost, and so on.

[2]The availability of a_p or a_c is equal to the ratio of mean time between failures to mean repair time plus mean time between failures of the equipment in question [SAN 63]. The availability function for other types of network-routing algorithms and/or other types of equipment-failure distributions will be more complex than Eq. (19.1).

$$X_{kj}a_{ijk} \leq T_{ij} \quad \text{for } i \neq k, \quad 1 \leq j \leq m \tag{19.5}$$

For a fully connected network, a_{ijk} is equal to the sum of the expected queueing delay at the ith computer for the channel to the kth computer W_{ik},[3] the expected queueing delay at the kth computer for the channel to the ith computer W_{ki}, and the expected computer processing time for the jth file t_{kj}. Hence

$$a_{ijk} \doteq W_{ik} + W_{ki} + t_{kj} \tag{19.6}$$

For a non-fully connected network, the expected query response time, a_{ijk}, depends on network topology, routing, and flow control policy, which is difficult to estimate. However, under simplified assumptions such as Poisson message arrivals, nodes statistically independent from each other, and a known fixed routing policy (i.e., a unique allowable path exists from origin to destination for each origin–destination pair), we are able to determine the message delay averaged over all messages flowing through the network [KLE 76].

For a network with M communication links with equal transmission rate R, let the total offered traffic to the network be γ, and let the total traffic within the network be $\lambda = \sum_{s=1} \lambda_s$, where λ_s is the total traffic on the sth channel which includes data traffic (with average message length l) and control traffic (e.g., acknowledgement). Further, let the average time to transmit a message (control or data message) be $1/\mu'$, the average time to transmit a data message (segment a file required by a transaction) be $1/\mu = l/R$, nodal processing time t_n and query processing time t_q be the same for all computers, and propagation delay be t_p. Then the expected response time for a computer to perform a transaction on a file at a remote computer is

$$a_{ijk} \doteq A \doteq 2 \sum_{s=1}^{M} \frac{\lambda_s}{\gamma} \left[\frac{\lambda_s/\mu'}{\mu' - \lambda_s} + \frac{1}{\mu} + t_p + t_n \right] + t_q \tag{19.7}$$

The factor of 2 in Eq. (19.7) is required to include the expected delay from the query originator to the destination and back to the originator.

Finally, we express the operating cost (objective function) in terms of the allocation (X_{ij}'s). Suppose that we know the storage cost of the jth file per unit length and unit time at the ith computer C_{ij}, the communication cost[4] from the kth computer to the ith computer per unit length C_{ik}', the request rate for the entire or part of the jth file at the ith computer per unit time u_{ij}, the frequency of modification of the jth file after a transaction at the ith computer P_{ij}, the average length of the segment of the jth

---

[3]For an appropriate expression of W_{ik}, the interested reader should refer to [CHU 69].

[4]In a non-fully connected network, because of alternate routing, C_{ik}' should be viewed as the average communication cost from the kth computer to the ith computer per unit length. In some packet-switching systems, C_{ik}' are distance independent and can be simplified to a constant C'.

file requested by a transaction l_i, and the number of redundant copies of the jth file stored in the system r_j. Then the overall operating cost per unit time C for processing m distinct files required in common by n computers is

$$C = \sum_{ij} C_{ij} L_j X_{ij} \; + \; \sum_{i,j,k} \frac{1}{r_j} C'_{ik} \, \ell_j u_{ij} X_{kj} (1 - X_{ij}) \; + \; \sum_{i,j,k} C'_{ik} \, \ell_j u_{ij} X_{kj} P_{ij} \tag{19.8}$$

(storage cost) \hspace{4cm} (communication cost)

which can be rearranged in the form

$$= \sum_{ij} D_{ij} X_{ij} - \sum_{i,j,k} E_{ijk} X_{kj} X_{ij} \text{ where } D_{ij} > 0, \; E_{ijk} > 0 \tag{19.9}$$

When $r_j = 1$, $1 \leq j \leq m$, then $X_{kj} X_{ij} = 0$ for $k \neq i$. Further, since $C'_{ii} = 0$, Eq. (19.9) reduces to

$$C = \sum_{ij} D_{ij} X_{ij}$$

We want to minimize Eq. (19.9) subject to availability, storage, and access time requirement constraints given in Eqs. (19.1) to (19.4). As the X_{ij}'s take on values zero or one, the allocation problem becomes one of solving a nonlinear zero–one programming problem. The nonlinear zero–one equations can be reduced to a linear zero-one equation [CHU 69]. With this technique, the file allocation problem can be then solved by standard linear zero-one programming [GOM 63].

A recent study [PRI 78] reported on use of the APEX III system, an integer programming software package supported by CDC 6000 series computers, to solve the file allocation problem. The system is capable of solving a problem consisting of 8000 constraint equations and 2500 unknowns. A file allocation problem with 15 computers and 15 files, consisting of 6330 constraint equations and 1801 unknowns, requires only a few minutes of computation time on that system.

Other file allocation studies performed in past years include channel switching [WHI 70] and assignment of channel capacity to achieve minimum operating cost [MAH 76]. Under the assumption that query response time is always satisfactory, Casey [CAS 72] studied the optimal number of copies of a file contained in the system such that it minimizes the cost of storing the copies of the file and of transmitting the file queries and updates. Let ρ be the minimum of the update to query traffic ratio for all sites in the network. An upper bound on the optimal number of copies is given by the minimum value of integer r that satisfies the expression $\rho \geq 1/(r - 1)$. There are other factors, such as file availability [CHU 73] and file response time [CHU 69, MAH 76], that determine the optimal number of copies of a file. The higher the number of duplicate copies of a file in the system, the greater the availability of a file and the lower the response time. However, duplicate copies also create problems of synchronization and consistency for concurrent updates, which are discussed in Sec. 19.5.

Morgan and Levin [MOR 77] formulated a model for file allocation that considers interaction between programs and data files. Data files are accessed by programs that may not be located at the same site. The user-generated requests for access to a file utilize various programs with different probabilities. A mathematical model is developed which is based on parameters such as unit query communication cost, unit update communication cost, and file storage cost. The model distinguishes the lengths of messages traveling between users and programs from the lengths of messages traveling between programs and files.

After the files have been created and allocated in a network, a directory is needed to specify the physical, logical, operational, and security characteristics of the files so that the user or system can locate and access a shared file in the distributed data base. Directory organization and its distribution influence query and update traffic patterns in the network. They not only affect the operating cost of the data base, but also the performance of the system in terms of security, reliability, and query response time.

19.3   FILE DIRECTORY SYSTEM DESIGN

A file directory is a listing of information about files available to users of the distributed data base in a computer network. Such a directory enables a user at any node to determine where in a network a specific sharable file is located. Such a directory can be considered to be similar to a card catalog in a public library. Users at each node may offer to list their files in this directory of public files for sharing purposes. A user may interrogate this list to determine its contents or obtain information on the location and characteristics of specific sharable files. The nonshared files are assumed to be stored at the computer known to the user and are therefore not considered here. We assume that each computer has its own directory, which consists of information on all sharable files stored in that computer. To search for a file that is not listed in that directory at his or her computer, the user must consult the file directory system.

There are several ways to design the file directory system: centralized file directory system, multiple master directory systems, local file directory system, and distributed file directory system. Based on the computer network topology, operating cost (communication cost, storage cost, and code translation cost), directory query rate, and directory update rate, mathematical models may be used to study the operating cost and response time of these directory systems as a function of directory query rate, directory update rate, and the ratio of storage cost to communication cost [CHU 79].

19.3.1   Information Contents of the Directory
System

The directory system should consist of physical, logical, security, and operational information about a file as shown in Tab. 19.1. For more information about the contents of the directory system, the interested readers should refer to [ALL 82].

The contents of the directory system may be logically partitioned and organized into several levels. Each level contains a certain amount of information and description about a file. The user terminates his or her query at the directory level when he or

Table 19.1. *Content of a Directory System.*

Physical (Static)	Logical (Dynamic)	Security	Operational
Name of file	File status (R, W)	(file, user, C)	Data reduction function (type of operation, query parameters)
Location (site)	Number of backlog jobs	C = read/write	Query processing optimizer
Creator	Computer site availability	Read only	Statistical data gathering algorithms
Version number of the file	Resource requirement	Write only	Deadlock avoidance algorithm
File size			
Code format			
Processing cost			
Communication cost			
Translation cost			
Number of duplicate copies of a file and their locations			
Date of last update			

she acquires information sufficient to process a file. Since using the directory at different levels may require different access rights, this file directory system provides different degrees of security protection at different levels.

The directory may include a query processing optimizer. When a user presents a query to the system, the directory first locates the files referenced by the query. Then based on the directory information, the current operating state of the data base, and resource requirements, the query processing optimizer generates a procedure for retrieval and a choice of locations for processing the query that yields minimum operating cost. An optimal query processing model is presented in Sec. 19.7. Further, the information in the directory system is updated after each operation. The directory system thus presents the up-to-date status of the system and plays an important role in processing queries in a distributed data base.

19.3.2 Centralized Directory System

In the centralized file directory system, a master directory is located at one of the computers. Should a user require a file that is not listed in the local directory, he or she consults the master directory for the location and contents of the requested file. Further, the centralized directory must be updated when a new version of a file is created or a change in storage location is required. The advantage of such a system is its ease in updating. The disadvantage is the high communication cost of each transaction.

The extended centralized file directory is a variation of the centralized file directory. In this case whenever a user uses the centralized file directory, and once the user finds the location and description of a file, he or she can append this information to the local directory. Should the user use this file again, the directory information for this file can be obtained from the local directory, thereby reducing the communication cost as well as time for querying the master directory. However, when the information on that file at the master directory is updated, we also require updating the information on that file in the local directories. Therefore, for notification of future updates in the master directory, the list of local directories that have appended file information is recorded in the master directory. This directory system provides an adaptive feature. After a certain time period, each extended directory consists of directory information about frequently referenced files.

19.3.3   Multiple Master Directory System

When computers in a network are clustered in groups, it is often cost effective to provide a master directory for the entire network at each cluster. The savings in communication cost for queries in a multiple master directory system could far outweigh the cost of storing and updating the file directories. To organize the multiple directory system, we partition the n computers in the system into r clusters ($r \leq n$). During normal operation, computers in a given cluster will query the directory, which is located at a member of that cluster. One way to partition n computers into r clusters is to base the partitioning on the network topology so that the partitioned clusters yield minimum communication costs. Another way is to base the partitioning on directory query rates and directory update rates for achieving minimum directory query response time.

19.3.4   Local File Directory System

In the local file directory system, there is no master directory in the system. When a requested file is not stored in the user's local directory, the user queries all the other local directories in the system until the requested file has been located. Assuming that the directory can be updated only by its owner, updating is done at its local directory. This does not require communications cost. On the other hand, such a directory system requires high communication cost and translation cost, as well as search time for locating the file. For a system of n computers, it requires an average of $(n-1)/2$ directory queries to locate a nonlocal file. However, if each of the computers contains a routing table that routes the directory query directly to the other computers rather than returning the negative query reply to the sender, the expected total communication cost can be greatly reduced, particularly if the routing sequence takes into consideration the probability of finding the file in the directory. The total operating cost can be reduced by a factor of ξ $(0 < \xi \leq 1)$, which depends on the network topology and the policy used in the routing table. A simple implementation of the routing table is to let each computer contain a directory locator which specifies the directory locations of all the shared files in the system. Whenever a file is created, deleted, or changes its directory location, all the directory locators in the system will be updated to reflect this change. Since such changes are not often, the contents of the directory locator should be fairly static. With the aid of such directory locator, the time required to search for a non local file is independent of the number of computers in the system. This greatly reduces the communication cost for searching the directory locations of the non-local files.

The advantage of such a directory is the ease of directory update as well as being particularly suitable for distributed data-base systems operating in a local network environment. The disadvantages are high communication cost and high directory query response time for locating and obtaining the file directory information if directory locator is not used.

19.3.5 Distributed File Directory System

In the distributed directory case, each computer in the system has a master directory. The advantage of this sytem is its fast response time. The disadvantage is the cost of storing a master file directory at each computer in addition to the communication cost for updating all these directories.

19.3.6 Operating Cost Trade-offs among Directory Systems

Let P be the normalized directory update rate, which is defined as the ratio of directory update rate to directory query rate and is assumed to be the same for all sites. Let $C_x(P)$ and $C_y(P)$ be the operating cost for directory systems x and y, respectively. The intersection of $C_x(P)$ and $C_y(P)$ represents the cost trade-off point (in terms of normalized update rate) for directory systems x and y. If we assume that all computers in the system have identical directory update rates, the operating cost is a linear function of P [CHU 76]. Thus $C_x(P)$ and $C_y(P)$ can be expressed as

$$C_x(P) = a_x P + b_x$$

and

$$C_y(P) = a_y P + b_y$$

(19.10)

where a_x and a_y are incremental costs (e.g., communication cost and translation cost) which increase with directory update rates. Both b_x and b_y are fixed directory operating costs (e.g., storage cost) which are independent of directory update rates. The intersection of $C_x(P)$ and $C_y(P)$, $P(x, y)$, satisfies

$$P(x, y) = \frac{b_y - b_x}{a_x - a_y}$$

(19.11)

Let us now consider the intersection of the cost curves for the centralized (C) and extended centralized (CE) directory systems. We assume that

1. Communication cost is much higher than storage cost so that storage cost becomes negligible.
2. All computers in the system have the same directory query rate.
3. All computers use the same software code; thus translation cost is not required.
4. The probability of updating each extended directory given that the master directory has been updated, μ, is the same for all computers.

Then it can be shown that [CHU 76]

$$P(C, CE) = \frac{2}{(n-1)\mu} \tag{19.12}$$

For example, if $n = 10$ and $\mu = 1/3$, then $P(C, CE) = 2/3 = 0.667$. Thus for a network with 10 computers operating in the environment described above, when the directory update rate of each computer is less than 67% of its query rate, the extended centralized directory system yields a lower operating cost than that of the centralized directory system.

We will now consider the directory operating cost trade-offs between the centralized directory system and the distributed directory system (D). If we assume that the directory query rate generated at each computer is the same and no translation cost is required, and that the communication cost between nodes i and k, the communication cost between node i and the directory node C_{id}, the distance between nodes i and k, S_{ik}, and the distance between node i and the directory node, S_{id}, satisfy the condition $C_{ik}^I S_{ik} = C_{id}^I S_{id}$, then it can be shown that [CHU 76]

$$P(C, D) = \frac{2}{n-1} \tag{19.13}$$

For a network with 10 computers operating in such an environment, $P(C, D) \doteq 0.22$. This implies that when the directory update rate is less than 22% of its query rate, the distributed file directory yields a lower operating cost than the centralized file directory.

We will now consider the cost trade-offs of the local file directory (L) cost curve with the distributed file directory cost curve. When the communication cost is high compared to the storage cost, and when the directory update rate is less than the directory query rate, the distributed file directory system yields a lower operating cost than that of the local -le directory system; that is when $C_{ik} \ll C_i$, then $P(L, D) \rightarrow 1$.

From performance studies based on the 10-node distributed network shown in Fig. 19.1, we notice that the operating cost of the file directory depends greatly on the directory query rate and the directory update rate (Fig. 19.2). Because of the large amount of data communication and translation associated with the directory updates in the distributed directory system, the rate of increase in operating cost with respect to the normalized directory update rate for the distributed directory system is higher than that of the centralized directory system. In the local directory system, we need only update the local directory of the computer that generates the

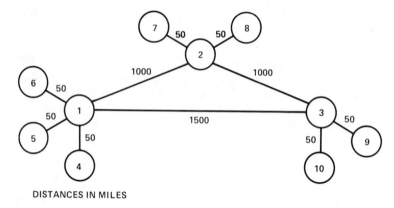

DISTANCES IN MILES

Figure 19.1. Distributed network for performance studies. Unit communication cost/unit storage cost $= C^t/C^s = 10$ months/mile.

update, and no transmission is required. The operating cost is therefore independent of the directory update rate.

Assuming that the communication cost is higher than the storage cost, our study reveals that when the directory update rate is low (e.g., less than 10% of the query rate), the distributed directory system yields lower operating cost than the centralized directory system. As directory update rate increases, the centralized directory system yields lower operating cost than the distributed directory system.

Comparing the two types of centralized directory systems, the extended centralized directory yields a lower operating cost than the centralized directory at lower directory update rates (less than 50% of the query rate), and the performance reverses at high directory update rates. This is because of the excessive amount of data transmission required to update all the extended local directories. The crossover point of the operating cost curves for these two types of directory systems depends on network topology and such parameters as storage costs, transmission costs, translation costs, and so on. As the directory update rate increases, the performance characteristics of the extended centralized directory system become similar to those of the distributed directory system.

The influence of the distribution of the directory query traffic on the operating cost has also been studied. In order to provide a common base for comparison, the total number of queries generated by the computers was kept constant, and the query traffic among the computers was varied. It was found that traffic distribution does not affect directory operating cost when all the computers are equal distances from each other, and does affect operating cost when distances among the computers are different.

19.3.7 Directory Query Response Time

Let us now consider the query response times for various directory systems. The expected response time for the *i*th computer to query its directory is defined as the

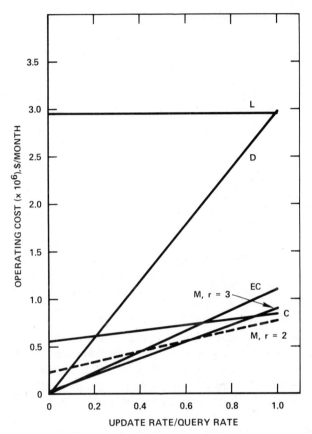

Figure 19.2. Performance of multiple directory systems for the distributed network. $C^t/C^s = 10$ months/mile, and query rate = 1000 queries/month. For $r = 2$, master directories at computers 1 and 2; for $r = 3$, master directories at computers 1, 2, and 3.

time from initiation of a query at the ith computer until the start of the reception of the results of the query. The expected response time consists of the waiting time at the input queue of the directory for processing the query t_1 (i), the waiting time at the output queue of the directory for transmission t_2 (i), the time to transmit the query to and its reply from the directory t_3 (i), and the directory processing time t_4 (i). The processing time consists of code translation, searching, and accessing. It depends on the file structure of the directory as well as the access time of the storage device, which could be different from one system to another, and should be known to the users. Here, therefore, we consider only the delay incurred at the input queue and output queue(s) of the directory, and the time to transmit the query on the communication channel. Let us denote the sum of these components as $t_{i,d}$ known as the directory query response time for the ith computer to the directory. Thus

$$t_{i,d} = t_1 (i) + t_2 (i) = t_3(i) \qquad (19.14)$$

Clearly, the real query response time incurred by the users is equal to the sum of $t_{i,d}$ and t_4 (i).

The arrivals at the input queue of the directory are the queries and updates generated by all the computers. The arrivals at the output queue(s) of the directory are the query replies generated at the directory. Let us first consider the centralized directory system. The set of requests arriving at the directory consists of directory queries and updates from all computers in the system. Since the directory does not have to reply to update traffic, and since each destination has its own output queue, the arrival rate at the output queue for the ith computer is equal to its directory query rate. For the computer that stores the master directory, $t_2(d) = t_3(d) = 0$. The expected query response time reduces to $t_1(d)$.

For multiple master directory systems, since the traffic load of the directory queries are shared by the multiple master directories, the expected waiting time for processing the directory queries at each master directory is much lower than the waiting time of the single master (centralized) directory system. Therefore, the response time for the multiple master directory is lower than that of the single master directory system. The query reply rate at the output queue for the ith computer is equal to the directory query rate from the ith computer. When the directory queries are generated by those computers that store the master directories, these query replies do not require transmission. Thus the response time equals $t_1(d)$.

For the local directory system whose replies are returned directly to the sender (i.e., without routing), the ith computer may locate the information on the file before the request reaches the kth local directory. Therefore, on the average only half of the queries generated at the ith computer will reach the kth computer.

When a carefully designed routing strategy is used in a local directory system, the input traffic rate to each directory can be greatly reduced. As a result, the query response time for the system with routing could be much smaller than that without routing.

For the distributed directory system, each computer has a master directory. File directory information can be obtained at each computer. Thus t_2 $(i) = t_3$ $(i) = 0$. The input traffic to the directory consists only of queries generated from its own computer and the directory updates generated from the rest of the computers in the system.

An expression for $t_{i,d}$ for different types of directory systems can be generated from well-known queueing theory results, assuming that arrival rates at the directory input and output queues can be approximated as Poisson arrivals, and that the communication lines have a fixed transmission rate. Then the query response times are shown in Fig. 19.3. The queueing delay increases as the query rate increases. Except in the local directory case, the queueing delay increases as the directory update rate increases. This is because only the nonlocal update messages are considered as input traffic to the directory. Since the input traffic to the multiple master directory system is shared among the master directories, it yields lower queueing delay than the centralized directory system. For the range of query rates we have studied, the time spent in transmission to and from the directories constitutes a large portion of the delay. Since the distributed directory system does not require such transmission, it yields the lowest query response time.

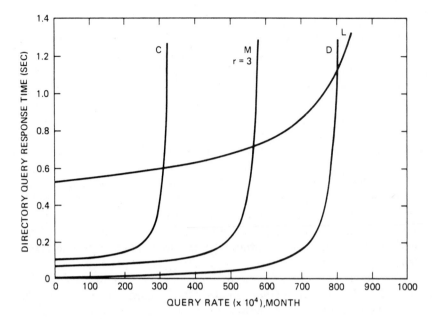

Figure 19.3. Expected directory query response time versus directory query rate for various directory systems. Normalized directory update rate = 0.5. C = centralized directory; L = local directory; D = distributed directory; M = multiple master directories. (From [CHU 76].)

Let us now consider the extended centralized directory system. For those files that have not yet been queried at the directory by the ith computer, the response time is similar to the centralized directory system except that the directory query rate is much smaller. The output queue at the centralized directory for a given computer should include the update traffic (generated by all the computers) for the extended directory of that computer. For those files whose directory information has already been appended to the local directory at that computer, there is no need for that computer to consult the master directory about these files. Therefore, the query response time has similar characteristics to that of the distributed directory system.

19.4 DEADLOCK IN DISTRIBUTED DATA BASES

A deadlock exists whenever two or more processes vying for the same resource reach an impasse. For example, suppose that both processes 1 and 2 require resources A and B to complete their tasks. At a certain point in time, process 1 has locked resource A and requested resource B; similarly, process 2 has locked resource B and requested A. Therefore, neither process 1 nor process 2 can obtain the necessary resources to complete its task. Thus a deadlock has occurred. When a deadlock occurs, if a job is aborted, the resulting partially completed process often represents a serious inconvenience to the user. He or she must, in many cases, reconstruct partially altered files. For this reason, deadlock is an important consideration in the design of operating systems, even though in practice it seldom occurs.

When the resources required by any process can be obtained prior to starting it, a deadlock prevention mechanism examines the resource requirements of all processes and allows a process to proceed only when a deadlock cannot occur. Therefore, deadlock can be prevented. On the other hand, when the resources required by any process cannot be obtained a priori (or it is too costly to do so), or when the system uses dynamic resource allocation (e.g., virtual memory systems), resource requirements may change dynamically. In these cases, deadlock detection must be used. The system detects and resolves the deadlock by eliminating an offending process from contention. It is possible to combine these mechanisms so that certain resources are serviced by a detection mechanism while other resources are serviced by a prevention mechanism.

Many studies of deadlock protection schemes have been reported [HAV 68, HAB 69, HOL 72, KIN 73], but the emphasis in these studies has been on centralized data-base systems. Here we will emphasize distributed data-base systems, which are complicated by the necessity for coordinating several computers without impeding their progress.

19.4.1   Access Control

In many cases, such as program libraries, it is necessary for two or more processes to have simultaneous access to the same file. However, a process that modifies a file cannot share with any other process access to that file at the same time. In order to provide users with this flexibility, a system must provide two methods of access to every file, either *shared* or *exclusive*. The user specifies which method of access is desired when the file is requested. If no process has been granted exclusive access to a file, a request for shared access to that file by any process can be granted. If no process has been granted either shared or exclusive access to a file, a request for exclusive access to that file by any process can be granted. This protocol provides multiple readers *or* one writer with access to a specific file.

19.4.2   Deadlock Prevention Mechanisms

One way to implement deadlock prevention in a computer network is to assign a node (computer) as a monitoring node, which examines the file requirements of all processes and allows a process to proceed when a deadlock cannot occur. This is rather inefficient since the monitoring node has to examine the file requirements before the process can be allowed to start, and a process will not be allowed to start if a future deadlock is possible. A more efficient way to implement deadlock prevention is to assign a fixed examining path in the network by assigning every node in the network a number [CHU 74]. Then the *examining path* is determined uniquely by the node numbers as shown in Fig. 19.4. When requests for files are passed around the network according to this path, intersite communication is greatly reduced. Further, node n_k (with node number k) has knowledge of the resource requests of the nodes that have node numbers less than k, therefore node n_k is able to determine if the request resource could cause deadlock. Such distributed control scheme improves the efficiency of the deadlock prevention mechanisms.

Since the lower-numbered nodes have better access to the deadlock prevention mechanism than higher-numbered nodes, one way to assign the node numbers is to assign lower numbers to the nodes that contain files that have a high usage frequency and a high volume of data required per transmission.

19.4.2.1 Simple Deadlock Prevention Mechanism

Deadlock prevention mechanisms require the user to specify the files that a process requires prior to initiation of that process. These requests are usually made through the job control language of the system. The information is used by the system to prevent a deadlock from occurring.

One means of preventing deadlock is for the system to obtain control of all the files requested by a process before initiating the process. For one process at a time, the system collects the requests for files and examines each one to determine if access to the file can be granted, as outlined in the preceding section. If all requests can be granted, the process is given access to the files and is initiated. Otherwise, the process is delayed until all processes that have access to the requested files terminate. While the process is delayed, the requested files are available to other processes [HAV 68].

In a distributed data base, the system examines the requests for files to determine if all the requests are for local files. If they are, the requests are processed as outlined above. Otherwise, the requests for files are passed from node to node via the examining path, starting with the first node. Each node examines the requests for files located at that node as outlined above. As soon as all the requests for files have been granted, the node at which the requesting process resides is so informed and the

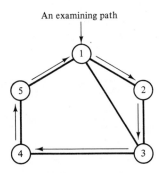

Figure 19.4. An examining path of a network.

process is allowed to proceed. Clearly, in a distributed data-base system, intercomputer communication is required when remote files are requested.

The simplicity of this mechanism enables easy implementation and requires low system overhead. In addition, interactive users can avoid waiting by simply terminating a delayed process, since such a process has not been initiated.

19.4.2.2 Deadlock Prevention with Process Set [CHU 74]

In order to more effectively determine if access to a file can be granted, processes having requests for the same file(s) can be grouped into process sets. A system may have any number of process sets. The membership criterion is, if a process requests exclusive access to a file, that process and all other processes which have requested access (exclusive or shared) to that file are members of the same process set. Further, each process belongs to one process set.

Such a group of process sets is formed as follows. Whenever a new process arrives, certain process sets that have possession of file(s) that are requested by the new process are combined and the new process is added to the resulting process set. (Of course, if no process sets possess a file or a set of files requested by a new process, the new process forms a process set by itself.) The rules for combining process sets are as follows. If shared access to a file is requested by the new process, the process set containing one or more processes which have requested exclusive access to that file is combined with the new process. If exclusive access to a file is requested by the new process, all the process sets containing one or more processes which have requested access (exclusive or shared) to that file are combined, and the new process is added to the resulting process set. When a process terminates, the remaining members of the process set may be reexamined with respect to each other by the same mechanism to reform their process set or sets.

The advantage of establishing process sets is that once a process has been allocated to a set, the progress of that process is independent of all processes in other process sets. Further, in contrast with the simple deadlock prevention mechanism, a process in a process set does not require complete control of all its files. The use of process sets for deadlock prevention considerably reduces the amount of computation required to determine whether or not all the processes can be completed. However, there is a certain amount of overhead in forming the process sets.

19.4.3 Deadlock Detection

Deadlock detection allows the user to request access to files at any time. The system monitors these requests by maintaining two lists, a list of processes P1, P2, . . . , and a list of requested files A, B, . . . , as in Fig. 19.5. The symbol Λ indicates that the process is not waiting for any file. Lack of the symbol indicates the process is waiting for a file. Each element of the lists has a pointer which is used by the system to determine if a deadlock has occurred. When the system receives a request for access to a file from a process, if the request can be granted, the pointer of the corresponding file is set to

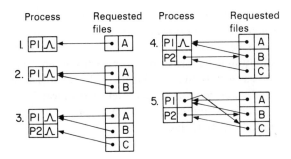

Figure 19.5. Deadlock detection in a distributed data base.

point to that process and the process is allowed to proceed. Otherwise, the pointer of the process is set to point to the requested file. The file list and process lists starting from the requested file are traversed along the path formed by the pointers until either an open process pointer Λ is found, in which case the requesting process is delayed, or the pointers return to the requesting process, in which case a deadlock exists [HOL 72].

As an example, consider two processes which make the following series of requests for files:

Request 1.   Process 1: requests for file A
Request 2.   Process 1: requests for file B
Request 3.   Process 2: requests for file C
Request 4.   Process 2: requests for file B
Request 5.   Process 1: requests for file C

The process and file lists are formed as shown in Fig. 19.5.

The open process pointer in request 4 is found when the path P2–B–P1 is detected. In this case P2 is delayed until P1 releases file B. If process P2 is not delayed, the deadlock in request 5 is found when the loop P1–C–P2–B–P1 is detected by the detection algorithm. When a deadlock is detected, the system returns one of the processes involved back to its initial state, releasing and restoring the files it controls. Since the files must be restored, a backup copy of each file must be available. The removed process is restarted at a later time [KIN 73].

The implementation of the deadlock detection mechanism in a distributed data base is accomplished by appointing one node of the network to monitor requests for files and detect deadlocks. The appointed node maintains the process and file lists, and every node is required to transmit to the appointed node information concerning the initiation and termination of each process and all requests for and releases of files. A process is allowed to proceed without waiting, even if a future deadlock is possible. For the purpose of improving reliability, a second node may be appointed as a back-up to monitor requests for files.

Deadlock detection can be easily implemented and has an advantage in that the user is not required to know in advance which files a process requires. On the other hand, even though actual deadlocks are infrequent, when they do occur, considerable system overhead must be accounted for. For example, an interactive user who is restarted must resupply all the information he or she had given the process, since the original information has lost its integrity. Finally, although this mechanism requires considerable intercomputer communication even when local files are being used, processes will not be delayed by the mechanism as long as all its requests for files (made at various times) can be granted.

19.5   MUTUAL AND INTERNAL CONSISTENCY IN MULTICOPY DATA BASES

To improve the availability and response time of distributed data bases, multiple copies of files may be stored in the distributed data base system. As a result, the loss of a processor or channel link will not result in the loss of the entire data base, and storing files at those sites that use them frequently provides faster access. However, storing multiple copies of files in the system creates the problem of synchronization of concurrent updates. Many studies [ALS 76, ELL 77, LAM 76, HAM 78, SHA 78, THO 78, GEL 78, MEN 78, GAR 80, BER 81] have been done. In the following, we shall discuss a few of the methods.

19.5.1   The Problem

Every transaction that causes a change in any data item stored in the data base must be followed by update messages to all nodes (sites) that have a copy of the data. Each site has a data base management system (DBMS) which applies those updates to the data it maintains. As an extreme case we may have one complete copy of the data base in each node.

Considering a file stored at both sites A and B, an update may cause the loss of mutual consistency as shown in the following:

Site A		Site B	
Part number	*Price*	*Part number*	*Price*
•	•	•	•
•	•	•	•
•	•	•	•
1021	$10.00	1021	$10.00
•	•	•	•
•	•	•	•
•	•	•	•

At site A, a transaction may change the price of part 1021 from $10.00 to $13.00 and at site B an almost simultaneous transaction changes the price of the same item from

$10.00 to $12.00. After these local executions and transmissions of the update messages to each other, a possible result is:

Site A		Site B	
Part number	*Price*	*Part number*	*Price*
•	•	•	•
•	•	•	•
•	•	•	•
1021	$12.00	1021	$13.00
•	•	•	•
•	•	•	•
•	•	•	•

The mutual consistency is not preserved because each site performs the local transaction before receiving the update message from the other site. Mutual consistency means that all copies of the same data must be identical to each other. It is not possible to have instantaneously identical copies at all times because of the communication delays. However, they must converge to an identical final state when transaction activity is terminated.

Besides the problem of mutual consistency of the redundant copies of the data base, we must also consider the preservation of invariant relations among items within the data base, also known as *integrity constraints*. This is called *internal consistency*, or *data integrity*. The following example shows how internal consistency of each data base may be lost due to updates.

Suppose that we have a file consisting of three data fields (x, y, and z) which must satisfy the condition $x + y + z = 3$. This file is stored at sites A and B, and initially these three variables have value 1. Now, if a user at site A executes $x = -1$, $y = 3$, and almost immediately another user, at site B, executes $y = 3$, $z = -1$, we have the following possible result:

	Site A		Site B	
	Before Update	*After Update*	*Before Update*	*After Update*
x	1	-1	1	-1
y	1	3	1	3
z	1	-1	1	-1
$x + y + z$	3	1	3	1

Mutual consistency among the multiple copies is preserved here, but internal consistency of each data base is not. However, each transaction does preserve data integrity if it is executed alone.

In conclusion, we must then observe two criteria to preserve data consistency: mutual consistency between redundant copies of data bases and internal consistency of each copy.

19.5.2 Solutions to the Consistency Problem

To provide mutual consistency, any alteration of a data item must be performed in all the copies of the data base, and alterations to the same data item must be performed in the same order in all copies of the data base. To provide internal consistency on a distributed data base, a lock mechanism should be used to synchronize transactions, provided that each transaction when executed alone does not violate data integrity.

Despite the delays in the communication lines, it is possible to force updates to take place at all the copies in the same order if we assign timestamps (TS) to them [THO 78]. These timestamps are generated by a local clock at each site. Synchronization of these clocks is discussed in [LAM 78]. These timestamps represent the time that the local transactions, which generated the updates, happened and are propagated together with the update messages. Each data item in each copy of the distributed data base has also its own timestamp.[5] This timestamp represents the time that the data item was last updated. Upon arrival of an update message to a node, the local data management process compares the timestamp of the update message to the one assigned to the local data item. The update is performed only if the timestamp of the received update message is more recent than that of the data item in the local copy.

Consider the following message for updating values of two data items in all redundant files in the distributed data base where the timestamp format is (year, month, day, hour, minute)

$$TS = (84, 3, 15, 12, 01)$$

ID	Value
1021	$4.00
1035	$7.50

ID	Value	TS
1021	$2.50	(83, 5, 15, 9, 12)
•		
•		
•		
1035	$7.90	(84, 3, 15, 12, 14)
•		
•		
•		

The second data item shown above will not have its value changed because its timestamp is more recent than that of the update message. It can be shown that by

[5]Using timestamps in this way clearly increases the storage requirements for the data base.

using timestamps, all copies of the data base converge to a final value as required by mutual consistency. However, the timestamp method is not sufficient to preserve internal consistency.

To provide internal consistency, the update transactions must be done with mutually exclusive access to every copy of the data items to be modified; that is, the transactions must be serialized. This is a direct extension of the problem in a centralized data base. The portions of the data base being read or written must be locked by the process executing the transaction. Further, there is a necessary restriction on the order of "lock" and "unlock" operations by a transaction. Suppose transaction A locks, reads, and unlocks a data item, then locks and reads a second data item. If another transaction, transaction B, updates both data items during the interval between the first unlock and the second lock of transition A, the set of data read by transaction A may be inconsistent. It can be shown that transactions must use "two-phase" locking to prevent such inconsistency [ESW 76]; that is, a transaction must consist of a "growing phase" where it sets all its locks and does not release any locks, followed immediately by a "shrinking phase" in which the locks are released and no locks can be set. Therefore, in two-phase locking, no lock may be set by a transaction after it has released a lock.

To implement the synchronization there is a straightforward algorithm. However, for a network with n nodes, it requires $5n$ intercomputer messages, which consist of n lock requests, n lock grants, n update messages, n update acknowledgments, and n lock releases. Because of the amount of communications involved, this is a time-consuming and expensive method.

A good synchronization algorithm must be deadlock free, speed independent, and allow partial operability. It must be speed independent because one cannot guarantee the order in which messages sent by two nodes will arrive at a third. The time required to transmit messages between any two nodes is not fixed. Partial operability implies the ability to operate even in case of failure of part of the network.

19.5.2.1   Synchronization Message Propagation via a Loop

The number of transmissions can be reduced from $5n$ to $2n$ (n lock requests, n update messages) by organizing the nodes in a loop structure for propagating the synchronization messages as shown in Fig. 19.4.

When receiving an update request, the local DBMS sends a request to its neighbor. The update request propagates around the loop, setting the necessary locks at each site, and when it arrives back to the sender, it is interpreted as a request-grant message. The local transaction is performed and the resulting update message also propagates around the loop. As a side effect it also acts as a lock release. Furthermore, the update message is its own completion acknowledgment when arriving back to the update originating node. Different priorities assigned to the nodes resolve the conflict of simultaneous requests. A node does not forward a lower-priority request while it has an outstanding one of its own.

Use of the loop structure for propagating the synchronization makes the system deadlock free because there are no cyclic dependencies. Further, it is speed independent because every transmission is serialized. Partial operability is achieved if there is the possibility of detecting node failures and bypassing the failed nodes or links. Since the messages propagate serially in the network, using such a method requires much delay. Therefore, it is suitable for small networks.

19.5.2.2   Majority Consensus Algorithm
[THO 78]

This algorithm is based on the principle that an update can be performed only if the majority of the data-base management systems in the network agree with a request for that update. This is because if two update requests have been accepted by a majority of the nodes, it means that at least one node has voted OK for both, and consequently they do not conflict.

Each request contains the list of the variables that participate in the update computation with their respective timestamps and the values for the updated variables. Each DBMS upon receipt of a request must either vote OK, REJECT, PASS, or defer voting. A vote of REJECT is issued by a node if any of the variables in the request is already obsolete (i.e., has a timestamp older than the one in that node's copy). A vote of OK is given if all variables are up to date and there is no conflict with any pending request. PASS is voted if the variables are up to date but there is a conflict with a higher-priority request. Voting is deferred if the variables are up to date but there is a conflict with a lower-priority request.

If the majority vote OK, the transaction is executed. In case of receiving a REJECT, the originating station must try again at a later time. If no REJECT is given but, because of PASS votes, the number of OK votes do not make the majority, the originating station must try again later.

For a network with n nodes, the transmission may be in broadcast mode or on a loop basis. In the broadcast case, the number of transmissions to perform an update is $2.5n$ and in the loop case it is $1.5n$.

Speed independence is achieved by the use of timestamps, and the use of priorities together with timestamps makes the algorithm deadlock free. Partial operability is also guaranteed. However, if more than half the network is not accessible, no updates can be performed.

19.5.2.3   Primary Site Locking [STO 79]

PSL is a cost effective locking protocol for concurrency control. In PSL, each file has a designated primary site (PS) that controls access to the file. For a task at a non-PS to obtain read access, a lock-request message for read-only access is sent to the PS. The reading task then waits until the PS replies with a lock-grant message which indicates that all updates to the requested file are completed. Contained in the lock-grant message is the sequence number of the last update made to the file. If the requesting site has not posted this update, then it waits until all outstanding updates have been posted before the reader is permitted to commence processing. Once the reader completes its processing, a lock-release message is sent to the PS. If there is no other task using the file for read-only access, then update access could be permitted at this time.

Figure 19.6 shows the file update protocol for PSL. If the requesting task does not reside at the PS of the file, a lock-request message (for update access) is sent, and the PS must reply with a lock-grant message before the requesting task can proceed. The requesting task may incur additional waiting if the sequence number in the lock-grant message indicates that there is an outstanding update message. Once the task completes its processing, its updates are distributed. The sequence number of the update is equal to the sequence number in the lock-grant message plus one. A site receiving the update will post it if the update is in sequence. Otherwise, the new update is queued until outstanding updates arrive. At the PS, an update message has the additional interpretation as an implicit lock-release.

In PSL, the number of messages required for file access varies with task assignment. In particular, if F_i is updated by a task assigned to F_i's primary site, then no lock-request, lock-grant, or lock-release message is required.

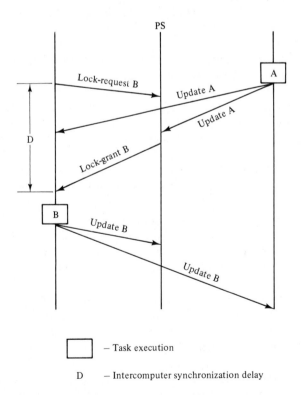

☐ — Task execution

D — Intercomputer synchronization delay

Figure 19.6 Protocol diagram for primary site locking (PSL).

19.5.2.4 Variable Level of Synchronization Control [BER 81, ROT 80]

Most synchronization techniques are ultimately equivalent to global locking by each transaction of the items in the data base that it reads or writes. However, a careful analysis of the conflicts between transactions shows that other synchronization mechanisms, weaker than global locking, can often be used instead. Such weaker synchronization mechanisms are faster and allow a greater degree of concurrency in transaction execution; thus they bring about more efficient operation of the distributed data-base system. This work describes the design and implementation of a concurrency control that uses four different synchronization mechanisms. Conflicting transactions are run using the mechanism that is most efficient and still generates consistent results.

The data-base environment consists of transaction modules, which supervise execution of transactions, and data modules, each of which manages storage of a portion of the data base. Parts of the data base are duplicated in multiple data modules. A transaction in execution performs read operations on a set of items in the data base, and write operations on another set of items. These sets are called the "read set" and the "write set" of the transaction. A conflict between two transactions occurs when the write set of one transaction intersects either the read set or the write set of another transaction.

The proposed synchronization mechanisms are called *protocols* and are expressed as rules for the relative sequencing of read and write operations in individual data modules. These read and write operations are generated by transactions that are being run concurrently. The relative sequence of read and write operations depends on the nature of the conflict between the transactions and on the transaction timestamp. Each transaction is assigned a globally unique timestamp by its transaction module.

The protocols define the relationship between transactions in execution; that is, one transaction runs under a particular protocol with respect to one or more conflicting transitions. Thus transaction A may run under protocol 1 with respect to transaction B but (simultaneously) under protocol 3 with respect to transaction C. Four protocols are proposed, and are numbered in order of the strictness of their synchronization requirements. Protocol 1 is for conflicts that occur only between the read set of one transaction and the write set of another. Protocol 2 is for read-only transactions that conflict with several other transactions. Protocol 3 is as strong as global locking, and synchronizes a pair of transactions where both the read set and write set of one transaction interfere with the other transaction. Protocol 4, for individual transactions that have a large number of conflicts with others, specifies that the transaction is to be run serially; that is, no conflicting transactions can be run concurrently with it.

In order to decide which protocols to use for synchronization at runtime, the transactions are first classified off-line according to their read sets and write sets. Each class has a read set and a write set. A transaction is a member of a particular class if its read set is contained in the class' read set and its write set is contained in the class' write set. The conflicts between classes are analyzed using a graphical technique called a conflict graph. The result of this analysis is a concurrency table which specifies which protocol to use when synchronizing transactions from conflicting classes. The table is referenced by transaction modules at runtime.

This concurrency control is implemented by the use of "read conditions." A transaction module begins execution of a transaction by sending out read messages containing read conditions which specify that:

1.   Read operations for the current transaction cannot be executed until the write operations generated by specified transaction classes have been completed.
2.   The read operations (except for protocol 1) must be executed before write operations for other transactions that might interfere with the executing transaction.

Protocol 4 requires an additional exchange of messages between transaction modules that takes place before the read messages are sent. A *concurrency monitor* at each data module schedules the read and write operations.

19.5.2.5   *Atomic Transactions and Two-Phase Commit*

Regardless of the mechanisms used to synchronize transactions, we must ensure that each transaction's execution is *atomic*; that is, the transaction either completes at all nodes of the network or does not happen at all. If the resulting data-base state at any node reflects a partial effect of the transaction, or if the transaction aborts at some nodes and completes at others, then consistency has not been preserved. Furthermore, it is undesirable to require any node to "back-out" or "undo" a transaction whose updates have already been written into that node's data base.

Two-phase commit is a useful mechanism that provides transaction atomicity, and can be used effectively with many synchronization algorithms. We say that a node *commits* a transaction to its data base when it writes the modifications and updates required by the transaction onto its permanent data-base storage, thus changing the data-base state. Two-phase commit provides a way to co-ordinate the decision of all nodes as to whether to commit or abort the transaction.

In two-phase commit, one node, acting as the *coordinator,* makes the final decision of whether to commit or abort the transaction. In the first phase. the coordinator sends a PREPARE message to all nodes. When receiving a PREPARE message, a node enters a state where it can recoverably either commit or abort the transaction. This is called the READY state, and normally requires that some local log entries be made at the node to facilitate recovery or a retry of the transaction, should it become necessary at a later time. It may also require that some local locks be set on the resources required to commit the transaction. The node then informs the coordinator that it is READY. Once a node enters the READY state, it cannot unilaterally decide whether to commit or abort; only the coordinator can make that decision. When the coordinator receives replies from all nodes, it then decides whether to commit or abort. The second phase then begins with a commit or abort message from the coordinator to all nodes. When receiving this second message, each node performs the appropriate action (commit or abort), releases resources locked by the transaction and replies to the coordinator. This step either completes execution or aborts the transaction.

By leaving the final decision of whether to commit or abort in the hands of a single node, the two-phase commit procedure helps ensure consistency. Further, forcing all nodes to come to the READY state before commitment, where they are prepared to either commit or abort and to recover from either action, the procedure minimizes the possibility of expensive back-out or recovery operations which might be required otherwise, such as in the case where a node crashes while updating. For more extensive and detailed treatments of two-phase commit, the reader is referred to [LAM 76, GRA 78].

19.5.2.6   The Exclusive Writer
Protocol (EWP)

In the previous sections, we have discussed techniques for updating replicated files including locking and timestamps. While the processing costs and message volume of locking and timestamps can be substantial, this overhead may not be significant for database management systems in which shared files reside on secondary storage. However, for real time systems in which files consist of data in RAM and which use no high level data model, the overhead of locking or timestamps may be prohibitive. Therefore, a new approach to data consistency has been introduced. In it, accesses to shared data are structured so that there is only one predetermined task which is allowed to write a shared data item. Referred to as the *exclusive-writer protocol* (EWP), this approach can provide a low cost technique for ensuring mutual consistency that is suitable for distributed real time systems.

In the EWP, a task can read a local copy of a data item at any time. However, *each shared data item is written by only one predetermined task which does not change during system operation*. To handle situations in which multiple tasks must write the same data (referred to as multiwriter situations), the following approach can be used: (1) an exclusive-writer (EW) is designated for each shared data item, and (2) to update a shared data item, a task sends an update-request message to the data item's EW. Such an approach has been used by the Distributed Processing Architecture Design (DPAD) [GRE 80]. Here, we assume that exclusive-writers are dedicated to receiving update-request messages, distributing updates, and performing operations to ensure data consistency.

Using the EWP to ensure mutual consistency results in two advantages over employing non-exclusive writer techniques such as timestamps and locking. First, the EWP avoids delays due to locking protocol overhead and waits for locking synchronization. A second advantage relates to deadlocks. Since the EWP does not use locking, the *EWP can eliminate deadlocks due to shared data access.*

Internal Consistency Considerations

Although the EWP can ensure mutual consistency, it does not necessarily ensure internal consistency as illustrated in the example (Section 19.5.1).

To ensure internal consistency in multiwriter situations without the use of locking or timestamps, the *interdependent data set (IDS) update rule* is proposed as follows:

1. When a data item is modified, the resulting update must include the values of all data for which the modified data item has an interdependency. (Applying the IDS update rule to the example in Section 19.5.1 assuming that site A is the exclusive writer, the user at site A must include z in its update, and the user at site B must include x, as shown in Fig. 19.7.) This implies that EWP updates may be larger than those for locking and timestamps.
2. When a site posts an update, it must guarantee that the entire update is processed atomically (i.e., without interruption).
    Under these conditions internal consistency (but not serializability) will be preserved.

Using the IDS update rule may increase the size of the update message. This motivates us to introduce the following variation of the EWP which does not use the IDS update rule. Each copy of a file has an update sequence number, SN. The update-request messages (rather than the entire IDS), contains the modified data and

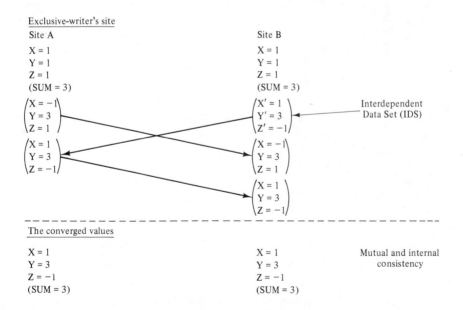

Figure 19.7. Preserving internal consistency in the EWP with interdependent data set update rule.

the SN. To determine if there was a conflict due to concurrent update-requests, the EW compares the SN in the update-request message with that of the corresponding file at its site. If they are not equal, then data conflict has occurred. To avoid violating internal consistency, conflicting update-requests are discarded.[6] If no conflict has occurred, the EW increases the SN by one and distributes the updates (which include the SN) as shown in Fig. 19.8

Discarding update requests may not be acceptable for some applications, so we extend the EWP to include a locking option (EWL). When an update conflict occurs, the EWP then switches to Primary Site Locking (PSL): the EW site is the primary site for all the files in the conflicting update-request, and the conflicting update-request is treated as a PSL lock request. Once all of the files required by the update request have been locked, the primary site issues a lock-grant message to the site that originated the update-request message. The originating site then re-executes the transactions and increases the SN of the files it updates by one, and then distributes the updates. When the EW receives an update message, it is treated as a lock-release. The detailed protocol is shown in Fig. 19.9.

To conclude, the EWP eliminates intercomputer synchronization delays but does not provide serializability (only internal and mutual consistency). The EWL does provide serializability (as well as internal and mutual consistency) and has the advantage of eliminating the intercomputer synchronization delay when there is no

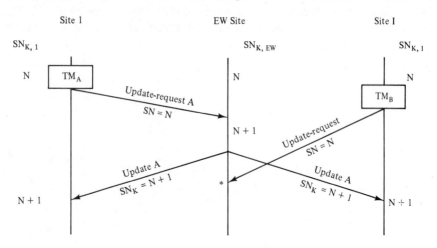

*Update-request discarded due to data conflict

$SN_{K, I}$ = Update sequence number for the copy of File F_K at Site I

(TM_A and TM_B only access file F_K)

Figure 19.8. Protocol diagram for the EWP with sequence numbers.

[6]For some applications (e.g., object discrimination in signal processing applications), occasional discard of updates may not be a problem.

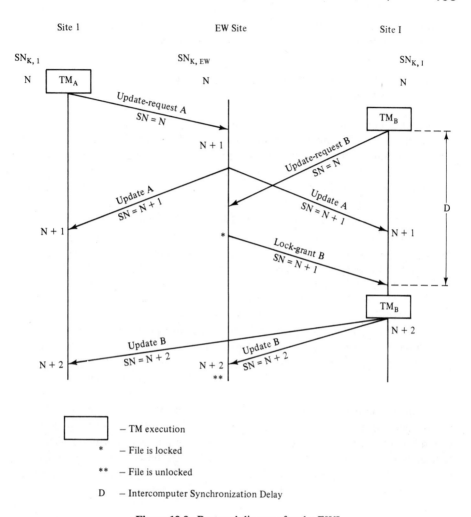

Figure 19.9. Protocol diagram for the EWL.

data conflict. Thus, the EWP and EWL have great appeal for updating replicated files in distributed real time systems. For more discussions on EWP, the interested reader should refer to [CHU 82B, CHU 85].

19.6   FAULT TOLERANCE AND RECOVERY IN DISTRIBUTED DATA-BASE SYSTEMS

Various techniques have been proposed to maintain consistency of a multiple-copy data base (i.e., a distributed data base in which redundant copies of data are maintained at more than one site) in the event of site failures, and to facilitate proper recovery of a failed site. We first discuss techniques used to maintain consistency of the surviving copies of the data base after a crash occurs.

19.6.1 Maintaining Consistency of the Data Base If a Site Crashes

A number of approaches to this problem have been proposed. One of them is based on a scheme for organizing the computer network such that one host site is designated as a primary site and several others are designated as backup sites. Protocols are used that guarantee that a resource-sharing service such as multiple-copy update synchronization will be disrupted only if n hosts fail simultaneously during a critical phase of the service, where n is determined by the design of the protocols. Such a scheme is said to satisfy the n-host *resiliency criterion* [ALS 76].

A number of simpler techniques can be used to maintain consistency. A two-phase message sending procedure for update messages was proposed in [HAM 78]. In this technique, the first phase of the procedure is the sending of a message to all sites informing them that an update message is forthcoming, including the names of the sites that should receive the message. The second phase is the update message itself, sent to all sites. Any sites that received the first-phase message but do not receive the expected update message (possibly because of a failure of the originating site) will consult the other sites named in the first-phase message to ascertain whether any of them received the update. As a result of such consultation, the update will be applied either to all of the intended sites or to none of them, thus preserving mutual consistency.

An alternative technique [SHA 78] is to have each site keep a list of the last n updates generated by itself (where the choice of n depends on the characteristics of the system). Each site agrees not to initiate an update until its nth previous update has been acknowledged by all sites. When a site crashes, all the sites compare the lists of updates that were originated by the crashed site. This comparison indicates the possible inconsistencies resulting from the crash. The surviving sites can then be made mutually consistent.

19.6.2 Recovery of a Crashed Site [SHA 78]

When a crashed site recovers, it must be brought up to a state consistent with the other copies of the data base. There are two major problems here: the first is to make sure that the crashed site performs all the updates that originated at other sites while it was down, and the second is to complete any update transactions that were initiated by the crashed site and were interrupted by the crash.

Provided that the local data-base copy was not destroyed by the crash, the first problem is solved by properly storing all the updates that occur while the site is down. This can be accomplished by using a history file at each site which records all updates to the data base and is marked to indicate the times when reconfigurations (crashes or recoveries) occurred. When a crashed site comes back up, one of the surviving sites sends a copy of the portion of the history file made between the time of the crash and the time of recovery.

If a site crashes before completing an update transaction, we have two consistency problems to contend with:

1.   The site may have broadcast update messages before modifying its own data base.
2.   The site may have completed the updating of its local data base, but had not yet begun to send update messages.

Problem 1 can be dealt with using the history file technique described above. For problem 2 we can require each site to record the updates to be made for a transaction before beginning to modify its own data base. This list of recent updates must survive any crash. When the site recovers, this list will be checked for outstanding updates so that the surviving sites can be made consistent with the crashed site.

In case the data-base copy at a site is completely destroyed by a crash (e.g., disk head crash), another site must be selected to make a copy of its data base after the crashed site becomes operational. During the time-consuming process of generating the copy, the previously crashed site is still treated as inoperative. Once the copy is installed, the recovery procedure described above is followed, using history file segments to ensure that recent updates are entered.

For more reading on fault tolerance and recovery in distributed data-base systems, the interested reader should refer to [GAR 82, KOH 81].

19.7   OPTIMAL QUERY PROCESSING POLICY

In this section we discuss policy for query processing in a distributed data base [WON 77, EPS 78, HEV 79, CHU 82A]. The main problem is the following: If a query can be decomposed into subqueries that require operations at geographically separated data bases, determine the sequence and the sites for performing this set of operations such that the operating cost (communication cost and processing cost) for processing this query is minimized. The problem is complicated by the fact that query processing policy depends not only on the query operations, but also on the parameter values associated with these operations.

In this section we present a method for generating the optimal query processing policy that jointly optimizes the processing cost and communication cost. Further, the method includes a variety of query operations.

We first discuss the representation of a query by a set of query trees and describe the procedure for generating the set of query processing graphs from the query trees. Next, theorems are given for optimal site selection for performing the operations and for determining local optimal query processing policies among the set of query processing graphs. Then a mathematical model is developed to compute the operating cost for a given query processing policy. Finally, an example is included to illustrate the procedure for finding the optimal query processing policy for processing a given query.

19.7.1 Query Trees

We assume that a given query can be decomposed into a sequence of operations with serial and parallel relationships, which will yield the correct result. We shall use a query tree as shown in Fig. 19.10a to express these relationships. For example, in Fig. 19.10a, the PROJECTION operation on F_2, and the PROJECTION and SELECTION operations on F_3 are performed in parallel and then input to the JOIN and PROJECTION operations, which are performed serially. The output from these operations together with F_1 are processed by UNION and SELECTION serially, and so on. In general, for a given query, there are many query trees that will produce the correct result of the query. We shall call these the set of feasible query trees for this query, as shown in Fig. 19.12. Algorithms based on commutativity, associativity, and distributivity of operations are available to generate the set of feasible query trees.

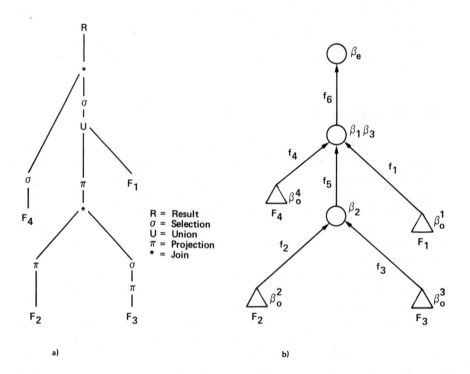

Figure 19.10. A query tree and a resulting query processing graph.

19.7.2   Query Processing Graphs

To reduce communication cost in distributed data base systems, it is often desirable to perform a group of operations at a single site and then transmit the results to other site(s) for further processing. Therefore, we collect sets of connected operations in the query tree into groups (local operation groups). These groups have the property that any pair of operations in a group can be linked by a path in the query tree such that all the operations on the path are in the group. These groups may be selected as candidates to be performed at a single site. Further, under such arrangements the communication cost for processing this query becomes the algebraic sum of the communication cost among the selected groups. Therefore, this motivates us to transform the query tree into a graph representation. We shall call this new representation the *query processing graph.*

There are three types of operations in a query processing graph: initial operations, intermediate operations, and final operations. Initial operations are designated by β_0^i, $i = 1, \ldots, s$, which mainly involve SELECTIONS and PROJECTIONS performed at the site that stores the file. Therefore, the initial operation selects the desired subset of the file for query processing. Intermediate operations are designated by β_i, which is either a single binary operation or a binary operation combined with one or more adjacent unary operations from a query tree to be executed at a single site. The final operation, β_e, presents the query result to the query initiator.

The query processing graph consists of execution nodes, storage nodes, and arcs, as shown in Fig. 19.10b. The *execution node* (denoted by circles) represents execution of a local operation group (either a single operation β_j or multiple operations, $\beta_i \ldots \beta_j$) which are performed at a single site. The sites for execution by two neighboring execution nodes are distinct. Therefore, the *arcs* connecting the execution nodes represent data communication between sites. The *storage node* (denoted by triangles) represents a file permanently stored at a specific site. The arcs connecting storage nodes to execution nodes represent input data to the execution nodes. Therefore, a query processing graph not only represents a sequence of operations for processing the query, but also provides the information about a single operation or groups of operations to be performed at the same site or at different sites.

For example, β_2, an intermediate operation, in the query processing graph (Fig. 19.10b) represents the JOIN and PROJECTION operations of the query tree (Fig. 19.10a) which is to be performed at a single site. β_0^3 in the query processing graph represents the initial operations of PROJECTION and SELECTION on file F_3 of the query tree. Files $f_1, \ldots, f_6$ are intermediate files that are transferred from one execution site to another. The transfer of intermediate file f_5 is represented by an arc between the site that performs β_2 and the site that performs β_1 and β_3. This graph represents the operation sequence $\beta_2\beta_1\beta_3\beta_e$ such that β_2 is executed at one site, followed by β_1 and β_3 at a second site, followed by β_e at the query originating site, which presents the final result file f_6 to the query initiator.

In some cases the contents of a file are required to be sent to several sites for performing query operations; for example, in the SEMIJOIN operation, part of the file stored at site Z may be sent to site X and the other part of the file may be sent to site Y for processing. Therefore, two arcs connecting different execution nodes (Z to X, and Z to Y) are needed to represent the communications for these query operations. Since sites X, Y, and Z represent different sites, adding an additional arc still satisfies the properties of the query processing graphs. In some cases, after performing the operation, site X may need to return some data to site Z (file storage location) for further processing. We need an additional execution node to represent the processing at site Z. Since the site for the processing of this additional execution node is different from the sites for the processing of its adjacent execution nodes, the additional graph still satisfies the properties of the proposed query processing graphs.

Since there are many possible ways for selecting local operation groups and for assigning sites for processing the operations, there are many possible query processing graphs for a given query tree.

19.7.2.1 Properties of Query Processing Graphs

The operating cost for processing a query with a given policy consists of communication cost and processing cost. We assume that the communication cost between each pair of computers is proportional to the volume of data, that the unit communication costs among different pairs of computers are the same, and that the processing cost for all computers depends on the operation performed and on the volume of data. For a given operation, the unit processing cost is the same for all the computers. Under these circumstances, we obtained the following theorems for site selection and computation reduction for the query processing graphs [CHU 82A].

Theorem 1. For each execution node of the query processing graph, selecting the site of the storage node that sends the largest amount of data to that execution node as the site for performing its operations yields minimum operating cost for that graph.

If this site-selection method generates an inconsistent site selection (selects the same site for two adjacent execution nodes of a graph), the graph can be reduced to a simpler graph (one that has fewer execution nodes) that yields a lower operating cost than that of the original graph.

Theorem 2. If the site selection for a given query processing graph based on Theorem 1 is inconsistent, that graph can be reduced to a simpler graph (one with fewer execution nodes) which has the same sequence of operations. Further, the reduced graph yields lower operating cost than that of the original graph.

If the set of operations at an execution node consists of more than one operation, we call such a node a *multioperation* execution node. Theorem 3 deals with graphs containing such execution nodes.

Theorem 3. For a given processing graph that contains a multioperation execution node that executes a set of operations $\{\beta_i \ldots \beta_j\}$, the sequence of operations from this set which has the lowest processing cost is used by the policy that has the lowest operating cost for this graph.

Corollary.   Theorem 3 is true for a query processing graph with more than one multioperation execution node.

Theorem 4.   If the sequence of operations for processing a given query is fixed, the query processing policy that minimizes the communication cost (total volume of traffic) yields the lowest operating cost among the set of policies that uses this fixed sequence of operations.

Theorems 1 and 2, together with the known file allocation information, provide guidelines in site selection for performing operations. Theorem 3 can be used to select local optimal query processing policies from certain query processing graphs that have multioperation execution nodes, and Theorem 4 provides a way of locating local optimal query processing policies from the set of policies that perform a given fixed sequence of operations (i.e., the set of query processing graphs generated from the same query tree). Using these theorems greatly reduces the computation requirements for determining the optimal query processing policy.

19.7.3   Query Operating Cost Model

The operating cost for processing a query consists of communication cost and processing cost. The communication cost depends partially on the sites selected for the operations. Both the communication and processing costs depend on the data reduction functions, sequence of operations, and on the data volumes of the files involved. The data reduction function, $\alpha(\beta_j, \bar{F}, \bar{\gamma})$, is the ratio of the output data volume to the input data volume for the operation β_j, input files $\bar{F}$, and the query operation parameter $\bar{\gamma}$. The data reduction function further depends on the previous operations. The data reduction function of operation β_i preceded by operations $\bar{\beta}$ with input files $\bar{F}$ and query operation parameter γ is denoted as $\alpha(\beta_i| \bar{\beta}, \bar{F}, \bar{\gamma})$. $\alpha(\beta_i, \bar{F}, \bar{\gamma})$ permits us to estimate the output temporary file length $l(f_i)$ for operation β_i from its input file size. Such data reduction functions may be estimated by simulation or measurement on a distributed data base [SMA 79] and their values are stored in the directory system.

Let C_0^i be the processing cost for operation β_0^i, and C_j be the processing cost for operation β_j per unit input file data (byte). Further, let C'_{ij} be the communication cost for transmitting a unit of data (byte) from the site that sends file f_i to the site of operation β_j. We will further define two indicating functions, Y_{ij} and Z_{ij}. We use Y_{ij} for indicating whether temporary file f_i is an input to operation β_j; that is,

$$Y_{ij} = \begin{cases} 1 & \text{if } f_i \text{ is an input to operation } \beta_j \\ 0 & \text{otherwise} \end{cases}$$

We use Z_{ij} for indicating whether f_i is available for processing at the site for performing β_j; that is,

$$Z_{ij} = \begin{cases} 1 & \text{if file } f_i \text{ is needed but is not available for} \\ & \text{processing at the site for performing } \beta_j \\ 0 & \text{otherwise} \end{cases}$$

Thus if $Z_{ij} = 1$, it is required to transmit file f_i to the site for performing β_j. Z_{ij} is determined from the file allocation and the query processing policy. The operating cost for processing a query with policy ψ equals

$$C(\psi) = \sum_{i=1}^{s} C_0^i \, l(F_i) + \sum_{j=1}^{k} C_j \sum_{i=1}^{q} l(f_i) \, Y_{ij} + \sum_{j=1}^{k} C_{ij} \sum_{i=1}^{q} l(f_i) \, Z_{ij} + \delta_{ez} \cdot C'_{qe} \cdot l(f_q) \qquad (19.15)$$

where

$l(F_i)$ = file length of F_i

$l(f_i)$ = file length of temporary file f_i

q = total number of temporary files required for processing of a given query

k = total number of operations $\beta_j, j > 0$, required for completing processing of a given query

$$\delta_{ez} = \begin{cases} 1 \text{ if } \beta_e \text{ is not at the same site of the last operation of } \psi, \beta_z \\ 0 \text{ otherwise} \end{cases}$$

C'_{qe} = unit communication cost for transmitting the query result to the originating site

f_q = result of the query

The first term of Eq. (19.15) is for the cost of the set of initial operations $\{\beta_0^i, i = 1, \ldots, s\}$, on the set of files $\{F_i, i = 1, \ldots, s\}$. The second term represents the total processing cost for performing operations $\beta_j, j = 1, \ldots, k$; the third term represents the total communication cost for transmitting temporary files $f_i, i = 1, \ldots, q$, to the sites of operations $\beta_j, j = 1, \ldots, k$; and the last term represents the cost of transferring the final query result file to the result destination site. The δ_{ez} function indicates whether this transfer is necessary.

Different query processing policies yield different sequences of query operations, as well as different locations for processing these operations. As a result, different policies yield different operating costs for processing a given query on a distributed data base. Equation (19.15) computes the operating cost for a given query processing policy. With the aid of the theorems described in the preceding section and the use of Eq. (19.15), we can determine the optimal policy that yields minimum operating cost for processing a given query.

Table 19.2. *File Characteristics of a Distributed Data Base.*

File	Location	Contents	Length (bytes)
F_1	1	Part number, part name	10^5
F_2	2	Supplier number, part number, quantity	10^5
F_3	3	Supplier number, supplier name, city	10^4

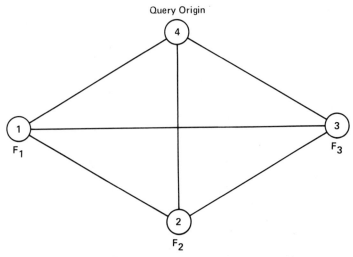

Query Origin

Figure 19.11. Computer network for the example.

19.7.4   Example

Consider a four-node computer network (Fig. 19.11) that contains an inventory relational data model and a data base consisting of three relations stored as files. The allocation and the descriptions of the files are given in Tab. 19.3.

   The following query is initiated at node 4: "Generate a listing of part number, supplier name, quantity for all 'calculators' produced in Los Angeles in a quantity greater than 1000 by any one supplier."

   From this query an algorithm may be used to derive the required operations to construct the query tree and after moving the unary operations to the lowest possible positions, we have the tree as shown in Fig. 19.12a. Based on the permutability of operations in the query tree, (i.e., adjacent JOIN operations are permutable), we can construct an additional tree for this query as shown in Fig. 19.12b. Let us now generate the query graphs from each of the query trees.

   In generating the processing query graphs from a query tree, we first generate the set of local operation groups from the operations in the query tree. Each of the local operation groups may be performed at an execution node in a query processing graph. Then we select the elements of the set of local operating groups and cascade them according to the sequence of operations in the query tree. The operations from the query trees are:

- $\beta_0^1 = \sigma_1 \pi_1$ are the initial SELECTION and PROJECTION operations on F_1.
- $\beta_0^2 = \sigma_2$ is the initial SELECTION operation on F_2.
- $\beta_0^3 = \sigma_3 \pi_3$ are the initial SELECTION and PROJECTION operations on F_3.

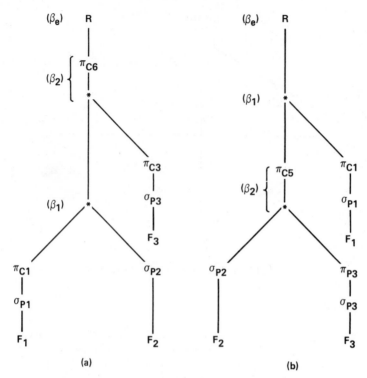

Figure 19.12. Feasible query trees for the example.

- β_1 is an EQUIJOIN on part number.
- β_2 is an EQUIJOIN operation on supplier number and a PROJECTION operation that eliminates the supplier number column.
- β_e is the operation that presents the query result to the query initiator.

The set of local operation groups for the query tree of Fig. 19.12a is $\{\beta_1, \beta_2, \beta_1\beta_2, \beta_e, \beta_2\beta_e, \beta_1\beta_2\beta_e\}$. The set of query processing graphs that are constructed is shown in Fig. 19.13a. The query processing graph for policy ψ_1 represents the policy of transmitting the files $f_1, f_2,$ and f_3 resulting from the initial operations $\beta_0^1, \beta_0^2,$ and β_0^3 to site 4 and processing them there by performing operation β_1 followed by β_2. The

Table 19.3. *Temporary File Characteristics.*

File	Contents	γ for β_0^i	$x\,(\beta_0^i, F_i, \gamma)$	$l(f_i)$ (bytes)
f_1	Part number	Part name is "Calculators"	0.05	0.5×10^4
f_2	Supplier number, part number, quantity	Quantity > 1000	0.1	1×10^4
f_3	Supplier number, supplier name	City is Los Angeles	0.3	0.3×10^4

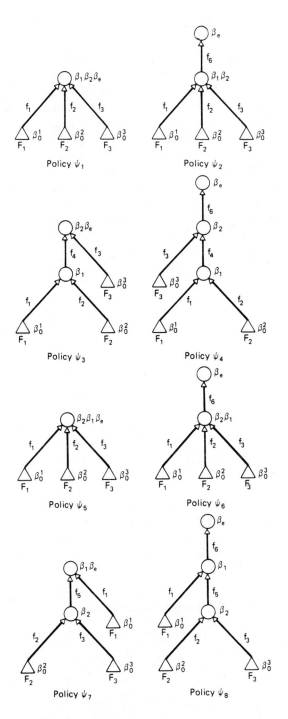

Figure 19.13. Query graphs for the example.
(a) Query graphs for the query tree of Figure 19.13a.
(b) Query graphs for the query tree of Figure 19.13b.

graph for policy ψ_2 represents performing the same sequence of operations, $\beta_1\beta_2$, at either site 1, 2, or 3 and then transmitting the query result to site 4. The graph for policy ψ_3 corresponds to performing operation β_1 at either site 1, 2, or 3, and then performing operation β_2 at site 4. The graph for policy ψ_4 represents performing operation β_2 at site 4. The graph for policy ψ_4 represents β_1 and β_2 separately at two of the sites 1, 2, and 3, by first performing operation β_1 at one site, then transmitting its result file to another site for processing by β_2, and then sending the final result to site 4.

In the same manner, the set of local operation groups for the query tree of Fig. 19.13b is $\{\beta_2,\ \beta_1,\ \beta_2\beta_1,\ \beta_e,\ \beta_1\beta_e,\ \beta_2\beta_1\beta_e\}$. The set of query processing graphs constructed from this set is shown in Fig. 19.13b. The query processing graph for policy ψ_5 represents the policy of transmitting the intermediate files $f_1, f_2,$ and f_3 to site 4 for processing by operation β_2 followed by β_1. The graph for policy ψ_6 corresponds to performing operation β_2 followed by β_1 at one of the sites 1, 2, or 3, then transmitting the result of operation β_1 (the query result) to site 4. The graph for policy ψ_7 represents first performing operation β_2 at one of the sites 1, 2, or 3, then transmitting its result to site 4 for processing by operation β_1. Finally, the graph for policy ψ_8 corresponds to performing operations β_2 and β_1 at separate locations among sites 1, 2, and 3 by performing β_2 first, transmitting its result to the site for β_1, performing operation β_1, and finally transmitting the query result to site 4.

The operations β_i^j, $i = 1, 2, 3$, reduce the files $F_1, F_2,$ and F_3 to $f_1, f_2,$ and f_3, respectively. The temporary file sizes $l(f_i) = \alpha(\beta_i^j, F_i, \bar{\gamma}) l(F_i)$ for $i = 1, 2, 3$. These temporary files have the characteristics summarized in Tab. 19.3.

We will study the example under three different cases by varying the parameter values. In all three cases, we assume that the unit communication cost is the same for all pairs of sites i and j and that the unit processing cost for each operation is the same for all the computers. Since file f_2 is an input to both operations, for simplicity we express the data reduction functions for operations β_1 and β_2 in terms of the length of file f_2.

We will first consider case A. The data reduction function values are $\alpha(\beta_i^j, F_i, \bar{\gamma})$ for $i = 1, 2, 3$ as given in Tab. 19.3, $\alpha(\beta_1, f_2, \bar{\gamma}) = 10^{-1}$, $\alpha(\beta_2, f_2, \bar{\gamma}) = 2 \times 10^{-1}$, and $\alpha(\beta_2, \bar{\beta}, f_2, \bar{\gamma}) = \alpha(\beta_1, \beta_1, f_2, \bar{\gamma}) = 5 \times 10^{-2}$. The unit communication cost value is $C'_{ij} = C' = \$10^{-3}$ per byte and the unit processing cost values are $C_0^i = C_0 = \$10^{-6}$ per byte for $i = 1, 2, 3$, and $C_1 = C_2 = \$0.5 \times 10^{-3}$ per byte.

Table 19.4.   *Optimal Sites for Operations.*

	Site for:		
Policy	β_1	β_2	β_e
ψ_1	4	4	4
ψ_2	2	2	4
ψ_3	2	4	4
ψ_4	2	3	4
ψ_7	4	2	4
ψ_8	1	2	4

The query processing graphs for policies ψ_2 and ψ_6 have a multioperation execution node that performs a set of operations $\{\beta_1, \beta_2\}$ such that this set of operations can be executed in either of the sequences $\beta_1\beta_2$ or $\beta_2\beta_1$. It can be shown that the processing cost of the sequence of operations $\beta_1\beta_2$ is lower than that of the sequence $\beta_2\beta_1$. Therefore, based on Theorem 3, we chose the policy ψ_2 over ψ_6. Similarly, we choose the sequence $\beta_1\beta_2\beta_e$, over $\beta_2\beta_1\beta_e$, thus choosing policy ψ_1 over ψ_5.

Next, we use Theorem 1 to select the sites of all the execution nodes in a given graph. This determines the optimal query processing policy for that graph. Table 19.4 displays the optimal sites selected for operations for all the query processing policies.

All the policies in the set $\{\psi_1, \psi_2, \psi_3, \psi_4\}$ have the sequence of operations $\beta_0^1\beta_0^2\beta_0^3\beta_1\beta_2\beta_e$. Both of the policies in the set $\{\psi_7, \psi_8\}$ have the sequence of operations $\beta_0^1\beta_0^2\beta_0^3\beta_2\beta_1\beta_e$. To find the best policy within each of these sets, we need to compute the total communication cost $C'(\psi)$ for each policy in the set.

$$C'(\psi_1) = C' \bullet [l(f_1) + l(f_2) + l(f_3)] = 18$$
$$C'(\psi_2) = C' \bullet [l(f_1) + l(f_3) + l(f_6)]$$
$$= C' \bullet [l(f_1) + l(f_3) + \alpha(\bar{\beta}_2 \mid \bar{\gamma}, f_2, \bar{\gamma}) \cdot l(f_2)] = 8.5$$
$$C'(\psi_3) = C' \bullet [l(f_1) + l(f_3) + l(f_4)]$$
$$= C' \bullet [l(f_1) + l(f_3) + \alpha(\beta_1, f_2, \bar{\gamma}) \bullet l(f_2)] = 9$$
$$C'(\psi_4) = C' \bullet [l(f_1) + l(f_4) + l(f_6)]$$
$$= C' \bullet [l(f_1) + \alpha(\beta_1, f_2, \bar{\gamma}) \bullet l(f_2) + \alpha(\beta_2 \mid \gamma, f_2, \bar{\gamma}) \cdot l(f_2)] = 6.5$$
$$C'(\psi_7) = C' \bullet [l(f_1) + l(f_3) + l(f_5)]$$
$$= C' \bullet [\gamma(f_1) + l(f_3) + \alpha(\beta_2, f_2, \bar{\gamma}) \bullet l(f_2)] = 10$$
$$C'(\psi_8) = C' \bullet [l(f_3) + l(f_5) + l(f_6)]$$
$$= C' \bullet [l(f_3) + \alpha(\beta_2, f_2, \bar{\gamma}) \bullet l(f_2) + \alpha(\beta_1 \mid \beta, f_2, \gamma) \bullet l(f_2)] = 5.5$$

Since $C'(\psi_4) < C'(\psi_2) < C'(\psi_3) < C'(\psi_1)$, based on Theorem 4, ψ_4 is the optimal policy among the set of policies $\{\psi_1, \psi_2, \psi_3, \psi_4\}$. Similarly, ψ_8 is the optimal policy among the set of policies $\{\psi_7, \psi_8\}$.

Finally, we use Eq. (19.15) to compute the operating cost of policies ψ_4 and ψ_8. Based on policy ψ_4 and the file allocation information in Tab. 19.2, we construct the following indicating functions:

$$Y(\psi_4) = \begin{vmatrix} 1 & 0 \\ 1 & 0 \\ 0 & 1 \\ 0 & 1 \\ 0 & 0 \\ 0 & 0 \end{vmatrix} \qquad Z(\psi_4) = \begin{vmatrix} 1 & 0 \\ 0 & 0 \\ 0 & 0 \\ 0 & 1 \\ 0 & 0 \\ 0 & 0 \end{vmatrix}$$

Substituting the parameters into Eq. (19.15), we have

$$C(\psi_4) = C_0 \bullet [l(F_1) + l(F_2) + l(F_3)] + C_1 \bullet [l(f_1) + l(f_2)]$$
$$+ C_2 \bullet [l(f_3)] + l(f_4)] + C'(\psi_4)$$
$$= 9.71 + 6.5 = 16.21$$

Similarly, for policy ψ_8, we have

$$Y(\psi_8)=\begin{vmatrix} 1 & 0 \\ 0 & 1 \\ 0 & 1 \\ 0 & 0 \\ 1 & 0 \\ 0 & 0 \end{vmatrix} \qquad Z(\psi_8)=\begin{vmatrix} 0 & 0 \\ 0 & 0 \\ 0 & 1 \\ 0 & 0 \\ 1 & 0 \\ 0 & 0 \end{vmatrix}$$

In the same manner, the operating cost of ψ_8 equals

$$\begin{aligned} C(\psi_8) &= C_0 \cdot [l(F_1) + l(F_2) + l(F_3)] + C_1 \cdot [l(f_1) + l(f_5)] \\ &\quad + C_2 \cdot [l(f_2) + l(f_3)] + C'(\psi_8) \\ &= 10.21 + 5.5 = 15.71 \end{aligned}$$

We note that $C(\psi_8) < C(\psi_4)$; therefore, ψ_8 is the optimal query processing policy for case A (see Tab. 19.5).

Let us now consider case B. All the parameter values remain the same as for case A except that the unit processing cost for operation β_1, C_1, has been reduced from $\$0.5 \times 10^{-3}$ per byte to $\$0.25 \times 10^{-3}$ per byte. The communication costs $C'(\psi_1)$ for $i=1$, $2, \ldots, 8$ of case A remain the same for case B. Therefore, based on Theorems 1, 3, and 4, policies ψ_4 and ψ_8 remain as the two local optimal policies for processing the query. The reduction in unit processing cost C_1 results in $C(\psi_4) < C(\psi_8)$. Therefore, ψ_4 becomes the optimal policy for processing the query, as shown in Tab. 19.6.

Finally, let us consider case C. The unit processing costs C_0^i and C_j, $j = 1, 2$, the unit communication costs C'_{ij}, and the data reduction functions for operations β_0^i, $\alpha(\beta_0^i, F_i, \bar{\gamma})$, remain the same as for case B. However, the value of the data reduction functions for operations β_1 and β_2 have been increased. Their new values are: $\alpha(\beta_1, f_2, \bar{\gamma}) = 0.3$, $\alpha(\beta_2, f_2, \bar{\gamma}) = 0.45$, and $\alpha(\beta_2|\bar{\beta}, f_2, \bar{\gamma}) = \alpha(\beta_1|\bar{\beta}, f_2, \bar{\gamma}) = 0.4$. From Theorem 1, we know that site selections for the execution nodes are independent of the data reduction functions for operations β_1 and β_2. Therefore, the sites for performing β_1 and β_2 remain the same as in cases A and B.

Because of the increase in the value of the data reduction functions for operations β_1 and β_2, the output data volumes from these operations have increased. As a result, policy ψ_3 yields the lowest total communication cost among the set of policies $\{\psi_1, \psi_2, \psi_3, \psi_4\}$. Therefore, by Theorem 4, ψ_3 is the optimal policy among that

Table 19.5   *Operating Costs of the Three Cases.*

Case	Policy[a]	Cost		
		Communications	*Processing*	*Operating*
A	ψ_4	6.5	9.71	16.21
	ψ_8	5.5	10.21	15.71
B	ψ_4	6.5	5.96	12.46
	ψ_8	5.5	8.46	13.96
C	ψ_3	11.0	6.96	17.96
	ψ_8	11.5	9.08	20.58

[a]The optimal policy for each case is shown circled.

set of policies. Similarly, policy ψ_8 is the optimal policy among the set of policies (ψ_7, ψ_8). Comparing ψ_3 and ψ_8, we note that $C(\psi_3) < C(\psi_8)$. Thus the policy ψ_3 is the optimal policy for case C.

19.8   AREAS OF FURTHER INVESTIGATION

In this chapter we have discussed the principles of distributed data-base design with reference to areas of file allocation, directory design, deadlock prevention and detection, integrity and consistency in multiple-copy data bases, fault tolerance, and query optimization, which represent the 15 years of progress since the first publication in this field [CHU 69].

There are many areas that still need investigation, such as data translation among heterogeneous data bases with different data structures, interprocess communication protocols for distributed data bases, joint optimization between file allocation and query optimization, fault tolerance and error recovery, performance monitoring and measurement, and security and privacy issues.

ACKNOWLEDGMENTS

This research is supported by the Department of Army, Contract DASG60-79-C-0087.

The author wishes to express his thanks to Paul Hurley of Bell Telephone Labs, N.J. and M.T. Lan of UCLA for their careful reviews of and comments on a draft of this manuscript.

REFERENCES

ALL 82   Allen, F. W., Loomis, M. E. S., and Mannino, M. V. "The Integrated Dictionary/Directory System," *Computing Surveys,* 14(2), June 1982, pp. 245–286.

ALS 76   Alsberg, P. A., and J. D. Day, "A Principle for Resilient Sharing of Distributed Resources," *Proc. 2nd Int. Conf. Software Eng.,* 1976, pp. 562–570.

BER 81   Bernstein, Philip A. and Nathan Goodman, "Concurrency Control in Distributed Database Systems," *Computing Surveys,* Vol. 13, No. 2, June 1981, pp. 185–221.

CAS 72   Casey, R. G., "Allocation of Copies of a File in an Information Network," *SJCC 1972,* Vol. 40, AFIPS Press, Montvale, N.J., 1972.

CHU 69   Chu, W. W., "Optimal File Allocation in a Multiple Computer System," *IEEE Trans. Comput.,* October 1969, pp. 885–889.

CHU 73   Chu, W. W., "Optimal File Allocation in a Computer Network," in *Computer Communication Networks,* N. Abramson and F. F. Kuo, eds., Prentice–Hall, Englewood Cliffs, N.J., 1973.

CHU 74 Chu, W. W., and G. Ohlmacher, "Avoiding Deadlock in Distributed Data Bases," *Proc. ACM Natl. Symp.,* Vol. 1, March 1974, pp. 156–160.

CHU 76 Chu, W. W., "Performance of File Directory Systems for Data Bases in Star and Distributed Networks," *AFIPS Proc.,* Vol. 45, 1976, pp. 577–587.

CHU 79 Chu, W. W., "Design Considerations of File Directory Systems for Distributed Data Bases," *INFOTECH, State-of-the-Art Rep.,* Distributed Data Bases, Vol. II, invited papers, Infotech International Ltd., Maidenhead, Berkshire, England, 1979.

CHU 82A Chu, W. W., and P. Hurley, "Optimal Query Processing for Distributed Database Systems," *IEEE Transactions on Computers, Vol. C-31, No. 9,* September 1982, pp. 835–850.

CHU 82B Chu, W. W., J. Hellerstein, and M. T. Lan, "The Exclusive-Writer Protocol: A Low Cost Approach for Updating Replicated Files In Distributed Real Time Systems," The *Proceedings of the 3rd International Conference on Distributed Computing Systems,* October 1982, pp. 269–277.

CHU 84 Chu, W. W., and J. Hellerstein, "The Exclusive-Writer Approach to Updating Replicated Files in Distributed Processing Systems," to appear in *IEEE Trans. on Computers,* 1985.

ELL 77 Ellis, C. A., "A Robust Algorithm for Updating Duplicate Databases," *Proc. 2nd Berkeley Workshop Distributed Data Manage. Comput. Networks,* May 1977, pp. 146–158.

EPS 78 Epstein, R., M. Stonebraker and E. Wong, "Distributed Query Processing in a Relational Data Base System," *SIGMOD Proc.,* May 1978, pp. 169–180.

ESW 76 Eswarn, K. P., et al., "The Notions of Consistency and Predicate Locks in a Database System," *Commun. ACM,* Vol. 19, No. 11, November 1976, pp 624–633.

GAR 80 Gardarin, G. and W. W. Chu, "A Distributed Control Algorithm for Reliably and Consistently Updating Replicated Databases," *IEEE Transactions on Computers,* December 1980, pp. 1060–1068.

GEL 78 Gelenbe, E., and K. Sevick, "Analysis of Update Synchronization for Multiple Copy Data-Bases," *Proc. 3rd Berkeley Workshop Distributed Data Manage. Comput. Networks,* August 29–31, 1978, pp. 69–90.

GOM 63 Gomory, R., "All-Integer Integer Programming Algorithm," in *Industrial Scheduling,* J. Muth and G. Thompson, eds., Prentice-Hall, Englewood Cliffs, N.J., 1963, pp. 195–206.

GAR 82 Garcia-Molina, H., "Reliability Issues for Fully Replicated Distributed Databases," *IEEE Computer Magazine,* September 1982, pp. 34–42.

GRA 78 Gray, J. N., "Notes on Database Operating Systems," in *Operating Systems: An Advanced Course, Lecture Notes in Computer Science 60* (ed. Goos & Hartmanis), Springer-Verlag, 1978, pp. 393–481.

GRE 80 Green, M. L., et al., "A Distributed Real Time Operating System," *Proceedings of the Symposium on Distributed Data Acquisition, Computing and Control,* December 1980.

HAB 69 Haberman, A. N., "Prevention of System Deadlocks," *Commun. ACM,* Vol. 12, No. 7, 1969, pp. 373–377, 385.

HAM 78 Hammer, M., and D. Shipman, "An Overview of Reliability Mechanism for a Distributed Database," *Proc. COMPCON 78,* March 1978, pp. 63–65.

HAV 68 Havender, J. W., "Avoiding Deadlock in Multitasking Systems," *IBM Syst. J.,* Vol. 7, No. 2, 1968, pp. 74–84.

HEV 79 Hevner, A. R., and S. B. Yao, "Query Processing in Distributed Database Systems," *IEEE Trans. Software Eng.,* Vol. SE-5, No. 3, 1979, pp. 177–187.

HOL 72 Holt, R. C., "Some Deadlock Properties of Computer Systems," *Comput. Surv.,* Vol. 4, No. 3, 1972, pp. 179–196.

KIN 73 King, P. F., and A. J. Collmeyer, "Database Sharing—An Efficient Mechanism for Supporting Concurrent Processes," *Proc. 1973 Natl. Comput. Conf. Expos.,* Vol. 42, June 1973, pp. 271–275.

KLE 76 Kleinrock, L., *Queueing Systems,* Vol. 2: *Computer Applications,* Wiley-Interscience, New York, 1976, pp. 320–323.

KOH 81 Kohler, W. H., "A Survey of Techniques for Synchronization and Recovery in Decentralized Computer Systems," *Computing Surveys,* Vol. 13, No. 2, June 1981, pp. 149–184.

LAM 76 Lampson, B., and H. Sturgis, "Crash Recovery in a Distributed Data Storage System," Internal Report, Xerox Palo Alto Research Center, 1976.

LAM 78 Lamport, L., "Time Clocks, and the Ordering of Events in a Distributed System, *Commun.*", *ACM,* Vol. 21, No. 7, 1978, pp. 558–564.

MAH 76 Mahmond, S., and J. S. Riordon, "Optimal Allocation of Resources in Distributed Information Networks," *ACM Trans. Data Base Syst.,* Vol. 1, No. 1, 1976, pp. 66–78.

MEN 78 Menasce, D. A., and R. R. Muntz, "Locking and Deadlock Detection in Distributed Databases," *Proc. 3rd Berkeley Workshop Distributed Data Manage. Comput. Networks,* August 28–31, 1978, pp. 215–234.

MOR 77 Morgan, H. L., and K. D. Levin, "Optimal Program and Data Locations in Computer Networks," *Commun. ACM,* Vol. 20, No. 5, May 1977, pp. 315–322.

PRI 78 Price, P. L., and D. W. Smith, "Analysis and Use of an Integer Programming Model for Optimally Allocating Files in a Multiple Computer System," DTNSRDC-78/102, David W. Taylor Naval Ship Research and Development Center, Bethesda, Md. 20084, November 1978.

ROT 80 Rothnie, J. B., et al., "Introduction to a System for Distributed Databases (SDD-1)," *ACM Trans. Database Syst.,* Vol. 5, No. 1, 1980, pp. 1–17.

SAN 63 Sander, G. H., *System Reliability Engineering,* Prentice-Hall, Englewood Cliffs, N.J., 1963, pp. 112–144.

SHA 78 Shapiro, R. M., and R. E. Millstein, "Failure Recovery in a Distributed Data Base System," *Proc. COMPCON 78,* March 1978, pp. 66–70.

SMA 79 Small, D., and W. W. Chu, "A Distributed Data Base Architecture for Data Processing in a Dynamic Environment," *Proc. COMPCON,* March 1979, pp. 123–127.

STO 79 Stonebraker, M., "Concurrency Control and Consistency of Multiple Copies of Data in Distributed INGRES", *IEEE Transactions on Software Engineering,* SE-5, 3, May 1979, pp. 188–194.

THO 78   Thomas, R. H., "A Solution to the Concurrency Control Problem for Multiple Copy Databases," *Proc. COMPCON 78,* March 1978, pp. 56–62.

WHI 70   Whitney, V. K. M., "A Study of Optimal File Assignment and Communication Network Configuration," Ph.D. dissertation, University of Michigan, 1970.

WON 77   Wong, E., "Retrieving Dispersed Data from SSD-1: A System for Distributed Databases," *Proc. 2nd Berkeley Workshop Distributed Data Manage. Comput. Networks,* May 1977, pp. 217–235.

Index